W9-ACO-393

UNDER THE EDITORSHIP OF

Leonard Carmichael

SECRETARY, SMITHSONIAN INSTITUTION;

FORMERLY PRESIDENT, TUFTS COLLEGE, AND DIRECTOR, TUFTS

RESEARCH LABORATORY OF SENSORY PSYCHOLOGY AND PHYSIOLOGY

Behavior
Pathology

Norman Cameron, M.D., Ph.D.

YALE UNIVERSITY

AND *Ann Magaret,* Ph.D.

UNIVERSITY OF ILLINOIS

Houghton Mifflin Company • *Boston*

The Riverside Press Cambridge

Editor's Introduction

Unlike some others, this book does not reveal psychiatrists discussing psychology they have not studied or psychologists dealing with psychiatric matters on which they lack full training. Both the present authors have had unusually complete training in psychology and psychiatry as well. Dr. Cameron holds the M.D. degree from the Johns Hopkins University and the Ph.D. degree in psychology from the University of Michigan. For a number of years he was associated with the late Dr. Adolph Meyer at Hopkins, and today he is Professor of Psychology at the University of Wisconsin and of Psychiatry at the medical school of that university. Dr. Ann Magaret, Professor of Psychology at Wisconsin, formerly held a research appointment in neuropsychiatry at Stanford University Medical School and has had wide experience in both psychology and psychiatry.

Behavior Pathology is not a partisan defense of any one-sided school, or other specialized approach to the abnormalities of human behavior. Above all it avoids in any form the dualistic approach to mental illness. Throughout, the authors discuss the behavior of the total human being as determined by his inherited biological make-up and especially as molded by his individual and unique social experience.

In developing this biosocial point of view the authors never deny or attempt to explain away any facts concerning behavior or its determination which can be disclosed by objective or scientific means. As a result their consideration of the socially determined learning that has taken place during the individual's entire life is unusually comprehensive.

Chapter by chapter there is a discussion of the close relationship between normal and pathological behavior and the steps which can be taken to insure the real diagnosis of and the wise therapy for individuals who display reactions which deviate from socially accepted norms. This means that the reader comes to see the pathological phenomena of behavior, be they serious or trivial, as dependent upon explanations which ultimately are not divorced from the scientific procedures which are basic to general modern medicine and to contemporary scientific psychology.

v

As the writer reads many good new books in the field of psychology, he is frequently struck by the importance that certain aspects of the growing science of psychology have for those who would understand the general business of living in our complex modern world. Certainly the present volume is a notable example of such a book. It is hard to believe that any physician, psychiatrist, or psychologist will not profit by studying it carefully. But a possible value of this book would be lost if it were to become merely a useful professional guide to those who already have wide expert knowledge of man's normal and abnormal behavior. Actually the present volume is so clearly written and its scientific and yet eminently sensible point of view is so effectively presented that it is hard to believe that any educated man or woman who reads it can fail to acquire a new kind of understanding of why normal as well as abnormal people act as they do. In its pages there is no trace of the strange intellectual procedure by means of which objective and scientifically observable human behavior is "explained" by the use of hidden mechanisms with mythological names.

The student of biology in general or of physiology in particular who studies this book will not be asked to put aside any of the accepted principles of his science. The present authors never pretend to explain what they observe, record, or measure as resulting from hypothetical "forces" or from the interaction of a conceptualized "mind" or "psyche" working upon a conceptualized "body" or "soma."

If the sane and scholarly point of view of the present volume becomes more widely understood the world will be spared much of the grief that it now knows because of malicious gossip about human deviations from the sort of behavior that is expected by society. This does not mean that the authors support the view that to understand all transgressions of social codes is to excuse such transgressions. Rather the book makes it clear that praise and blame and punishment are not the only methods of adjusting the peculiarities of human social behavior. It thus helps to make possible a modern and rational approach to an understanding of normal as well as pathological reactions.

The present volume is not a new edition of Dr. Cameron's previous book, *The Psychology of Behavior Disorders* (Houghton Mifflin Co., 1947). This book and the former one are written to supplement each other. In the earlier volume a principal emphasis is given to the modern understanding of the major varieties of mental illness. In the present book the basic emphasis is upon an understanding of the patient as an individual who has a given hereditary make-up and a unique history of fortunate as well as unfortunate social learning.

LEONARD CARMICHAEL

Contents

vii

Preface

The field of behavior pathology was at one time dominated by a need to construct rational groupings of related signs and symptoms, so as to reduce the unwieldy mass of descriptive data to some kind of system. After many decades of effort, in many countries, there finally emerged a generally accepted classification of pathological syndromes which consisted, for the most part, of fairly clear-cut neuroses and psychoses. This accomplished, the major emphasis shifted to an attempt to achieve skill and precision in differential diagnosis — an attempt to sharpen the distinctions between different syndromes. The hope which sustained these efforts sprang from a realization that, in some medical areas, differential diagnosis had led to differential therapy, and previously resistant illnesses had been brought under therapeutic control. Something like this was once confidently anticipated in behavior pathology; but the confidence has turned out to have been unjustified.

Long before the structure of syndrome formation and differential diagnosis in psychiatry had been completed, serious dissatisfaction with the product appeared among experienced clinicians. The classification that finally emerged, and was officially adopted, reflected fundamental uncertainties and disagreements even in the definitions through which it sought to clarify and formalize the process of differential diagnosis. There was — and still is [1] — much overlap and unclearness in syndrome description; and the revisions that have been at various times proposed have not eliminated uncertainty and controversy. Confusion is obvious even in official attempts to distinguish among the standard neurotic syndromes. The feeling in some quarters is that the distinctions, as set down, are arbitrary and exceedingly difficult to defend, excepting perhaps in the extreme case. In short, the syndromes in our field have been modelled upon the relatively inflexible end-products of behavior pathology; and they give scant recognition to the developments underlying and preceding the crystallization of neurosis and psychosis.

[1] Cheney, C. *Outlines for psychiatric examinations.* Utica, New York: State Hospitals Press, 1934.

The rise of twentieth century behavior pathology has been characterized by two developments which hold the promise of a solution for this situation. One is a tremendous growth of interest in the genesis of symptoms and their utilization as defense, aggression or evasion; the other is an increasing realization that therapy in this field is fundamentally a process of maturation and learning. The two are obviously interrelated; and what holds them together is the fact that both recognize the vital importance of progressive modification of the human organism through its interaction with its biosocial environment. The genetic approach focusses upon the formative years of life, the periods of infancy, childhood and adolescence; it looks for crucial changes in individual organization in relation to the dynamics of family constellations and of other primary groups. Contemporary therapy focusses upon recall, reconstruction and working through — upon the reorientation and reorganization of a person in terms of his present behavior as this reflects his genetic past.

These two interrelated trends have brought into prominence the basic importance of social learning in the genesis of behavior pathology and in the modification or elimination of its phenomena. Thus, by an indirect route, we have arrived at a point where, as a result of the concentrated and devoted study of individuals, we have established the primacy of the group in personal development. We begin where birth begins, with the unmistakable needs of the neonate, and the succession of inescapable frustrations to which he is exposed because of his helplessness and the complexity of the social milieu. This points up the inevitability of conflict and anxiety; and it clears the way for our recognition that all persons must acquire techniques for overcoming anxiety or at least making it tolerable. The acquisition of such techniques and their modification are both examples of social learning; and this holds good, of course, for the acquisition and modification of pathological techniques, as well as normal ones, and for therapy as well as pathogenesis.

This book is an expression of these trends. Throughout it we have utilized the principle of continuity — that pathological behavior is related to and derived from normal behavior, and that therapy is dependent upon this relationship. We have begun with the conception of the human being as a biological organism, with hereditary and constitutional background, operating as one component of a dynamic social environment. We have presented the development of behavior pathology as essentially a process of maturation and learning in such a setting. We have laid particular stress upon those functions which are characteristically human — the functions that seem responsible for the vast difference between the behavior pathology found in man and that found in infrahuman mammals. Hence the symbolic and role-taking activities maintain a conspicuous place in our presentation. And, finally, we have attempted, through repeated cross-reference, to relate behavior pathology to those disciplines upon which it must depend, and to which it can greatly contribute — psychiatry, psychology, sociology and anthropology.

We wish to acknowledge with gratitude the assistance we have received in the preparation of the manuscript. Dr. Wilfred J. Brogden has read the chap-

ter on Learning and Behavior Pathology; and Dr. Clare Thompson has read
the chapter on Developmental Retardation.   Both have made numerous constructive suggestions.   Dr. Hulsey Cason has generously placed at our disposal
his encyclopedic annotated bibliography on psychopathic personality.   Mrs.
M. Bakken, Mrs. L. Coleman and Mrs. F. Mote have rendered the manuscript
into legible form.

NORMAN CAMERON
ANN MAGARET

Introduction

Behavior pathology is the concern and the responsibility of us all. The patients who suffer from it are not the only persons who feel its effects; and the general practitioners, psychiatrists, psychologists and social workers, who deal with it professionally, are not the only ones who need to understand it. Today we are coming to believe — as well as to state in words — that pathological behavior always derives from and is related to normal behavior, that is, from those reciprocal reactions which we are all constantly giving in our relations with other persons in a social environment. One of the most important consequences of this belief is a new appreciation for the inexact and shifting boundaries between normal and pathological behavior.

We all live out our lives in a complex field of social interaction. Because we are trained from birth in anticipating and reciprocating the reactions of others, most of us develop considerable skill in predicting the behavior of ourselves and other persons. We learn to allow for our friends' eccentricities and idiosyncrasies, to take into account their talents, their preferences and their biases. And we learn also to overlook, ignore or suppress those parts of our own behavior which contradict the conception we have formed of ourselves. In this way, we fashion a frame of reference within which we can locate our own reactions, and the reactions of other persons with whom we interact.

This frame of reference not infrequently encompasses behavior which is unusual, deviant or mildly pathological. Everyone knows young children who hide behind their mothers and cry, or who run away when visitors come to call. Most people know someone who is wary and quick to take offense, who replies to innocuous statements with a prompt *"Just how did you mean that?"* Most social groups include at least one person who seems excessively rigid, self-righteous and conforming — a person who condemns as sinful human frailties which most of us overlook. It is a rare community which does not

1

contain a child who cannot progress in school, a housewife who fatigues easily and has vague bodily complaints, a husband who drinks steadily and sometimes to excess, or an aged individual who occasionally goes out for a walk and then cannot find his way home unaided.

We see, and allow for, these mild deviations in our own behavior also. We all have periods of irritability, times when we are unaccountably depressed, or bouts of fatigue and malaise. We have nights of sleeplessness and days of distractibility. We may conclude at one time that others are talking about us, and later on light-heartedly dismiss our suspicions as obviously groundless. We may become temporarily argumentative and accusatory, or transiently over-controlled; we may grow involved for a time in compelling fantasies and disturbing dreams, only to relinquish them when daily events become more satisfying. Such slight deviations as these we can accept and locate easily within our learned frame of reference.

Occasionally, however, we find behavior, in ourselves or in others, which falls outside our familiar frame of reference. A young boy, always shy and timid, abruptly refuses to go to school; pressure to attend makes him tense, rigid and negativistic by day, and a prey to terrifying nightmares at night. An ageing uncle, always proud and suspicious, begins sending us bewildering letters, in which he threatens to cut us off from a fortune we know he never had. Our neighbor across the street, a carefree, jolly man, takes to playing his radio loudly all night, accompanying the program with his own loud singing. The evening paper headlines a case of amnesia; we recognize the picture of the unknown patient, found wandering about in a remote city, as that of an attractive, talented girl we once knew. Those spells of breathlessness which used to bother us become so frequent and so worrisome that we begin to suspect heart disease, when the heart is actually sound. Our characteristic periods of annoyance and irritability become difficult and finally impossible to control; and we indulge in temper outbursts that are as inexplicable and uncomfortable for us as for our friends.

In such instances as these, our relatives and close friends suddenly become strangers to us; and we become for a time strangers to ourselves. The carefully-learned skills in anticipating, predicting and reciprocating behavior are somehow ineffectual. The comfortable frame of reference which supported everyday social interaction does not encompass timidity exaggerated into school phobia, insecurity distorted into grandiose delusion, or tense gaiety stretched to overexcitement. Nor does the common frame of reference embrace anxiety controlled through repression or mistaken for cardiac illness. Consequently, a great many persons interpret such pathological behavior as weird, occult or incomprehensible. They consign the symptoms of fear, insecurity, tension and anxiety to some remote, inconsequential or extramundane place.

What the untrained observer cannot see, of course, is the essential similarity between normal, everyday behavior and the exaggerated and distorted reactions he calls incomprehensible. He misses the intervening steps between childhood shyness and school phobia, between defensive suspiciousness and aggressive delusion, between chronic anxiety and protective amnesia. He is unable to accept respiratory distress as a sign of intense anxiety, or temper outbursts as indicators of tension which has outstripped the limits of personal tolerance. In popular thinking, and in the discourse upon which it depends, there is a chasm between pathological behavior and the normal reactions from which it must always derive. To span this chasm between normal and deviant behavior is one of the chief goals of behavior pathology.

The Field of Behavior Pathology

The study of *behavior pathology* embraces those human reactions which are culturally so deviant, or personally so unrewarding, as to render the individual characteristically tense, dissatisfied or ineffectual. The reactions which we term *pathological* always represent the exaggeration, distortion or impoverishment of everyday normal behavior. Sometimes we can specify precisely and trace accurately the development of behavior, from its normal pattern through the exaggeration, distortion or impoverishment which makes it finally pathological. Often we lack the factual information or the investigative techniques necessary to reconstruct completely the transformation of normal into pathological behavior. But even when we cannot trace each step in the development, such information as we have points irresistibly to an unbroken line of relationship between normal reactions and behavior pathology. The patients whom we study, when we come to know them well, seem no longer odd, bizarre or grotesque. They always turn out to differ from the rest of us only in their extravagant, restricted or inappropriate use of techniques which everybody uses in attempting to reduce the tensions of need and anxiety.

There are many different fields of investigation which study deviant human reactions. Physiology and biochemistry, for example, include within their subject-matter shifts in blood chemistry, cellular changes in the central nervous system, and alterations in muscle and nerve potential, many of which can be considered pathological. Indeed, we find many studies of the physiological and biochemical deviations of human organisms which are aimed specifically at providing explanations for behavior pathology. In a similar way, sociology and anthropology include within their problems for study such topics as social disorganization, group disintegration and cross-cultural differences in behavior which may also be pathological. And many studies of sociological and anthropological variables seek to explain pathology in the human individual as a function of changes in the structure of the groups to which he belongs.

The subject-matter of *behavior pathology* is neither primarily the cell nor the social group, but rather the total individual. Behavior pathology does not ignore the biological properties of human organisms, nor does it overlook the social field in which human beings move and interact. It recognizes the human individual as a biological system, with all its variations in receptor, neuro-muscular, secretory and integrative functioning. It recognizes also that human beings are always members of social groups, whether these are family groups, neighborhoods, geographically-defined communities, economic strata or social classes. Behavior pathology, however, investigates pathological phenomena, and seeks their explanations, in the biological organism as it operates in a particular social milieu. It is concerned with the ways in which human beings, with their individual patterns of need and frustration, work out their ways of behaving through and by means of their own family and community groups. It is characterized, in other words, by the *biosocial* approach to the study of human behavior.

A biosocial view of behavior pathology

Let us now define *behavior pathology* as *the study of those forms of human behavior which render the individual persistently tense, dissatisfied, incompetent or ineffectual*. There are two general criteria for behavior pathology as we define it. (1) *Behavior may depart markedly from cultural expectation.* Thus an individual may remain so immature, or become so aggressive or withdrawn, as to be unable to participate in social intercourse; or he may, on the basis of his own need, arrive at conclusions regarding himself and others which are unwarranted in terms of the consensus. (2) *Behavior may adhere closely to cultural expectation, but still be personally unrewarding.* Thus an individual may control his own behavior rigidly, permitting himself not the slightest deviation from the cultural norm; but he may do this at the high personal cost of constant tension and fatigue, or of severe behavioral impoverishment. Either cultural deviation or increased personal tension, or both, may characterize the behavior we term pathological.

All of us occasionally show behavior which is socially inappropriate. We may develop immature attitudes for a time, remaining dependent after a long illness, or seeking a return to parental protection when adult stresses grow too severe. We may sulk or become markedly aggressive after prolonged frustration; or we may withdraw and temporarily isolate ourselves from a social situation which has grown too complex for us to handle. All of us also show, now and then, the inhibited, overcontrolled reaction pattern which stifles freedom and spontaneity, and brings us tension and dissatisfaction. For most of us, however, these episodes are transient; and we can resume our more appropriate and satisfying ways of behavior with little difficulty or delay. It is when these forms of reaction persist, and constitute a significant part of an individual's total behavioral repertory, that we consider the reactions *pathological.*

Were we to accept our definition of behavior pathology in its widest and most literal sense, we would investigate the conditions and consequences of deviations in all the reactions of which human organisms are capable. We would be concerned with myopia and hyperopia, with sluggish and hyperactive tendon reflexes, with deafness and auditory hypersensitivity, as examples of deviant reactions. We would be concerned also with extremely high and extremely low wage-earning capacity, with only children and with offspring of families of ten or more, with illiterate persons and college graduates — again as examples of deviations from a cultural norm. Behavior pathology would then become the study of the extremes of all possible human reactions in which there occurs a wide range of performance.

From the *biosocial* point of view, however, the behavior pathologist is interested primarily in those deviant reactions which have significance for the individual's social behavior. We may, for example, study myopia as a deviant response; but we do not then concentrate upon the refractive error and its correction. We look rather for the many interpersonal consequences which nearsightedness has for the person who suffers from it. A myopic person ordinarily has trouble in recognizing others at a distance; he is consequently always in danger of being branded unfriendly or disdainful by persons he cannot see and does not promptly greet. Relief of myopia can be obtained, of course, from properly fitted spectacles. But a great many nearsighted persons are either reluctant to mar their appearance by wearing glasses, or they wear them at the cost of growing sensitivity toward the comments others make about them. Both his difficulty in recognizing others and his acquired sensitivity to slight may thus prevent the nearsighted person from effective social intercourse.

The behavior pathologist may also study "only children" and children from large families; but he is not concerned with family size as a statistical phenomenon. As we shall see, it is in their families that children gain much of their practice in role-taking and social sharing. A child in a large family has more immediate and extensive opportunity for playing with other children, and for learning the privileges of being older and the advantages of being younger, than has the only child. We shall also see that children ordinarily learn security or insecurity with their parents in rivalry with their siblings. A child who must share his parents' time and affection with brothers and sisters is in a different position, with regard to parental acceptance and rejection, from the situation in which the only child grows up. We shall find also that the child learns typically masculine or feminine role-taking behavior partly through identification with older individuals in his family. The only daughter among several children may learn to live out her role with different emphases from those developed by one of five girls in a family. It is always social nuances such as these, and the interpersonal implications of behavioral deviation, which concern the behavior pathologist.

This emphasis upon the social implications of deviant behavior determines not only the general viewpoint of the contemporary behavior pathologist, but also the particular kinds of behavior which he studies. We shall see that there are some sorts of normal human behavior whose variations are more closely related than others to the development of behavior pathology. The tension which may underlie and perpetuate pathological reactions, for example, is often the consequence of prolonged unfulfilled *need;* and the pathological reactions themselves are typically distorted or exaggerated techniques of need-satisfaction. These techniques often develop first under conditions of *stress* and *frustration;* and they persist and even spread because they alleviate the stressful and frustrating circumstances under which they first arose.

Many persons who suffer from behavior pathology, as we shall find, are caught in multiple, unresolved *conflicts* among incompatible reactions. The persistent tension of unresolved conflict has its consequences in *anxiety*, which for the past half-century has been singled out by behavior pathologists as a common forerunner of behavioral distortion and impoverishment. Anxiety takes many forms in behavior pathology, but whatever its character in a particular instance, it is always predominantly an *emotional reaction*, in which visceral responses play an important part. Indeed, we shall find no variety of pathological behavior to which emotional reactions do not in some fashion contribute.

All of us, as we shall see, learn to react not only to others but also to ourselves as social objects. In this way, each of us develops a system of *self-reaction*, derived from the reactions which other social persons — parents, siblings, peers and spouse — make to us. Like other forms of human behavior, a system of self-reaction may grow distorted, socially invalid, or overly restricted, and thus contribute to the initiation and perpetuation of behavior pathology. All of us learn also the interlocking organizations of behavior which we shall call social *roles*. If these roles conflict severely with one another, become socially inappropriate, or grow rigid and inflexible, as they occasionally do, then their distortions may lead toward behavior pathology. Self-reactions and roles typically begin in overt social reactions, but they are usually extended and altered through the private, unshared reactions of *thinking* and *fantasying*. And the covert behavior of thinking and fantasy may grow progressively remote from social reality, and thus lead irresistibly toward behavior pathology.

By now it should be clear that the behavior pathologist is concerned deeply with the ways in which human beings satisfy need, meet stress and frustration.

and resolve conflict. He is interested in the rise and fall of anxiety, and in any behavior which involves visceral participation. He must understand individual patterns of self-reaction and of role-taking behavior. He cannot stop with a study of the obvious, overt reactions which human beings show, but he must go on to investigate their private forms of thinking and their characteristic fantasy themes. These are the sorts of normal behavior whose exaggeration and distortion lead to pathology; and these are consequently the topics which will be emphasized in the chapters that follow.

Behavior pathology and behavior disorder

Behavior pathology, we have said, involves reactions which render the individual persistently tense, dissatisfied, incompetent or ineffectual. But pathological reactions are not always so widely generalized as to cause sweeping changes in the total personality. An individual may develop pathology in one restricted area of his total behavior and remain reasonably competent as a social person in other areas. Thus a housewife may become tense, anxious and even somewhat disorganized whenever a particular guest comes to call, but remain calm, efficient, and skilled in her reactions to other guests, to her parents, her husband and her children. Occasionally, however, a patient develops a persistent constellation of pathological reactions which consistently occur together. To such a relatively fixed, crystallized pattern of symptoms we give the general name, *syndrome*.[1] In the field of behavior pathology, syndromes are ordinarily called *behavior disorders*.

Throughout the history of behavior pathology, considerable attention has been given to the problem of classifying the various patterns of pathological reaction into discrete syndromes. A common first dichotomy, for example, was the distinction between *neurosis* (minor disorder) and *psychosis* (major disorder). The neuroses were then subdivided into various syndromes, such as psychasthenia, neurasthenia and hysteria; and the psychoses were likewise further subdivided into separate syndromes, including mania, depression and schizophrenia. Some of the early behavior pathologists, among them Bleuler [2] and Kraepelin,[3] made careful observations of their patients' symptoms, wrote meticulous descriptions of these symptoms, and fashioned schemes for classifying syndromes which are still in wide use today.

No one doubts that some system of ordering symptoms into syndromes is a necessary and desirable aspect of the study of behavior pathology. However, as our information about behavior pathology, and our attitudes toward it,

---

[1] For an analysis of "syndrome" as a correlational concept, see Marzolf, S. S., "Symptom and syndrome statistically interpreted." *Psychol. Bull.*, 1945, vol. 42, pp. 162–176.

[2] Bleuler, E., *Lehrbuch der Psychiatrie.* Berlin: Springer, 1930. (English translation of earlier edition, New York: Macmillan, 1924.)

[3] Kraepelin, E., *Psychiatrie: ein Lehrbuch für Studierende und Ärtze.* (4 vols.) Leipzig: Barth, 1909–1913.

have altered through the years, our bases for classifying syndromes have also undergone change. Some contemporary behavior pathologists have become dissatisfied with the more traditional classificatory schemes, and are proposing new ones, based upon new premises.[4] One approach is to begin with the various forms of normal behavior which are typically exaggerated and distorted in behavior pathology, and then employ syndromes as illustrations of the sorts of end-product to which pathological reactions may lead. Let us take, as an illustration of this approach, the pathological reaction of *disorganization*.[5]

In the process of developing maturity there occurs a progressive *organization* of behavior, through inclusion and exclusion, along lines of social conformity.[6] At any age beyond infancy, the mature individual can perform a great many acts, including thinking, fantasying and social interacting, with relative precision and skill. Under certain conditions, the normal mature individual may temporarily lose the precise organization of his behavior. If he is fatigued, ill or intoxicated, if he is under stress, distracted or frightened, he may become for a time *disorganized*. And if any of these conditions persist for an unduly long period of time, the consequent disorganization in behavior may likewise persist. In the exceptional case, the disorganization becomes self-perpetuating, and the individual's behavior is then so inappropriate or ineffectual as to deserve to be called *pathological*.

Disorganization as a form of behavior pathology is to be found in a great many behavior disorders. It is characteristic of *anxiety attacks* and of *panic*.[7] It occurs in *delirium*,[8] whether from acute intoxication, febrile illness or traumatic brain damage. It is typical also of *schizophrenic disorders*.[9] But each of these behavior disorders includes other forms of behavior pathology, in addition to the pathological disorganization which occurs in all of them. No one of these disorders, consequently, can be considered the direct end-product of disorganization alone.

To take but one example, patients who develop *schizophrenic disorder* typically show — in addition to disorganization — pathological desocialization, delusional pseudocommunity behavior, excessive fantasy and hallucination. These are all examples of behavior pathology, and characteristically they occur together as the syndrome we call schizophrenic disorder. But the development of this syndrome does not eliminate individual differences among patients. Some schizophrenic patients are predominantly *aggressive*, others are *submissive*, and still others are *detached*. Some show little delusional behavior, or never develop hallucination. And the better we come to know our

[4] Veterans Administration, "Nomenclature of psychiatric disorders and reactions." U.S.V.A. Technical Bulletin, TB 10A–78. Washington, D.C., 1947; Strecker, E. A., Ebaugh, F. G. and Ewalt, J. R., *Practical clinical psychiatry* (6th ed.). Philadelphia: Blakiston, 1947.

[5] For an extended discussion of disorganization, see pages 448–469.

[6] Exclusion and inclusion are described on pages 74–75.

[7] See pages 306–310.   [8] See pages 469–477.   [9] See pages 494–515.

schizophrenic patients, the more difficult it becomes to place them in a particular classificatory pigeonhole.

This difficulty in locating patients within some arbitrary classification of behavior disorder has important consequences for the student of behavior pathology. For one thing, it should not surprise him to come upon patients suffering from the same disorder who differ widely from one another. Nor should it be surprising to find patients who in many ways depart from the typical description of the syndrome which has been generally accepted. For another thing, we cannot realistically study syndromes or symptoms as patterns which are abstracted from the total behavioral organization of the particular patient who develops them. We will do a more accurate and a more complete job of understanding our patient if we begin by investigating the ways in which he overplays and underplays the various techniques of adjusting to tension and anxiety. If we trace these reactions through a lifetime of learning, always within a social context, we shall arrive at length at a genuine comprehension of the symptoms and syndromes which define the patient's pathology.

Problems of Behavior Pathology

Pathological behavior, we have said, is always derived from and related to normal, everyday reactions. We are all capable of showing, under certain conditions and for brief periods of time, behavior which resembles the inappropriate reactions of our patients. But not all of us develop the persistent, enduring, maladaptive responses which define behavior pathology. One of the most compelling problems in this field is the question of why some persons acquire behavior pathology while others, under comparable environmental conditions, seem relatively immune to it.

Susceptibility to behavior pathology

Repeatedly throughout our study we shall find that stress, frustration and conflict underlie the development of pathology in our patients. We shall see also that unconsummated emotional behavior, which we call anxiety, contributes significantly to the initiation and the persistence of maladaptive reactions. But stress, frustration, conflict and anxiety are the lot of all of us. What seems to distinguish the patient from those persons who do not develop severe maladjustment is his low *tolerance* for the tensions which stress, frustration, conflict and anxiety bring him. The patient's threshold for the endurance of tension seems somehow lower than the thresholds of other persons.

There are many possible reasons for the lowered tolerance which characterizes the patient who develops behavior pathology. Commonly he is a person who, throughout his life, has acquired sensitivities to certain forms of stimulation which render him exceptionally responsive. Because of his particular course of social learning, he may be unusually sensitive to slight, for example, or to signs of his own bodily functioning, to fear-provoking stimulation, to affectional demands upon him, or to competition with others. Such learned readiness-to-react — or *reaction-sensitivity*, as we shall call it — is to be found in the development of attitudes of extreme dependence and extreme hostility, in the construction of pseudocommunities and delusional behavior, in the growth of autistic communities and hallucination, and in many other forms of pathological behavior. The patient notices, reacts and takes reciprocal steps where most persons would ignore, overlook or inhibit. Lifelong training in particular patterns of reaction-sensitivity may thus provide the *predisposing* factors to low tolerance which lead to behavior pathology.

Along with a history of predisposition, we often find specific events which seem to set off pathological reactions in our patients. Occasionally these events involve a sudden change in biological competence — as in systemic illness, intoxication or central nervous system damage — that ushers in a period of pathological behavior which then persists. More often, it is a severe thwarting, a grave personal loss, or an intolerable fright which precedes the appearance of pathological reactions. Such events as these are ordinarily called *traumatic*. They may contribute to predisposition to behavior pathology, but they are also counted among the *precipitating* factors in the development of maladjustment.

It cannot be too strongly emphasized that so-called traumatic events are never isolated precursors of behavior pathology. All of us contract illness, suffer grave disappointment and become frightened; but most of us do not develop behavior pathology on these bases. It is always the personal construction which the patient places on these events — their meaning, in terms of his own needs, fears and aspirations — which gives the events their traumatic flavor. We often hear of persons who, after years of skillful and rewarding adjustive behavior, seem suddenly and without a background of predisposition to develop behavior pathology on a traumatic basis. But these reports are always based upon incomplete information. The particular pattern of reaction-sensitivity which makes behavior pathology possible for such persons may have been submerged — inconspicuous to others and inaccessible to the patient himself — but it is a necessary background for the development of pathology. In determining the development of behavior pathology, in other words, predisposing and precipitating factors work hand in hand.

Behavior pathology as an acquired reaction

Today it is an accepted principle that behavior disorder is the end-result of progressively inappropriate and unrewarding social *learning*.[10] Pathological

[10] For a detailed consideration of learning and behavior pathology, see Chapter 3.

reactions, as we have seen, do not occur by chance, nor are they the certain consequence of sharply lowered physiological competence. Neither are they merely the inevitable resultant of a genetic strain which may seem to characterize a particular family line. Constitutional and hereditary factors undoubtedly play a part — in what way and to what extent we cannot yet precisely state — in the development of behavior pathology. But human constitutional and hereditary factors can have no existence independent of human organisms, who live out their lives in a particular social context in interaction with other persons. In our study of behavior pathology, we can never afford to forget the years of social learning, much of it casual, incidental and unrecognized, which define the life history of every human being.

It is for this reason that we begin, in the study of behavior pathology, with the expectations which parents have for their children, with matters of parent-child interaction, and of sibling relationship. It is for this reason also that we trace, in the study of our patients, the early history, the events of infancy, of childhood and adolescence, which have directed the course of their social learning. When we make such a *genetic* approach to our subject matter, we are struck repeatedly by the consistency of behavioral development, by the inevitability with which some forms of early learning seem to lead toward pathological reactions. We are struck also by the frequency with which certain phenomena of learning — as clear in our clinical studies as in our laboratory experiments — seem to be involved in the development of behavior pathology.

For one thing, it is apparent that attitudes, responses and relationships learned early in life *generalize* to new situations throughout the individual's history. The child of rejecting parents, for example, tends to anticipate rejection from other social persons with whom he later comes in contact; and he tends equally to invite from others, through his own reactions to them, the rejection he is receiving at home. This suggests another characteristic of the social learning which underlies behavior pathology: that it is *reciprocal*, in terms of the expectations and reactions of other persons. We shall find such learned reciprocating not only in parent-child and sibling relationships, but also in the delusional and hallucinatory developments of our patients. The guilty patient invites punishment from others; if it is not forthcoming he may delusionally attribute punitive attitudes to persons who do not in fact have them. Or he may mistake his own punitive self-reactions for the voice of someone else, and thus hallucinate the punishing responses to which his guilt impels him to reciprocate.

For another thing, it is clear in our studies of social learning that reactions which generalize widely tend to become *cumulative* and at length *self-perpetuating*. The child who is trained by his parents to note and comment upon his bodily functions, for example, may learn his lessons all too well. He may become helpless to ignore the little shifts in heart rate and breathing rhythm, the visceral gurgling and rumbling, the patterns of muscular tension and relaxation, which most persons never notice. If he is anxious, insecure or unhappy, he may then place upon these normal events a frightening or depressing construction, until he develops a full-blown syndrome of anxiety, invalidism or depressive disorder.

In the same way, the child who fails to learn the easy give-and-take with others, the sharing and role-taking skills necessary for social participation, may arrive at adulthood ill-prepared for mature interbehavior. His long practice in social withdrawal and isolation makes it altogether impossible for him to play a satisfying adult role, no matter how strongly he may wish to do so. We see the product of such cumulative and self-perpetuating social maladjustment particularly in immaturity reactions and in schizophrenic disorders. Patients whose inappropriate behavior grows thus cumulative and self-perpetuating are caught in a vicious circle which often can be interrupted only with expert assistance, and sometimes not at all.

Social learning, we have said, is in large part training in conformity to the reactions and expectations of other persons. In the course of their development, however, human beings learn to react to themselves as social objects, always in terms of the reactions which others — their parents, siblings, friends or spouse — make to them. The system of learned *self-reactions* which thus develops has important consequences for the acquisition of behavior pathology. From it are derived the reactions of self-regulation, self-control and self-criticism which in some persons may be carried to pathological extremes. A great many reserved, detached, anxious, guilty patients are persons whose patterns of self-regulation have become seriously exaggerated or distorted. And a great many otherwise inexplicable symptoms — compulsive rituals, depressive delusions, hysterical inactivations and suicidal fantasies, for example — are the products of progressively inflexible self-reactions.

Behavioral duplicity and behavior pathology

One of the most perplexing aspects of pathological behavior is its apparently contradictory and inconsistent nature. From the vantage-point of our everyday frame of reference, as we have seen, patients often seem unpredictable in what they do. They invite pain or punishment which others would try to avoid. They arrive at conclusions which, in terms of the social consensus, seem unwarranted and invalid. They may speak in language that communicates nothing meaningful to the untrained observer. They act out in motor behavior attitudes which they deny and repudiate in words; or they deny in fantasy and dreaming what they accept in waking conversation. It is hardly surprising that the student of behavior pathology, confronted with such contradictions as these, often concludes that patients who suffer from behavior disorder are peculiar, bizarre or inexplicable individuals.

What the untrained observer may dismiss as inexplicable in the patient's reactions is actually an indication of that *behavioral duplicity* which is as common to normal as to pathological behavior. We all learn to practice selectivity among our own reactions, to accept what fits in with our ideal picture of ourselves and to reject that which seems at variance with it. We all learn to achieve in fantasy what is denied us in reality, to place satisfying constructions on ambiguous or threatening situations, to be able to say one thing in public and think the opposite in private. We all become so expert in these skills of disguise and concealment that we rarely appreciate the contradictions they involve. Indeed, most of us can seldom afford to recognize our own behavioral duplicities; for if we did so we would thus be forced to confront the very contradictions, tensions and anxieties which our learned disguises hold in check. Often it is only in the exaggerated and extravagant reactions of patients that we can recognize the dichotomies which characterize the everyday behavior of us all.

There are many dichotomies in the organization of human reactions which constitute behavioral duplicity. One of these is the division between *verbal* and *nonverbal* behavior. We shall see that a great many important and enduring attitudes and responses develop in infancy, before language has become a tool in communication. We shall see also that other significant reactions occur in states of emotional tension and disruption which prevent a sequential organization of language. And repeatedly we shall come upon fantasy themes which may affect a person's entire behavior organization, but which elude precise formulation in words. In this way we all develop dichotomies between what we say and what we do, until our words may become poor indicators of our total behavior. When now we say that a patient is "talking nonsense" or acting contrary to his verbal statements, we are actually recognizing in him a division between verbal and nonverbal reactions, a division that differs from our own only in its deleterious effects upon his total behavior.

Another factor which contributes to behavioral duplicity in normal individual and patient alike is the *relative accessibility* of some behavior to one's own self-reactions. People differ markedly in the extent to which they can recall, specify and comment upon their own activities. For all of us, there are past events or present attitudes — often highly significant ones — which are inaccessible to our own self-reactions. These events and attitudes are still part of our total behavior organization, and therefore still participate in our current behavior, even though we cannot identify or describe them. Some behavior pathologists have characterized such unavailable reactions as "unconscious," and some have constructed systems of personality theory built upon the concepts of "conscious" and "unconscious" experience. What actually distinguishes the "conscious-unconscious" continuum, however, is the relative accessibility of one's behavior to one's own self-reactions — the extent to which a person can accurately report upon his own performance.

The behavioral duplicity which grows out of self-inaccessible reactions is often the product of *repression*. It is to be found in the selective forgetting, the slips of speech, the fragmentary gestures and the dreams and fantasies of normal individuals. It is found to an exaggerated degree in the symptoms of amnesia, paralysis and anesthesia which characterize hysterical inactivation, and in the trance, fugue, seizure and multiple personality of hysterical autonomy. We shall find indications of self-inaccessible behavior in the rituals of compulsive patients, the disorganization of schizophrenic disorder, and the vague, unidentified bodily complaints of intensely anxious persons. The occasional dramatic example of wide discrepancy between accessible and inaccessible reactions, however, must not blind us to the fact that we are all inaccurate reporters of our own behavior. Much that is significant and determinative in our everyday lives is unformulated, unshared and unreportable.

Methods of Studying Behavior Pathology

Any science, in the course of its history, develops its own methods of investigation. These methods, however, always depend upon a variety of conditions. They are devised initially to answer particular questions, or to obtain certain sorts of information which seem important. When the questions change in character, or new and different information is needed, then the methods of investigation must change in corresponding ways. But investigative methods also depend upon advances in neighboring sciences, upon developments in techniques employed by other fields, and upon the current philosophical and theoretical positions which support science at any given period of history. The methods of studying behavior pathology reflect all of these conditions.

Because the science of behavior pathology has grown out of psychology, out of medicine, physiology, sociology and anthropology, its investigative methods have been largely borrowed from these related fields. There are both advantages and disadvantages in such appropriation of techniques. A great many methods of studying behavior which have been evolved by the experimental psychologist, for example, are entirely suitable to problems of behavior pathology. Borrowing these methods and applying them to the study of pathological behavior short-cuts the time and effort of the behavior pathologist at no sacrifice of precision. But for many of the problems which the behavior pathologist confronts in his research, the techniques of experimental psychology are inadequate or inappropriate. Borrowing and applying unsuitable methods are likely to produce research which is trivial or irrelevant. Methods of investigation must always be appropriate to the actual problems confronting the investigator. One of the greatest needs in contemporary behavior pathology is the need for research techniques which are appropriate to the complexity and significance of the problems in this field.

Longitudinal methods of study

Due largely to its emphasis upon *genetic* factors, behavior pathology lends itself well to a study by means of longitudinal methods. In these methods, systematic observations or measures are made of the behavior of subjects, at regular time intervals, over a period of years. This approach has been used most frequently in the studies of child development, upon which many of our hypotheses concerning the etiology of behavior pathology depend.[11] Typically, of course, such studies begin by employing random or unselected samples of a total population of infants as subjects. Because frank behavior disorder does not develop in everyone, even extensive longitudinal studies of an unselected group of subjects may yield little information which is directly relevant to behavior pathology. It is always the complaint of the research worker in this area that, if he could know in advance which children would develop behavior disorder, he could amass many more significant cases for longitudinal study than are otherwise possible.

This difficulty is circumvented in part by the method of the *case history*, which in its usual form reverses the longitudinal procedure, but still provides genetic information regarding behavior pathology. Most behavior pathologists who work intensively are in possession of much information concerning their patient's infancy, childhood and adolescence — some of it obtained from the patient himself, and some from his parents, siblings, spouse and others who know him intimately. This information may then be arranged in temporal order, and presented as a longitudinal case history of a particular person. The case history approach has always been the most popular method of studying behavior pathology; but it has grave limitations as an investigative technique.

One of the disadvantages of the case history method stems from its dependence upon one individual for information. Clinicians who work with patients are oriented toward the unique individual; they are interested in what this particular past event means for this particular patient. If they interest themselves in the *prediction* of human behavior, their concern is with prediction in a single case. If they are interested in *postdiction* — the specification of past events from present behavior — again it is postdiction in a single case. Most experienced clinicians believe they are relatively accurate predictors and postdictors for individual patients they know well. At present we are beginning to devise techniques for the quantification of the single case, and for the study of the accuracy of prediction and postdiction of a given patient's behavior by a given clinician.[12]

[11] For examples of these approaches, see pages 23–25.

[12] As illustrations of this trend, see Allport, G. W., "The use of personal documents in psychological science." *Soc. Sci. Res. Council Bull. 49.* New York, 1942; Baldwin, A. L., "Statistical problems in the treatment of case histories." *J. clin. Psychol.*, 1950, vol. 6, pp. 6–11; Cattell, R. B., Cattell, A. K. S., and Rhymer, R. M., "P-technique demonstrated

What the behavior pathologist needs to know, however, is the generality of factors which may be found in the case history of the individual patient. It is not enough to know, for example, that infantile feeding frustration has led to adult oral aggressiveness in a single instance. One must discover also how general this relation is in the total population, and particularly how often infantile feeding frustration has *not* led to adult oral aggressiveness. This sort of information cannot be obtained by one case history, or even by a series of case histories unless the series is randomly selected. It can be obtained only by the slow, laborious, painstaking longitudinal research, which begins with a random sample of infants, and studies all the individuals in its sample in an orderly fashion until they reach adulthood.

Cross-sectional methods

Partly because of the time-consuming nature of longitudinal studies, much research in behavior pathology employs cross-sectional techniques. These methods are aimed at the study of behavior occurring at a particular point in time; they neglect, for the most part, the events which preceded and led up to the behavior being studied. Consequently, they are more concerned with the phenomena of behavior pathology than with its genetic development. There are at least three cross-sectional methods which may be singled out for special mention: the *statistical method*, the *field approach* and the *experimental method*.

The *statistical method* in behavior pathology is directed toward the question of the relative frequency of occurrence of various forms of pathological behavior under different conditions. For the most part, studies of this kind begin with some classification of behavior disorder, and consequently they are limited by all the limitations of arbitrary diagnostic categories which we discussed earlier. From studies of this sort, however, we have information concerning the occurrence of behavior disorder at different ages, sex differences in behavior disorder, and geographical distributions of behavior disorder.[13] The statistical approach also permits us to study, through correlational techniques, the relationship between the occurrence of behavior pathology and such other factors as maternal overprotection, parental maladjustment, family membership, school failure and bodily disease.[14] Occasionally, our statistical studies begin not with syndromes of behavior disorder, but with forms of behavior pathology. Thus,

in determining psycho-physiological source traits in a normal individual." *Psychometrika*, 1947, vol. 12, pp. 267–288; Cattell, R. B. and Luborsky, L. B., "P-technique demonstrated as a new clinical method for determining personality and symptom structure." *J. gen. Psychol.*, 1950, vol. 42, pp. 3–24.

[13] See, for example, Faris, R. E. L., "Ecological factors in human behavior." In Hunt, J. McV. (Ed.), *Personality and the behavior disorders*. New York: Ronald, 1944, pp. 736–757; Dayton, N. A., *New facts on mental disorders*. Springfield, Ill.: C. C. Thomas, 1940; Landis, C. and Page, J. D., *Modern society and mental disease*. New York: Rinehart, 1938; Pollock, H. M., *Mental disease and social welfare*. Utica, N.Y.: State Hospitals Press, 1941.

[14] Examples of such studies are to be found on pages 56–63.

for example, we have information concerning the relative frequency of visual and auditory hallucination, and information about the popularity of various fantasy themes.

One application of the statistical method which is of especial interest to the behavior pathologist is to be found in the use of *psychometric tests*. It is occasionally possible to quantify, and then to scale, certain forms of behavior which are significant in behavior pathology. We shall see, later on, that intelligence scales play an important part in the understanding of developmental retardation; [15] that the degree of deterioration occurring in some disorders may be roughly scaled; [16] and that, under strictly specified conditions, the degree of behavioral regression may also be measured.[17] Many of the most significant and frequent reactions in behavior pathology, however, have not yet been precisely quantified. Scales of frustration tolerance, of anxiety-readiness and of aggressiveness, dependence and disorganization, would be extremely useful in the description of our patients' reactions. However, behavior pathologists have not yet devised adequate techniques for measuring these important variables.

The *field approach* — or *cross-cultural approach*, as it is sometimes called — involves comparative studies of behavior pathology in different cultural settings. This technique was first developed by anthropologists. It is still employed by them, as well as by behavior pathologists, in the study of pathological behavior.[18] We have already seen that the designation of reactions as pathological is relative to what is expected or appropriate in a given social group. This factor of *cultural relativity* can be studied most directly through a field approach. Trance, hallucination or frenzied overexcitement, for example, is taken to be a sign of grave pathology in contemporary Western society. But cross-cultural investigations indicate that trance, hallucination and overexcitement are not only accepted but sought after, as signs of divinity or superiority, in social groups other than our own.

Field studies of different cultures often provide instances of practices and attitudes which cannot be duplicated, either in case histories or in experiments, in our own society. Parents in some societies, for example, traditionally bind their offspring and severely thwart their activity during early infancy. Parents in other cultures exert no control whatever over their infants' feeding and eliminative activities. Mothers in still other cultures establish with their infants a relationship of teasing frustration, in which they stimulate the child to excitement and then leave him. These methods of child-rearing have no exact counterpart in our own society. The study of adults who have undergone severe thwarting as infants, or have been left entirely free of restriction in feed-

[15] See pages 157–160.   [16] See pages 518–531.   [17] See pages 267–269.
[18] See, for example, Kardiner, A., *The psychological frontiers of society*. New York: Columbia University Press, 1945; Erikson, E. H., *Childhood and society*. New York: Norton, 1950.

ing and eliminating, or stimulated to unconsummated excitement, should provide us with much-needed information concerning the relationship between these forms of child-rearing and adult personality constellations.

The *experimental method*, in its purest form, is the most precise and well-controlled of the techniques of studying behavior pathology. This method requires that all variables but one be controlled or held constant, and that the one be varied systematically, with a view to determining the effect of its change upon the other variables. If, for example, the research worker is interested in determining the effect of *delay* upon the occurrence of aggressive behavior, he must systematically vary the time interval elapsing between the initiation of an act and its consummation, and then somehow measure the degree of aggressive response which his subjects show. If he is interested in determining the effect of *unresolved conflict* upon muscular tension, then he must induce conflict in his subjects, prevent conflict-resolution, and then measure the consequent changes in his subjects' muscular tension. It goes without saying, of course, that in such experiments as these, control procedures must be employed, to provide reference points against which the changes occurring under experimental conditions may be compared.

There are relatively few cross-sectional studies in behavior pathology which meet the strict criteria of an experiment. A number of factors conspire to prevent the behavior pathologist from designing and executing a true experiment on his subject matter. For one thing, the conditions which may initiate, intensify and perpetuate pathological reactions are so numerous and so intricately interrelated that untangling them, and then systematically varying them, constitute exceedingly difficult tasks. For another thing, the significant variables in behavior pathology — self-reactions, social roles, needs, conflict, reaction-sensitivities and inaccessible reactions — are hard to specify and even harder to measure. Furthermore, the behavior pathologist cannot manipulate experimentally any reactions which might have lasting personal significance for his human subjects. His primary responsibility to his subjects as human beings prohibits him from investigating the absolute limits of frustration tolerance, from inducing severe behavior disorganization, or from experimentally producing in his subjects delusional, hallucinatory, or phobic reactions which might then persist.

One solution which experimental behavior pathologists have found to these difficulties has been to employ infrahuman animals as subjects for study.[19] Consequently, we have a great many investigations of "experimental neurosis" in rats, cats, sheep and pigs, numerous studies of conflict in rats, studies of feeding frustration and satiation in puppies, and investigations of displace-

[19] For summaries of such studies, see Liddell, H. A., "Conditioned reflex method and experimental neurosis"; Finger, F. W., "Experimental behavior disorders in the rat"; Miller, N. E., "Experimental studies of conflict." In Hunt, J. McV. (Ed.), *Personality and the behavior disorders*. New York: Ronald, 1944, pp. 389–465.

ment, disorganization and "anxiety reduction" in rats. Experiments of this sort can employ precise delineation and measurement of variables, and they permit the application of extreme conditions and the production of genuinely pathological behavior which are impossible with human subjects. At best, however, experimental studies based on infrahuman animals provide only analogues of behavior pathology in the human organism.

An occasional experimental investigation with human subjects seems to approach closely the criteria of an adequate experiment, and still to deal with a genuine problem of behavior pathology. We shall find such investigations in our study of conflict, stress and frustration; and we shall find them also in our study of repression and selective forgetting. The techniques of conditioning, especially as applied to visceral reactions and subliminal stimulation, seem also to be appropriate to the experimental investigation of behavior pathology. Hypnosis appears to offer some promise as a technique of inducing and controlling self-inaccessible reactions for experimental purposes. And experimentally-produced distraction has proved a fruitful means of stimulating language disorganization in otherwise normal persons. With these rather rare exceptions, however, the traditional experimental approach has developed few techniques which are appropriate to the study of significant variables in behavior pathology.

The growing interest in the development of more precise investigative methods is one sign that behavior pathology today is gradually changing in character. It began as a more or less descriptive study, grounded largely in clinical observation. Its development was delayed and distorted by the popular view that patients are somehow shameful — possessed by demons and driven by magical forces — and that they merit punishment, ostracism or deliberate neglect. But behavior pathology has extended its scope and sharpened its procedures until it now approaches the status of an independent science. And along with the gradual growth of behavior pathology as a field of scientific investigation have come changes in the public attitude toward patients who suffer from behavior disorder. Slowly, and still with great difficulty, we are replacing the old caricatures of patients as guilty, inferior outcasts with pictures that correspond more faithfully to the facts.

As we turn now to the study of behavior pathology, we shall find many indications of these changed attitudes. Today we no longer rest content with a description of syndromes, or of their odd, confusing and sometimes alarming symptoms. We look beyond these products of pathological trends and see the patient as basically an ordinary human being whose particular course of social learning has led him toward behavior pathology. We can see him as one for whom the tensions of unfulfilled need, or the pressures of stress and frustration, have become at last intolerable. Even his most extravagant symptoms seem somehow intelligible to us, as we find in them only exaggerations and distortions of adjustive techniques we all employ.   And in trying to understand the patient, we must depend, for our information, not only upon the case history, but upon experimental investigations, field research and longitudinal studies. It is only by beginning with the patient as a social person, and studying his behavior by means of every appropriate method we can devise, that we will arrive at length at a clear view of behavior pathology.

2

Behavior Organization

I. NEED, STRESS AND FRUSTRATION

To say, as we do, that behavior pathology is always related to and derived from normal behavior is to acknowledge the immediate importance of some challenging problems. For one thing, we must face the question: From what normal reactions is the exaggerated and inappropriate behavior of our patients derived and to precisely what is it related? What are the conditions under which normal reactions are likely to be distorted or show impoverishment, and to persist as a frankly pathological mode of living? Why, under comparable conditions of need, stress and frustration, do some persons develop behavior disorders while others do not? It is to such matters as these — problems of individual susceptibility or immunity, individual differences in need and satisfaction, in tolerance for stress and frustration, and in the direction and efficiency of social learning — that we turn in the present chapter and the next one.

There are a great many sources to which we may go for information on these points. Research on infantile behavior, for example, and studies of social interaction among children, adolescents and adults, yield clues as to how pathological behavior develops. The fertile experimental literature of human learning contains promising leads concerning the exaggeration of normal reactions and their resistance to change. Although the lines of relationship between biosocial health and behavior pathology are not as yet perfectly drawn, the data which the contemporary behavior pathologist has at his disposal all point in the same direction. They all suggest that we can account for the evolution of pathological reactions from normal ones without relinquishing our generally accepted principles of human behavior. But we can accomplish this end only if we take as our material the total human organism, with all its biological properties, operating in a complex social field.

21

Individual Differences in Responsiveness

The development of behavior, whether normal or pathological, depends upon the responsiveness of the growing organism.   An active, irritable infant participates in a wider environment than does a quiet, phlegmatic one, and he invites different reactions from those who share the environment with him. The baby who turns, reaches, and kicks restlessly in his crib; who cries, smiles or coos a great deal; or who nurses actively and long, inevitably exposes himself to situations which differ from those which the placid, unreactive child encounters.   What these differences in reactivity may mean for the infant's behavior organization is also importantly determined, of course, by the needs and attitudes of his parents and of the others who respond to him.   An exuberant, accepting family may welcome noisy activity in its newest member which quieter, more restrictive parents would consider irritating, frightening, or bad.

Any parents who have more than one child will testify that infants differ widely from one another in responsiveness, and any experienced pediatrician will confirm this testimony.   To their more or less casual observations, we may add data from many of the conventional studies of infantile activity.   In one typical investigation, for example, the movements of infants were recorded, during the first ten days of their lives, both instrumentally and by trained observers.[1]   Even in the first day of life, some of these infants showed five times as much general activity as others.[2]   Differences as wide as these were recorded throughout the ten-day observation period.   Other investigators report differences in the tendency of newborn infants to develop generalized muscular tension,[3] and still others find they can reliably differentiate infants as "very active," "moderately active" and "quiet" by the end of the lying-in period.[4] The same range of responsiveness is seen when nursing activity alone is studied.[5]   Kanner has described a series of children referred to his clinic, in whom the parents report pronounced unresponsiveness from the first weeks of life.[6]

[1] Irwin, O. C., "The amount and nature of activities of new-born infants under constant external stimulating conditions during the first ten days of life." *Genet. Psychol. Monogr.*, 1930, vol. 8, pp. 1–92.

[2] The extremes for day 1, in number of oscillations recorded by the polygraph, are 4,444 and 23,289.

[3] Bergman, P. and Escalona, S. K., "Unusual sensitivities in very young children." In Freud, A. (Ed.), *The psychoanalytic study of the child.* New York: International Universities Press, 1949, vol. 3/4, pp. 333–353; Ribble, M. A., "Infantile experience in relation to personality development." In Hunt, J. McV. (Ed.), *Personality and the behavior disorders.* New York: Ronald, 1944, pp. 621–651.

[4] Fries, M. E. and Lewi, B., "Interrelated factors in development: a study of pregnancy, labor, delivery, lying-in period and childhood." *Amer. J. Orthopsychiat.*, 1938, vol. 8, pp. 726–752.

[5] Balint, M., "Individual differences of behavior in early infancy, and an objective method for recording them: I. Approach and the method of recording." *J. genet. Psychol.*, 1948, vol. 73, pp. 81–117.

[6] Kanner, L., "Problems of nosology and psychodynamics of early infantile autism." *Amer. J. Orthopsychiat.*, 1949, vol. 19, pp. 416–426.

At the other extreme are reports of infants who, often in relation to birth injury or endocrine dysfunction, show an unremitting hyperactivity.

Infantile differences appear in general social responsiveness as well as in activity level. Babies differ reliably from one another in the frequency with which they smile, laugh or cry.[7] Heightened emotional reactivity seems so characteristic of prematurely born infants that one writer speaks of a "syndrome of sensitiveness" in premature children.[8] Infants differ also in constellations of such socially-derived traits as petulance, tendency toward escape, and attention given to the experimenter in test situations.[9] In the preschool years, some children initiate a great many social contacts, while others begin few;[10] and some play more frequently in groups than do others.[11] During the same years, children differ from one another in their conflict behavior.[12] Indeed, there is no study dealing with measured behavior in infancy and childhood which does not report, directly or indirectly, evidence of differences in responsiveness from the earliest days of life.

The fact of early individual differences in responsiveness provides the behavior pathologist with an attractive hypothesis to account for differences in personal susceptibility to behavior disorder.[13] An energetic, highly responsive infant, from the first day of his life, may behave in ways which raise the tension level in his environment, and which perpetuate his own overactivity. It is altogether possible that with this beginning, he may continue to respond characteristically throughout his life with excitement and overactivity. If he were to develop behavior pathology, we should expect him to maintain his excitement and overactivity, perhaps in an exaggerated form, as panic, anxiety attack or manic disorder. In the same way, the apathy that characterizes an unreactive infant may deprive him of many of the reactions from others which are essential to his biosocial maturation. His unresponsiveness may discourage

[7] Washburn, R. W., "A study of the smiling and laughing of infants in the first year of life." *Genet. Psychol. Monogr.*, 1929, vol. 6, pp. 403–537; Brackett, C. W., "Laughing and crying of preschool children." *J. exper. Educ.*, 1933, vol. 2, pp. 119–126; Bayley, N., "A study of the crying of infants during mental and physical tests." *J. genet. Psychol.*, 1932, vol. 40, pp. 306–329; Ames, L. B., "Development of interpersonal smiling responses in the preschool years." *J. genet. Psychol.*, 1949, vol. 74, pp. 273–291; Spitz, R. A., "The smiling response: a contribution to the ontogenesis of social relations." *Genet. Psychol. Monogr.*, 1946, vol. 34, pp. 57–125.

[8] Shirley, M., "A behavior syndrome characterizing prematurely-born children." *Child Develpm.*, 1939, vol. 10, pp. 115–128.

[9] Shirley, M., *The first two years*, vol. III. *Personality manifestations*. Minneapolis: University of Minnesota Press, 1933.

[10] Jones, M. C. and Burks, B. S., "Personality development in childhood: a survey of problems, methods and experimental findings." *Monogr. Soc. Res. Child Develpm.*, 1936, vol. 1, no. 4.

[11] Green, E. H., "Friendships and quarrels among preschool children." *Child Develpm.*, 1933, vol. 4, pp. 237–252.

[12] Jersild, A. T., *Child psychology* (Rev. ed.). New York: Prentice-Hall, 1942.

[13] For one analysis of this point, see Cameron, D. E., "Facilitation and inhibition as factors in behavioral deviations." *Amer. J. Psychiat.*, 1949, vol. 105, pp. 693–696.

his parents and other adults from fondling him, talking to him or providing him with new and challenging toys, so that the poverty of his social environment sustains his passivity and social isolation. If such a child develops behavior pathology, he is likely to show an exaggeration or distortion of his own characteristic reactions in the form of retardation, chronic fatigue or desocialization.

We shall find, in our case material, patients whose infantile responsiveness seemed to set the course of their social learning in the direction of some specific pathology. Indeed, some adult pathological reactions follow so consistently from characteristic childhood patterns that the development of a particular variety of behavior pathology seems inevitable. We may also find exceptions to this principle, however, in cases where changed social relationships, sudden traumatic illness, and deep personal loss seem to restructure and even reverse the patient's characteristic behavior. Both varieties of onset — gradual development and relatively abrupt reorganization — will become understandable when we have considered in greater detail the principles of behavior organization. Consequently, we turn now to studies of the *consistency* of personality patterns, and to contemporary research on *constitutional factors* in human behavior. We shall find the most significant information, however, only after we have carried our search into the field of social learning.[14]

Consistency in behavior organization

Early differences in reactivity would have little meaning if they were not maintained and woven into a consistent pattern of individuality. If the differences we have described were all chance and momentary ones, for example, we would have no basis, in our everyday lives, for predicting what other people would do. Nor could we describe in any systematic fashion the development of normal behavior, or its caricature and malformation in the reactions of patients. But human beings, whether through biological structure or progressively selective learning, or through both, typically develop ways of behaving which are consistent. The older they grow, the more like themselves they are apt to become.

Many of the studies we have just considered provide information on the beginnings of individual uniqueness. In Shirley's longitudinal study, for example, careful observations and ratings of the children's behavior were made regularly for the first two years of life.[15] Although the infants differed measurably from one another, many exhibited patterns of behavior which were for them characteristic. Shirley concluded her investigation by writing brief personality sketches of each child. Fifteen years later, a great many of

---

[14] For a discussion of learning in relation to behavior pathology, see Chapter 3.

[15] Shirley, M., *The first two years*, vol. III. *Personality manifestations*. Minneapolis: University of Minnesota Press, 1933.

these same subjects, now in their adolescent years, were located by another investigator, and new personality sketches of them written.[16] Experts to whom the identities of the subjects were unknown were able to match the later with the earlier personality sketches, with a degree of accuracy far beyond chance expectation. In short, individual consistency in personality development, over a fifteen-year period, was striking enough to permit impartial judges to identify an adolescent subject from a description of him as an infant.

Other studies yield additional evidence favoring the long-time persistence of unique personality patterns. Thus Gesell's twins T and C, who were remarkably similar in many ways, each had unique attitudes and responses which were maintained over a fourteen-year period.[17] In an analysis of the school behavior of sixteen children over a five- or six-year period, McKinnon obtained data which also support the view that individual behavior is consistent.[18] Her results indicate that tendencies toward withdrawal from social situations are most likely to persist unchanged during this time-span, and that the changes in behavior which do occur are most often in the direction of *greater* conformity. In this study, as in all instances of human development, however, individual consistency is neither perfect nor necessarily permanent. Thus environmental change, new interpersonal relationships, or the acquisition of particular skills, operated in individual cases to alter the characteristic pattern of personality development.

As we might expect, striking exceptions have been found to the principle of developmental consistency, just as there occur striking examples of traumatic reorganization of behavior in individual cases. Macfarlane, for example, reports that among preschool children, studied over a one- or two-year period, problem behavior is more likely to be transitory than permanent.[19] Often, however, a change of problem behavior seems to represent rather a change in symptom than an over-all reorganization of behavior. A fearful child, for example, may scream as an infant, run away when he is a little older, and later become shy and withdrawn; and all of these apparently diverse reactions may still reflect his basic fearfulness. In the great majority of cases, later behavior seems to continue along general lines which are discernible in early infancy.

The fact of early, continuing individual differences in behavior provides a focus for much controversy in contemporary behavior pathology. For some writers, this finding represents proof of an hereditary constitutional tendency

---

[16] Neilon, P., "Shirley's babies after fifteen years: a personality study." *J. genet. Psychol.*, 1948, vol. 73, pp. 175–186.

[17] Gesell, A. and Thompson, H., "Twins T and C from infancy to adolescence: a biogenetic study of individual differences by the method of co-twin control." *Genet. Psychol. Monogr.*, 1941, vol. 24, pp. 3–121.

[18] McKinnon, K. M., "Consistency and change in behavior manifestations as observed in a group of sixteen children during a five-year period." New York: Teachers College, Columbia, Bureau of Publications, 1942.

[19] Macfarlane, J. W., "The guidance study." *Sociometry*, 1939, vol. 2, pp. 1–23.

toward health or illness — a predisposition so strong that people seem almost foreordained to develop behavior pathology or to escape it. By others, individual consistency in behavior organization is interpreted as the product of selective learning in a social context, which favors the self-perpetuation of certain ways of behaving and not others. In the interest of a biosocial view of normal and pathological behavior alike, we cannot afford to ignore either party to this controversy.

Constitutional factors in behavior pathology

Human organisms differ from one another in many aspects of their biological machinery — in height, weight and body build, in strength, sensory acuity, cortical potentials and energy level, in endocrine function and blood composition, and in the reactivity of their central and autonomic nervous systems. All of these factors, singly and in combination, have at one time or another achieved prominence as possible causes of behavior pathology. Occasionally, to be sure, "constitutional make-up" has been invoked as a reason for the development of behavior pathology only because no other explanation seems to hold.[20] Much more frequently, however, technical advance in medicine, and in its supporting sciences of physiology, biochemistry and pathology, has opened the way toward sober and well-planned investigations on the biological properties of the human organism. Indeed, the majority of our contemporary research projects in the field of behavior pathology are still conceived in the faith that, somewhere in the structure and functioning of the patient as a biological animal, lies the ultimate explanation of his pathological behavior.

Each present-day attempt to correlate skeletal, muscular, neural, circulatory, endocrine or chemical change with enduring behavior deviation has a long history.[21] Systems of personality diagnosis based on bodily "humors" — the forerunners of contemporary endocrine studies — began in the ancient belief that, in his own structure, man contained the same basic elements which made up his universe. Interest in the relationships between body type and temperament goes back at least to 425 B.C., to the writings of Hippocrates, and is probably much older even than that.[22] As knowledge has increased and techniques improved, the direction of research has changed; but the problem of correlating constitutional factors with behavior disorder remains today alive and still unsolved. A vast amount of carefully-directed research effort still yields results which are largely negative. From the wide field of investiga-

---

[20] This seems to be the case in the older conventional formulations of "constitutional psychopathic inferiority." See Chapter 7.

[21] See Allport, G. W., *Personality: a psychological interpretation.* New York: Holt, 1937, pp. 55–97.

[22] Sheldon, W. H., "Constitutional factors in personality." In Hunt, J. McV. (Ed.), *Personality and the behavior disorders.* New York: Ronald, 1944, pp. 526–549.

tions on constitutional factors, we shall select just two examples: those on *blood chemistry* and those on *body type*.

Blood chemistry. The task of establishing a relationship between behavior pathology and chemical composition of the blood is a particularly difficult one. The balance of creatinine, phosphorus and cholesterol in the blood of a human organism changes so widely from one day to the next that it often obscures any possible differences between individuals.[23] It is therefore not surprising to discover that efforts to describe a pattern of blood composition typical of patients suffering from particular behavior disorders have yielded results which are discouragingly negative. Critical reviews of hundreds of such chemical studies filter out only a few meager results which can be considered dependable; and even these are exceedingly difficult to interpret.[24] One positive finding, for example, is that patients in manic excitement tend to have slightly increased blood calcium. This increase may, of course, represent a constitutional variation which existed before the patient became ill, and which predisposed him toward the development of a manic disorder. It is equally possible, however, that elevated blood calcium levels may result from the manic patient's typically increased exertion, and thus may represent the consequence, rather than the antecedent, of his illness. Many of the positive findings in studies of blood chemistry do not dispose of this sort of ambiguous interpretation.[25]

Body type. The same difficulty of interpretation exists in contemporary studies of body type. The most vigorous proponent of physical typology today is Sheldon,[26] whose system of somatotyping on the basis of four components represents an advance over the earlier, more rigid classification. With high reliability, Sheldon was able to characterize the degree to which each anatomical component contributes to the total body structure of a given individual. He also found high correlations between somatotype and "temperament" type.[27] In his experimental group, for example, delicate, poorly muscled individuals with fragile bones (*ectomorphs*) were characterized, according to Sheldon's reports, by restraint, inhibition, desire for concealment and aversion

[23] See, for example, Goldstein, H., "The biochemical variability of the individual in relation to personality and intelligence." *J. educ. Psychol.*, 1935, vol. 18, pp. 348–371.

[24] See, for example, McFarland, R. and Goldstein, H., "The biochemistry of dementia praecox." *Amer. J. Psychiat.*, 1938, vol. 95, pp. 509–552; McFarland, R. and Goldstein, H., "Biochemistry of manic-depressive psychosis." *Amer. J. Psychiat.*, 1939, vol. 96, pp. 21–58; Malamud, W. and Miller, W., "Psychotherapy in the schizophrenias." *Amer. J. Psychiat.*, 1931, vol. 88, pp. 457–480.

[25] For critical reviews of this material see Cameron, N., "The functional psychoses." In Hunt, J. McV. (Ed.), *Personality and the behavior disorders.* New York: Ronald, 1944, pp. 861–921; Cameron, N., "The functional psychoses." In *Ann. Rev. Physiol.*, 1943, vol. 5, pp. 453–464; Cameron, N., "The place of mania among the depressions from a biological standpoint." *J. Psychol.*, 1942, vol. 14, pp. 181–195.

[26] Sheldon, W. H., Stevens, S. S., and Tucker, W. B., *The varieties of human physique.* New York: Harper, 1940.

[27] Sheldon, W. H. and Stevens, S. S., *The varieties of temperament.* New York: Harper, 1942.

to social activity (*cerebrotonia*). Those subjects who were sturdy and muscular (*mesomorphs*) were characterized as typically active, vigorous and assertive (*somatotonia*); while those who had massive and highly developed digestive viscera (*endomorphs*) were reported to be relaxed persons, who loved comfort and sociability, and who were hungry for affection as well as for food (*viscerotonia*).[28]

Serious criticisms have been aimed at Sheldon's methods and at his statistical analysis.[29] Even disregarding these, however, we may still question whether a given somatotype represents a constitutional predisposition toward a particular temperament type. Perhaps the individual with one variety of body build calls forth reactions from others which train him in characteristic ways of behaving. Thus the biological fragility of the ectomorph may make him inacceptable to his peers and unable to compete with them; he may then acquire, in social interaction, the techniques of withdrawal and isolation which characterize the "cerebrotonic" temperament. Conversely, the strong and stalwart mesomorph may learn, in successful competition with his peers, the techniques of vigorous assertiveness which define the "somatotonic temperament." In studies of body type, as in the case of the biochemical investigations, the critical question of interplay between constitution and social learning remains unanswered.[30]

In other studies of constitutional factors the findings have been similar. Important information is often obtained from them regarding the chemical, physiological and anatomical properties of the human organism; but correlations between these properties and the signs of behavior pathology are few. In general, negative results predominate, and positive results are open to conflicting interpretations. Consequently, such studies have thus far made only a negligible contribution to our understanding of the development and persistence of pathological behavior. The same limitations, and the same discouraging results, characterize investigations of the relationships between behavior pathology and *heredity*.

Hereditary susceptibility to behavior pathology

The student of human genetics has as great difficulty as the biochemist or physiologist has, in gathering sound data, and in interpreting them in the light

[28] For an application of the technique of somatotyping to the problem of psychiatric diagnosis, see Wittman, P., Sheldon, W. H., and Katz, C. J., "A study of the relationship between constitutional variations and fundamental psychotic behavior reactions." *J. nerv. ment. Dis.*, 1948, vol. 108, pp. 470–476.

[29] See the review of Sheldon, W. S. and Stevens, S. S., "The varieties of temperament," by Anastasi, A. *Psychol. Bull.*, 1943, vol. 40, pp. 146–147.

[30] Similar criticisms have been aimed at Kretschmer's typology in the work of Cabot. See Cabot, P., "The relationship between characteristics of personality and physique in adolescents." *Genet. Psychol. Monogr.*, 1938, vol. 20, pp. 3–120. For a direct challenge to Sheldon's work along the same lines see Fiske, D. W., "A study of relationships to somatotype." *J. appl. Psychol.*, 1944, vol. 28, pp. 504–519.

of his assumptions. No family line, of course, is without its cases of eccentricity or frank behavior pathology. But because behavior disorder is still widely considered shameful, families knowingly conceal and unwittingly forget instances of behavior pathology among their relatives. Even if a painstaking search through family histories unearths a preponderance of cases of behavior disorder in certain family lines, this fact does not necessarily demonstrate an inherited susceptibility. A prevailing family pattern of handling tension and need may create a familial predisposition toward behavior pathology as surely as if the susceptibility were transmitted through a pattern of dominant genes.[31]

The possibility that constitutional predisposition to behavior pathology is inherited is by no means a remote one. Selective breeding of rats, for example, can produce strains of animals which differ from one another in what may be called "temperament." It has been found that "emotionality," as defined by excessive micturition and defecation in the rat,[32] and "wildness," as defined by the animal's fighting and hiding tendencies,[33] vary systematically when genetic strains are crossed. In lines of both human and infrahuman organisms, structural characteristics, such as eye color and sensory defect, appear with frequencies which follow certain principles of genetic transmission. But neither eye color nor rodent wildness constitutes an important part of behavior pathology in the human being. It is rather with social ineptness and the inappropriate use of adjustive techniques, with tendencies toward anxiety, toward depression, excitement or persistent misinterpretation, that the behavior pathologist must concern himself in his search for origins and possible predispositions.

A few contemporary geneticists maintain the conviction that constitutional factors determine immunity or susceptibility to behavior pathology. These investigators accordingly study, in family lines, the occurrence of body type, of particular patterns of blood composition, and of autonomic responsiveness.[34] The greatest share of our research on heredity in behavior pathology, however, is based upon syndromes of behavior disorder rather than upon physiological or chemical variables. The investigator searches hospital records to see whether a particular disorder appears more frequently among close relatives of hospitalized patients than among persons unrelated to them. Research of this kind is ordinarily confined to a few syndromes. Exaggerated anxiety and

---

[31] Evidence for such "cultural transmission" is to be found in Ingersoll, H. L., "A study of the transmission of authority patterns in the family." *Genet. Psychol. Monogr.*, 1948, vol. 38, pp. 225–302.

[32] Hall, C. S., "The inheritance of emotionality." *Sigma Xi Quart.*, 1938, vol. 26, pp. 17–27.

[33] Stone, C. P., "Wildness and savageness in rats of different strains." In Lashley, K. S. (Ed.), *Studies in the dynamics of behavior.* Chicago: University of Chicago Press, 1932.

[34] Jost, H. and Sontag, L. W., "The genetic factor in autonomic nervous system function." *Psychosom. Med.*, 1944, vol. 6, pp. 308–310; Sontag, L. W., "The genetics of differences in psychosomatic patterns in childhood." *Amer. J. Orthopsychiat.*, 1950, vol. 20, pp. 479–489.

fatigue reactions, hysterical and paranoid illnesses, for example, are not usually considered to be hereditarily determined, and are consequently excluded from study. Those disorders which are most commonly suspected of having their origin in hereditary predisposition, on the other hand, are subjected to detailed study. These include developmental retardation, "constitutional psychopathic inferiority," depressive and manic illnesses, and schizophrenic disorders.

Perhaps the most extreme proponent of the hereditary viewpoint toward behavior pathology is Kallmann. In a series of books and papers, he has vigorously supported the doctrine that schizophrenia depends upon a specific genetic factor.[35] He begins by selecting a large number of schizophrenic patients in state hospitals, and then locates as many as possible of the patients' near and remote relatives, in whom he attempts to identify the presence or absence of schizophrenic disorder. His results seem to show that more close relatives of schizophrenic patients than distant ones have at some time suffered from schizophrenia. The frequencies of occurrence of schizophrenic disorder among close and remote relatives are used by Kallmann as a basis for the conclusion that predisposition toward schizophrenia is a recessive genetic trait.

Kallmann is not the only adherent of the hereditary view, nor is schizophrenia the only disorder for which specific genetic determination is claimed. A great many investigators have been impressed by the greater frequency of behavior pathology in some family trees than in the general population.[36] Recurring depressive and manic disorders — often included officially in the so-called "manic-depressive psychoses" — appear in certain families to a degree that encourages some investigators to conclude that susceptibility to these disorders must also be inherited.[37] The frequencies of occurrence of depressive and manic reactions, however, do not fit a specific genetic pattern of simple recessiveness or simple dominance.[38]

To these findings, and to their interpretation, a great many contemporary research workers raise serious and fundamental objections. The results of some studies, for example, conflict sharply with those of Kallmann and his associates. Moreover, the methods of investigation employed by Kallmann are

[35] Kallmann, F., *The genetics of schizophrenia.* New York: Augustin, 1938; Kallmann, F., "The genetic theory of schizophrenia." *Amer. J. Psychiat.*, 1946, vol. 103, pp. 309–322.

[36] See, for example, Landis, C. and Page, J., *Modern society and mental disease.* New York: Rinehart, 1938; Lewis, N. D. C., *Research in dementia praecox.* New York: National Committee for Mental Hygiene, 1936; Myerson, A., *Inheritance of mental diseases.* Baltimore: Williams and Wilkins, 1925; Pollock, H., Malzberg, B. and Fuller, R., *Hereditary and environmental factors in the causation of manic-depressive psychoses and dementia praecox.* Utica, N.Y.: State Hospitals Press, 1939.

[37] Rosanoff, A. J., Handy, L. M. and Plesset, I. R., "The etiology of manic-depressive syndromes, with special reference to their occurrence in twins." *Amer. J. Psychiat.*, 1935, vol. 91, pp. 725–762; Slater, E., "The inheritance of manic-depressive insanity." *Proc. Roy. Soc. Med.*, 1936, vol. 29, pp. 981–990.

[38] For a review of these studies, see Bellak, L., *Dementia praecox (The past decade's work and present status: a review and evaluation).* New York: Grune and Stratton, 1947, pp. 40–47.

open to criticism on at least four grounds: [39] (1) the validity of his *diagnosis* of schizophrenia is questionable, since he included "doubtful" cases, occasionally had recourse to anecdotal material and, in some instances, apparently called patients schizophrenic if they came from families in which the incidence of this disorder was high. (2) The *sampling* of schizophrenic patients' descendants was necessarily selected, since a great many of the original group of patients did not marry or have children. (3) The *expectancy* of occurrence of schizophrenia among related and unrelated groups cannot be stated with accuracy, since there is little agreement among geneticists as to the proper methods of calculating expectancy figures for this disorder. (4) *Environmental factors* are largely ignored, in spite of the fact that the early schizophrenic illness of a parent may seriously disrupt the family pattern in which the offspring are reared.

Criticisms such as these can be directed against most contemporary studies of hereditary susceptibility to behavior pathology. As in the case of studies of constitutional factors in behavior disorder, so in the case of research on hereditary predisposition, we cannot today point to a single study which gives a definitive answer to the question of etiology. The situation would be hopelessly discouraging were it not for one point on which constitutional typologists, staunch hereditarians and vigorous environmentalists alike agree. This is the indisputable fact that human organisms, whatever their biological predispositions, must work out in a social context their characteristic ways of behaving.

It is for this reason that we shall deal, in our study of behavior pathology, with total human organisms in a complex social field. We shall talk more about self-reactions than blood chloresterol, more about role-taking than cortical potentials, and more about socially-derived need than about recessive genes. In so doing, we continue the reversal of traditional trends which is beginning to characterize the field of behavior pathology. For it is a curious fact that, up to the present time, research in behavior disorder has concentrated more upon hereditary, prenatal and physiological factors, present in the organism at the moment of birth, than upon the decades of social learning which follow. This is all the more surprising when we recall the meager positive findings which such research yields. In choosing to study the lifetime of the total biosocial organism, we are selecting an approach which, from our present perspective, gives promise of greater and more immediate return.

The life history of a postnatal human being is the history of a slow, irregular, and often painful initiation into human society. Sometimes through direct tuition, but more often through providing models, his parents and his peers interpret for him the ways of behaving which prevail in his culture. This progressive social learning may produce behavior which ranges, in different individuals, from that which is personally satisfying and socially appropriate, to

[39] This criticism follows that of Pastore, N., "The genetics of schizophrenia: a special review." *Psychol. Bull.*, 1949, vol. 46, pp. 285–302.

that which is so unrewarding and invalid as to be called pathological. Whether or not the individual reaches adulthood firmly established in his culture depends upon the continuing, lifelong interplay of personal need and social expectation. If we are to understand the organization of normal and pathological behavior, therefore, we must begin by considering need, stress and frustration.

Need

Human infants, we have said, differ from one another in their responsiveness to stimuli, and in the readiness with which they become active. Some of these differences undoubtedly represent congenital variations in irritability. Some of them, however, appear regularly in conjunction with conditions of deprivation and satiation. For example, infantile activity increases as the period lengthens between feedings and it decreases when a child has been fed.[40] An infant becomes restless if the temperature of his surroundings drops, if he is thirsty or is deprived of sleep; and his restlessness subsides when a blanket is added, when he has a drink of water or a nap.

As a child grows, these simple relationships gain in complexity and significance. Now activity may increase with his mother's absence and wane when she enters the room. The quiet which earlier followed sucking the nipple, and getting food, now attends sucking a rattle or a thumb. The baby continues restless at nap-time until he has a particular blanket or a special toy, regardless of temperature change or degree of fatigue. Throughout the lifetime of any human being, his requirements increase and multiply, and the things which satisfy him become more numerous and more specific.

The concept of need

A list of the definitions of need which behavior pathologists have at one time or another advanced, would be an outline of trends in the history of behavior pathology. When nineteenth century biologists and psychologists, influenced by Darwinian evolution, explained human activity by means of instinctual theories, behavior pathologists also talked in terms of instincts. Because a dualistic philosophy of mind and body flourished at the same time, some behavior pathologists applied the instinct hypothesis to the "psyche" and spoke of "psychic" needs and instincts.

Two developments have altered these earlier definitions of need. One is the accumulation of information regarding the biological properties of living organisms, which led to the principle of *homeostasis*.[41] According to this prin-

[40] Balint, M., "Individual differences of behavior in early infancy, and an objective method for recording them: I. Approach and the method of recording." *J. genet. Psychol.*, 1948, vol. 73, pp. 81–117.
[41] Cannon, W. B., *The wisdom of the body* (2nd ed.). New York: Norton, 1939.

ciple, living tissue tends to maintain its stability and to return to a stable organization if its equilibrium is disturbed. The need-satisfaction sequence of
food deprivation — restlessness — feeding — quiescence can thus be taken as an
illustration of the disturbance and restoration of physiological equilibrium.

The other development is the increasing emphasis which contemporary
behavior pathologists give to the socially-learned aspects of pathological behavior. The principle of physiological homeostasis may explain the simple
sequence of *tension — feeding — relaxation*. But it tells us little about infants
who suck their thumbs, about children who develop food fads, obese adolescents who cannot stop overeating, emaciated depressed patients who refuse to
eat, and schizophrenic adults who believe that eating gradually changes their
bodies until they become superhuman or immortal. Today, any concept of
need which is useful in behavior pathology must allow for the elaboration of
simple sequences of tension and relaxation into intricate and personalized
patterns of socially derived need and satisfaction.

Definition of need. Let us then define *need* as *a condition of unstable or disturbed equilibrium in an organism's behavior, appearing typically as increased or
protracted activity and tension.* The signs of tension are many. They may include increased reflex responses, elevated heart and respiratory rate, low skin
resistance, and action potentials from contracting muscle fibers. In grosser
terms, they include tremors, grimaces, exaggerated startle reactions, sleeplessness, and any indicators of heightened reactivity — ranging from overt restlessness, distractibility and talkativeness, to increases in such covert reactions
as thinking, fantasying and dreaming. In many people, extreme unreactivity —
rigid posture and unaccustomed silence, for example — may also be indicators
of protracted tension. It is from *changes* in activity and tension that the
observer infers the behavioral disequilibrium of unsatisfied need.

Disequilibrium in behavior may follow upon a variety of conditions.
Changes in the surrounding temperature or in the individual's metabolic
processes, as we have seen, typically give rise to increased activity and tension.
But changes in the *social* climate also characteristically bring behavioral disequilibrium; and so do symbolic and covert reactions. A frown or a gesture
from the mother, the sound of her footsteps or of her voice in an adjoining
room, the activity of thinking about a rival sibling, may precipitate increased
tension and activity in a child. Reading, talking and fantasying on aggressive
or erotic themes may arouse and intensify adult need. Need is thus part of any
ongoing sequence of activity, and in consequence it is closely bound up with
motivation.

The precise identification of the conditions which arouse need, in a particular
person and at a given time, is an exceedingly difficult task. Because need-
satisfaction sequences undergo intricate modification through covert and symbolic reactions, the factors which instigate need-satisfaction sequences are

seldom open to inspection. Often our own behavior deceives us until we cannot say what it is that makes us tense, or what might bring us tension-reduction. Occasionally our attempts at self-analysis fail altogether; and only expert behavior analysis by an impartial person can then identify the instigators of our need.

Definition of motive. The factors which appear, upon analysis, to be significant in initiating and continuing organized behavior, are customarily called *motives.* We designate as *motive whatever factor seems to be of special significance in instigating and sustaining a given need-satisfaction sequence.* At one time it was fashionable in behavior pathology to identify and classify motives, as if one could encompass in a catalog of verbal tags all the sources of human action. During this period, motives were thought of in the same way as were the instinct-like needs we discussed earlier: they were considered "forces" or "energies" added to behavior, much like the addition of the critical charge that detonates a bomb. Today we recognize that *motive is a product of behavior analysis.* It is a construct of our own making, the result of our own operations in analyzing behavior.

During the same period in which motives were viewed as "forces," those motives which could be specified by the individual himself were called "conscious." Motives which eluded his search but could be designated by another person were called "unconscious." In line with the philosophical position of the time, conscious and unconscious motives were originally located in two distinctly different realms of the "psyche." These distinctions were at one time exceedingly useful in calling attention to the many motives of which all of us are unaware, and in stimulating study of the defensive technique of selective forgetting which we call *repression.* Unfortunately, however, the distinctions belonged to an earlier philosophical position which does not support contemporary psychological theory and methods of investigation. At present, the many definitions of unconsciousness are ambiguous and confusing,[42] and the differentiation between conscious and unconscious motives has become less and less distinct.

Consequently, we prefer to speak of *degrees of accessibility* of motives to one's own analysis, rather than of conscious and unconscious motives. No one doubts that people differ in the adequacy with which they can identify and formulate in words the significant factors in their own behavior. Nor is there any doubt that a given individual can formulate some aspects of his own behavior more adequately than others, or that acts which wholly mystify him are often those in which repression has played a part. Indeed, the problem of repression is crucial to our understanding of behavior pathology, and we shall give it detailed consideration in a later chapter.[43]

[42] Miller, J. G., *Unconsciousness.* New York: Wiley, 1942.
[43] See pages 337–351.

Primary and derived needs

The concept of need would have little value for the behavior pathologist if it included only simple patterns of muscular or visceral tension and relaxation. Hunger, thirst, oxygen-deficit and sexual tension, in their basic physiological forms, are rarely important in behavior pathology. But excepting for the neonatal period, immediately after birth, these needs rarely appear as uncomplicated physiological disequilibrium in any human behavior. Birth introduces the organism into a social environment within which needs are immediately complicated, satisfied, or frustrated through the activities of other persons. Within a context of complete dependence upon others, the human neonate begins a lifelong course of social learning which brings him new needs, new techniques of meeting them, and new frustrations. The possibilities of developing individual and unique patterns of need-satisfaction are endless; so also are the potentialities for acquiring the inappropriate and socially invalid sequences which define behavior pathology.

The multiplication of needs through social learning has led to a popular distinction which is misleading but persistent. This is the distinction between "primary" or "physiological" need, on the one hand, and "derived" or "social" need on the other. According to this view, tensions which are closely related to the organism's or the species' survival, such as those associated with hunger, thirst, oxygen deficit and sex, are primary. Needs which develop in a social context, such as tensions associated with the presence or absence of other persons or with their reactions are "secondary." In practice, this distinction is impossible to maintain. Behavioral disequilibrium in any organism necessarily involves physiological responses. But physiological disequilibrium, at least in human organisms, is so early and so thoroughly modified by social learning that pure or "primary" needs do not exist, except in theory.

This dilemma cannot be resolved by calling those needs primary which seem prepotent in the organism's behavior. Among normal persons and patients alike there may be found hierarchies of needs which reverse the expected order of significance. One man may starve rather than submit to demands which to his neighbor seem unimportant. Another may choose to exist at a level of bare subsistence because his religious beliefs, his political convictions, or the procedures of a scientific experiment demand it. Death may be courted and even welcomed by the inspired military leader, the martyr, the anxious penitent and the depressed patient. The evidence is all against a universal order of need-prepotency in human behavior. Hierarchies of needs there are, but they form highly personalized patterns, the products of different emphases in the social learning of different individuals.

The acquisition of personalized hierarchies of need begins at birth. From the infant's first nursing period, in his first day of life, the physiological disequilibrium of *hunger* occurs in a significant social context. The mother is much more than a food supply; she is her child's first and most important social contact.[44] The newborn infant is introduced at once to delay, to thwarting and to dependence upon another person. His mother may feed him gently or roughly, tensely or in a relaxed fashion, on a strict time schedule or on demand. Each of these contingencies represents a different sort of training in social interaction, and each may determine the direction which the elaboration of the hunger need takes.

The mother who feeds her infant tensely and on a strict time schedule, for example, prolongs and intensifies his behavioral disequilibrium through the delay, and through her own sudden, sporadic movements. Many infants react in such situations by sucking inefficiently, rejecting the breast or regurgitating their food. And most mothers then become more tense and concerned over these signs of feeding disturbance. Under such circumstances, the approach of nursing time and the preparatory sights and sounds of feeding are likely to arouse tensions in both infant and mother which are *intensified* rather than relieved by the act of feeding. Indeed, these tensions may appear whenever the mother is present, and later whenever any adult is present, whether the infant is hungry or not. As the infant grows into childhood, his language and other motor behavior serve further to elaborate and complicate these needs, until they are far removed from the simple metabolic disequilibrium which first defined them. At no stage in this development, however, can we say that the hunger need has shifted from a primary and biological to a derived and social one. The progression from the physiological disequilibrium of hunger, to irritability, restlessness and tension in the presence of adults, has been one of continuing, reciprocal social interaction.

In an equally complicated fashion, the disequilibrium of *sex need* becomes extended, through social learning, into individual hierarchies of need. It is a common observation that young infants show patterns of behavior which adults would endow with specific sexual and procreative significance. Erections occur as part of a generalized tension in the male infant, for example, and most babies and young children discover and handle their genitalia in the course of exploring their own bodies.[45] Such reactions seem to be practically universal; and they apparently occur more frequently in infants who have developed adequate relationships with their mothers than in those who are deprived of maternal affection. In one study of 250 children -- including some cared for by their own parents at home, some by their mothers in a nursery, and some by nurses in an orphanage — genital activity was found to be most

---

[44] See pages 134–137.

[45] Halverson, H. M., "Infant sucking and tensional behavior." *J. genet. Psychol.*, 1938, vol. 53, pp. 365–430; Halverson, H. M., "Genital and sphincter behavior of the male infant." *J. genet. Psychol.*, 1940, vol. 56, pp. 95–136.

frequent where there were close affectional relationships between mother and infant.[46]

In view of the prevalence of genital play in infants, and its significance as an early indicator of satisfactory social relationships, it is unfortunate that many parents are unable to accept objectively their infants' genital responsiveness. Due mainly to their own acquired sensitivities, parents often place infantile genital manipulation or sex reactions within an adult ethical framework. They interrupt, control or punish their offspring's sex responses, in such a way as to increase rather than decrease the need of the infant or growing child who exhibits such behavior. For the child, of course, both sex behavior and its restriction lack the adult accents which his parents give them. It is therefore not surprising that he comes to confuse sex with evil, punishment and the withdrawal of parental affection. At no point in the progression, from the generalized tensions which include genital responsiveness, to the complex attitudes of fear, shame or guilt over sex behavior, can we isolate "primary" sex need from the matrix of social learning within which it develops. Like hunger, thirst, oxygen-deficit or temperature imbalance, the disequilibrium of sex need begins in a social context, and is never separated from it.

Need-satisfaction sequences

Need and its satisfaction together form a pattern of tension and reduction of tension. This pattern is a temporal one whose extent may range from a few seconds, at one extreme, to a period of years, at the other extreme. The simple disequilibrium induced by stumbling, for example, constitutes a need which the righting reflexes immediately and automatically terminate or "satisfy." Food deprivation arouses needs which may be denied for hours, or even for days, before feeding reduces the tension. And sex need may continue without direct satisfaction for a span of years. But regardless of the time-span involved, it is this temporal pattern of tension and tension-reduction or termination to which we give the name *need-satisfaction sequence*.

Feeding a restless, hungry infant restores the organism to a condition of equilibrium, and thus terminates the tension and activity of need. The termination of need, when it is the consequence of such action, we call *direct satisfaction*. Termination of need through direct satisfaction is less common — and less important in the organization of normal and pathological behavior — than its termination through a shift in activity, some distraction, or a learned substitution. The reduction of tension by such means we call *indirect* or *substitute satisfaction*. Thus the hungry infant sucks his thumb, the starving

[46] Spitz, R. A. and Wolf, K. M., "Autoerotism. Some empirical findings and hypotheses on three of its manifestations in the first year of life." In Freud, A. (Ed.), *The psychoanalytic study of the child*, vol. 3/4. New York: International Universities Press, 1949, pp. 85–120.

prisoner of war fantasies a feast, and both achieve some reduction in the tension of their hunger need.

The satisfaction of need, whether immediate or delayed, direct or substitute, has four consequences of importance to the student of behavior pathology. In the first place, need-satisfaction eventuates in tension-reduction. In the second place, the techniques of need-satisfaction which a person develops often become ends in themselves, and thus in effect generate new needs. Moreover, need-satisfaction sometimes favors the appearance of needs which are lower in a person's hierarchy. And, finally, need-satisfaction sequences can elicit after-reactions which may themselves be either positive or negative with respect to the original satisfaction. We shall turn now to a more detailed consideration of each of these four possible consequences of the satisfaction of need.

1. *Need-satisfaction eventuates in reduction of tension.* We shall see later [47] that tension-reduction is one of the conditions which favors prompt and efficient learning. This means that reactions which terminate need are likely to be learned easily, and to persist in the learner's repertory of behavior. To put the point in more precise language, tension-reduction serves to reinforce the learning of those acts which induce it.

Because it facilitates learning through the reduction of tension, need-satisfaction may contribute to the fixation of behavior. Hesitations in bio-social maturation are common in the normal development of human beings, and prolonged delay in some phase of maturing underlies much behavior pathology. Such delays or terminations of maturation we call *fixation.*[48] Thumb-sucking in an infant, for example, is a commonly learned tension-reducer; but thumb-sucking in a school-age child represents fixation. More inclusive need-satisfactions may lead to more comprehensive fixations. Thus the child whose affectional needs are satisfied through overprotective reactions from his mother may arrive at his adult years with immature, dependent attitudes toward other people. And because of overlearning in this area, he may be wholly unable to shift his ways of behaving to a more adult level.

2. *Techniques of need-satisfaction, whether direct or substitute, often become ends in themselves and so generate new needs.* This is closely related to our previous point. Because tension-reduction facilitates learning, the techniques which the individual employs in satisfying need tend to persist as an integral part of his behavioral repertory.[49] The child who sucks his thumb as part of his preparatory feeding behavior, for example, may find comfort in thumb-

---

[47] See pages 75–79.

[48] Maturation and fixation are discussed in Chapter 5.

[49] This is similar to Allport's concept of "functional autonomy" of motives; see Allport, G. W., *Personality; a psychological interpretation.* New York: Holt, 1937, pp. 190–212. For a review of experiments with infrahuman animals on this point of "acquired drives," see Miller, N. E., "Acquired drives and reward." In Stevens, S. S. (Ed.), *Handbook of experimental psychology.* New York: Wiley, 1951.

sucking whenever he is restless or forlorn. And he may be restless and forlorn when he is not hungry, so that his learned means of tension-reduction appear in contexts other than the feeding situation. In this way, the techniques of need-satisfaction come to reduce tensions which are remote from the original need. This point is so important to behavior pathology that we must give it special consideration.

A great many instances of behavior pathology represent the persistence of techniques of need-satisfaction which were originally appropriate, but which have grown exaggerated or distorted until they become at last socially invalid.

Let us take, as an illustration, the behavior of a young unmarried woman who came to a psychiatric clinic complaining of fatigue, ineffi- ciency, excessive daydreaming and a voracious appetite. She said she had been growing increasingly tired and lethargic since her graduation from college two years before. Although she had accepted several tempo- rary jobs teaching dramatics in small schools, she neglected her work more and more, spent long periods lying on her bed, and memorized and recited lengthy excerpts from religious tracts. Finally she gave up working alto- gether and remained at home alone in her room.

Six months before she came to the clinic, our patient began to eat vora- ciously. She took three or four generous helpings at each meal, and be- tween meals ate large quantities of food from the refrigerator. Although the pantry was always open to her, on several occasions her parents found her in the barn, eating grain and garbage which had been put there for the farm animals. She excused this behavior merely by saying that she was hungry. During this six-month period she gained forty pounds. Exam- inations in the clinic excluded the possibility of endocrine or general metabolic disturbance; but there was considerable evidence to indicate that the uncontrollable eating had become a substitute satisfaction which reduced the tension of her unappeased affectional needs.

The patient was the oldest of seven children. For the first five years of her life she had been the only child, indulged and overprotected by her mother. Then came the second child, a girl, and the patient was abruptly cut off from the fondling, petting, praise and attention which had formerly been hers. Later in childhood, the younger sister consistently excelled her in school and made friends more easily than she. In adolescence the sister enjoyed pretty clothes, dancing and the company of boys, which the patient herself characterized as "having a good time in a wicked way." Throughout her life, the patient compared herself unfavorably with her sister, calling herself "dumb," shy and "old-maidish." She had few boy friends, went to college dances alone, and was always critical of any young man who came to call on her. Her fantasies and dreams, however, cen- tered around love affairs, marriage and child-bearing. Her younger sister became engaged and then married six months before the patient came to the clinic — the time at which, it will be recalled, the patient began her voracious eating.

In the hospital, the patient appeared apathetic, preoccupied, and some- what disorganized in her behavior. Asked about her overeating, she said,

"I guess it's my sex . . . I'm a little eager for marriage, I ought to be taken care of. . . . My hands are weak." Her spontaneous comments were usually confined to complaints of hunger. On an obesity diet she achieved only a negligible loss of weight; she continually attempted to take food surreptitiously from the other patients. Prolonged therapy directed, not toward her overeating, but toward the needs for affection and acceptance which food had come to satisfy indirectly, brought some improvement. She remained, however, a shy, withdrawn person who easily became fatigued and who continued to find solace and release from tension by eating. For her, eating had become fixed as a technique of satisfying needs other than hunger; and it persisted in her repertory of behavior in a context of increasingly maladaptive reactions which eventually crystallized as a chronic schizophrenic disorder.

Many persons learn to eat when they are lonely, frustrated, frightened, bored or restless for any reason, whether or not they are suffering from food-deprivation. A systematic study of eating as a substitute satisfaction is to be found in the cases of obese children and adults studied by Bruch.[50] These persons, like our patient, were without organ pathology to account for their obesity, but were typically starved for affection and security early in their lives. For them, eating seemed to provide reduction of the tensions of rejection and insecurity rather than reduction of the tensions of hunger. The significance of eating as a need in these patients is shown in their universal inability to remain on a diet or to respond to any other form of treatment, unless it also included satisfaction of their *affectional* needs.

The same relationships can be seen in many of the reactions originally implicated in the feeding situation. Thumb-sucking, object-sucking or tongue-sucking, for example, are reactions which often occur in conjunction with hunger-satisfaction in the infant. They may come to be more generally tension-reducing, however, and may persist as one of the so-called "oral mannerisms." The infant who refuses or regurgitates his food, and thereby arouses maternal concern, may come to respond with food finickiness and vomiting in any situation in which he is rejected or needs affection. We find extreme examples of this variety of need-satisfaction occasionally in adults suffering from behavior disorder who so persistently vomit that their lives are placed in jeopardy.

A young married woman, for example, was brought to a general hospital in an ambulance, in a severe state of starvation and dehydration. Her husband explained that, for the past year, she had grown increasingly

---

[50] Bruch, H., "Obesity in childhood: III. Physiologic and psychologic aspects of the food intake of obese children." *Amer. J. Dis. Child.*, 1940, vol. 59 (II), pp. 739–781; Bruch, H. and Touraine, G., "Obesity in childhood: V. The family frame of obese children." *Psychosom. Med.*, 1940, vol. 2, pp. 141–206; Bruch, H., "Obesity in childhood and personality development." *Amer. J. Orthopsychiat.*, 1941, vol. 11, pp. 467–474; Bruch, H., "Psychological aspects of obesity." *Psychiatry*, 1947, vol. 10, pp. 373–381.

unable to retain food, until now she vomited anything, solid or fluid, which she swallowed. Repeated laboratory investigations, prior to her admission and while she was in the hospital, disclosed no organ pathology to account for her symptoms. In the hospital, the patient seemed willing enough to take food, but promptly regurgitated it. Intravenous injections of glucose also resulted in vomiting. Because the patient was *in extremis*, intravenous injections were given while she was under sedation. Although these enabled her to survive, they did not bring any noticeable improvement in her general condition. Attempts to explore with her the difficulties which might have led to this persistent vomiting failed, both because of the patient's resistance and because her extreme weakness made it difficult for her to respond to questioning. After three weeks of bare survival, with no improvement, she was removed from the hospital by her husband and died soon thereafter.

The background of this extreme reaction, as furnished by the husband, seemed to lie in the patient's attitude toward marriage and its responsibilities. Both the patient and her husband were citizens of a country where marriages were arranged by the couple's parents, and where neither party involved knew one another until their wedding day. Our patient had been fearful of marriage and unprepared for it, and had refused twice to go through with the ceremony which her parents had arranged. Her rejection of food actually began several weeks before her wedding; but afterwards it increased steadily in severity until it included vomiting. In this patient, as in many others to a less extreme degree, intractable vomiting seemed to represent rejection of the responsibilities of maturity, and possibly even rejection of life itself.

Techniques of tension-reduction which involve the sex organs may also become compelling needs. Genital manipulation may provide release of tension for the infant, and then persist as a satisfaction in any needful situation, whether sexual or not. Because of many parents' punitive attitudes toward such behavior, however, children often make their earliest sex responses in a setting of pain and punishment. It is therefore not surprising to find adults who intermingle sex reactions, pain and punishment, and adults for whom the acts of inflicting or suffering pain have themselves become new needs.

The need to inflict pain, punishment, domination and restraint upon others we call *sadism;* and the reciprocal need to suffer these we call *masochism.* It was generally believed among the earlier behavior pathologists that sadistic and masochistic needs were always sexual in character. It is, of course, true that in heterosexual relations, one individual ordinarily imposes restraint, domination and sometimes pain, which the other accepts and often seeks. But by no means is all need to inflict or to suffer pain and punishment necessarily sexual in origin. If the infliction of punishment or pain upon another person reduces tension of any kind, sadistic reactions may persist as new, insistent needs. A great many individuals — overzealous reformers and overanxious sinners, for example — relieve their own tensions by condemning and punishing the failings of others.

In the same way, if punishment breaks up intolerable tensions of any kind, it may be sought by an individual as a welcome source of release. We shall see that the rigidly trained child or adult who believes he has transgressed, remains anxious and tense until he gains punishment from others or from his own self-reactions. We find in the painful rituals of many compulsive patients, and in the self-mutilation of some schizophrenic patients, additional examples of satisfaction in punishment. Thus one female schizophrenic patient extinguished cigarettes by squeezing the burning end, and applied lighted cigarettes to her wrists and forearms until she was badly scarred. She explained, "I burned myself there because I felt I had been wicked. I felt I should be punished."

Anxious depressed patients often seek punishment for acts or thoughts which they consider sinful and unpardonable.

> One patient in agitated depression, for example, becoming tense and fearful, implored nurses and physicians to torture her. "I ought to be put on a table and strapped down and smothered to death," she said. "When are they coming after me? This is the day I'm to be killed. . . . I know I'm the next. They'll tie my hands and put me in the fire and burn me to death. . . . Put me in a tub of boiling water. Make the water boiling hot. I want somebody to kill me. . . . What are those guns I hear?"

Sometimes, as in this patient, masochistic need eventuates in delusions and hallucinatory developments.[51] The patient believes others are reviling and persecuting him, or hears voices which threaten and accuse him and, in the exceptional but tragic case, obeys a voice which impels him to suicide.

3. *Need-satisfaction may favor the appearance of needs which are lower in the individual's hierarchy.* Each person, as we have seen, acquires a unique pattern of needs which differ among themselves in relative prepotency. When needs are satisfied which occupy a prepotent position in an individual's private scale of values, the person often discovers that now other needs have become significant.[52] Thus the man for whom economic security is all-important may find, when he is at last financially secure, that relaxation, recreation and conviviality are now essential for his well-being. We have indirect evidence of this consequence of need-satisfaction in reports of prisoners of war who came close to death by starvation.[53] For, during food-deprivation, matters of personal interrelationship, political conviction or bodily appearance became insignificant as compared with those of sheer survival; but after the nutritional needs

---

[51] For an extended discussion of *delusion*, see Chapter 13, and of *hallucination*, see Chapter 14.

[52] For a theoretical analysis of this point see Maslow, A. H., "'Higher' and 'lower' needs." *J. Psychol.*, 1948, vol. 25, pp. 433–436; Maslow, A. H., "Some theoretical consequences of basic need-gratification." *J. Personality*, 1948, vol. 16, pp. 402–416.

[53] See, for example, Bettelheim, B., "Individual and mass behavior in extreme situations." *J. abn. soc. Psychol.*, 1943, vol. 38, pp. 417–452; Bondy, C., "Problems of internment camps." *J. abn. soc. Psychol.*, 1943, vol. 38, pp. 453–475; Friedman, P., "Some aspects of concentration camp psychology." *Amer. J. Psychiat.*, 1949, vol. 105, pp. 601–605.

had at last been satisfied, these other needs reappeared. An analogous phenomenon is often seen in the course of therapy in behavior disorder. When the patient's need for acceptance and security is satisfied, through the relationship he establishes with his therapist, other needs become prepotent for him.[54]

4. *Need-satisfaction sequences evoke after-reactions which may be either positive or negative.* After the tension of need is terminated, human beings can still react to the now terminated need-satisfaction sequence. This *after-reaction* may be one of pleased acceptance, as when, following a hearty meal, a person comments favorably upon the food and upon his state of relaxation or pleasant satisfaction. The after-reaction may, however, be one of irritation, revulsion or chagrin, as when the food has been poor, the company annoying, or one's own behavior embarrassing. After-reactions, whether positive or negative, may follow directly upon the termination of a need-satisfaction sequence, or they may be delayed weeks, months or even years.

After-reactions to the termination of need have two important consequences. For one thing, the after-reaction may become an end in itself. The individual may come to derive greater satisfaction from talking, thinking or reading about food and drink, or about sex need and satisfaction, than from direct feeding or sexual behavior. For another, the after-reaction often changes in sign with the passage of time. A great many war veterans, for example, react immediately to the hardships and privation of battle with fear and disgust, but years later may recall and comment upon the same conditions with humorous pleasure. Conversely, an individual may react to sexual or hostile need-satisfaction sequences at the time with gratification, only to recall the same events later with shame and sorrow. The latter change in sign from positive to negative is particularly common in anxious and depressed patients. Indeed, we shall often find it in the *crucial shift* which characterizes agitated and retarded depressive disorder.[55]

From this analysis it is clear that satisfaction of need has important consequences for behavior pathology. Because it is tension-reducing, satisfaction facilitates overlearning and hence may favor the fixation of behavior at immature levels. By the same principle, acquired techniques of need-satisfaction may persist and become needs in themselves. Moreover, the satisfaction of prepotent needs often permits needs lower in a person's hierarchy to appear and to become compelling. And when a need-satisfaction sequence is terminated, the human being can still after-react to it, positively or negatively. As important in behavior pathology as need-satisfaction, however, are the conditions which prevent need-satisfaction, and which thereby keep the organism in a state of prolonged tension and activity. These are the situations of stress and frustration, to which we next turn.

[54] See pages 611–615.
[55] The crucial shift is discussed on pages 321 and 324.

Stress and Frustration

As common in everyday life as the sequence of need and satisfaction are situations in which need and its tensions persist unrelieved. Every infant meets such contingencies at birth. The immediate and automatic need-satisfaction which characterizes life in the uterus gives way to schedules of feeding, elimination, naps and play. The daily routines interrupt an infant's ongoing behavior and bring him thwarting of need, and delay of its satisfaction. His is to be no passing acquaintance with stress and frustration. For throughout life, everyone continues to encounter situations in which sequences of activity are altered, distorted, delayed or permanently halted. And every individual develops his own means of coping with unfulfilled need, as well as his own thresholds of tolerance for it.

There are two different but closely interrelated situations which intensify or prolong the tensions of unsatisfied need. In one, pressures from others, or from his own reactions, markedly change the individual's ongoing behavior from its customary pattern. Thus, for example, a young child who in his own home handles knife and fork reasonably well, may astonish his parents by his behavior when he is in the highly charged atmosphere of a company dinner away from home. Under such pressure, a few children improve in skill and dexterity, while many more hesitate, falter and even disorganize in their eating behavior; but in either case the reactions are changed from their customary pattern. This first variety of situation we shall designate as *stress*.

A second situation which intensifies or prolongs tension is one in which ongoing activity is prevented from reaching consummation. A child who sets out to get an ice-cream cone loses his nickel on the way and returns home crying. An adolescent girl buys a new dress for a high-school dance but sits at home on the appointed evening because no boy has invited her to go. A bookkeeper, whose length of service merits a promotion and a raise, sees a younger member of the firm placed in the position he covets. A man loses his job because he has grown old, and lives out his life thereafter unhappy, functionless and unwanted. To this variety of situation we give the name *frustration*. Stress and frustration are both inevitable parts of human existence, and both contribute to the development and persistence of pathological behavior.

Stress

Let us define *stress* as *a situation in which a person's ongoing behavior is altered from its customary pattern, because of continuing pressure from others or from his own reactions*. There are many changes in ongoing behavior which occur in situations of stress. Skeletal and visceral reactions may accelerate or slow down.[56] The individual's pattern of activity may become simplified to the

[56] Darrow, C. W. and Henry, C. E., "Psychophysiology of stress." In National Research Council, *Human factors in undersea warfare.* 1949, pp. 417–439.

point of stereotypy, or tightened in organization until it seems inflexible. The pattern may become loose, overinclusive or even thoroughly disorganized. Under stress, the efficiency of skilled acts may decline or they may improve; but if they improve, this usually occurs at great personal cost, in terms of energy output, prolonged tension and unremitting strain.[57] Common to all these characteristics of stress, however, is a *change* in the behavioral sequence, from one which is customary for the individual, to one which is decidedly different.

The pressures which define a stressful situation also vary greatly in kind. An imposed acceleration in the *tempo* of a performance may alter the character of the ongoing activity. Thus the housewife who discovers that important guests are arriving earlier than she had expected, hurries her tasks, takes shortcuts in her cleaning, omits an elaborate sauce from her menu, and arrives tense and tremulous at the door to greet her visitors. In an analogous way, any increase in the *intensity* of external stimulation may prove stressful. The man who answers questions calmly and judiciously in an office interview typically behaves quite differently if he is in the focus of an intense light, and the target of insistent, shouted accusations by a hostile cross-examiner.

Much of the stress of everyday life is the product of our own reactions to ourselves rather than the direct consequence of the behavior of other people.[58] The early arrival of her guests will be more stressful to the average housewife if her reputation, or her husband's status, is at stake, than if the occasion is a casual one. A cross-examination with third-degree tactics will change the victim's customary behavior much less if the situation is a parlor game than if it is a court-martial where conviction may bring execution. It is the immediate construction which a person places upon a situation that decides whether it is stressful or not. If the housewife transforms a chance incident into a test of personal adequacy, or if the defendant answers questions in a context of anticipated death, then these situations become highly stressful — regardless of the particular reactions of early guests or energetic prosecutor.

Many vivid examples of stress in normal individuals are to be found among military personnel. No fighting man can ignore the threat of injury and death in modern gunfire, in flak, and in falling bombs. No fighting man is without concern over himself, his family and his companions in battle. To the universal fear of destruction, and his responsibility for others, a multitude of external pressures is added. The man fights under absolute orders, in foxholes, in planes or in boats, which restrict his actions and keep him vulnerable to deadly attack. Exposed to the intense and terrifying sights and sounds of battle, he is expected to execute skilled performances at high speed and with perfect accuracy. Under such stress some men suffer temporary or permanent

---

[57] Haggard, E. A., "Psychological causes and results of stress." In National Research Council, *Human factors in undersea warfare.* 1949, pp. 441–461.

[58] For a discussion of self-reactions, see pages 95–104 and 284–289.

impairment in their customary behavior. A great many more men, however, are able to maintain their performance at a high level of efficiency, although usually at the cost of severe personal strain.

Because stress is the primary feature of wartime operations, the procedures employed for selecting men for dangerous missions has often included artificially stressful situations.[59] From these techniques we can obtain further information regarding the character of stress. Candidates for the intelligence service, in the German and British as well as in the American forces, were subjected to two or three days of tests designed to produce stress. They were required to fabricate false personal histories, and to maintain them despite the most strenuous efforts of expert lawyers, psychologists and psychiatrists to break their stories. They were accused of crimes, and interviewed and cross-examined by trained prosecutors. They were forced to undertake a variety of difficult and impossible tasks, such as dragging heavy logs over high, smooth walls, or building intricate bridges with inadequate materials; in some instances trained "helpers" badgered them and impeded their efforts. Most of these tests were conducted also under severe time pressure.

Such selection procedures were calculated to increase the demands which the candidates made upon themselves. These men had all volunteered for hazardous duty. Success meant a responsible, if dangerous, assignment in a special service. Many of the tests involved groups of candidates, so that competition among the men developed easily. The combination of pressures from external demand and from personal self-reactions made the situation comparable to military combat; and in general the men behaved as do men in the stress of combat. Some showed temporary disorganization or impairment of behavior, while others maintained or increased the efficiency of their performance under stress.

Like combat personnel and candidates for the intelligence service, a great many patients suffering from behavior pathology develop disorganization or inappropriate reactions in a setting of stress. Sometimes a brief traumatic event, such as a sudden change in personal relationships, the loss of a close friend or relative, or a bodily illness or injury, provides a situation stressful enough to precipitate behavior disorder. Much more typically, however, a long period of unrelieved stress gradually alters and distorts the person's customary behavior from the patterns which are common in his culture to those which are pathological. We shall find brief periods of increased personal stress preceding the occurrence of compulsive acts. Likewise, anxiety disorders, and depressive and manic illnesses, as we shall see, grow typically out of a background of chronic anxiety, intensified by personal stress.

[59] Office of Strategic Services. *Assessment of men.* New York: Rinehart, 1948.

Frustration

Even in highly stressful situations, need-satisfaction sequences are fre-quently completed, although their consummation may involve increased strain and effort for the individual. There are a great many circumstances, however, under which behavior sequences are prevented from reaching consummation, either temporarily or permanently. These circumstances usually induce dis-tortions of behavior such as those occurring under stress. Situations of this kind, in which the completion of behavioral sequences is prevented, we desig-nate as *frustration*. By *frustration* we shall mean a *situation in which a person's ongoing motivated behavior is temporarily or permanently prevented from reaching consummation.*

Frustration by simple delay. Simple postponement of the termination of an ongoing behavioral sequence is a daily occurrence for any member of a social group. Schedules of feeding and toilet training first introduce the infant to delay in the satisfaction of his need. As an individual grows through childhood and adolescence to adulthood, the cultural context of family and community, which controls his need-satisfaction sequences, becomes more complex, and delay grows more frequent and protracted. The direct satisfaction of sex need, to take but one example, is commonly postponed for years after the organism is biologically mature. For in most societies it must wait upon intricate, cul-turally-defined rites of courtship, engagement and marriage, which have legal, religious and social implications far beyond any strictly biological significance.

In a society such as ours, where prescribed delay is a common event, we may expect to find people anticipating, directly or indirectly, the termination of their need-satisfaction sequences. Indeed, parents often train their children directly in such anticipation by answering questions and requests for privilege with the admonition "Wait until you're older." The excursions into adult-like behavior which typify normal adolescence often represent anticipations of need-satisfaction which family and community ordain shall be delayed.[60] Some persons find that simple postponement of need-satisfaction produces tensions which cannot be tolerated unrelieved, and so proceed to terminate their on-going behavior regardless of cultural prohibitions. We find such reactions in the feeding and toilet "accidents" of all normal infants, in the brief, impulsive responses of normal children and adults and, in extreme distortion, in the characteristic behavior of selectively retarded social deviants.[61]

Frustration by thwarting. In the course of biosocial maturation, simple post-ponement of need-satisfaction is joined by the equally frustrating but more common condition of thwarting. Physical obstacles, the reactions of others, and one's own self-reactions, all enter to interrupt and distort the ongoing se-quence of behavior. Infants in all cultures undergo thwarting in the course

[60] See pages 141–143. [61] See pages 203–206.

of their early training. The swaddling, body-binding and cradling procedures which other cultural groups apply to their young are duplicated by the cribs, play-pens and fenced-in yards which limit the freedom of children in contemporary Western society.[62] In all societies, these barriers are gradually replaced by parental reactions to the child, which overtly, or by gesture, command, and warning look, move him from dangerous to safer places. And eventually the thwarting parental reactions are in turn succeeded by the growth of self-reactions, until in full maturity individuals efficiently restrict and control their own behavior.[63]

A great many laboratory experiments have been conducted to investigate the properties of thwarting conditions, and to define the relationships between severity of thwarting and the character of ensuing behavior.[64] One of the most lifelike of these is a study carried out at the University of Minnesota during World War II, to determine the effects of experimental semistarvation upon the human organism.[65] The subjects were thirty-six volunteer members of the Civilian Defense Patrol who, over a six-month period, subsisted on a diet so restricted that they lost on the average 25 per cent of their body weight. Since the subjects were free to do as they liked, except for eating or missing their daily test periods, the responsibility for cooperating fully in the experiment was largely in the men's own hands. Under these experimental conditions, therefore, severe thwarting of the hunger need occurred mainly as a consequence of the subjects' own self-reactions of control.

The men reacted to thwarting with a wide variety of substitute satisfactions. They soaked their food in water, chewed gum until their mouths became sore, collected recipes, talked and fantasied about food during the day, and dreamed of it at night. About one-fourth of the group developed reactions so deviant and inappropriate as to be considered at least temporarily pathological. In these cases the pathological behavior seemed to be the outcome of personally characteristic patterns of maladaptiveness, intensified by severe thwarting in the experimental situation. A few of the men, despite great effort, were unable to maintain the necessary level of self-denial, and so withdrew entirely from the experiment.

[62] For a discussion of recent literature concerned with these points, see Orlansky, H., "Infant care and personality." *Psychol. Bull.*, 1949, vol. 46, pp. 1–48.

[63] For a discussion of self-reactions, see pages 95–104. For a discussion of self-control, conscience and guilt, see pages 284–289.

[64] See, for example, Hovland, C. I. and Sears, R. R., "Minor studies of aggression: VI. Correlation of lynchings with economic indices." *J. Psychol.*, 1940, vol. 9, pp. 301–310; Mintz, A., "A re-examination of correlations between lynchings and economic indices." *J. abn. soc. Psychol.*, 1946, vol. 41, pp. 154–160; Marquis, D. P., "A study of frustration in newborn infants." *J. exper. Psychol.*, 1943, vol. 32, pp. 123–138; Sears, R. R., Hovland, C. I. and Miller, N. E., "Minor studies of aggression: I. Measurement of aggressive behavior." *J. Psychol.*, 1940, vol. 9, pp. 275–295.

[65] Franklin, J. C., Schiele, B. C., Brozek, J., and Keys, A., "Observations on human behavior in experimental semistarvation and rehabilitation." *J. clin. Psychol.*, 1948, vol. 4, pp. 28–44.

Somewhat more artificial than this study, but still intensely thwarting, is the common experimental technique of induced failure.[66] The experimenter sets his subject a task which cannot be performed and insists upon impossible criteria of speed and accuracy, or interrupts the subject before he has completed the assigned tasks and announces to him that he has failed.[67] In either case, the ongoing activity initiated by the experimenter's instructions never reaches consummation. Under such brief, sham conditions, laboratory subjects exhibit in miniature a good many of the reactions that characterize people who encounter more enduring and more severe thwarting in their daily lives. In these experiments, as in the semistarvation one, the subject's own interpretation of the tasks, the level of achievement he anticipates for himself, and his own criticism of his performance are important variables in determining the degree of thwarting. Often the subject seems torn between his desire to quit and his sense of obligation to the experimenter, so that the situation becomes one of conflict for him.

Frustration by conflict. Conflict between contradictory reactions is a common condition of frustration. People repeatedly encounter situations, whether trivial or significant, in which one ongoing sequence of behavior cannot be consummated except at the expense of another sequence. Resolving such a conflict, therefore, means terminating one pattern of activity but leaving the other one thwarted. Partly because it is exceedingly common, but largely because it is closely related to the development of anxiety, conflict has been subjected to careful investigation as a determinant of behavior pathology. For this reason, we shall defer our discussion of conflict to a later chapter, where we can give it detailed consideration.[68]

Individual differences in tolerance

It is a commonplace observation that individuals differ widely from one another in their ability to withstand stress and frustration.[69] Some persons seem to tolerate extreme pressure without showing behavioral impairment or disorganization. Most persons endure lifelong delay in the satisfaction of

---

[66] For a critique of these procedures, see Glixman, A., "An analysis of the use of the interruption-technique in experimental studies of 'repression.'" *Psychol. Bull.*, 1948, vol. 45, pp. 491–506.

[67] For examples of such experiments, see Glixman, A. F., "Recall of completed and incompleted activities under varying degrees of stress." *J. exper. Psychol.*, 1949, vol. 39, pp. 281–295; McClelland, D. and Apicella, F., "A functional classification of verbal reactions to experimentally induced failure." *J. abn. soc. Psychol.*, 1945, vol. 40, pp. 376–390; Yarrow, L. J., "The effect of antecedent frustration on projective play." *Psychol. Monogr.*, 1948, vol. 62, no. 6, pp. 42; Zander, A. F., "A study of experimental frustration." *Psychol. Monogr.*, 1944, vol. 56, no. 3, pp. v, 38.

[68] See Chapter 9.

[69] Lacey, J. I., "Individual differences in somatic response patterns." *J. comp. Physiol. Psychol.*, 1950, vol. 43, pp. 338–350; Leitch, M. and Escalona, S., "The reaction of infants to stress." In Freud, A. (Ed.), *The psychoanalytic study of the child*, vol. 3/4. New York: International Universities Press, 1949, pp. 121–140.

certain needs, or accept severe thwarting and conflict without apparent adverse effect. A few people, in situations which may seem objectively less stressful or less frustrating, become inefficient, or develop reactions so inappropriate as to be called pathological. Moreover, the same individual may successfully withstand stress and frustration in some areas of his own behavior, but succumb readily when other need-satisfaction sequences are involved. *Tolerance for stress and frustration* we define as *the ability to endure pressure, delay, thwarting and conflict without developing maladaptive reactions.*[70]

Under conditions of extreme pressure and thwarting, individual differences in the ability to withstand stress and frustration become dramatically apparent. Military combat, for example, pushes nearly every fighting man close to his limits of tolerance. Medical reports from many theaters of World War II, however, point out that fighting men typically withstand an unbelievable amount of stress and frustration without developing maladaptive reactions.[71] British submariners, for example, exposed to unremitting operational strain and severe restriction of freedom, showed a negligible proportion of psychiatric breakdown; and those men who developed behavior pathology often did so as the result of personal and domestic rather than military strain.[72] Flying personnel universally developed reactions of fear and anxiety, but continued nevertheless to fly with efficiency and endurance. Indeed, so many men went on performing their duties with skill, despite symptoms of anxiety, that one military psychiatrist has questioned seriously the adequacy of our contemporary definitions of "pathology."[73]

The reasons for individual differences in tolerance for stress and frustration are exceedingly complex. There is some indication, from studies utilizing the techniques of experimentally-induced failure, that frustration-tolerance may increase with *age*. Older children, for example, more frequently than younger ones choose to repeat tasks on which they were previously made to fail.[74] This ability to return to situations which formerly brought frustration is considered to be one index of frustration-tolerance. Persons suffering from *behavior pathology* often seem, in experimental situations, to have low thresholds for stress and frustration. Thus a group of schizophrenic adults, also subjected to artificially induced failure, chose to repeat tasks on which they had previously succeeded. Somewhat related to this finding is evidence that patients suf-

[70] Rosenzweig, S., "An outline of frustration theory." In Hunt, J. McV. (Ed.), *Personality and the behavior disorders.* New York: Ronald, 1944, pp. 379–388.

[71] Curran, D., "Functional nervous states in relation to service in the Royal Navy." *Inter-Allied Conf. War Med.* (1942–45), 1947, vol. 1, pp. 219–224.

[72] Curran, D., "Operational strain: psychological casualties in the Royal Navy." *Inter-Allied Conf. War Med.* (1942–45), 1947, vol. 1, pp. 233–238.

[73] Wright, D. G., "Operational strain: stress in combat flyers." *Inter-Allied Conf. War Med.* (1942–45), 1947, vol. 1, pp. 244–246.

[74] Rosenzweig, S., "Further comparative data on repetition-choice after success and failure as related to frustration tolerance." *J. genet. Psychol.*, 1945, vol. 66, pp. 75–81.

fering from behavior disorder do not differ from a control group in the threshold of pain perception; but they react to a painful stimulus by wincing and withdrawing at lower levels of intensity than do the controls.[75]

One experiment with young children suggests that differences in tolerance for stress and frustration may be largely *learned*.[76] These children were given a six-week training period on problems of gradually increasing difficulty. Under such a regime, the children grew able to tolerate increasingly severe demands without developing destructive reactions. It is altogether possible that the differences in tolerance which a given individual shows in different areas of his own behavior are also learned. We shall see [77] that *reaction-sensitivities* to particular excitants are acquired, and that they often dictate the degree to which a particular situation is stressful or frustrating.

To these factors must be added one more, derived from observations of military personnel. The *time relationships* in a need-satisfaction sequence often seem to determine whether an individual will pass the limits of his own tolerance. These relationships, however, are not simple. The long-continued stress and frustration involved in combat flying, for example, contributed less to the development of behavior disorder among flyers than did the number of actual casualties in a particular unit.[78] This suggests that the anticipation of hazard may carry the individual beyond the threshold of endurance. Moreover, the development of pathological reactions in a military setting often occurred some time after the stress and frustration were over. The candidates for the intelligence service described earlier, for example, were more likely to become inefficient and disorganized after the stress interview than during it. In the same way, combat personnel who performed with great skill and courage frequently developed pathological reactions after they had been removed to a rest camp.[79] We shall need to remember these points when we find patients developing behavior disorder in situations of anticipated stress, or some time after stress and frustration appear to have been relieved.

The most general consequence of stress and frustration is the persistence of unsatisfied need.[80] When need-satisfaction sequences are prevented altogether

[75] Malmo, R. B. and Shagass, C., "Physiologic studies of reaction to stress in anxiety and early schizophrenia." *Psychosom. Med.*, 1949, vol. 11, pp. 9–24; Malmo, R. B. and Shagass, C., "Physiologic study of symptom-mechanisms in psychiatric patients under stress." *Psychosom. Med.*, 1949, vol. 11, pp. 25–29.

[76] Keister, M. E. and Updegraff, R., "A study of children's reactions to failure and an experimental attempt to modify them." *Child Developm.*, 1937, vol. 8, pp. 241–248.

[77] See pages 70–74.

[78] Reid, D. D., "Neurosis on active service: experience among aircrew on a bomber station." *Inter-Allied Conf. War Med.* (1942–45), 1947, vol. 1, pp. 230–233.

[79] Curran, D., "Operational strain: psychological casualties in the Royal Navy." *Inter-Allied Conf. War Med.* (1942–45), 1947, vol. 1, pp. 233–238.

[80] For an analysis of the sorts of behavior which characterize frustration, as well as for a systematic analysis of frustration as a special kind of behavior, see Maier, N. R. F., *Frustration, the study of behavior without a goal.* New York: McGraw-Hill, 1949, pp. xiii, 264.

from consummation, then tension increases or persists unrelieved. And protracted, unrelieved tension often has this important outcome: it may culminate in the impairment and disorganization of patterned behavior. We shall find this phenomenon in the anxiety attacks which punctuate cumulative anxiety, and in the panic reactions which occasionally follow.[81] The end-result of unrelieved tension we shall see in the deliria of cerebrally incompetent persons,[82] and in the behavioral disorganization and desocialization of patients suffering from schizophrenic disorder.[83]

There is, however, a second important consequence of frustration. Prolonged tension which does not yield to head-on attack may lead the individual to acquire socially inappropriate techniques of substitute satisfaction. And it is just such non-valid and distorted ways of handling frustrated need which constitute a great many of the symptoms characteristic of behavior disorder. The autonomy and inactivation of hysterical disorder, the compulsive rituals of anxious patients, and the progressive misinterpretations which characterize delusional and hallucinatory behavior, represent substitute satisfactions which are tension-reducing but socially inappropriate. Like all techniques of need-satisfaction, those which eventuate in behavior pathology are the outcome of social learning, and to this topic we shall proceed in the following chapter.

[81] See pages 305–310.   [82] See pages 469–477.   [83] See Chapter 16.

Behavior Organization

II. LEARNING AND BEHAVIOR PATHOLOGY

The development of complex social behavior, whether it is skilled or unskilled, appropriate or inappropriate, is always dependent upon learning. Human beings are not born with dominant attitudes of hostility, resentment, withdrawal or anxious overconcern; they learn them in social interchange with others. Some human beings, in the same general context, acquire inexplicable fears of darkness, of high places or of animals. Others become progressively less and less able to participate in social communication, or to share their thoughts with their friends. They may develop private ways of looking at the world, and may arrive finally at the unwarranted conclusion that others are ridiculing, victimizing, or worshipping them. Such non-valid and unskilled reactions as these are common in a great many of the behavior disorders we are about to study; and all of them are products of social learning.

Valid and skilled behavior, of course, is as certainly an outcome of learning as are the reactions we consider pathological. Human beings learn attitudes of relaxed, out-going friendliness just as they learn attitudes of resentment and suspicion. Most people acquire techniques of effective social intercourse, and a reasonably adequate appreciation of the perspectives of other people. Only a minority exhibits ineptness and rigidity. Over the entire range of complex human behavior, from the normal, through the gauche and eccentric, to the frankly pathological, each reaction is the product of social learning. Moreover, the range is continuous; there are no boundaries which set off normal from pathological reactions.

Our patients, like all the rest of us, are human beings who become involved in stressful and frustrating situations, and develop varying degrees of skill or ineptness in handling them. Consequently, we should be able to identify principles of learning which account equally well for ordinary successful problem-solving, the misinterpretations of suspicious people, and the delu-

53

sional convictions of paranoid patients. When, however, we try to apply to behavior pathology the conventional descriptions of learning familiar to students of normal behavior, we face at once the following series of paradoxes.

(*a*) The literature of learning is rich in results and hypotheses that come from brief, *carefully-controlled* laboratory experiments on nonsense-syllable memorizing, maze-running and problem-solving. In the pathological reactions of patients, on the other hand, as in the everyday behavior of us all, what we find is the resultant of a *lifetime of casual, incidental learning*, much of it occurring in the context of parent-child, sibling or marital interrelationship.

(*b*) Our laboratory investigations indicate that in many instances of human learning, the *favorable consequences* of an act in part determine its persistence in the learner's repertory. Reinforcement, reward and punishment seem to bear systematic, though not simple, relationships to learning efficiency. Yet we shall find patients suffering from behavior disorder who persist for years in reactions which are *inept, non-adjustive, unrewarding and often painful*. And they persist in such behavior in spite of opportunities for change, and even in spite of strong pressures and repeated encouragement to change.

(*c*) In the conventional laboratory experiment, the cues to the reactions being learned are *open to the observation* of the subject, as well as of the experimenter. The patient, however, is frequently in a less fortunate position than the experimental subject in this regard. For him, the cues are often *inaccessible to his own self-reactions*. He can neither observe nor report the excitants that have made him tense, irritable, fearful or withdrawn; and his behavior is consequently inexplicable to himself.

(*d*) The learning tasks set for the subject in a laboratory experiment usually favor a *slow and gradual acquisition* of reactions. Our conventional learning curves all reflect our faith that a given performance becomes progressively more efficient with repeated trials. We shall find analogies of this phenomenon in the slow, progressive social ineptness which brings some patients to desocialization and schizophrenic disorder. But we shall also meet anxious, hysterical and paranoid patients who seem to acquire inappropriate reactions abruptly, almost as if for them *one trial* were sufficient for learning.

Such apparent contradictions as these might seem to require two sets of explanations — one to account for normal learning and another to account for pathological. A careful analysis of our contemporary information regarding human learning, however, will soon show that such double explanations are neither necessary nor desirable. The learning of pathological behavior proceeds according to the same methods, and under the same general conditions, as does the acquisition of normal reactions.[1] The patient does not deviate from

[1] For examples of the application of learning theories to behavior pathology see Dollard, J. and Miller, N. E., *Personality and psychotherapy: an analysis in terms of learning, thinking and culture.* New York: McGraw-Hill, 1950; Misbach, L., "Psychoanalysis and theories of learning." *Psychol. Rev.*, 1948, vol. 55, pp. 143–156.

the laboratory subject in the ways in which he learns. It is only the direction and the emphasis of his learning which are different.

Among the characteristics of learning which are common to all human organisms, there are six which we single out as particularly relevant to behavior pathology. These six are by no means mutually exclusive, nor do they alone describe completely the intricate details of human learning. We select these characteristics because they represent the aspects of normal learning through which pathological reactions most commonly develop. In what follows, accordingly, we shall see that (1) *learning occurs in a social situation;* (2) *learning involves temporal sequences of behavior;* (3) *learning is selective;* (4) *learning is facilitated by tension-reduction;* (5) *learning depends upon excitants which may be incidental and self-inaccessible;* and (6) *learning involves the rapid reorganization of behavior.*

Learning in a Social Situation

Human learning typically occurs in an environment of other individuals and cultural products, in directions defined by the prevailing cultural patterns. This is as true of laboratory learning as it is of the child's gradual induction into the ways of his family. In most experiments on human learning, however, the responses of others in the situation — the experimenter and his assistant, for example — are rigidly controlled and restricted, so that the social contributions to learning are minimized. In casual, everyday learning, on the other hand, the situation is reversed. The behavioral changes which define learning make their first appearance in the social context of the family, and they persist or undergo modification throughout life in an environment of other persons.

As we have already seen, the net of parental attitude and response within which active and irritable infants grow is different from that which encloses the dull and apathetic baby.[2] We shall see later how parents' demands and expectations in relation to feeding and affectional behavior train the child not only in handling cup and spoon, and in attitudes of filial dependence, but also in the reciprocal social behavior and the growing independence which lead toward biosocial maturity.[3] We shall see also that many instances of pathological behavior in adults represent the end-result of particular emphases and concerns which have their beginnings in early parent-child relationships. In studying the contribution of learning to behavior disorder, therefore, we begin where the patient often begins his misguided learning — in the social situation of the family.

There are two techniques, usually more casual and incidental than planned, by which the child learns in the everyday environment of his home. His parents may guide, restrict or instruct him in specific ways; and their teaching may

[2] See pages 23–24.   [3] See pages 134–143.

go on to include indoctrination as to whom he should select as friends, what religious and social attitudes he should maintain, what vocation he should enter and whom he should marry. This approach to social learning we shall call learning by *direct tuition*. On the other hand, parents may employ a minimum of direct instruction, but instead, through the example of their own behavior, provide models of how one eats, talks, thinks, loves, fears and hates — models which the child may grow to duplicate in his own reactions. This second approach to social learning we shall call learning by *adoption of the prevailing pattern*.

Direct tuition

A clear-cut illustration of social learning by direct parental tuition is to be found in Levy's study of maternal overprotection.[4] Levy selected, from the files of a child guidance clinic, twenty children whose mothers had maintained extreme and enduring attitudes of overprotection toward them. The mothers typically kept their children close to them by giving them excessive fondling during infancy, sharing sleeping quarters with them and limiting the children's activity to a restricted territory near the home. They kept their children infantile and dependent by prolonging each stage of biosocial maturation well beyond the usual time. They discouraged their children from making friends outside the home, selected with care the few friends they permitted, accompanied their offspring to and from school and interpreted their children's behavior to the teacher. Thus, by means of detailed instruction, close restriction and direct intervention, these mothers overtrained their sons and daughters in immature, dependent behavior.

This direct maternal tuition had specific and far-reaching effects upon the complex social behavior of the children. The mothers utilized two different patterns of overprotection: *indulgence* and *domination*. The child whose mother was indulgently overprotective continued his infantile aggressions throughout his later years; he carried his fighting and bullying tactics into the neighborhood and the school. The child whose mother gave domineering overprotection learned dependent, submissive reactions; he continued to withdraw from his contemporaries and cling to adults for protection, outside as well as in his own home. Neither uncontrolled aggression nor passive dependence was successful for these children in playground or school situations. Nevertheless, direct tuition by the mother had so effectively overtrained the children in aggression or dependence that, even when their techniques failed, they were unable to shift to more mature ways of behaving. The children remained socially inept and isolated from companionship with their peers.

An additional result of Levy's study introduces us to a facet of social learning which we shall find repeatedly in the development of behavior pathology. In

[4] Levy, D., *Maternal overprotection*. New York: Columbia Univ. Press, 1943.

their indulgent or domineering relationships with their offspring, these mothers seemed to be satisfying their own personal needs. Some of the mothers had wanted a child for years, or had lost an infant through miscarriage or through death. For these mothers, a child fulfilled a compelling need; but a child also represented a delicate and precious organism which, to survive, required vigilant protection. There are some mothers, however, who reject their children and view them as an unwelcome interruption or a threat to a close marital relationship. These mothers apparently develop attitudes of extreme overprotection in a compensatory way, as if by donning the cloak of concern and control they could cover up their own disappointment and irritation at having a child. But in all instances, overprotective maternal attitudes and immature child behavior develop in a context of reciprocal relationships between the needs of the mother and those of her child.

There are other studies of child development, both longitudinal and cross-sectional, which support Levy's findings regarding direct parental tuition. The Fels Institute long-time research on children and their parents, for example, identifies constellations of parental control which appear to be related to child behavior.[5] In this study, two diverse patterns of parental tuition — rejecting and accepting — lead to diverse patterns of child behavior. Children of rejecting parents are typically active, emotionally responsive, quarrelsome, hostile toward their siblings, and resistant to adults. Children whose parents are easy and accepting, on the other hand, are less active, more placid and, in their later years, more sociable.

Another study, which investigated the persistence of maternal attitudes in a cross-sectional laboratory situation, brings out further important relationships.[6] Its results indicate that mothers maintain attitudes toward their children of permissiveness, control or intervention, which are consistent from one observational period to the next. Moreover, some of the mothers in this second study interpreted the experimental situation as a test of their own maternal adequacy, and consequently attempted to show off the child by pushing and prodding him. It was evident that, as we saw also in the Levy study, the mother's needs helped dictate her procedures with her child.

To these systematic studies of direct parental tuition we may add further data from clinical observation. In clinical work, it is not uncommon to find an adult patient suffering from behavior pathology who has been trained by

---

[5] Baldwin, A. L., Kalhorn, J. and Breese, F. H., "Patterns of parent behavior." *Psychol. Monogr.*, 1945, vol. 58, no. 3.

[6] Merrill, B., "A measurement of mother-child interaction." *J. abn. soc. Psychol.*, 1946, vol. 41, pp. 37–49. For a study on the attitudes which distinguish the parents of "problem" from "non-problem" children, see Shoben, E. J., Jr., "The assessment of parental attitudes in relation to child adjustment." *Genet. Psychol. Monogr.*, 1949, vol. 39, pp. 101–148. For a study of the stability of family authority patterns from one generation to the next, see Ingersoll, H. L., "A study of the transmission of authority patterns in the family." *Genet. Psychol. Monogr.*, 1948, vol. 38, pp. 225–302.

his parents in patterns of overconcern. A hypochondriacal young man was the son of a mother who continually worried over her own health. As soon as her son could talk, she began conducting daily inquisitions, in which she questioned him insistently regarding each system of his body, and tried to discover whether he might possibly have this or that symptom. The patient's early training in anxious reaction-sensitivity to his own body and its processes led to indigestion, abdominal pains and vomiting when he was only five years old, and prepared the ground for an alarming array of hypochondriacal symptoms which brought him to the clinic at the age of twenty-two.[7] In much the same way, a patient's exaggerated concern over food intake, regularity of elimination, rest and cleanliness frequently reflects childhood overtraining by anxiously watchful parents.

Not only the direction of patients' specific symptoms, but also their comprehensive systems of attitude, may be the outgrowth of direct parental tuition.

> One college student, for example, developed behavioral disorganization, with tension, sleeplessness, religious preoccupations and suicidal thoughts in a setting of overwork, fatigue and academic failure. But it was obvious that his difficulties had begun long before this. For he had been trained throughout childhood and adolescence, by his mother, in self-examination regarding the fundamental tenets of his religion, and by his father in ambitions which far exceeded his abilities. The patient described his mother as a fanatically religious person who repeatedly discussed with him controversial and insoluble problems of sin and punishment, evil and damnation. He described his father as a brilliant but unyielding man who would tolerate nothing less than perfection in his son. In college, the boy began to question for himself the tenets of his mother's faith, and at the same time he found himself unable to meet the academic standards his father set for him. His training had provided him no defense against religious uncertainty and no tolerance for imperfection in himself. "I am affected with a troublesome conscience," he said, "and I have the unfortunate attitude that winning the game is more important than playing it." With his supporting attitudes thus threatened, the patient grew tense, depressed, suicidal and finally seriously disorganized in his behavior.

In many patients, as in this one, anxious self-examination and worry over minor and remote failures in adulthood follow directly from the tuition supplied them by their parents. Later on, we shall encounter other patients whose attitudes of apprehensiveness and fearfulness began originally in parental training.[8] Fear of failure and apprehensiveness in new situations, for example, may be the production of parents' direct teaching that failure means weakness, and that new situations are tests of strength and fortitude. A

[7] For a further discussion of body overconcern and chronic invalidism, see pages 231–242.
[8] See pages 294–295.

great many patients are adults who learned too well the lessons from their parent tutors.

Adoption of the prevailing pattern

Not all of the social learning which goes on in the family is the consequence of direct tuition. It is a commonplace observation that young children learn to duplicate many of their parents' reactions, without either understanding the significance of the parental behavior or being trained directly in it.[9] The little girl adopts her mother's choice of words, her postures and her gait, borrows her mother's clothing, and puts her doll through the routines her mother follows with the new baby. The little boy repeats his father's vigorous expletives, strides with hands in pockets, demands long trousers and centers his play around themes of going off to work. We shall see that practice in such role-taking behavior is an important constituent of biosocial maturation.[10]

Children also learn to adopt their parents' aversions to certain foods or to particular persons. They come to duplicate their parents' attitudes toward the sinful and the good, toward cleanliness, body care, diet and illness. They mirror the irritabilities, the fear, the anxieties and mood changes which their parents have developed.[11] It is such adopted ways of behaving as these which typically color also the pathological reactions of patients. Their beginnings are often to be found in the tensions which infants develop in response to signs of generalized disturbance and anxiety in their parents.[12]

Even infants in arms may react to muscular tenseness in their mothers by crying, becoming restless, and rejecting food. In a twenty-month observational study of infants in a prison nursery, for example, Escalona found instances in which infants less than four weeks old refused the breast when their mothers trembled, held them tightly, or moved restlessly while nursing.[13] These same babies, on the same day, accepted the bottle when it was offered by someone other than the mother. Escalona also observed that the incidence of infantile tantrums, food refusal and vomiting was always higher each month on "parole day" than at other times, although the feeding routines remained exactly the same. For the prisoner mothers, parole day was a tense time,

[9] We are not here referring to a direct and complete reproduction of behavioral patterns which literally defines "imitation," but rather to a more gradually learned duplication of prevailing reactions. For an analysis of this point, with experimental support, see Miller, N. E. and Dollard, J., *Social learning and imitation*. New Haven: Yale University Press, 1941.

[10] See pages 114–122.

[11] For one approach to this problem, see Roff, M., "Intrafamily resemblances in personality characteristics." *J. Psychol.*, 1950, vol. 30, pp. 199–227. See also Bach, G. R., "Father-fantasies and father-typing in father-separated children." *Child Develpm.*, 1946, vol. 17, pp. 63–80. The latter study indicates that children's attitudes toward their fathers may be in part the product of the mother's characterization of the father to her child.

[12] See pages 295–296.

[13] Escalona, S. K., "Feeding disturbances in very young children." *Amer. J. Orthopsychiat.*, 1945, vol. 15, pp. 76–80.

since it marked the day when decisions were made regarding their release from prison. To these periodic increases in their mothers' tension, the infants reacted with generalized eating disturbances.

By the time they reach their preschool years, many children who live in an environment of parental tension have themselves developed tense and disturbing ways of behaving. In one study of nursery school children and their parents, for example, those children whose parents were dissatisfied with one another showed more behavior disturbances than did those whose parents were accepting of one another.[14] Particularly if their parents were dissatisfied over affectional relationships or over attitudes of dominance and submissiveness, the children tended to develop inappropriate social behavior in the nursery school situation. The children did not seem to acquire specific problems in response to specific parental concerns; rather, they developed generalized tension in a context of generalized parental dissatisfaction.

A few experimental investigations describe the more specific duplication of parental reactions in child behavior which is often seen in clinical observation. In the study mentioned earlier, Escalona reports that whether an infant accepts or rejects tomato juice or orange juice depends in some cases upon the likes and dislikes for these foods which characterize the adult who feeds him. An infant with an established preference for orange juice, for example, will reverse his preference and reject orange juice if he is assigned to a different adult who herself dislikes orange juice. Along the same lines, Macfarlane finds that children are most likely to develop disturbing behavior in the areas which most concern their parents.[15] Thus in her study, the child of parents who are themselves meticulous in their choice of foods, and anxious over the relation of food intake to size, strength and health, is more likely to develop food finickiness than other behavior problems. Such findings as these are consistent with our view that the adoption of the prevailing family pattern is an important aspect of learning in both normal and pathological behavior.

Identification

A common reaction which favors the adoption of the prevailing pattern is *identification*. By *identifying* we mean *reacting to the attributes of other persons, groups, objects and symbols as if these attributes were also one's own*. Identification arises inevitably in the course of early family living. The child begins life as part of a family unit from which he is only later differentiated as a unique individual. At first, his possessions, his status, and his characteristics are almost exclusively those of his parents and siblings, and he reacts to these as

[14] Baruch, D. W., "A study of reported tension in inter-parental relationships as co-existent with behavior adjustment in young children." *J. exper. Educ.*, 1937, vol. 6, pp. 187–204.

[15] Macfarlane, J. W., "The relationship of environmental pressure to the development of a child's personality and habit patterns." *J. Pediat.*, 1939, vol. 15, pp. 142–154.

if they were indeed his own. Most of us maintain throughout our lives at least some of the remnants of our early identification with the family group. We react to achievements or failures in our relatives as if we ourselves had won or lost. And most of us extend our reactions of identifying beyond the family, and find satisfaction and release of tension in gangs, clubs and social organizations, in the victories of school or company teams, in the superiority of powerful automobiles or expensive clothing, and even in the exploits of fictitious characters.

Family identification is important in social learning, however, because it leads the child's behavior in the direction which the reactions of his parents take. The boy who uses his father's words and inflections, or swaggers across the yard wearing his father's hat, is reacting to these characteristics and objects as if they were his. But in so doing he is also duplicating his father's reactions, and learning to act as his father acts.[16] In more significant aspects of behavior it is the same. A child in cowering when his mother trembles at a brilliant lightning-flash, in rejecting food which his father does not like, or in viewing a visitor with the same alarm and suspicion his parents show, is reacting as if his parents' characteristics were also his. He is learning a family pattern of fear, aversion or suspicion which will one day indeed become his own.

In pathological cases, we often see similarities in behavior between patients and their parents which reflect the adoption of a prevailing pattern through identification.

> A clear-cut but not exceptional example of this variety of learning can be seen in the behavior of a young woman of twenty-one, who became unable to complete even the simplest acts. In bathing, dressing or eating, she had to perform each step over and over, so that she never finished these daily routines. If she tried piano-playing, for which she had outstanding talent, she was forced to turn each page of music again and again, and to repeat each phrase so often that the thread of the composition was lost. She grew progressively ineffectual at her work, could not touch anything for fear it was unclean, and became unable to eat. She explained her behavior by saying that she feared she was sinful; it was not she but God who performed each act for her, which necessitated her repeating every reaction in order to make it her own. It was at this point that she came to a psychiatric clinic for help.
>
> This was the patient's fourth episode of illness. She had first become fearful of sin and dirt when she was seven years old, and again at the ages of eleven and of sixteen she grew temporarily unable to touch things and filled with the conviction that God was everywhere. The background of her concerns lay in lifelong social and economic insecurity, in ridicule

---

[16] For studies of the behavior of young children who are deprived of a paternal identification-figure, see Bach, G. R., "Father-fantasies and father-typing in father-separated children." *Child Develpm.*, 1946, vol. 17, pp. 63–80; Sears, R. R., Pintler, M. H. and Sears, P. S., "Effect of father separation on preschool children's doll play aggression." *Child Develpm.*, 1946, vol. 17, pp. 219–243.

which she received because of a disfiguring facial scar, and in attitudes of dependency which, by preventing her from making close attachments to her peers, kept her immature and socially unskilled. The patient was strongly attached to her mother, and demonstratively affectionate toward her; she seemed somewhat fearful of her father and said she had not embraced or kissed him since she was one year old. She preferred the company of women to that of men, spoke disparagingly of the opposite sex and, at twenty-one, had gone out with a boy only twice in her life. In this context, it is highly significant for our present purpose that there was a striking parallel between the woman's pathological reactions and those which her mother had earlier developed.

During her own childhood, the patient's mother had suffered from episodes of insistent anxiety which, she said, were the same as those of the patient. While she was pregnant with the patient, the mother again developed fears — this time fear that she would burn her child, that she would commit a sin, that if she touched anything she would become unclean, and that food she prepared might poison others. These reactions persisted and grew worse after the birth of the child, so that our patient was never without a dramatic model of behavior pathology in the person with whom she was most strongly identified. During interviews with the psychiatrist the mother minimized her own "foolish ideas," and rejected the suggestion that her reactions might have contributed to the direction of the daughter's illness. The patient, for her part, denied that she was in any way affected by her mother's behavior. "She can't upset me — I'm used to her," she said. What the patient denied in words, however, she had accepted in her non-verbal behavior, until as a young adult she was a faithful reproduction of the prevailing female pattern in her home.

Cases of this sort indicate clearly that the adoption of the prevailing pattern encourages and sustains similarities in behavior among members of the same family. And this fact is of great importance in behavior pathology. For we often find occurrences of similar behavior pathology in parents and their children, and in siblings reared together. As we have already seen, such family similarities in the development of behavior pathology are often taken to be evidence for the inheritance of susceptibility to a specific behavior disorder.[17] But, whether or not specific hereditary tendencies can some day also be established, there is no doubt that the prevailing family pattern distinctly favors the learning of a particular kind of pathological behavior.

Social learning, whether by direct tuition or through adoption of the prevailing pattern, is not confined to the parent-child relationship. The presence of other children in the home provides additional guides, and additional models of appropriate and inappropriate behavior.[18] In his relationships with his own peers outside the home, the child becomes part of a new social situation,

[17] See pages 28–32.
[18] Krout, M. H., "Typical behavior patterns in twenty-six ordinal positions." *J. genet. Psychol.*, 1939, vol. 55, pp. 3–30.

within which he may learn ways that vary widely from his domestic pattern.[19] And throughout his lifetime, teachers, employers and marital partners continue to participate in the individual's social learning. In all these contexts, as in any social situation, the relationships are reciprocal. The needs of his siblings, peers, teachers, employers and spouse — like the personal needs of his parents — contribute inevitably to the direction and extent of the individual's social learning.

Learning and Temporal Sequences of Behavior

The reactions involved in human learning are patterned sequences which are temporal in character. Any reaction, whether human or infrahuman, normal or pathological, can be described in terms of a beginning and an end. A hungry rat enters the starting-box of a maze, runs to the right, then twice to the left, then to the right, reaches the food compartment and eats. A preschool child in a sand-box reaches for the shovel, finds it held by another child, pulls on it, pleads, demands and screams, and is removed to another part of the yard by his teacher. A carpenter arrives on the job, collects his tools, measures, saws and planes his lumber, nails the pieces together in a particular order, checks on level and angle, and goes off to lunch. A compulsive patient gets up in the morning, arranges razor, blade, brush and shaving cream in a particular pattern before he can begin shaving, bathes according to a prescribed sequence, dons each piece of clothing in an unchangeable order and, because of all this ritualistic detail, arrives at breakfast late, exasperated and weary.

These examples all represent *temporal sequences* of behavior, defined by a beginning-phase and an end-phase. We may describe any reaction — whether brief or protracted, circumscribed or inclusive — in similar temporal terms. A compulsive patient's ordered acts of first placing the shaving cream on the left side, and arranging razor, blade and then shaving brush at the right, constitute a sequential pattern within the framework of his complete ritual. The same patient's childhood relationships with his parents, his early training in anxiety, his adolescent conflicts and adult frustrations, and even his plans for the future, constitute a much more comprehensive but still temporally-defined organization of behavior.

Of course, a temporal analysis is not the only kind of analysis that can be made.[20] But it is the most convenient and acceptable one to us simply because

[19] See, for example, Jack, L., "An experimental study of ascendant behavior in preschool children." *Univ. Iowa Stud. Child Welfare*, 1934, vol. 9 (no. 3); Page, M., "Modification of ascendant behavior in preschool children." *Univ. Iowa Stud. Child Welfare*, 1936, vol. 12 (no. 3); Tryon, C., "Evaluation of adolescent personality by adolescents." *Monogr. Soc. Res. Child Develpm.*, 1939, vol. 4, pp. 1–88; Tryon, C., "The adolescent peer culture." *Yearb. Nat. Soc. Stud. Educ.*, 1944, vol. 43, pp. 217–239.

[20] For a systematic presentation of psychology from the point of view of temporal units, see Muenzinger, K. F., *Psychology: the science of behavior.* New York: Harper, 1939.

training in our culture is largely a matter of time relationships. We grow up in a world of schedules for eating, working, playing and sleeping — a world of alarm clocks and railroad time tables, of days for washing clothes and days for ironing them, of times for starting work and times for quitting, of seasons for gardening and seasons for shovelling snow, of years for preschool, grade school, high school, college and work. Our lives are punctuated by time demands which sort our reactions into shorter or longer temporal sequences. It is therefore not surprising that it is easiest for us to view human behavior as a complex temporal organization.

We choose to employ a temporal analysis in our study of behavior pathology for two further reasons. In the first place, we shall find that anticipant reactions occupy a prominent place in the organization of both normal and pathological behavior. In the second place, we shall find that the extension of behavior in time opens the way to a wide variety of appropriate and inappropriate learning. We have already pointed out the relationship between the temporal extension of need-satisfaction sequences and the learning of new needs and new satisfactions. We turn now to a more detailed consideration of *anticipant reactions* and of *learning within a temporal framework*.

Attitudes and responses

There are two aspects of any ongoing behavioral sequence which we may distinguish from one another: the diffuse background and the specific focus. To these two constituents of any reaction we give the names *attitude* and *response*. *The attitude is the widespread, diffuse, behavioral background which prepares for, supports and prolongs certain responses and not others.* A *response*, on the other hand, is *the more specific, localized aspect of a reaction which emerges from and is supported by the attitude.*

Let us take as an example the reactions of a man who is driving to his place of work in his car. The tensional patterns that bring him to the car, hold him in the driver's seat, and keep him alert to pedestrians, other cars, traffic lights and policemen, are part of the diffuse behavioral background — the *attitude*. His movements in shifting gears, accelerating, braking and steering are *responses* which the attitude facilitates and supports. Responses and their supporting attitudes are constituents of the unitary, temporal organizations we call *reactions*.

Of course, behavior is more than a series of discrete reactions strung together in time. Total behavior is an intricate, interrelated pattern which has both unitary and contradictory aspects. In complex, everyday living, reactions typically overlap with one another; they undergo interruption and mutual interference. For the man driving his car, proceeding from his home to his place of work may be part of a wider sequence which includes making an appointment with his employer, protesting against his treatment and asking for a raise. If his preoccupation with these matters becomes too complete, he may miss a stop light, drive beyond his destination or even hit another car. At work, he may find that his employer is out of town or refuses to see him; and when he is finally able to speak to him, the employer may discharge him instead of increasing his pay. Life is made up of just such contingencies as these, which evoke shifts of attitude, new responses and contradictions among reactions.

Reactions in which simultaneously opposing trends play a prominent part we call *ambivalent reactions.* Ambivalence often results when a contradictory excitant appears in the context of ongoing behavior — as when a man driving to work suddenly recognizes a landmark which is beyond his destination. But ambivalence in normal and pathological behavior alike is most significant when it develops in relation to affectional attitudes. Children inevitably acquire ambivalent reactions toward their parents, who not only reward and comfort them, but also bring them punishment and denial. For many children, this ambivalence is sharpened by sibling or parental rivalry.[21] Filial ambivalence may persist almost unchanged throughout an individual's life, and it often generalizes to other sources of affection. We shall find among our patients examples of adult marital relationships which seem to duplicate the ambivalent reactions of child toward parent. And we shall see the consequences of persistent ambivalence in the vacillation and indecisiveness, the guilt and self-reproach, which characterize many of our patients.

Occasionally, ambivalent reactions are seen in the impulsive, unpredictable and often dangerous behavior of schizophrenic patients.

> One of our patients, for example, was riding in the car with his father, who was driving at high speed along a transcontinental highway. A friend of the family was a passenger in the back seat. Father and son conversed amicably for many miles; then, after a moment of silence, the patient abruptly lunged over and seized his father by the throat. The car shot wildly out of control as the father struggled to free himself, and only the intervention of the family friend, and the fact that the highway was free of other traffic, prevented a fatal accident. Afterward the patient seemed frightened, tense, stiff and somewhat chagrined, but wholly unable to account for his behavior. Another patient, during a visit of his mother to the hospital, threw his arms impulsively around her neck, saying, "I love you, I love you, I love you," over and over. Then, after a slight pause, he shouted venomously, "You're the cruellest person in the world and when I get out of here I'll get a gun and shoot you!"

Anticipant attitudes

An attitude, because it functions as a background, serves also as a preparation for the appearance of certain responses. This preparation we may call

[21] There is some indication that, when the mother depreciates the father, the child develops ambivalent fantasies toward the father. See Bach, G. R., "Father-fantasies and father-typing in father-separated children." *Child Develpm.*, 1946, vol. 17, pp. 63–80.

anticipation. As a simple example of this let us take the hungry infant who, early in life, reacts to oral contact with the nipple by means of grasping and sucking responses which are supported and facilitated by a background attitude of movement and tension. As the baby grows older, these supporting patterns appear earlier and earlier in the sequence of feeding behavior. At first the infant begins his diffuse and restless movements of nursing while the nipple is approaching, later when he merely hears the sounds his mother makes in preparing to feed him, and eventually when the mother only appears or speaks to him. In thus responding to the early phases of a situation, with reactions originally given later in the sequence, the infant is showing *anticipant attitudes.*

Let us define an *anticipant attitude* as the *backward temporal extension of the attitude, which prepares a behavioral background in advance of the appropriate responses.* We shall see that anticipant attitudes play an exceedingly important part in behavior pathology. The sustained tensions of exaggerated anxiety, for example, represent anticipant attitudes in an ongoing sequence of behavior which remains unconsummated.[22] Often the worry and apprehension of a chronically anxious or agitated depressed patient arise from the anticipation of real or fantasied punishment. Occasionally among patients suffering from behavior disorder the anticipant attitude is socially invalid, and facilitates responses which are bizarre and sometimes even dangerous. Thus a schizophrenic patient, after weeks of silent brooding, may conclude that a hostile mob is waiting outside his door to kill him; and he may meet this anticipated attack by unexpectedly battering down his door and attempting to escape. When he finds the hall empty of armed men, he may be unable to shift his attitude to a more valid one, and his now pointless violence may lead him into severe behavioral disorganization.

Learning in a temporal context

The temporal character of behavioral sequences, and the protracted extension of attitudes in time, provide conditions which facilitate learning and determine its direction. For one generally accepted principle of human learning is that excitants which are part of a context within which a response is occurring may serve at a later time to elicit the same response.[23] Thus a child who takes his castor oil thinly disguised in orange juice, and who dislikes castor oil, may come to react with aversion and vomiting to pure orange juice. In the same way, a child who gets his first lessons in reading at the hands of an unsympathetic or hostile teacher may develop dislike or fear of reading itself.

[22] See pages 278–279.
[23] This appears in learning theories variously as the law of contiguity (Guthrie, Robinson); associative shifting (Thorndike); redintegration (Hollingworth). For a discussion of these points, see Hilgard, E. R., *Theories of learning.* New York: Appleton-Century-Crofts, Inc., 1948, pp. 27; 52–75; 148–149; 332.

For our study of behavior pathology, it is important to note that excitant and response need not occur in strict simultaneity for the excitant later to evoke the response. Indeed, there may be considerable delay between the two and learning still go on. Furthermore, at least in complex forms of human learning, excitants which are responded to by the individual as part of the original context, or which recur in symbolic or fantasy forms, are often effective in reinstating earlier responses.

> Thus a twelve-year-old boy had been unable, throughout his life, to meet the expectations of his ambitious foster-parents. He developed a severe febrile illness; and while he was convalescing, in a setting of over-protective concern, he heard a nurse tell his foster-parents that he might become blind. Thereafter he had difficulty in keeping his eyes open, particularly in situations which seemed to him difficult or threatening. Even talking or thinking about school intensified the heaviness of his eyelids. By the time he appeared in a child guidance clinic for help, two years later, his formerly periodic inability to raise his eyelids had developed into a continuing hysterical inactivation; he could no longer raise them at all. Here, a chance remark which occurred in the context of unaccustomed but desperately needed affection favored the learning of pathological reactions which recurred and finally persisted on the basis of personal interpretation.

These facts suggest that the reactions constituting an ongoing behavioral sequence may later be evoked by any part of the original stimulating situation. If the sequence spans a long period of time, then the number and variety of potentially effective excitants is correspondingly great. The interval between a tap on the patellar tendon and the ensuing knee jerk, for example, is hardly long enough to permit the operation of intervening stimuli. Far more significant in behavior pathology than brief, reflex-like sequences, however, are generalized states of tension that begin as anticipant attitudes, persist in time, and precipitate important after-reactions which continue long after the termination of an act. We discussed such extended behavior patterns earlier, when we described the protracted tension, satisfaction and after-reaction which characterize need-satisfaction sequences.[24] And we shall later consider prolonged behavioral sequences in which visceral participation is dominant and sustained, when we come to the problem of anxiety.[25] For the present, however, it is enough to note that when ongoing reactions persist in time, there is a strong possibility that excitants which appear during the protracted time interval may come later to initiate the same reactions.

One consequence of great importance to the student of behavior pathology follows from this analysis. We have said that excitants which occur in the same temporal context with ongoing reactions may later initiate them. But these excitants need bear no verbally logical relationship to the reactions they

---

[24] See pages 37–43.   [25] See pages 122–129 and 278–280.

initiate. It is sufficient that excitant and reaction be part of the same temporal pattern; often they are part of the same situation only because of concomitance. Human reactions thus acquire new excitants which are entirely inexplicable on grounds of verbal logic. Indeed, the logic involved in much symptom-formation, as in much normal human behavior, is predominantly the logic of non-verbal operations, of concomitance in space and time.

Let us take an example to clarify these somewhat complex relationships.

A little boy of six and his three-year-old sister owned a cat which was about to have kittens. The children's parents, who were easy and accepting persons, had promised that the children might watch the birth, and had given them a simple, unemotional description of what they would see. For days before the event, brother and sister made elaborate preparations for the cat's comfort, watched over her unceasingly, and talked of little else but the coming birthday. One evening when parents, children, and a close friend of the family were gathered in the living room, the guest abruptly announced that the cat appeared ill. There was a wild scramble, during which the little boy picked up the cat and ran into the basement room which had been prepared for the kittens' birth. The little girl followed in high excitement. Both children pushed and shoved to get a better view of each newborn kitten until the boy accidentally stepped backward and came down heavily on his sister's finger with his cleated shoe. The little girl screamed in pain and terror and could not be quieted until her father had put her to bed.

This episode describes a relatively long sequence of behavior in which anticipant attitudes, specific responses and after-reactions are all involved. It represents also a situation studded with chance excitants which later called forth the reactions of pain and fear attending the girl's accident. During the ensuing week, the child avoided the adult guest, her brother, her father, and the basement room which she had formerly helped to prepare. She could not be induced to look at the new kittens; and she ran away if the cat appeared near her. For a few nights she refused to go to bed at the usual time, and insisted upon a night light — two reactions which were unusual for her. Because of the calm acceptance her parents gave her behavior, she gradually lost these unaccustomed patterns and returned to her usual ways of acting.

For our present purpose, the significant thing about this episode is the variety of concomitant excitants which came to initiate avoidant reactions. To father, brother, adult guest, basement room, cat, kittens and bedtime the girl reacted in the same way as she had to the injury to her finger. These new excitants bore no verbally logical relationship to the birth process in cats. They were chance events which happened to be part of a relatively long behavioral sequence — a sequence which was accidentally terminated by pain and fright. Of course, if we had not known the details of the incident, we could, through our own verbal logic, have related the child's new fear-excitants to some meaning which birth might have held for her. But in this situation, as in many instances of pathological reactions, the new excitants seem to have been acquired on the basis of space-time concomitance.

A great many of the distorted and bizarre reactions of patients can be accounted for in the same way. All protracted sequences of behavior are subject to endless modifications in terms of whatever excitants may be operating at the same time. Important as this fact is, however, it does not mean that all human learning is grounded in temporal concomitance. Every human being is selectively more reactive to some aspects of a situation than to others; for, in the course of ordinary living, human beings are likely to learn in accordance with their own *needs*.

Selective Learning

Human learning in a complex or unstructured situation proceeds in large part according to the personal needs of the learner. Let us take as an example of this point the reactions of the different members of an audience to a popular lecture on a medical topic. If we question each listener at the close of the lecture, we are sure to find not only that he recalls different aspects of the talk, but also that what he has learned is importantly affected by his own personal hierarchies of need. The medical student remembers details which the office worker scarcely hears. The housewife learns a list of ingredients for a balanced diet from words which her husband dismisses as trivial. Her husband, on the other hand, takes away with him from the lecture a plan for the improved medical care of his employees which other members of the audience cannot remember.

If our hypothetical audience included patients with pronounced behavior pathology, we would hear some reports of the lecture which seemed to us to bear little relationship to what the speaker said. A seriously depressed patient might tell us that the lecturer spoke of terrible diseases and lingering death, and he might accept these details as ominous portents of a frightful punishment awaiting him for his own guilt and unworthiness. A paranoid patient, on the other hand, might take from the talk whatever statements agreed with his dominant delusional system, and elaborate upon what he recalled in such a way that the whole address seemed directed personally at him. The hypochondriacal man, with chronic severe worries centered about his gastrointestinal tract, might come away from the lecture strongly fortified in his belief that his stomach or his bowel was diseased; and he would then be able to cite things said, or things he thought had been said, that were confined largely to the gastrointestinal tract. Every member of an audience selects and learns what is relevant to his own personal need.

Individualistic learning of this sort begins with the selective interpretation of a stimulating situation, which is itself the product of past learning. For some time, clinicians have capitalized upon this human tendency toward personalized interpretations in their diagnostic use of the so-called "projective techniques," which in effect provide an unstructured stimulus-situation for the patient to reorganize according to his needs. More recently, findings from laboratory experiments have contributed systematic information regarding the personal nature of interpretation. There is some evidence, for example, that straightforward judgments of the size of a stimulus-object vary according to the previous training of the subject.[26] There are also indications that the extent to which a subject is personally involved in a task affects the efficiency with which he later recalls it.[27] Moreover, whether a laboratory subject considers his own performance successful or a failure seems to depend at least as much upon his own private standards of achievement for himself as upon the actual level of his accomplishment.

These clinical and experimental findings force us to reconsider and widen our view of the relationship between the effects of an act and the efficiency with which it is learned.[28] At least in complex social learning, the effects of reward and punishment, of success and failure, operate often in terms of individual hierarchies of need. In accordance with their needs, human beings are differently responsive to different aspects of the same stimulating situation. And their differential sensitivities are important determiners of the direction and efficiency of their social learning.

Reaction-sensitivity

The selective reactivity which distinguishes one learner from another is not the consequence of sense-organ efficiency; neither is it the product of specific acquired responses. The medical student may have no more acute hearing than the office worker, but he learns facts from the medical lecture which the latter honestly insists he has not even heard. The employer who obtains from the lecture a plan for medical care of his employees looks at his plant and his workers differently on the following day. He sees hazards he never knew ex-

[26] For examples of such experiments, and the criticisms directed toward them, see Bruner, J. S. and Goodman, C. C., "Value and need as organizing factors in perception." *J. abn. soc. Psychol.*, 1947, vol. 42, pp. 33–44; Bruner, J. S. and Postman, L., "Tension and tension release as organizing factors in perception." *J. Personality*, 1947, vol. 15, pp. 300–308; Bruner, J. S. and Postman, L., "Symbolic value as an organizing factor in perception." *J. soc. Psychol.*, 1948, vol. 27, pp. 203–208; Carter, L. F. and Schooler, K., "Value, need and other factors in perception." *Psychol. Rev.*, 1949, vol. 56, pp. 200–207.

[27] Rosenzweig, S., "The experimental study of repression." In Murray, H. A. *et al. Explorations in personality.* New York: Oxford, 1938, pp. 472–490. We shall consider this point at greater length in our discussion of repression on pages 337–351.

[28] For a discussion of the controversy over the "law of effect," see Hilgard, E. R., *Theories of learning.* New York: Appleton-Century-Crofts, 1948, pp. 282–288; Koffka, K., *The growth of the mind.* London: Kegan Paul, 1924, p. 102; Koffka, K., *Principles of gestalt psychology.* New York: Harcourt, Brace, 1935, p. 552; Tolman, E. C., "The law of effect." *Psychol. Rev.*, 1938, vol. 45, pp. 165–203; Allport, G. W., "Effect: a secondary principle of learning." *Psychol. Rev.*, 1946, vol. 53, pp. 335–347; Mowrer, O. H., "The law of effect and ego psychology." *Psychol. Rev.*, 1946, vol. 53, pp. 321–334.

isted. Dangerous and unguarded tools are suddenly apparent to him, and so are inadequate lighting, dust-filled air and the cramped postures of his workers. The employer is operating in terms of a general readiness-to-react, which obliges him to organize an old, familiar situation into a new and unaccustomed pattern. This selective readiness-to-react we call *reaction-sensitivity.*

By *reaction-sensitivity* we mean *a selective readiness-to-react to certain components of a stimulating situation and not to others.* Reaction-sensitivity is the consequence of one's having acquired a system of related attitudes and responses. An individual with a persistent attitude of anxiety, for example, becomes selectively responsive to the threatening or fear-provoking components of his life-situation. A person with aggressive or domineering attitudes is thrown into attack or argument in situations which, to the person with attitudes of passivity, seem unimportant or repulsive. Friendly attitudes support outgoing responses in one man, while attitudes of suspicion support responses of flight or covert, brooding resentment in another. Such acquired systems of related attitudes and responses produce reaction-sensitivities which account for a great many of the differences in interests and in aptitudes which we find among normal people. The little girl's acquired concern with dolls, clothing and houses represents a pattern of reaction-sensitivity quite different from her brother's learned responsiveness to mechanical toys and active, competitive games. Adult men and women in our culture reflect the persistence of these early learned reaction-sensitivities in their divergent interests and skills.

Patients suffering from behavior disorder, as we shall see, often differ significantly from other persons in the direction which their reaction-sensitivities have carried them. Hypochondriacal patients who develop body overconcern, for example, become highly skilled in observing and reporting upon ordinary physiological activities which most persons ignore in themselves. Compulsive and depressed patients often become acutely sensitive to the faintest signs of guilt or sin in their own reactions or in those of other persons. Patients suffering from paranoid disorders typically develop sharp sensitivities to any possible slight, and often interpret casual remarks as personally-directed insinuations. Profound *reaction-insensitivities* are to be found in hysterical and sometimes in schizophrenic patients. The patient grows unresponsive to certain components of stimulating situations, and often becomes incapable of participating in the social life around him. Such developments as these, which may be transient in normal behavior but enduring in behavior pathology, are commonly the outcome of reaction-sensitization which is *progressive.*

By *progressive reaction-sensitization* we shall mean *the process in which a person, once he has become reaction-sensitive in a specific direction, continues to develop further readiness-to-react in the same direction, on the basis of successive acquired reactions.* This process, as we have seen, may account for differences between individuals which become progressively greater as time goes on. Acquired sensitivities which are progressive have great potential significance, not only for normal personality organization, but also for the development of behavior pathology. Indeed, progressive reaction-sensitization may determine personal immunity or susceptibility to behavior disorder.

Let us take, for example, the children of domineering and indulgent over-protective mothers whom we have earlier described.[29] Maternal domination, it will be recalled, trained these children in passive, submissive behavior which generalized to their relationships with their peers and with adults. Maternal indulgence, on the other hand, trained the children in stubborn, aggressive reactions which they employed in school and neighborhood situations as well as at home. The dominated children thus acquired one constellation of selective readiness-to-react and the indulged children another. The two groups entered new situations in school and neighborhood with two different patterns of expectancy — the one with anticipation of restriction and the other with anticipation of unlimited freedom — and both reacted selectively to those components of the new situations which fit their expectancies.

It is in this way that progressive reaction-sensitization may result in behavior modifications which are cumulative. If, under prolonged stress and frustration, a dominated child were to develop behavior pathology, we would expect him to show the exaggerated social isolation, withdrawal and fantasy toward which his progressive reaction-sensitization has been directing him. On the other hand, should an indulged child develop behavior pathology, he would be more likely to show the exaggerations of his characteristic aggression and impulsiveness in various forms of antisocial behavior.[30] Such progressive deviations, begun in childhood, seem to underlie a great many pathological developments of adolescence and adulthood.

The fact that progressive reaction-sensitization favors cumulative behavioral sequences is of great importance to our understanding of the causes of behavior disorder. It suggests that behavior disorder may persist and grow worse, even though the conditions which originally gave rise to it improve. Thus an anxious patient may acquire reaction-sensitivity to the bodily changes of his own anxiety. If his reaction-sensitivity becomes progressive, he may grow increasingly perceptive of his own visceral changes, and become more anxious over their possible significance to his health. His increased anxiety may then spiral into a disabling body overconcern — not so much because of what originally initiated his anxiety as because of these newly developed skills in self-examination that he has acquired.

[29] Levy, D., *Maternal overprotection*. New York: Columbia University Press, 1943; Kasanin, J., Knight, E. and Sage, P., "The parent-child relationship in schizophrenia: I. Overprotection-rejection." *J. nerv. ment. Dis.*, 1934, vol. 79, pp. 249–263.

[30] Levy, D., *Maternal overprotection*. New York: Columbia University Press, 1943. Four of Levy's cases showed in later life behavior which was described as "psychopathic." For a more detailed consideration of this point, see pages 203–211.

The persistence and spread of reactions through progressive reaction-sensitization is, of course, closely related to the concepts of *generalization* and *stimulus-equivalence* which students of human learning have long employed. These concepts are derived from laboratory experiments on conditioned response and associative learning in infrahuman animals, and are most strictly defined in terms of individual, specified stimuli and responses. In a looser sense, however, they are applicable to such more inclusive and more socialized reactions as the behavior pathologist studies. When the child who is aggressive toward his mother at home becomes similarly aggressive toward his teacher, as in the case of Levy's indulged children, he may be said to have *generalized* his reactions from one stimulating situation to a similar one. To put the matter another way, teacher and mother are *equivalent* excitants, since both evoke aggression from the child.

In many contemporary theories of learning, the extent and frequency of generalization are said to be a function of the degree of similarity of new excitants to the original one.[31] If the teacher looks like the indulgent mother, for example, or uses her words, or maintains the mother's attitudes toward him, a child may develop aggressive reactions toward the teacher more readily than if the similarity is less close. However, in many cases of normal and pathological behavior, it is the personal, selective construction which the individual places upon the new situation that determines his reaction. To most people, an exit sign with pointing finger and a chance wrong number on the telephone do not resemble each other at all. To the paranoid patient, who is reaction-sensitive to possible threat, however, both may become part of an expanding plot against him, and both may be excitants to apprehension and anxiety. Progressive reaction-sensitization, in other words, often determines which stimuli are equivalent for the individual, and in what direction his reactions shall generalize.

By now it is clear that selective learning, through progressive reaction-sensitization, may have two general consequences in behavioral organization. (a) Selectivity typically channels and restricts the individual's repertory of acquired reactions to an interrelated pattern which for him is characteristic. This variety of organization we may term *stable and exclusive.* (b) The channeling and restriction of patterns through reaction-sensitivity, however, cannot be rigid and inflexible. The organization of behavior must remain sufficiently elastic so that the individual can alter his reactions, or shift readily from one behavioral sequence to another.[32] This variety of organization we term *un-*

[31] Hull, C. L., *Principles of Behavior.* New York: Appleton-Century-Crofts, 1943, p. 199; Lashley, K. S. and Wade, M., "The Pavlovian theory of generalization." *Psychol. Rev.*, 1946, vol. 53, pp. 72–87; Hull, C. L., "Mind, mechanism and adaptive behavior." *Psychol. Rev.*, 1937, vol. 44, pp. 1–32.

[32] For studies of "flexibility" and "rigidity" as personality characteristics, see Fisher, S., "Patterns of personality rigidity and some of their determinants." *Psychol. Monogr.*,

stable and inclusive. Normal behavior organization depends upon an optimal balance between exclusion and inclusion. The organization of certain kinds of pathological behavior, however, is characterized by exaggerated exclusion or exaggerated inclusion.

Exclusion and inclusion in behavior organization

The acquisition of skill in typewriting provides an illustration of balanced exclusion and inclusion in normal behavior organization. The student typist writhes on the edge of her chair, grits her teeth, grimaces, tenses her fingers and wrists, whispers each letter as she types it, and covertly rehearses the arrangement of symbols on the keyboard. As her skill increases, these irrelevant reactions are excluded from her behavior. Indeed, the marks of the expert typist are her relaxed posture, easy finger movements and lack of covert rehearsal of word or letter patterns. Her typing behavior has become *stable and exclusive.*

Stability and exclusion in behavior organization are never absolute in skilled performances. It is essential to the office typist's efficiency, for example, that she be able to include many variant reactions within her typing behavior. She must be able to answer questions as she types, maintain her speed even when she has a bandaged finger, and use different machines with slightly different keyboards. This relatively inclusive pattern of behavior, however, may become overinclusive if the typist is tense or disorganized. In a public contest over typing speed, for example, the expert may again include reactions which she ordinarily excludes; she grimaces, tenses her hands and whispers the words until precision is lost and she flounders awkwardly. Skilled performance thus depends upon a balance between a stable, exclusive organization and one which is relatively *unstable and inclusive.*

In certain of the behavior disorders, the optimum balance between exclusion and inclusion is lost, and the patient's behavior becomes overexclusive or overinclusive. *Overexclusion,* for example, is typically found in cases of hysterical inactivation. A patient who is involved in an incident which he cannot accept may forget not only the inacceptable incident but also his own name, his job, his home address, the names of friends and relatives — in fact, any information which might serve to identify him. Such instances of hysterical forgetting clearly represent extravagant overexclusion which develops in relation to the patient's own need. Therapy aimed at removing or satisfying this need ordinarily permits the patient to include again in his behavioral repertory the reactions which had been excluded from it.

1950, vol. 64 (no. 1); Rokeach, M., "Generalized mental rigidity as a factor in ethnocentrism." *J. abn. soc. Psychol.,* 1948, vol. 43, pp. 259–278; Rokeach, M., "The effect of perception time upon rigidity and concreteness of thinking." *J. exper. Psychol.,* 1950, vol. 40, pp. 206–216. This point is further discussed on pages 119–122, and on pages 406–413.

In *overinclusion*, the generalization of reactions is extended until the individual cannot maintain boundaries between the various behavioral sequences in which he participates. Such behavior organization characterizes compulsive patients and those suffering from manic disorder and delirium. It is among cases of schizophrenic disorganization, however, that we find our most dramatic illustrations of overinclusion. The schizophrenic patient's behavior organization is ordinarily so unstable that he cannot restrict his reactions to the few coherent ones necessary for his daily living. This extravagant overinclusion has been found repeatedly in simple test situations, such as that in which the task is one of sorting blocks of different sizes, shapes and colors into groups of those which seem to the subject to belong together. The following verbatim comments, given slowly and deliberately by a schizophrenic patient performing this test, illustrate typical overinclusion.

> "See that circle there (on the test board)? You have to swing a radius here — 31416 pi in surveying, eat a pie, survey — before you can do something with *that* (white trapezoid). White like the paper (on the examiner's desk). You have to lift that up and cover it with ink. It's where food comes from. I'm a cook. Like the Russian revolution. I can cook a hundred pies to prove that you people are dependent on food. You're supposed to make food because everyone can't eat peas. There's fifty people down there (ward) and only forty-nine peas on the plate . . . (pointing to red blocks), You've got terra cotta there and red rubber on pencils. As soon as you rub out that, you rub away the whole game."

The patient begins with a white circular block, but goes on to include in his group the radius, the value of pi, pie as a food, the experimenter's paper and the ink he is using, allusions to economic problems based on food, and his fellow-patients on the ward. When, later, he selects a red block, again he cannot limit his reactions to the test objects, but includes red paint, and then red erasers which for him can obliterate the entire situation. In similar tests, which employ cut-outs of people and of household objects rather than blocks, the same extravagant overinclusion is reported.[33] The schizophrenic patient typically goes beyond the boundaries of the test categories to include office materials, examiner, and the products of his own fantasy in his indeterminate classifications.

Learning and Tension-Reduction

In human learning, reactions which eventuate in tension-reduction are readily acquired and persist in th learner's behavioral repertory. It often appears as if patients suffering from behavior disorder acquire and maintain reactions in

---

[33] Shneidman, E. S., "Schizophrenia and the MAPS test: study of certain formal psychosocial aspects of fantasy production in schizophrenia as revealed by performance on the make-a-picture-story (MAPS) test." *Genet. Psychol. Monogr.*, 1948, vol. 38, pp. 143–223.

ways which directly contradict the principle of *effect* in learning.[34]   A depressed patient, for example, may persistently rehearse and exaggerate past events whose recall brings him only pain and remorse.   A patient with a compulsive hand-washing ritual may scrub his hands with hot water and a strong abrasive even though they are already painfully cracked and bleeding.   An hysterical patient may develop contractures, paralyses or seizures when these severely limit the range of his social participation and keep him a dependent invalid. The inept social deviant typically repeats the same aggressive, antisocial acts that have earned him fines or imprisonment.   Thus, learning in a large variety of pathological behavior seems to run counter to the effects of reward and punishment as these operate in the experimental laboratory.

This seeming paradox can be at least in part resolved if we take into account the fact that learning is facilitated by tension-reduction.   The principle of tension-reduction — or drive reduction, as it is sometimes called — is part of most systematic explanations of learning.   Indeed, it is implicit in Freud's early statement that release of libido or vital energy is pleasurable while its accumulation without release is painful.[35]   Contemporary behavior theorists of learning ordinarily hold that primary reinforcement, or the strengthening of learned responses, depends in part upon the magnitude of need-reduction.[36] Writers who are influenced by field theories likewise recognize the contribution of tension-reduction to learning, although they state the matter somewhat differently.   For them, a situation to be learned is incomplete; incomplete situations evoke a tension pointed toward completion.[37]   The learner consequently achieves reduction of tension through completing the incomplete situation — or, as these writers would say, through *closure*.

In our earlier discussion of need, we have already suggested the importance of tension-reduction in the acquisition of pathological behavior.[38]   There we said that acts which served to consummate need-satisfaction sequences tended to persist, and indeed to become needs in their own right.   This seems to happen whether or not the tension-reducing acts are socially valid and appropriate. To the anxious person, alarmed by his own anxiety-produced gastrointestinal changes, the unjustified conclusion that someone must be poisoning him may

[34] For a discussion of the controversy over the "law of effect," see Hilgard, E. R., *Theories of learning.*   New York: Appleton-Century-Crofts, 1948, pp. 282–288; Koffka, K., *The growth of the mind.*   London: Kegan Paul, 1924, p. 102; Koffka, K., *Principles of gestalt psychology.*   New York: Harcourt, Brace, 1935, p. 552; Tolman, E. C., "The law of effect." *Psychol. Rev.*, 1938, vol. 45, pp. 165–203; Allport, G. W., "Effect: a secondary principle of learning." *Psychol. Rev.*, 1946, vol. 53, pp. 335–347; Mowrer, O. H., "The law of effect and ego psychology." *Psychol. Rev.*, 1946, vol. 53, pp. 321–334.

[35] Freud, S., *Beyond the pleasure principle* (Trans. by C. J. M. Hubback).   New York: Boni and Liveright, 1924, p. 1.

[36] Hull, C. L., *Principles of behavior.*   New York: Appleton-Century-Crofts, 1943, p. 66.

[37] For a discussion of this point, see Hilgard, E. R., *Theories of learning.*   New York: Appleton-Century-Crofts, 1948, pp. 184, 219; Koffka, K., *The growth of the mind.*   London: Kegan Paul, 1924, p. 102.

[38] See pages 37–43.

provide temporary relief from his bewilderment and confusion. The fact that his conclusion is socially invalid seems to be less important than the fact that it is tension-reducing. Many unwarranted conclusions persist and become delusional convictions on the basis of such tension-reduction.

Needs, as we have seen, multiply in the course of biosocial maturation; hierarchies of need also develop, which differ widely from one person to the next. Indeed, the number and variety of activities which may be tension-reducing is endless. The laboratory experiments from which the hypothesis of tension-reduction ("drive-reduction") is derived, are somewhat limited in their application to human behavior pathology. Thus, they use infrahuman animals and ordinarily employ such acts as eating or avoiding shock as tension-reducers, instead of the more complex social acts comparable to those which human organisms acquire as need-satisfiers. Nevertheless, one series of laboratory studies, utilizing fear and anxiety-reduction in infrahuman animals, provides us with at least an experimental analogue for the learning of pathological behavior by human beings.

These experiments begin with the hypothesis that fear-reduction is "rewarding" and hence reinforces the learning of new reactions.[39] Let us take one study by Mowrer as an example.[40] Laboratory rats are placed in an alley which is entirely floored with an electric grill. Whenever current is applied to the grill, the animals can escape the shock by running to a small safety compartment. After a number of trials, the rats run directly to the safety box the moment they are placed in the alley, and thus completely avoid receiving electric shock. The experimenter now alters the procedure so that in order to get to the safety compartment, the rat must pass over a portion of charged grill and must therefore always take electric shock. On the other hand, the rat might now avoid shock entirely by remaining in the uncharged part of the alley. Instead of staying in the uncharged area, however, the animals already used in this experiment continued, for hundreds of trials, to run at once across the electrified grill and into the safety compartment.

The persistence of such non-valid, punishing behavior reminds us at once of the persistence of painful, self-defeating reactions which we find in behavior pathology. And Mowrer's analysis of his experimental results gives us a hint as to the way in which inappropriate reactions may be acquired and perpetu-

[39] See, for example, Farber, I. E., "Response fixation under anxiety and non-anxiety conditions." *J. exper. Psychol.*, 1948, vol. 38, pp. 111–131; Brown, J. S., and Jacobs, A., "The role of fear in the motivation and acquisition of responses." *J. exper. Psychol.*, 1949, vol. 39, pp. 749–759. For reviews of such studies, see Miller, N. E., "Acquired drives and reward." In Stevens, S. S. (Ed.), *Handbook of experimental psychology.* New York: Wiley, 1951; Dollard, J., and Miller, N. E., *Personality and psychotherapy: an analysis in terms of learning, thinking and culture.* New York: McGraw-Hill, 1950, pp. 62–94.

[40] Mowrer, O. H., "Learning theory and the neurotic paradox." *Amer. J. Orthopsychiat.*, 1948, vol. 18, pp. 571–610.

ated. According to Mowrer, the initial trials with shock trained the rat to fear the total experimental situation. During these initial trials, also, the animal learned to escape shock by running to the safety box. The act of running to safety was thus reinforced through fear-reduction. In the latter part of the experiment, however, running to safety brought shock; and shock reinforced the rat's fear of the apparatus. Consequently each time the animal was put into the fear-provoking alley, it repeated the act which had been reinforced by fear-reduction — the act of running into the safety compartment.

Anxiety in human behavior, as we shall see, is infinitely more complex than the fear of electric shock in a laboratory rat.[41] At the same time, certain parallels can be drawn between the persistently inappropriate behavior of these rats and the persistently non-valid reactions of patients. For behavior which in human beings is reinforced by tension-reduction often operates in such a way as to increase rather than to alleviate anxiety. Thus the compulsive patient whose anxiety is temporarily reduced by his hand-washing ritual may become further concerned over the possibility of infection in his raw and bleeding hands. Now the tension-reducing reaction of scrubbing the hands itself augments his anxiety; and to his increased anxiety level the patient reacts with further hand-washing and consequently still further anxiety.

It is this characteristic self-perpetuation of inappropriate reactions which leads some behavior pathologists to speak of the "vicious circle" of pathological behavior.[42] An anxious patient may acquire reactions of nail-biting, masturbating or drinking as tension-reducers, become more anxious over the possible effects of these habits, and consequently grow less able to control them. A paranoid patient may conclude that his anxiety-produced gastrointestinal symptoms mean that he is being poisoned, become increasingly anxious over the poisoning, and develop more severe gastrointestinal symptoms which only reinforce his delusional conviction and encourage its expansion. The same reactions paradoxically provide tension-reduction while they increase anxiety, and the patient is thus caught in a circle of inappropriate behavior.

Few patients who have acquired persistent and circular nonadjustive reactions of this sort can alter them without expert assistance. There are many reasons for the resistance of such pathological behavior to change. For one thing, the reactions are ordinarily overlearned, since they occur repeatedly in a context of tension-reduction. For another, such reactions are often acquired in problem situations which for the patient are insoluble. If the patient is caught in a conflict of multiple-avoidant reactions, for example, in which he finds no acceptable basis for choice, he may acquire and maintain stereotyped, ritualistic behavior. In a sense he gives up trying alternative reactions.[43] We

---

[41] See Chapter 10.

[42] See, for example, Horney, K., *The neurotic personality of our time.* New York: Norton, 1937.

[43] For a discussion of this point of view see Hilgard, E. R., *Theories of learning.* New York: Appleton-Century-Crofts, 1948, p. 340.

shall see this variety of nonadjustive behavior in cases of compulsive and depressive disorder. We shall find it, also, in schizophrenic and cerebrally incompetent patients who, in terms of their own overinclusive behavior, confront a hopelessly chaotic world.

By far the most crucial reason for the resistance of nonadjustive behavior to change, however, lies in the self-inaccessibility of the patient's reactions. Often in behavior disorder, a patient cannot identify the excitants which initiate and increase tension and anxiety in him. This suggests that human beings must acquire reactions in an incidental way, to stimulation which they do not recognize, and in ways which they cannot formulate in words. We turn next to a consideration of learning which is incidental and self-inaccessible.

Incidental and Self-Inaccessible Learning

In the organization of complex human behavior, both the excitants to learned reactions and the learning process itself are often inaccessible to the self-reactions of the learner. Human beings typically formulate in words, comment upon and describe to others their own reactions. Our formulations of our own behavior, however, vary greatly in clarity and precision. A man may return from a business trip, for example, and report with accuracy to his friend the route he took, the towns he visited, the people he met and the sales he did or did not make. Or he may afterward formulate in thinking the details of his trip without communicating them to anyone. He may, however, return from his travels unable to describe his behavior in any detail except, perhaps, to recognize that he is tense, tired or uneasy; and these general reactions also he may either share with others or keep to himself. In rare instances, a man may return wholly unable to formulate to himself or communicate to others the reasons for his trip, where he went, what he did, whom he saw or why he has now come back.

These illustrations represent varying degrees of accessibility of behavior to an individual's own self-reactions, ranging from the accurate reporting of a commonplace event to the total amnesia which characterizes an hysterical fugue. A person's behavior may be totally accessible, only partially accessible, or completely inaccessible to his own self-reactions. We have already seen that *motives*, although readily identified by someone else, may be inaccessible to a person's self-reactions.[44] We shall see later that the competing reactions which constitute *conflict* may also be self-inaccessible.[45] Motive and conflict, however, are only part of a wide class of phenomena which often remain inaccessible to the individual: the conditions and consequences of his everyday learning.

The organization of normal and pathological behavior alike is full of aver-

[44] See pages 33–34.   [45] See pages 248 and 274.

sions and attachments, fears and hopes, ambitions and discouragements, aggression and passivity, enduring attitudes and fleeting responses, whose origins and later course a person cannot trace. A business man suffers from recurring irritability and depression, and a compulsive patient intermittently counts his possessions and arranges them in order; but neither can identify the excitants which initiate their reactions. A laborer develops a strong dislike for his foreman, and an anxious patient acquires an intense terror of open spaces; but neither can say how his reactions began. A shy and withdrawn housewife avoids social situations, and a schizophrenic patient becomes unable to participate in social interrelationships; but to neither are the steps in lifelong social learning accessible, which led to their adult ineptness.

It is not surprising that a good share of human learning remains inaccessible to the reactions of the learner. We have already seen that most everyday, non-laboratory learning goes on in a casual and incidental way, and that its background is an exceedingly complex social context of reciprocal interrelationships among people. We have also seen that ongoing behavior which extends over long periods of time undergoes modification on the basis of chance space-time concomitance. Such concomitance is not likely to impress the learner, nor lend itself readily to formulation in terms of verbal logic. For these reasons, we should expect to find, in the behavior of normal people and of patients, a large proportion of learned reactions which are self-inaccessible.

Definitive experiments are few in which human subjects have learned to react either to self-inaccessible excitants, or in ways which they cannot report. This is partly because the requirements for adequate and realistic experimentation on inaccessible behavior are exceedingly difficult to meet. Visceral reactions, for example, represent a kind of behavior which seems typically to be learned without the subject's control. But visceral reactions are variable, and they often cannot be satisfactorily quantified for precise experimentation. Excitants to learning may be made inaccessible to the laboratory subject through hypnosis, but this is in itself a difficult and often equivocal procedure. In spite of the serious obstacles in the way of such experimentation, however, we have at present a few studies which show how inaccessible learning proceeds in the laboratory.

One group of relevant experiments involves the conditioning of vasomotor responses to stimuli that are subvocal. An example of this approach is to be found in a study of Roessler and Brogden.[46] The subjects employed were college students who, in preliminary trials, had been found to respond with constriction of the blood-vessels of the hand (vasoconstriction) when the wrist was given electric shock. (1) These selected students were now given the electric shock with two other forms of simultaneous stimulation — they heard a

---

[46] Roessler, R. L. and Brogden, W. J., "Conditioned differentiation of vasoconstriction to subvocal stimuli." *Amer. J. Psychol.*, 1943, vol. 56, pp. 78–86.

buzzer signal, and at the same time they themselves spoke a nonsense syllable. This procedure was continued until the combination of buzzer sound and nonsense syllable, without electric shock, produced the vasoconstriction. (2) Next the subjects were trained with electric shock and the spoken nonsense syllable, but without the buzzer signal; and (3) finally a series was carried through in which the spoken syllable with shock was now combined with a different spoken syllable, not accompanied by shock at all. The result of this procedure was that a conditioned differentiation was established, so that when one syllable (the one accompanied by shock in the training series) was spoken by the subject, vasoconstriction appeared in his hand; but when the other syllable was spoken by him, no vasoconstriction appeared.

Once this conditioned differentiation had been set up, the experimenters moved ahead to the final and crucial phase of the procedure. They instructed the subjects to "think" the syllables actively — but not to speak or whisper them. A few of the students actually gave consistent responses of vasoconstriction to the appropriate syllable when repeating it subvocally. Such results as this suggest that, under proper laboratory conditions, human beings can learn to give visceral responses — here vasoconstriction — which are ordinarily inaccessible to the regulation of one's self-reactions. It is, moreover, a highly significant fact that these subjects learned to respond to excitants which they themselves initiated and which they did not in any way communicate to others.

There are many analogies of this variety of inaccessible learning in the development of pathological behavior. Indeed, there are many patients who become tense or apprehensive, and who show all the autonomic changes of acute anxiety, while fantasying on anxiety-provoking themes. And often these patients, like our experimental subjects, neither identify nor communicate the fantasies which seem to initiate and intensify their anxiety.

It should be emphasized that there are wide individual variations involved in this kind of responsiveness. Ordinarily, only a small fraction of the total group of laboratory subjects can acquire stable vasomotor reactions under such experimental conditions. Furthermore, many of these studies — particularly those dealing with pupillary constriction to subvocal excitants — yield conflicting or negative results when they are duplicated.[47] In at least one further

[47] For examples of such experiments, see Hudgins, C. V., "Conditioning and voluntary control of the pupillary reflex." *J. gen. Psychol.*, 1933, vol. 8, pp. 3–51; Steckle, L. C. and Renshaw, S., "An investigation of the conditioned iridic reflex." *J. gen. Psychol.*, 1934, vol. 11, pp. 3–23; Steckle, L. C., "Two attempts to condition the pupillary reflex." *J. gen. Psychol.*, 1936, vol. 15, pp. 369–377; Menzies, R., "Conditioned vasomotor responses in human subjects." *J. Psychol.*, 1937, vol. 4, pp. 75–120; Menzies, R., "Further studies of conditioned vasomotor responses in human subjects." *J. exper. Psychol.*, 1941, vol. 29, pp. 457–482; Henneman, R. H., "An attempt to condition the galvanic skin response to subvocal stimuli." *Psychol. Bull.*, 1941, vol. 38, p. 571; McCleary, R. A. and Lazarus, R. S., "Autonomic discrimination without awareness: an interim report." *J. Personality*, 1949, vol. 18, pp. 171–179; Hilgard, E. R., Dutton, C E., and Helmick, J. S., "Attempted

study, however, which we shall consider in our discussion of anxiety, auto-nomic reactions were successfully conditioned to excitants which were, of course, recognized and identified by the experimenter, but not at all by the subjects.[48] These findings, also, support the common observation that human beings do learn to react in stable and predictable ways to stimulating situations which are inaccessible to them.

As an illustration of the use of hypnosis in research on self-inaccessible learning, let us take the studies of Leuba. In one of these experiments, deeply-hypnotized subjects were instructed to look attentively at a red square on a white card while listening to a buzzer.[49] After a few trials, the sound of the buzzer alone led the subjects to report that they saw the red square. The subjects were then told that they would recall none of the events that had occurred during hypnosis, and were then awakened from the hypnotic state. Nevertheless, the subjects reported in the waking state that they saw a red square appearing whenever the buzzer sounded, although no red square was present. Such a phenomenon, of course, seemed inexplicable to these subjects. Their bewilderment, however, was certainly no greater and no more distressing than that reported by the phobic patient who becomes unaccountably terror-stricken when he hears a church bell or sees a cat.

In another experiment, Leuba instructed hypnotized subjects to adopt, at three different times, three different attitudes: happy, critical, and anxious.[50] During each hypnotic period they observed and commented upon the same series of pictures. Their interpretations of the pictures proved to be in har-mony with each hypnotically-induced attitude. A picture of a wounded sol-dier on a stretcher, for example, was seen by a subject whose attitude was happy as an illustration of medical efficiency; the same subject in an anxious mood, however, saw in the identical picture a soldier who might not reach the hospital in time, and who indeed might already be dead. Such results indicate that what the subjects saw in the pictures, and the constructions they placed upon what they saw, were colored by attitudes which were induced through hypnosis, but through hypnosis were also rendered inaccessible to the subjects' self-reactions. Again an analogy with the learning of pathological behavior is suggested. For in behavior pathology the patient is indeed common who places terrifying, threatening or erotic constructions upon innocuous situa-tions, apparently because of attitudes which he has acquired and continues to maintain, but which he does not identify or formulate in words.

pupillary conditioning at four stimulus intervals." *J. exper. Psychol.*, 1949, vol. 39, pp. 683–689.

[48] Diven, K., "Certain determinants in the conditioning of anxiety reactions." *J. Psychol.*, 1937, vol. 3, pp. 291–308. See also pages 270 and 297–298.

[49] Leuba, C., "Images as conditioned sensations." *J. exper. Psychol.*, 1940, vol. 26, pp. 345–351.

[50] Leuba, C. and Lucas, C., "The effects of attitudes on descriptions of pictures." *J. exper. Psychol.*, 1945, vol. 35, pp. 517–524.

A great deal of experimentation still remains to be done before we can define with any precision the operations through which self-inaccessible learning occurs, and state the conditions which favor it. Our informal observations of everyday social learning, however, suggest at least three factors which are probably involved. (1) From case studies, it frequently seems that learned reactions are self-inaccessible because the individual acquired them before he acquired language, and consequently never formulated them in words. (2) As we shall see later, the process or the product of learning is often rendered inaccessible through repression. (3) In some instances, the excitant which comes to evoke a reaction appeared originally in a context of stress, excitement or disorganization, as is the case in anxiety attacks or panic. Under such circumstances, the emergency character of the original situation prevents the identification of the effective excitant. The subsequent occurrence of the excitant, however, is often sufficient to bring about a prompt reorganization of behavior.

Learning as Rapid Reorganization of Behavior

Human learning in complex or unstructured situations often involves the sudden reorganization of ongoing behavior into new patterned sequences which then persist. This final aspect of learning is of special significance in behavior pathology. For patients appear often to acquire pathological reactions with such ease and rapidity that they seem to contradict the principle that efficient learning requires repeated reinforcement. Certainly we shall find patients who develop fears, acquire and maintain rituals, or arrive at unwarranted conclusions, with a suddenness that is astonishing in view of the complexity of the behavior involved. And we shall occasionally meet patients who develop symptoms so promptly after a traumatic event that we are at once reminded of one-trial learning.

The questions of whether learning is sudden or gradual, one-trial or multitrial, insightful or automatic, carry us deep into controversial learning theories. For some contemporary writers, all learning theoretically occurs in one trial;[51] for others, repeated reinforcement is essential;[52] and for still others, learning depends upon means-end relationships which may or may not involve the restructuring or reorganizing of an hypothetical field.[53] Many aspects of these controversies arise from the particular kinds of learning tasks which experimenters set their subjects. Many of them also reflect the particular theoretical positions which these writers assume in dealing with behavioral data. Let us begin by recognizing that, whatever the theoretical implications in-

[51] See, for example, Guthrie, E. R., *The psychology of learning.* New York: Harper, 1935; Guthrie, E. R., *The psychology of human conflict.* New York: Harper, 1938.

[52] Hull, C. L., *Principles of behavior.* New York: Appleton-Century-Crofts, 1943.

[53] For a discussion of this point of view, see Hilgard, E. R., *Theories of learning.* New York: Appleton-Century-Crofts, 1948, pp. 177–324.

volved, rapid and successful problem-solving does occur in the course of human learning. There is considerable experimental evidence to indicate that, once a learner has arranged in a particular order the tools supplied him, he can solve certain types of problem promptly and efficiently. Moreover, he repeats his correct solution readily on subsequent occasions, so that obviously he has learned it to a reasonably reliable degree. The classical observations of this variety of learning, of course, are those which Köhler made upon the problem-solving behavior of chimpanzees;[54] but later studies by other experimenters, employing other animals and different problems, have yielded similar findings.[55] To learning which proceeds in this way some theorists give the name *insight*.[56]

For our purposes as students of behavior pathology, we may define *insight* as *the occurrence of a reaction, or a system of reactions, which precipitates a sudden and comparatively stable behavioral reorganization*. The reactions which appear are often overt, as in the case of an adult subject working a mechanical puzzle who, after a time of unsuccessful *pulling* on a wire, turns the puzzle over, *pushes* the wire and suddenly succeeds in assembling the gadget. The reactions are just as often covert and unshared, however, as when an anxious person, after weeks of silent brooding, abruptly concludes in private that his unremitting headache is a sign of brain tumor. Frequently, as in this instance, it is a system of self-reactions which precipitates behavioral reorganization. We shall find such learning through self-reactions in the delusional conviction of depressed patients that they are unworthy and hopelessly damned; but we shall find it also in the fresh view of their own behavior which patients often acquire in the course of therapy.[57]

Prompt reorganization of behavior is in itself neither good nor bad, neither valid nor invalid, in terms of cultural norms. The sudden occurrence of a new pattern of reactions may eventuate in successful problem-solving or in recovery from behavior pathology; but it may also represent conclusions which immediately increase the person's anxiety or convince him that he is beyond help.[58] Furthermore, abrupt reorganization always occurs in some relation to an indi-

[54] Köhler, W., *The mentality of apes* (Trans. by E. Winter). New York: Harcourt, Brace, 1925.

[55] See, for example, Alpert, A., "The solving of problem-situations by preschool children: an analysis." *Teach. Coll. Contr. Educ.*, no. 323, 1928; Duncker, K., "On problem solving" (Trans. by L. S. Lees from the 1935 original). *Psychol. Monogr.*, 1945, vol. 58, no. 270; Klüver, H., *Behavior mechanisms in monkeys*. Chicago: University of Chicago Press, 1933; Maier, N. R. F., "Reasoning in white rats." *Comp. Psychol. Monogr.*, 1929, vol. 6, no. 29, p. 23; Tolman, E. C. and Honzik, C. H., "'Insight' in rats." *Univ. Calif. Publ. Psychol.*, 1930, vol. 4, pp. 215–232.

[56] Although this term had been previously used by a number of students of animal learning, it was first systematically employed by Köhler, and then by Yerkes, R. M., "The mind of a gorilla. I." *Genet. Psychol. Monogr.*, 1927, vol. 2, pp. 1–193.

[57] See pages 620–623.

[58] Compare Boisen, A. T., "Onset in acute schizophrenia." *Psychiatry*, 1947, vol. 10, pp. 159–166.

vidual's ongoing behavioral sequences. Typically, a period of unsuccessful tries, of anxious self-examination, or of private, retrospective brooding precedes the sudden occurrence of reactions which restructure an individual's behavior organization. What characterizes insight, as we define it, is a reorganization which emerges from a person's previous reactions, but which comes rapidly, and persists with comparative stability in his subsequent behavior.

From the foregoing analysis, it is clear that rapid reorganization involves many of the aspects of learning which we have already discussed. (1) The reactions which precipitate a continuing pattern of behavior reorganization are ordinarily the product of the person's *reaction-sensitivity*. The chronically anxious person who is reaction-sensitive to his own bodily changes, for example, is ready to organize his reactions into a frightening constellation which for him spells incurable illness.

(2) The reorganized pattern of behavior, whether it is valid or invalid, persists in the individual's repertory because it is *tension-reducing*. Restructuring completes an ongoing sequence of behavior which is incomplete, and consequently brings closure. Thus a sudden conviction that he has committed the unpardonable sin terminates the painful uncertainty and diffuse self-reproach of a depressed patient. His delusion may bring him further sorrow and hopelessness, but at least it provides a more secure basis for organized activity, even though the activity be so inappropriate as to eventuate in suicide.

(3) Often the reactions involved in behavioral reorganization are those which have been *inaccessible to the learner's self-reactions*. We shall see later that the return of repressed reactions may usher in a period of disorganized behavior. Just as often, however, the recurrence of previously repressed attitudes and conflicts precipitates a restructuring of behavior which is stable and systematized. Thus a combat veteran who has successfully repressed the horrifying details of his buddy's death in battle may, upon recalling them, conclude at once that he was responsible for the death and brand himself a sinful murderer. In the same way, however, a phobic patient who for years has been unable to identify the excitants to his fears may, in the course of therapy, come to recall and formulate the situation in which he first became fearful; and his behavior may be immediately reorganized on the basis of these new reactions. When formerly self-inaccessible reactions are suddenly reincluded in the individual's repertory, the resulting behavioral reorganization can lead the person either toward pathology or toward biosocial health.

Most of the characteristics of learning through rapid reorganization are to be found in the following case.

A sixteen-year-old girl was transferred from a Midwest general hospital to a psychiatric clinic in a state of extreme excitement. Up to this time, she had always been a quiet, orderly, conscientious child who was considered a model daughter by her parents and a model student by her teachers. From early childhood, however, she had suffered from a urinary tract disorder which necessitated frequent examination and treatment. She seemed to accept her illnesses calmly, and always submitted to medical procedures cooperatively and without complaint. Two days before her admission to the psychiatric clinic, while preparations were being made for a trip to a general hospital for another urinary tract examination, the patient became suddenly overexcited and was rude and profane to her father. She refused to believe that her father was real, and talked constantly about a young physician with whom she said she was deeply in love. The trip to the hospital was made, and a genitourinary examination completed, but the girl became so overtalkative, erotic and combative that she was transferred to the psychiatric service.

This sudden onset of excitement in a characteristically placid and submissive girl represents a dramatic reorganization of behavior into pathological patterns. As in all cases of sudden reorganization, however, this restructuring had its roots in selective reaction-sensitivities which prepared the girl for the abrupt onset of a particular constellation of reactions. The patient was an only child whose mother died early in her life. She had been reared by her dictatorial aunt and her stern father, neither of whom could offer the child the warmth and affection that she sought. She had no friends of her own age, and the few acquaintances she made were with older persons, toward whom she developed only fleeting attachments. When the patient was eleven years old, her father married a woman who vacillated in her attitudes toward the child between indifference and open hostility. This marriage ended in divorce after three years, during which time the girl heard frequent, violent arguments between her father and his wife over money and prestige which led frequently to charges and countercharges of infidelity.

In this setting there was no one to whom the girl could turn for reassurance, or with whom she could share her doubts and anxieties about herself and her recurrent illnesses. She obtained almost no sex instruction, was utterly unprepared for the anatomical and physiological changes of puberty, and was bewildered and frightened by the snatches of conversation she overheard from adolescent boys and girls at school. The repeated genitourinary examinations and medical procedures which her illnesses necessitated only added to her confusion. It is hardly surprising that she developed persistent erotic fantasies, in which themes of sex behavior, pelvic examination, genitourinary infection, pregnancy and childbirth were intermingled.

Against this background of increasing tension and sexual confusion, the decision that the patient should have still another complete genitourinary examination was distinctly threatening. The crisis came when, just prior to the trip to the hospital, the girl's father announced abruptly that he intended remarrying. It was this news that apparently precipitated a sudden violent reorganization of behavior into the erotic and combative patterns which we have described. Her covert sexual fantasy themes grew suddenly overt in the girl's excited description of an imaginary love affair with a fantasied physician. Repressed attitudes of aggression toward her father became suddenly self-accessible, and erupted into profane and obscene attacks upon the father, and into repeated denials that he was real. This new and sudden reorganization of behavior into pathological patterns persisted over a five-month period in the hospital. It then gave way gradually to the patient's accustomed reactions until, after seven months, she was able to return home well, and to resume her schooling.

We shall meet other patients who, like this one, develop a pathological reorganization of behavior on the basis of traumatic events toward which their acquired attitudes have made them reaction-sensitive. We shall see later on, also, that in a great many delusional developments, there occurs a phenomenon known as *sudden clarification*. This is only a special case of rapid reorganization; an anxious patient, made selectively reaction-sensitive by his past training, arrives precipitately at conclusions which turn out to be socially invalid. And we shall find other examples of equally rapid, but this time socially valid conclusions in the reactions of patients who are undergoing treatment through interview, discussion, and free verbalization.[59]

By now it should be clear that the learning of pathological behavior proceeds according to the same general principles as does any other human learning. It occurs in a complex social situation through direct tuition and through the adoption of prevailing ways of reacting. It involves extended temporal sequences of anticipation, response and after-reaction which favor the operation of chance concomitance. Like any other learned behavior, a particular pattern of pathological reactions will always reflect in part the needs of the learner, and once acquired it will be maintained as long as it proves to be tension-reducing. Finally, as we have just seen, learning in both normal and pathological behavior is often self-inaccessible and it may involve relatively rapid reorganization.

Implicit in our discussion of learning, of course, has been the fact that human learning is always complicated by its heavy dependence upon symbolic behavior. Language and thinking not only facilitate human learning and increase its complexity; they also provide the basis for innumerable confusions which contribute to the production of distorted and bizarre behavior in patients. Because of its central position in the development of both normal and pathological reactions, we have reserved, for special consideration, the development and operation of symbolic behavior, of socially-derived role-taking and of self-reactions, to which we shall now turn.

[59] See pages 561–574.

4

Symbolization, Role-Taking and Emotional Reactions

Language Behavior

Human society is built around and sustained by communication; and the behavioral organization of all individuals who participate in social interaction is continuously dependent upon communicative functions. Therefore, if we are to understand the behavior of any individual in human society, we must take into account man's chief instrument of communication, language behavior, and its complex product, socially organized thinking. For it is the development and systematic use of language and thinking which, more than any other characteristic, distinguishes man among mammals, and marks off his behavior pathology as fundamentally different from that of any other form of life.

Precursors of communicative speech

It is impossible to grasp the significance of language in relation to social thinking and behavior pathology unless we examine first some of the precursors of the spoken word. For language behavior is not the *source* of communication in young children, but its *outcome*. Communication arises out of need. The needs of a newborn infant, and the ways in which they are satisfied, or terminated, do not differ fundamentally from need-satisfaction sequences in other mammals. Hunger, for example, appears in the human neonate under the same general conditions that instigate hunger in puppies, kittens, lambs and colts.

Hunger is likewise satisfied in all mammalian forms, including man, by the conjoint operation of sucking and giving suck. Such reciprocal, cooperative behavior is "social" — since it involves the unitary shared activity of two individuals.[1] It is also an example of rudimentary communication, since the two individuals react, and modify their reactions, in terms of each other's behavior.

[1] See pages 134-137.

If the maternal nipple recedes, the infant may pursue it, make searching movements, or begin to cry. To this the mother responds by making the nipple once more available; and the pursuit, searching, or crying, is replaced by sucking. Nevertheless, communication such as this does not go beyond the simple direct interplay of specific reaction and specific body part. And other need-satisfaction sequences in human neonates, as in other newborn mammals, are similarly restricted in scope.

The human infant is able, even without the aid of language, to achieve far more than the acquisition of skill in satisfying his earliest needs. Long before he can talk or understand connected discourse, he succeeds in developing extensive systems of new need, and he learns a great variety of new techniques of satisfaction. Quite apart from communicative speech, the human being is a markedly superior organism when it comes to the elaboration and use of complex adaptive reactions. During infancy, the prelanguage child enters effectively into innumerable social interactions, and learns to carry through behavioral sequences in a multidimensional field of operations.

It is obvious that the advent of genuinely cooperative social behavior and reciprocal interplay does not wait upon communicative speech.[2] Rather cooperation and reciprocity form the matrix out of which language behavior develops. Nevertheless, the prelanguage child must live by means of a sharply limited environment that is structured in terms of relatively brief behavioral sequences. His anticipation is restricted to things happening around him. He cannot stimulate himself to recall; his recall can be stimulated for the most part only by events external to himself. He cannot cheer himself by predicting, "In another two hours I will be fed." He cannot remind himself that tomorrow is his birthday.

As long as a child lacks language, he is like other mammals also in having to meet direct frustration with overt attack, flight, evasion or complete inaction. He cannot fall back upon language symbols, which allow us older persons to escape the immediate effects of frustration without having to abandon all attempts at solving the difficulty. The older person may stand overtly still; but covertly he manipulates his symbolic counters, and plans his victory while he seems submissive in defeat. The infant's defeat in a frustrating encounter is final and complete; and his satisfactions have a similarly absolute quality. Without language, the child cannot be consoled for his losses by the specific reassurances of others, or by them be congratulated specifically for his gains. Neither has he the behavioral means of providing himself with reassurance and congratulation, as he later will have. His life is largely keyed to present occurrences.

[2] See, for example, the account of the smiling response in Spitz, R. A., "The smiling response: a contribution to the ontogenesis of social relations." *Genet. Psychol. Monogr.*, 1946, vol. 34, pp. 57–125.

The human being is able to free himself from this bondage to the present — in which all other mammals must continue living — because of his peculiar biological structure and his cultural inheritance. Man is apparently the only mammal biologically capable of acquiring the unique and infinitely complex system of communication that we call language behavior. And, from the moment of his birth, every human being is an integral part of a society and culture that is organized and transmitted in communicative terms. Under these circumstances, the sounds which every infant learns to make are gradually transformed into the conventional patterns of whatever language system prevails in his surroundings. Since this development is of enormous importance in behavior pathology, we shall next consider some of its salient characteristics in greater detail.

The beginnings of human speech [3]

Two general conditions are necessary for the emergence of communicative speech: (1) The child must have developed biosocially to the point at which he can emit and repeat specific sounds in a specific situation; and (2) he must be engaged in some participative activity with an older person who is using communicative speech. Indeed, there is no behavior that illustrates better than spoken language the dependence of all complex human learning upon biosocial maturation and interindividual participation. The first makes it possible; the second makes it actual.

It is the first condition, the child's biosocial development, which as a rule determines the time of the emergence of conventional speech. For, as we shall see, conjoint activity begins with the earliest feeding and body-care routines in which mother and child cooperate and reciprocate. In these and numberless other shared, social situations the mother pours forth the words, phrases and exclamations belonging to the language system she has made her own. The infant, early in his speech career, emits cooing sounds, cries, laughs, crows and gurgles. Later on he adds his own individualistic exclamations; he babbles and begins to play with sounds; he looks, reaches, points, manipulates or withdraws. These are the immediate antecedents of communicative speech, the biological beginnings that every child learns as part of his early social interaction. Thus, we see that language behavior has its origins in the movements and sounds which are instigated during the course of shared activities.

It was at one time supposed that the child collected isolated words and phrases one by one — as wealthy women once collected pearls — until his acquisition of a graded string of verbal elements gave him possession of a chain of speech. But actually, children begin by learning the broad patterns of the

[3] For a recent review of the literature on the development of language in children see McCarthy, D., "Language development in children." In Carmichael, L. (Ed.), *Manual of child psychology*. New York: Wiley, 1946, pp. 476–581.

talk they hear around them, before they have mastered single words and phrases. They speak in meaningless babble with intonations and inflections that sound at a distance like connected discourse (*expressive jargon*); [4] and in so doing they lay the foundations for their subsequent acquisition of meaningful sequential speech. The child thus unintentionally gains practice in the rhythms and undulations typical of the language in his society, just as he learns other basic rhythms and accents in manipulative and locomotory skills.

The babbling that goes to make up a young child's vocal play and expressive jargon contains a tremendous variety of sound. Indeed, students of language development maintain that every child at some time makes all of the sounds to be heard in all contemporary languages.[5] The problem in learning to speak, therefore, is not that of creating new sounds but of selecting, from an almost infinite behavioral store, the ones belonging to the language system of the surrounding society and culture. This selection, as we shall see, is the product of neither the child's behavior alone, nor of the reactions of his elders, but of the social interaction between child and elders as they participate in some conjoint activity.[6]

Learning to speak is selective and tension-reducing

Every infant, in his spontaneous babbling, ultimately reaches a phase of repetitive performance. His utterance of a particular sound, which he himself also hears, is immediately followed by repetition of the same sound, partly because he has heard it. The result is the appearance of such familiar couplings, or *reduplications*, as "na-na," "boo-boo," "ga-ga," and of successions of repetitive activity, like "la-la-la-la-la-la-la" (sometimes called *lalling*). It is widely held among students of child behavior that such self-stimulations and self-response are crucial in the process of learning to speak.[7] But reduplication and lalling, while necessary conditions for the acquisition of language behavior, are not alone sufficient. The intervention of an older person is apparently essential if sounds are to be fixed as communicative speech.

When a child's vocalizations resemble human language, the adult tends to repeat approximately what the child has just said. This stimulates the child to repeat also, in the same way that his own speaking leads to reduplication. Thus the older person, in effect, singles out from among the child's utterances

[4] Bayley, N., "Mental growth during the first three years." *Genet. Psychol. Monogr.*, 1933, vol. 14, no. 1, p. 92; Gesell, A. and Thompson, H., *Infant behavior: its genesis and growth.* New York: McGraw-Hill, 1935, pp. 243–257 and 286–291.

[5] See, for example, Irwin, O. C. and Curry, T., "Vowel elements in the crying vocalization of infants under ten days of age." *Child Develpm.*, 1941, vol. 12, pp. 99–109; Lewis, M. M., *Infant speech: a study of the beginnings of language.* New York: Harcourt, Brace, 1936.

[6] Brodbeck, A. J. and Irwin, O. C., "The speech behavior of infants without families." *Child Develpm.*, 1946, vol. 17, pp. 145–156.

[7] Lewis, M. M., *Infant speech: a study of the beginnings of language.* New York: Harcourt, Brace, 1936, pp. 79–80.

those sounds which belong in the language of the society and culture which both share. In this manner, the conventional sounds are reinforced and the unconventional undergo ultimate extinction through neglect. It is important to realize that, before language behavior becomes established in an individual's repertory, such adult repetitions and child reduplications occur, not once or a dozen times, but literally tens or hundreds of thousands of times.[8]

From what has been said, it is already clear that language behavior is acquired in the same general ways that other behavioral patterns are.[9] For speech is always learned in a social situation, as a part of conjoint activity; it shows a sequential character from the start, even before specific words or phrases have been stabilized in the child's repertory; and the acquisition of communicative speech is fundamentally a selective process, in which child and older person cooperate in emphasizing the conventional and neglecting the individualistic. But to limit our discussion of learning to these factors would be both fruitless and unnecessary, for learning to speak is also intimately tied up with tension-reduction and the satisfaction of need.[10]

We may begin with the fact that all infants make sounds as part of their general activity, and tend to respond to speech by other persons with their own vocalizations. The sounds a child emits are in themselves attention-getting, in the same sense that crying, wetting, breath-holding and vomiting may be attention-getting. When, however, his vocalizations elicit sounds in other persons, and lead to a little vocal game, the child's babbling becomes part of an important and rewarding shared activity. A lonely or ignored child soon learns to attract and hold another person as playmate by emitting sounds, and by responding to the attention he then gets with further babbling that prolongs the vocal game. Tension-reduction occurs under these circumstances because the child's acquired need for human company, and for the reciprocal stimulation that it brings, is satisfied. Solitude is replaced by partnership; monotony gives way to entertainment.

The selective adult response to infant babbling, which we have just discussed, also operates as tension-reduction. When an English-speaking mother, for example, hears her child utter some such reduplicative sound as "ma-ma" or "da-da," she is almost certain to respond with generally increased animation as she repeats the sound. She is likely to supplement this response with an affectionate demonstration — kissing, fondling, picking the child up, holding and cuddling him. To her the child seems to have learned a meaningful word

[8] For an indication of the persistence of such repetitions in adult speech, see Ritter, A. M., "Some conditions influencing the incidence of response duplication of verbal stimuli." *J. Psychol.*, 1949, vol. 28, pp. 93–118.

[9] See Chapter 3 for a detailed discussion of the characteristics of learning fundamental to behavior pathology.

[10] For information concerning the relationship between frequent words and personal need in preschool children, see Shirley, M., "Common content in the speech of preschool children." *Child Develpm.*, 1938, vol. 9, pp. 333–346.

— her name, in a sense, or his father's. To the child the situation has suddenly become more exciting and rewarding. The mother now lies in wait for a repetition of the sound; and when by chance it comes again, she pounces on it and there is more fun and stimulation for both participants. Thus, the satisfying maternal animation and approval must be reckoned among the crucial selective factors that transform reduplicative babble and expressive jargon into human speech.

The outcome of this process of selective learning, in a tension-reducing, socially-shared situation, is always the same. A child's babble gains first the patterns of intonation and inflection of the language he hears around him. Eventually, the individualistic syllable-reduplications in these learned sequences are crowded out by the sounds that adults reward and reinforce. As the conventional sounds increase in a child's vocalization, the adult may observe sudden and as yet unexplained increments of whole phrases or a short sentence in the child's speech repertory. These are probably instances of insightful learning,[11] in which we can identify the sudden reorganization, but so far not the reaction that precipitates it.

Speech as indicating and symbolizing behavior

For the student of behavior pathology, the phase of selection and fixation of conventional speech-sounds is of somewhat restricted interest. It becomes important chiefly in problems of developmental retardation, in specific language disabilities, and in language impairment as the consequence of cerebral damage. When, however, we turn to the elaboration of conventional sounds into instruments that indicate and symbolize, we come at once upon a phase of language development that is significant for almost the whole of behavior pathology. As we have already pointed out, the vastly complex behavioral organization of all human beings who participate in social interaction is built around verbal communication. And communicative speech, as we shall see, depends upon the properties of *indicating* and *symbolizing*.

(a) *Indication*. Every infant begins sooner or later to point toward objects that he cannot reach, and activities that he cannot enter; and vocalization is a common accompaniment of such manual indication. When the child has learned to restrict one of his utterances to a shared situation in which some one object appears — as "daw" when a dog is present — he has unwittingly seized hold of a response that has new properties for him. The child points, and says "daw," his mother repeats something similar, and he hears what both he and his mother say. The pointing, the hearing, the seeing and the sharing are all aspects of a unitary behavioral field, in which child and mother are responding selectively to the presence of the dog. This is the beginning of speech as indication.

[11] See pages 83–87.

The child inevitably extends this indicating use of sound by saying "daw," and pointing, as the dog goes past him and disappears from view. He can continue to say "daw" after the dog is out of sight. He learns to say it when the dog barks unseen, or scratches on the front door before being admitted to the house. The child may or may not point in the direction of the animal; most of us never quite give up pointing as we indicate through words. But the crucial fact in this development is that a fixed sound can now perform the functions of the indicating hand, and do a better job of it. Moreover, it is but a small step from this level of verbal indication to the infinite potentialities of symbolization.

(b) *Symbolization.* Indication becomes symbolization when the object or activity indicated is no longer present as direct stimulation. In our example, the child was approaching rudimentary symbolization when he responded with "daw" to the unseen barking or scratching dog. He was still closer to it when he spoke this specific syllable immediately after the dog had disappeared from sight and hearing. The child attains symbolization as soon as he reacts to the spoken syllable in ways that are appropriate to the advent, presence or disappearance of the dog, and when there has been no sign of the dog in the immediate past. The mother, for example, says "dog" or "daw" and thereby stimulates her child to search for the object to which both mother and child had previously responded with an equivalent sound. This, of course, is only a special case of anticipant behavior,[12] which here we find induced by the beginnings of verbal communication.

This symbolic use of a specific sound, in the complete absence of the object or activity to which it originally referred, is often called *representative.* The spoken syllable can represent or substitute for the absent thing or act. As the representative or symbolic function of the spoken word becomes established, the individual can begin to make statements about objects and activities which are located somewhere else, or which belong to the future and the past. With only a meager repertory of conventional words, a child can eventually say the dog is cold. He can say this when the dog is cold to the touch or can be heard whimpering outside in winter. But he can say it also — and this is the critical point for us — when the dog is whimpering but not cold, or when the day is freezing, but the dog has managed to come in unseen and creep into the warm basement.

We have dwelt upon the development of indication and symbolization because they are basic to the evolution of discourse in the human being, and because in discourse we shall find both the roots and the consequences of a large share of behavior pathology.[13] The distinction just made — between a verbal

[12] See pages 65–66, where anticipant behavior is defined and illustrated in direct relation to learning.

[13] For a discussion of these points, see Chapters 15 and 16.

statement that does and one that does not correspond with the actual situation — is fundamentally a distinction between the universe of discourse and the universe of non-discourse. It is the distinction, reduced to its simplest valid terms, which is usually intended in behavior pathology when we speak of *reality* and *unreality*.

A statement is realistic if it conforms to the object, activity or relationship to which it refers — the conformity being usually expressed in terms of a consensus. If it does not so conform it is unrealistic, and the situation it describes is called unreal. On this same general basis, such reactions as recall, belief, hope, expectation and prediction can be evaluated as to their degree of conformity or probability; and in terms of the evaluation, we characterize them as more or less real and unreal. As we shall see, the question of correspondence or non-correspondence between a person's statements — whether explicit or implied — and what the person is referring to, becomes of prime importance in the use and misuse of language and thinking, as play, entertainment, defense, compensation or escape.[14]

Verbal self-regulation

We have already encountered self-stimulation and self-reaction in the reduplication and the lalling of prelanguage infants. There we said that these couplings and serial repetitions of a syllable are considered of crucial importance for the emergence of communicative speech. Here we shall see that they are critical also for the evolution of self-attitude and self-response. By self-response we mean the response of an individual to his own behavior or appearance; and by self-attitude we mean the attitude that favors and sustains such responses.[15]

Without self-attitudes and self-responses there could be no self-evaluation in terms of the prevailing mores. There would be no remorse or pride concerning things past, and no personal conflict over actions planned. We should have neither feasting in exultation nor fasting in penance. Delusion would be robbed of nearly all its dramatic and effective components, and hallucination reduced to impersonal fragments of recall.[16]

Self-stimulation moves forward, from the merely repetitious to the *indicative* and *symbolic*, when a child speaks a conventional syllable and responds appropriately to the sound in terms of what it represents. The child who, in participative activity with his mother, learns to say "daw" in reference to the dog,

---

[14] For a discussion of the "unrealistic" use of language in early childhood, see Kanner, L., "Irrelevant metaphorical language in early infantile autism." *Amer. J. Psychiat.*, 1946, vol. 103, pp. 242–246; for an account of the development of "secret" language, see Howard, R. W., "The language development of a group of triplets." *J. genet. Psychol.*, 1946, vol. 69, pp. 181–188.

[15] For definitions of attitude and response, see pages 64–65.

[16] See Chapters 13 and 14.

learns also to react to what he says with searching and anticipant behavior. He can now initiate specific relevant reactions in his own behavior through the symbolic use of a conventional word.   In this act of verbal self-stimulation and appropriate response, the child has laid the behavioral foundation of verbal self-control, self-evaluation, self-punishment and self-reward.   He has unwittingly begun the process of subjecting his private actions and his private thought to the verbal representations of public scrutiny.

The public scrutiny comes first; its private verbal representatives are a later acquisition.   The child learns what he may and may not do before he has developed sufficient formal speech to comment meaningfully upon his actions. His earliest comments are simply repetitions of what his elders say as they assist him, thwart him, correct, reward or punish him.   He learns to make sounds resembling "No-no!" "Good boy!" "Bad boy!" in appropriate social situations which he shares with an evaluating parent.   At this stage it is usually no more than concomitant vocalization — an incidental sound effect which becomes stable and predictable before it takes on self-evaluative functions or grows into verbal self-control.   Thus a child may shake his head solemnly and say, "No-no!" when he is doing something of which his parents regularly disapprove; but he will for some time go right on doing it, as though no disapproval were being voiced.

Eventually, however, such consistently heard and consistently emitted sounds do acquire self-regulatory and self-critical properties.   The child begins to do something for which he has been interfered with repeatedly, restrained or punished; he says "No-no!" as his parent has also been saying; and he hesitates or desists.   The conventional word now leads to conforming behavior. The child acts in accordance with what he says; and what he says is a repetition of the sound his parent makes in thwarting the child, or in warning him. A domestic animal can learn to respond promptly and appropriately to verbal reprimand and warning; but it cannot take the initiative, sound the reprimand or speak the warning, and then interrupt what it was about to do.   The child can and does learn to take the initiative.   By means of sounds, which have become fixed as his vocabulary, through conjoint activity with a parent, he is able himself to object to what he is about to do, to express objection as his parent would, and then suit his own actions to his parent's words.

This is indeed a simple and a restricted achievement as it stands — to be able to negate an act with a syllable, and by that negation terminate the act. But its potentialities are limitless, like those arising from the invention of numbers and pictographs, which were also simple and restricted at the start. For ultimately the child, grown through adolescence to adulthood, will mingle self-regulatory symbols with almost everything he does that offers an alternative.   Sometimes the symbols will be speech; sometimes they will be frowns, smiles, nods, gestures and posturing.   Sometimes muted words, tensions and covert thinking will be used. The exact form of such self-regulation is second-ary; the principle remains basically always the same. An act stimulates the actor to symbolize as he proceeds to further action; the symbolization modifies the development of later acts; and symbol and later act combine to produce and modify the course of a person's own ongoing behavior.

We have used negation — the child's "No-no!" — as our example, because it induces dramatic hesitations and reversals that are easier to demonstrate than the effects of affirmations. But, of course, in any system of self-regula-tion, approval is every bit as important as disapproval. Children learn to give the parent's "Yes!" to their permitted and prescribed reactions, as well as "No!" to what is not allowed. Those activities which his elders encourage and reward with praise or privilege, the child learns also to encourage and re-ward in himself. He displays his approval and gratification publicly over what he has achieved; and he receives then a further reward in his parent's acquiescence. In time he comes to modify the *public* expression of both his self-approval and self-condemnation, in accordance with prevailing custom and self-interest.

It should not be supposed that symbolic self-regulation puts an end to the struggle between alternatives. On the contrary, symbols give to conflict new dimensions. Even the infant who says "No-no!" to his adient response goes on responding just the same. Indeed, he may slap his own hand and still go on. And when his words become effective obstacles, he hesitates and vacillates be-fore he stops. This wavering is the overt *conflict between simple responses*, about which we shall have more to say later on.[17] It is also another example of the discrepancies that can arise between verbal and non-verbal responses in the same activity [18] — here between what a person says and what he does. These conflicts between words and deeds, that first appear when we begin to speak, are never fully resolved until we cease to live. There is always what we do and what we say we ought to do; what we do and what we say we ought not to have done; what we do and what we tell others, and even ourselves, that we have done.

The war that words wage upon deeds, and deeds on words, is paralleled by an incessant conflict that develops among words themselves. The child who learned to speak about the dog, when no dog was near him, learns also to com-ment upon his own behavior, when that behavior is well past or not yet immi-nent. And he can comment, too, on what he says about an act, and then pass judgment on his comment.[19] He can next discuss his judgment, and so lift his self-reactions out of the arena of non-verbal behavior, and set them against

[17] For a detailed discussion of conflict, see Chapter 9.

[18] Compare pages 109–112.

[19] For extreme examples of children's tendency to comment upon their own behavior, see Kanner, L., "Irrelevant metaphorical language in early infantile autism." *Amer. J Psychiat.*, 1946, vol. 103, pp. 242–246.

each other wholly in symbolic terms. Symbolic representation, we know, does
not maintain a simple one-to-one relationship with what it represents.[20] So
the statement of attitude or intent, of need and frustration, of conflict and
anxiety, may bear only a vague resemblance to what is symbolized. The
verbal can never substitute completely for the non-verbal actuality. And the
conflicts between statements, between statement and fantasy, and even among
fantasies themselves, give to symbolic self-reactions and to the whole of behavior pathology, a still unfathomed depth.

Verbal self-evaluation

We have said that, without self-attitude and self-responses, human beings
could not develop self-evaluation in terms of the prevailing mores.[21] There
would be neither pride nor remorse, no conflict in advance of action, or afterwards, and only the most colorless, transient delusion and hallucination.
Under these conditions, human living would have the direct and immediate
quality that characterizes the life of other mammals. But, as we have pointed
out, the human mammal learns to react in verbal terms to what he himself
does, to what he himself says, and eventually to what he thinks. He thus
develops a symbolic system by means of which he is able, not only to regulate
his own behavior, but also to talk about it, describe it, weigh it, applaud or
stigmatize it.

In this symbolic system are the origins of what we have called the verbal
representation of public scrutiny in private behavior.[22] For verbal self-evaluation begins — as all other verbal acquisitions do — with the taking over from
one's elders of the evaluations which they voice in relation to one's own conduct and the conduct of others in the environment. These are at first simple
negations, affirmations and other contrasts — "no" and "yes," "good" and
"naughty," "clean" and "dirty," "quick" and "slow," "smart" and
"dumb." Children learn early in their linguistic careers to attach such terms
to whatever names they have acquired for people, animals and things. In this
way they begin an adjectival and adverbial division of their surroundings into
what should be approved and what condemned, what prized and what depreciated, what sought after and what shunned.

These crude evaluative reactions are mastered earlier than the more complex and inclusive ones which ultimately supplant them.[23] Every child's initial
uses of evaluative terms, like his first use of other words, are little more than
mere repetition of adult sounds made in shared situations. Indeed, adults
tacitly acknowledge the incompleteness of a child's early evaluative reactions

---

[20] See Chapters 15 and 16.   [21] See page 95.   [22] See page 96.
[23] Gesell finds examples of the comprehension of inhibiting, prohibiting and forbidding
words in children as young as 12 to 18 months of age. See Gesell, A., Thompson, H., and
Amatruda, C. S., *The psychology of early growth*. New York: Macmillan, 1938.

in their own behavior. For, when they make evaluative assertions to little children, they characteristically exaggerate, by means of impressive pantomime, the accompanying withdrawal or adience, the disapproving frown or accepting smile, and even the inflections and intonations of their words. Adults repeat these little melodramatic acts until the child seems to have caught some of the attitudinal flavor in his own evaluative statements. Thus the child acquires enduring, conventionally structured basic attitudes — negative and positive, hostile and friendly, approving and condemning, attracted and repelled.

The appropriately structured attitudes and responses, which the child acquires directly from speaking persons around him, always include evaluative reactions that refer to his own appearance, status and behavior. He hears that he is a big fellow, that he is mamma's darling and can feed himself. He is told that he looks like his father, that he is older than his baby sister, and that he loves her. He is called dirty, disowned and a bad boy; and then he is all clean, mamma's darling again, and now he will be a good boy. As the child learns such characterizations, he begins to make use of them in informing others of what others have informed him about himself. Since he also hears what he is then saying, he gains practice in making statements concerning his own appearance, status and behavior, which become statements also to himself. Now he has acquired a new ability: the ability to satisfy his own need for clarification, reassurance or correction, by means of opinions about himself, concerning what he does and says, and who he is.

The opinions that a child first forms of himself must inevitably mirror the opinions that others in his vicinity formulate. He can no more make up his own independent evaluation at this stage than he can invent his own communicative speech. For behavior pathology, this is one of the most important facts about evaluative self-attitudes and self-responses, that their origins lie always in the opinions of other persons. And, early in the life of every child, this must mean that his basic attitudes toward himself reflect directly the attitude toward him of his parents or his parent-surrogates. If his parents accept him and for the most part approve his conduct, the child will unwittingly adopt these attitudes as the models for his own acceptance and approval of himself. If, instead, his parents reject him and emphasize his inferiority or badness, he will initially learn to reject himself and treat his deeds as inferior or bad.

If self-evaluation had no more to it than this, one could predict from what parents said to a child, and what they said about him in his presence, exactly what the child would grow up to say and think about himself. One could also predict, from what a child had learned to say about himself at the age of three years, what he would say and think at thirteen and at thirty. But the development of verbal self-evaluation is neither as simple nor as inflexible as this. It is true that early parental reactions have been clinically demonstrated to have enduring consequences in a child's later years.[24] The modes of their operation, however, are far from simple.

(a) *Transient fluctuations in parental attitude.* One obvious source of complexity in the growth of self-evaluation is that the parent or parent-surrogate seldom maintains a fixed and single attitude toward his child. Even the most accepting parent regrets now and then the restrictions upon his freedom of action that parenthood inevitably entails. The regret may well come and go in relation to difficulties that are wholly unconnected with the child's behavior at the time. From the standpoint of what the child says and does, these fluctuations become in effect capricious, unintelligible and unpredictable. Because of this hidden factor, the same behavior may at one time be rewarded and at another punished or ignored. The child who has learned to gain praise and encouragement by dressing well, or by giving unsolicited domestic help, occasionally finds his self-display unaccountably annoying, and his assistance disparaged or spurned.

(b) *Long-term shifts and reversals in parental attitude.* There is another common variation in parental attitude which involves more than a transient fluctuation. This is the change, often progressive, in the kind and degree of acceptance that a child is given as he grows older. Some mothers take delight in caring for a helpless infant; for them a baby is the doll of their girlhood come to life. As the doll becomes more and more self-sufficient and grows into a person, such a mother may find her interest waning, and her thoughts turning to the prospect of another infant. Some mothers, on the other hand, find the care of an infant monotonous and burdensome. When, however, the child acquires locomotion, manipulative skill and communicative speech, the once indifferent or resentful mother may discover in him an interesting and appealing companion.

Fathers are much more likely than mothers to show the latter kind of attitudinal shift, from indifference to affectionate interest.[25] For one thing, they have not in boyhood been absorbed with doll play or parent roles. Neither have they usually been permitted, much less encouraged, to help care for relatives' and neighbors' infants as their sisters have. Accordingly, they seldom enter actively into feeding and body-care routines in relation to their own infants. It is only after the child begins to get about and to talk that paternal acceptance begins to be significant. The father to whom infant care seems as dull and unattractive as doll-play now finds an entertaining challenge in the independent activity and rudimentary conversation of his child. The burden of dependence has grown into a promise of autonomy.

The birth of a second child is one of the commonest and most widely recog-

[24] See pages 56–63.
[25] See, for example, Gardner, L. P., "An analysis of children's attitudes toward fathers." *J. genet. Psychol.*, 1947, vol. 70, pp. 3–28.

nized occasions for important changes in parental attitudes which are reflected in the self-attitudes of the first-born.[26] The baby of the family is discarded for a new baby; he is expected suddenly to become self-sufficient, to give up the spotlight for the side lines, and to give affection generously when he can get none for himself. Children often react to such deprivation by concluding that they are of little value and unloved.[27] If, as is often the case, they are reproached or punished for resenting their forced abdication and for loathing the usurper, they see themselves guilty, unworthy and hateful, without in the least being able to overcome their resentment and loathing. Thus they introduce, into their system of self-evaluation, attitudes that are strongly self-reproachful, self-punitive and self-depreciatory. These are foundations upon which compulsion, hallucination and delusion can in later years be erected.[28]

The effects of such maternal and paternal shifts, from acceptance to rejection or from rejection to acceptance, may complicate considerably the course of a child's development of self-evaluation. This is especially apt to be the case when a major change in parental attitude occurs while self-evaluation is being consolidated through the use of language, or after such consolidation has taken place. In the former situation, the child's self-evaluation is likely to consist of confusing ambiguities. Approving and accepting characterizations and opinions will coexist in his behavior organization with self-attitudes that clearly reflect disapprobation and repudiation by the parent. In the latter situation, the child is exposed to outright contradiction between his own self-evaluative statements — which he has acquired directly from the parent — and the parent's revised estimate of the child, which is now opposite in sign.

(c) *Interparental discrepancies.* A further complication in the development of self-evaluation arises from the simple fact that children are usually reared by two parents, each of whom brings to parenthood certain unique contributions. In the first place, each parent comes from a particular family background in which, for approximately two decades, each has participated in a dynamic familial organization.[29] From this participation, each parent has acquired many anticipant attitudes in relation to parenthood and filial behavior. Moreover, the father also represents the male subculture, with all its male traditions, while the mother similarly represents the female subculture with its female folklore. Each will reflect the needs and expect the satisfactions from parenthood which each has learned through identification in the past with father and mother. Thus, what one emphasizes in relation to the

[26] See the discussion of sibling rivalry on pages 287–289.

[27] Levy, D., "Studies in sibling rivalry." *Res. Monogr. Amer. Orthopsychiat. Assn.*, 1937, no. 2, pp. 1–96; Levy, D., "Hostility patterns in sibling rivalry experiments." *Amer. J. Orthopsychiat.*, 1936, vol. 6, pp. 193–257; Anon., "Ambivalence in first reactions to a sibling." *J. abn. soc. Psychol.*, 1949, vol. 44, pp. 541–549.

[28] Compare the discussion of masochism on pages 41–42.

[29] See Ingersoll, H. L., "A study of the transmission of authority patterns in the family." *Genet. Psychol. Monogr.*, 1948, vol. 38, pp. 225–302.

child, whom both share, the other may slight; what one praises, the other may belittle; what one gently condones, the other may severely criticize.

Such discrepancies, far from being exceptional, must be recognized as the rule in our culture. Under ordinary circumstances, their effects upon the child's self-evaluation are constructive, since exaggerations of attitude in one parent are likely to be tempered by the more matter-of-fact attitudes in the other. Indeed, parents tend to offset each other's overemphases in this way — sometimes deliberately, sometimes not. When, for any reason, a child is reared by only one parent, the resulting organization of self-attitude and self-response is nearly always one-sided. Depending largely upon the dominant attitudes of the remaining parent, the child will tend either to overplay or to underestimate the characteristics of the missing parent, and so overvalue or depreciate the appearance of corresponding characteristics in his own behavior.[30] The result of this, as we shall later see, is often to hamper the child in developing realistic role-taking in relation to one or the other sex.

The mere fact that both parents participate in the rearing of a child does not, of course, guarantee that each will contribute positively to the child's self-evaluation. The child whose mother worships him, and provides him with a ceaseless flow of love and praise, may be resented by his father for this very reason, and may by him be harshly treated. Similarly, the child who gets constant affectionate attention from his father may make his mother jealous and spiteful. In either case, the child will acquire sharp contradictions in his self-attitudes and self-responses. He may love himself dearly for some characteristics and hate himself for others, or even love and hate himself for the same characteristics. Later in childhood, in adolescence and adulthood, he may enter into some relationships with zest and confidence, but show apathy and vacillation in some others that are socially no less important and seem to an observer no less attractive and no more ambiguous.

If parents are at serious odds with each other, one of them may become suddenly hostile toward a child, whom he has previously accepted, including him now as part of a hated marital situation. The other may seek to compensate for lost marital affection by turning avidly toward the child who has perhaps been treated previously with only moderate warmth. Some quarreling parents use their child as a weapon against each other, subjecting him in this process to a confusion of doubly ambivalent attitudes, each parent hating and loving him as he represents for each a symbol of the other, and a fellow-conspirator against the other. Children under these circumstances cannot fail to develop multiple ambivalent attitudes toward their parents,[31] to derive from these contradictory identifications grossly conflicting opinions of themselves, and to lay

[30] Sears, R. R., Pintler, M. H., and Sears, P. S., "Effect of father separation on preschool children's doll play aggression." *Child Develpm.*, 1946, vol. 17, pp. 219–243.
[31] Compare the findings of Bach, G. R., "Father-fantasies and father-typing in father-separated children." *Child Develpm.*, 1946, vol. 17, pp. 63–80.

the foundations of warring systems of self-attitude and self-response that can be readily converted into delusion and hallucination under stress.[32]

(d) *Later self-reactions and counter-reactions.* Up to now we have been discussing the acquisition of self-evaluation almost as if a child were the passive recipient of his human environment. While this conception does relatively little violence to the actual situation early in the development of self-reactions,[33] it becomes less and less adequate as the child grows older. For the process of learning verbal self-evaluation is selective in character just as other human social learning is. At first the child repeats everything he can from what he hears around him. But as his systems of self-attitude and self-response become more and more complexly organized, he grows increasingly selective in what he most readily reacts to — in short he grows progressively reaction-sensitive in self-evaluation as in other things. And, even though ambiguities and contradictions never are eliminated from these self-reactions, the biosocially maturing child soon begins to show recognizable tendencies to resist certain characterizations of his behavior, status or appearance, and to welcome others gladly.

There is also an early phase in the development of self-evaluation which is characterized by vigorous counterreactions, by the wholesale *rejection* of what others say, that appears in many children between the third and fourth years. This phase is generally referred to as the *age of resistance*. The refusal to accept what others say is only one aspect of a general opposition to regulation, restraint and positive guidance. But it is unquestionably of considerable importance for a child's later autonomous development that he develop techniques which enable him to persist doggedly in maintaining self-opinions, when everyone around him disagrees. For it is only a little less unfortunate to be unable to sustain adequate self-attitudes, without continual outside reassurance, than to be unable to modify one's self-evaluation when persistence in it threatens one's integrity.

Another important selective factor in the development of self-evaluation is that of identification. The child, we have indicated,[34] acquires family patterns of behavior essentially through reacting to the possessions, status, and characteristics of members of his family as if these were his own. It is obvious, however, that the child cannot adopt a characteristic of one parent, along with its diametric opposite from the other parent, unless he reserves these opposed reactions for different social roles.[35] Moreover, in some of the conflicting situations which we have been discussing, the child is often forced to adopt the characteristics of one parent, and reject the corresponding but opposed

---

[32] For a further discussion of this development, see Chapters 13 and 14.

[33] See the discussion on pages 285–287.

[34] See pages 60–63, for a definition and discussion of identification.

[35] This separation into discrepant roles will be discussed later in the present chapter. See also pages 249 and 273, and the discussion of opposition on pages 386–387.

characteristics of the other parent. This adoption of the characteristics of another person is commonly referred to as "identifying with" the other one.

Because the father is away from home most of the young child's waking life, it is the mother who provides the greater part of the behavioral material for a child's identification in the early years. This is particularly true of learning to stigmatize forbidden acts and to applaud those of which the mother approves. The foundations of ethical self-reactions, and therefore of a child's conscience, are thus as a rule laid by maternal mores.[36] It is the mother, also, who tends to develop self-evaluation in her child with respect to behavior that reduces friction in interpersonal relations, such as courtesy, good manners, consideration for another's property and person, the bestowing of gifts and of compliments. The child learns to derive a certain degree of reward from performing these social rituals, as he acquires his mother's reactions and becomes able, through them, to praise himself and to react to what he does with attitudes of pride and self-acceptance.

The child's sex is a highly significant determining factor in the direction of later identification, and therefore operates selectively in the development of self-evaluation. The mother stresses her own ideal of femininity in guiding her little girl's daily conduct, and of masculinity in bringing up her little boy.[37] Contrasts and comparisons are repeatedly voiced which reinforce one behavioral trend and negatively affect the other. To this the growing disparity in relative size and strength contributes in determining the direction of his behavioral development. He learns to value highly the things he can do and the things he must learn to do as a little man, and to disparage the domestic and maternal achievements of his sister. He is taught the social implications for him of such terms as manly, strong, smart, good, brave and independent, and of sissy, weakling, dumb, slow, scared and mamma's boy. These and a thousand other verbal characterizations are given him at one time or another as his social fortunes rise and fall. And he learns to give them also to himself.

The identifying maneuvers continue to make their contributions as the child extends his activities into the neighborhood, the school, the church and other formal or informal social organizations. For many years children associate predominantly with those of their own sex and approximately their own age. The self-evaluations they learned primarily from their parents and from their siblings, are modified effectively by their contemporaries to conform more closely to the cultural norms than to the original family standards. This

[36] Conscience is defined, and discussed in relation to anxiety, on pages 284–289. Some of the early origins of ethical behavior are indicated on pages 136–140.

[37] For indications of the effect upon the development of masculine and feminine roles of the father's absence from the home, see Sears, R. R., Pintler, M. H., and Sears, P. S., "Effect of father separation on preschool children's doll play aggression." *Child Develpm.*, 1946, vol. 17, pp. 219–243.

process reaches its disturbing culmination during adolescence, when identification with one's like-aged, like-sexed peers becomes militantly dominant over identification with parents, childhood heroes or heroines, and civic leaders or public enemies. This is the period of the child's final counterreaction to parental suzerainty, the *second age of resistance*. It is this phase of development that frequently determines whether an adolescent shall become an autonomous adult, or continue indefinitely to draw upon his parents for his emotional security.

The conflict that everyone must face in adolescence is, of course, the conflict between childhood folkways, in which each adolescent has had years of practical experience, and adult folkways which are familiar to him only through hearsay, and have at most been practiced in play and fantasy. The principal opposition raised in adolescent self-attitudes and self-responses is in relation to things permitted to adults and forbidden to children. The adolescent dilemma in self-evaluation is thus one of seeing himself damned if he elects to claim adult privilege denied to children, and damned if he elects to deny himself adult privilege and remain a child. In the one he lines up with his peers against his parents; in the other he sides with his parents and defies his peers.[38]

For a great many persons this dilemma is never really settled. As we shall see in adolescent and adult behavior pathology, the voices of one's parents often continue throughout life to protest against the forbidden acts of childhood, whenever they are re-enacted in an adult setting. Usually, even in pronounced behavior pathology, the parental protest appears simply as one arm of a personal conflict which often remains self-inaccessible. When, however, delusional and hallucinatory behavior appears, the voices may be heard as those of envious calumniators, as warning cautions, as the pronouncements of God, or as interfering and controlling influences from human beings with supernatural powers. The words, heard often in one's childhood and incorporated in one's thinking, seem now again to come from someone else. Thus the process by which public opinion originally grew into private self-evaluation becomes reversed. Communicative speech which had once been transformed into thinking, seems to emerge again, and to resume its abandoned function of communication.

Socially Organized Thinking

The transformation of public, communicative speech into private, unshared thinking is one of the most powerful agencies in bringing about the socializa-

[38] Tryon, C., "Evaluation of adolescent personality by adolescents." *Monogr. Soc. Res. Child Develpm.*, 1939, vol. 4, pp. 1–88; Tryon, C., "The adolescent peer culture." *Yearb. Nat. Soc. Stud. Educ.*, 1944, vol. 43, pp. 217–239.

tion of human individuals. It is also one of the most important factors in producing behavior pathology. For, as a person takes over the language structure that prevails around him, and weaves his recall, his daydream and his fantasied intent into its form, he inevitably approximates his intent, his daydream and his recall to those prescribed by his society and culture. And it is this organization of thinking in linguistic form that makes possible the compulsive soliloquy, the stereotyped gesture of hysteria and schizophrenia, the expansive grandiosities of mania and the merciless self-condemnation of depression. It is the linguistic form of thinking, as we have pointed out, that allows the ghosts of a person's secret past to rail against him or to urge him on with unmerited applause.

Prelanguage thinking

One of the most vital problems facing everyone who is concerned with the infantile origins of behavior pathology is that of the nature of prelanguage thinking. There is some evidence to indicate that older children and adults are able to recall and describe discrete scenes and events which antedate the appearance of adequate communicative speech. This evidence must be treated with great caution. For even though the scene or event recalled is shown to have preceded the acquisition of commensurate language behavior, there is always the possibility that parental statements are the basis for the remembering, rather than the actual event or scene.

Attempts have been repeatedly made to carry recall far back into the prelanguage years, systematically, through the use of such techniques as free association, hypnosis, narcoanalysis and dream analysis.[39] Numerous prelanguage "memories" have been reported in the literature, as a result of these investigations; but there are still serious difficulties in the way of securing adequate validation of the reports. From what is known about the cultural distortion of the recall of even relatively recent events in adults, one must maintain an intelligently skeptical attitude as to the authenticity of reported infantile recall.

An appeal to non-verbal dreaming and daydreaming, as activity which is closely related to prelanguage thinking, has somewhat more to recommend it. Nevertheless, this too suffers from a paucity of acceptable corroboration. Dreaming and daydreaming, for example, seem at some times and in most persons, to be devoid of verbal formulation, and to be derived from the products of visual perception.[40] Thus scenes with spatial dimensions and chromatic properties appear to be imagined without formulation in language — even in

---

[39] For an example of this procedure see Lindner, R. M., *Rebel without a cause: the hypnoanalysis of a criminal psychopath.* New York: Grune and Stratton, 1944.

[40] See for example, Despert, J. L., "Dreams in children of preschool age." In Freud, A. (Ed.), *The psychoanalytic study of the child.* New York: International Universities Press, 1949, vol. 3/4, pp. 141–181.

the linguistic shorthand which we employ in making private inference, or in covertly planning some overt act. This kind of activity, it is maintained by many students of behavior, is apparently what the prelanguage child engages in when he faces an unsolved problem, when he is frustrated in an overt act, and perhaps when he is alone with nothing else to do.

If we accept the fact that we still lack incontrovertible evidence to support the claims for the faithful recall of infantile events, we must also realize that these claims have never received final refutation. Indeed, it seems exceedingly unlikely that the non-verbal dreaming and daydreaming, which children regularly report when they have learned communicative speech, should have no antecedents whatever in the prelanguage years. It is at least reasonable to assume that prelanguage thinking is closely related to the non-verbal aspects of our own familiar dreaming and daydreaming.

Accordingly, in what immediately follows, we shall take the position that non-verbal prelanguage thinking continues in a somewhat altered form into later childhood and adulthood. This is the activity traditionally called "imagery," which in decades past has been the object of considerable investigation, and for centuries has been a favorite focus for conjecture. It is generally agreed, by those students of behavior who admit "imagery" into their scientific orbit, that less and less reliance is placed upon it, as an individual develops and utilizes verbal symbolization more and more.[41] For most practical purposes, communicative speech and its symbolic derivatives are infinitely more useful instruments, in a verbally organized world, than are the apparently more colorful and spacious imaginings that do not stem from language.

The muting of communicative speech

The child who learns publicly to speak with others, learns also to speak privately with himself. This is a simple, direct statement of a relationship between language behavior and thinking that develops eventually into something immensely complex and intricately devious. The original practice of formulating problems in words, phrases and sentences, and speaking these aloud, is never wholly lost. The man who is caught talking to himself in public usually excuses himself by saying, "I was just thinking out loud." This is a socially acceptable excuse because everyone thinks aloud in words at some time or another, particularly when he is angry, in conflict or surprised.

The talking child at first says everything audibly. Indeed, this is the procedure through which he was able originally to acquire communicative speech. He made noises for many months, as part of his general activity, and eventually some of these noises in a modified form became language behavior. As a

[41] Compare the findings of Ames, L. B. and Learned, J., "Imaginary companions and related phenomena." *J. genet. Psychol.*, 1946, vol. 69, pp. 147–167; Murphy, L. B., "Childhood experience." In Hunt, J. McV. (Ed.), *Personality and the behavior disorders*. New York: Ronald, 1944, pp. 675–676.

child learns the naming of acts and things, he begins to provide a verbal accompaniment for the rest of his behavior. He repeats the characterization of what he and others do that he has previously taken over from adults and older children around him. He announces also what it is that he has just finished, or is about to start, and in this way keeps himself and others informed about his activities. He states conventionally expressed opinions about things in his surroundings, as soon as he has acquired the vocabulary that goes with the opinions. Thus, in time, the talking child develops a running commentary that roughly parallels a great deal of his other overt behavior.

Having slowly and with tremendous effort acquired this ability to play a verbal obbligato to his other activity, the child must next learn to silence himself. This is almost a matter of unlearning and relearning; and, as such, it represents one of the most difficult of all the sequences that biosocial maturation entails. As we shall later see, every maturing human being must repeatedly abandon some technique or relationship, which he has perfected and enjoyed, and acquire an often unwelcome and more difficult substitute. If he fails to do this, we call him fixated [42] and relatively immature. Thus, if a child of seven still speaks all his thoughts aloud, we would characterize this behavior as verbal fixation, and seek its roots in developmental retardation [43] or other behavior pathology.

Many factors conspire to silence the talking child. For one thing, the noises which adults at one time helped him to convert into communicative speech become noises again, for them, long before the child tires of repeating them. Moreover, there is usually a sleeping father, or a napping younger sibling, or a grandparent who must not be disturbed — and talking is disturbing. And perhaps the most difficult lesson of all is that of learning to be silent when someone else is speaking. It has been found that even prelanguage children tend to react to human speech with their own vocalization.[44] This tendency in most persons is never lost. Indeed, it is probably basic to the ready occurrence of discussion among strangers who have not been trained in diffidence or aloofness.

Another highly influential group of silencing factors has to do with a child's acquired need for privacy. This need grows out of the most practical, unromantic considerations. In learning to parallel his activity with an accompaniment of speech, the child has learned the unfortunate practice of announcing what he is doing, of advertising his intentions, and of making known his motivations and opinions. He soon discovers the grave disadvantages of such publicity. It keeps adults informed of his ongoing activity, and so places him at the mercy of their approval and disapproval. It warns them of what he is

[42] For a definition and discussion of fixation, see pages 143–153.
[43] For a definition and discussion of developmental retardation, see Chapter 6.
[44] See McCarthy, D., "Language development in children." In Carmichael, L. (Ed.), *Manual of child psychology.* New York: Wiley, 1946, pp. 494–495.

about to do in time to permit them to frustrate him. It reveals to them his analysis of his own behavior and his personal evaluation of the very adults who hear him. The disclosure of motivation prevents the child from disclaiming guilt, and his public statement of opinion may expose him to verbal rebuttal or to corporal punishment.

Indeed, public statements have so many disadvantages that they are soon curtailed. The child discovers that if he speaks softly enough to himself he can continue talking without awakening sleeping relatives and without annoying a cranky parent. He can go on talking to himself in the midst of adult conversations, or in church, at the theater, and in school. While someone is speaking directly to him, the child can prepare his answer *sotto voce*, and polish it up in advance of its delivery. Or he can withhold his answer if its delivery seems on re-examination to be unwise — and, again, it is the soft speaking that gives him the chance to re-examine and reconsider. For everyone finds that if he says something and then contradicts himself, or disclaims what he has just been saying, he seems sometimes to be held responsible for whichever of the two statements reflects the greater discredit upon him.

Behavioral duplicity

In dealing as he does with persons larger and more powerful than he, the child learns for himself the wisdom of agreeing quickly with his adversary. But he learns also that he may at the same time defy even his most vengeful opponent, provided he utters his defiance inaudibly. Thus a new dichotomy is born. Not only may words be at variance, and descriptions contradict what they describe, but covert speech now gives the lie to public statement. In what he says aloud, the child bows gracefully to force; but he can go on in silence to deny angrily his capitulation. Or he may speak out what he intends to do, while saying to himself that he has other plans.

In the same way, a child learns to proclaim publicly one opinion and hold its opposite in private. He ascribes socially acceptable motivation to his acts, for the benefit of an adult listener; but for his own benefit he gives them quite a different interpretation to himself. Through such behavioral duplicity, human beings develop complex techniques of self-protection, some of which contribute importantly to the preservation of individual integrity in the face of group pressures.[45] However, from the same techniques, as we shall see, the human being learns to deceive himself as well as others, to divide his own behavior into contradicting systems, and in extreme instances, to disown his reactions and ascribe them to real or fictitious persons other than himself.[46]

There are still other and more subtle uses to which verbal privacy can be

---

[45] See the discussion of rationalization and compensation on pages 376–381.
[46] See Chapters 13 and 14.

put.[47]   It may entertain the child to make fanciful and bizarre statements about people, activities and things. It may comfort him to deny that he has lost what he has lost, and that he will certainly be thwarted in something. Such contradictions of the consensus, and of his own public acknowledgments, can be maintained in private without fear of ridicule or refutation. The child learns to tell himself stories that magnify his achievements beyond anything he can possibly accomplish — indeed, beyond anything anyone can do. When he is lonely, or when he has been belittled and humiliated, he can in private verbally exalt himself and humble those who scorn him or neglect him.[48]   All these things he does with little effort in muttered or unspoken words; to do them otherwise would be laborious, dangerous or impossible.[49]

Economy of verbal effort is, in itself, of prime importance in the development of verbal privacy — less dramatic, perhaps, than some of the other factors, but no less significant for behavior pathology. Economy of verbal effort is clearly evident in a great deal of communicative speech, wherever the persons communicating have a common background and are in agreement as to the special symbols originating from it. A discussion involving mathematical or musical symbols, among persons experienced in the field, gives a nice illustration of verbal economy arising from a common background. Let an unsophisticated listener ask at some point in the discussion for a restatement in ordinary language, however, and the economy is likely at once to vanish. Communication that has been tripping along lightly, on mathematical or musical notation, now drags heavily and uncertainly through the ambiguous longhand of popular speech.

It is not necessary to go to technical discussions for examples of verbal economy. The members of any organization with a background of special shared activities illustrate it just as well. There is an abbreviated and highly expressive verbal code shared among war veterans, another among individuals belonging to a religious group, a trade or a social group, and still another that is peculiar to a subculture, a class or caste, a neighborhood gang or an adolescent peer culture. Chums in childhood develop their own shorthand speech — unintelligible to outsiders because it needs the shared context to complete it — and so do adult friends, lovers, marital partners, and close-knit families. Effective communication goes on among these smaller units even though the symbols used are reduced to a glance, a fleeting grimace, a grunt, shrugged shoulders, a manneristic movement, or a specially coined word that cannot be found in the dictionary of any language.

[47] For an account of "magic" solutions, see Lewin, K., "Behavior and development as a function of the total situation." In Carmichael, L. (Ed.), *Manual of child psychology*. New York: Wiley, 1946, p. 822.

[48] See Murphy, L. B., "Childhood experience." In Hunt, J. McV. (Ed.), *Personality and the behavior disorders*. New York: Ronald, 1944, pp. 652–690.

[49] We shall return to a discussion of these properties of muted speech when we consider delusion and hallucination, in Chapters 13 and 14.   "

Communication with oneself is communication among behavioral organizations having common backgrounds and sharing one organism. Under these conditions, the ultimate in verbal economy can be achieved. Self-conversation may and frequently does go on in full dress, as a soliloquy of completed sentences which even an eavesdropping stranger would understand. In overt self-conversation, however, a person also makes use of technical abbreviations, of the verbal codes he shares with other in-group persons, and of the minimal audible and visible symbols that have meaning only for his intimates and himself. The solitary debate of a man excited or in conflict is most likely to include a conglomeration of all the speech forms, which no one but the man himself may fully understand — phrases and words completely spoken, technical notations and in-group slang, symbols reserved for intimates, and a great deal audible and inaudible, visible and invisible, that still functions as self-communication.

Of course even when communicative speech is fully muted, all the soundless forms may be present in silent self-communication. One often sees a person in a public place who, not observing that he is being watched, goes through a quiet, fragmentary pantomime. He sits and faintly smiles, looks sober, gives a meager frown, and faintly smiles again. He nods his head, almost imperceptibly, in affirmation or acceptance, and shakes it slightly in negation or rejection. His hands make minute gestures, he shrugs his shoulders briefly, then rests his chin upon a hand and stares intently at the floor. From this fixed contemplation he may arouse himself by a sudden laugh or snort, notice that someone is looking at him, and so terminate his reverie.

If everyone engaged in silent self-communication were regularly to pantomime it, our trains and busses, our streets and public meeting-places, our churches and our conference tables would be far livelier and distracting than they are. But we all learn while we are children to inhibit the movements of self-conversation as we inhibit its sound. Speech sounds become covert or minimally overt speech movements, and these in turn may be reduced to tensional patterns of muscular response — just as the gestural and other pantomimic movements are. Some of these tension patterns and movement residuals in self-communication have been instrumentally detected and recorded; the rest must for the present be inferred.

What we have been calling self-communication makes up a great part of what is usually considered thinking. It is the use of symbolic systems as substitutes for other behavior. Such thinking may take the place of non-verbal behavior, as when a man plans a day's work or a woman plans a meal in silence. It may also take the place of verbal symbols, spoken or written, as when a child considers how best to gain a privilege from an adult, but does not phrase it in communicative speech or mouth the words. But the forms of self-communication that are most prominent in behavior pathology are those of silent soliloquy, dialogue, self-conversation and debate. These are the favored forms in conflict, the sources of compulsive vacillation, the materials of delusion and the origins of the voices that one hallucinates.

Thinking as fantasy

The progressive acquisition of communicative speech, we have said, tends in time to organize childhood behavior more and more in verbal terms. But this does not mean, of course, that all human activity is eventually carried out in words, or even that all we do is capable of verbal formulation. We learn and practice complex coordinations during the prelanguage and early language years — manual manipulations of a thousand kinds, conjugate following and guiding with the eyes, locomotion, and all the crawling, jumping, springing, running and curvetting that little children manage.[50] These and many more acts we continue and further complicate as we learn to play games and to perform work. They help make up a non-verbal universe that frequently comes into serious conflict with our universe of discourse.[51]

As a child grows increasingly verbal — as he acquires an adequate meaningful vocabulary — he employs the instrument of language more and more as an aid in manipulative and locomotory learning. But, even here, the tendency is gradually to leave the language out as the learned act grows nimble and precise. Indeed, deftness and precision in large part depend upon the elimination of talking from the act's structure. We may learn to drive a car by means of our own verbal instructions, memorized from a driver's manual. But when we have acquired ease and skill in driving, our language mechanisms can then be released for social conversation with a companion. Actions which we have learned with guiding words become smooth and automatic as we are able to dispense with them.

The growth of covert fantasy seems to follow a developmental sequence not unlike that described for skilled overt acts. The same verbal instrument that aids us in organizing complex coordinations in manipulation is also effective in complicating and restructuring our daydreams. What evidence we have appears to indicate that the imaginings of prelanguage children are fleeting, fragmentary and inconstant.[52] As language behavior is increasingly acquired, fantasy becomes enriched, grows more stable and is better remembered. The child hears stories and learns to tell them to himself. He learns likewise to tell others what he has dreamed or imagined, what he would like to do, what he

---

[50] For information concerning complex performances in the early language years, see Kuenne, M. R., "Experimental investigation of the relation of language to transposition behavior in young children." *J. exper. Psychol.*, 1946, vol. 36, pp. 471–490.

[51] See the discussion in Chapters 13 and 14.

[52] Dudycha, G. J. and Dudycha, M. M., "Childhood memories: a review of the literature." *Psychol. Bull.*, 1941, vol. 38, pp. 668–682; Waldfogel, S., "The frequency and affective character of childhood memories." *Psychol. Monogr.*, 1948, vol. 62, pp. 1–39

expects to look like, and who he would like to be. This is all practice in imagining as well as exercise in talk.

Language, it is now evident, confers upon imagination a rapid and enormous increase in complexity; but this is not to say, of course, that fantasy is all transmuted into words. All children, and most adolescents and adults, report their fantasy as having spatial, chromatic and kinetic properties that words do not have. They say they think of tunes, the quality of a familiar voice, the taste of ice cream, the smell of hot pie, and the feel of velvet — and none of these quite coincides with their most effective verbal formulation. They newly structure or recall a scene, and it seems to them to belong rather to the non-verbal than to the verbal universe. It is more like dreaming than like talking.

Dreaming, we know, commonly includes communicative speech and other symbols, as well as wordless sounds and shifting scenes. And so, of course, does fantasy awake. When we silently recall tunes and familiar voices, we may recall the words that belonged with them. Tastes, smells and textures, that we imagine to ourselves, frequently move us to exclaim or pass a fragmentary comment, aloud or quietly. Indeed, were we committed to the task of separating completely language behavior and its derivatives from fantasy, we could not do it. The very covert character of dreaming and daydreaming makes the intermingling with it of symbols and residuals of symbols inevitable. But our aim is not the dissection of imagination. We are concerned rather with laying a foundation upon which to build our later understanding of the pathology of human thinking.

The behavior pathology of human thinking we shall see most clearly demonstrated when we study delusion and hallucination. In delusion, we shall find exaggerations, distortions and misuses of the symbolic systems that make up communicative speech. In hallucination, we may witness the misidentification of one's remembered past and of one's past imaginings. In both delusion and hallucination, the marks of social origin will be obvious. The individuals who people delusional and hallucinatory communities are persons with social roles, drawn from ordinary life, or persons whose role-taking is attributed to them by current folklore — gods, demons, good and evil spirits. Even the predicaments that the patient structures in his imaginings are modelled after those in which he has found himself, or read about or heard described. His fantasy is firmly grounded in the social patterns of his milieu, however much his misinterpretations may distort or magnify.[53]

[53] For a detailed discussion of the biosocial origins of delusion and hallucination, see pages 387–392 and 414–426.

Social Role-Taking

Learning and social conformity

Human learning, as we have seen,[54] is social learning, structured from the very start of life in terms of a highly organized human environment. With all his innumerable potentialities for complex behavior, the newborn infant must face the task, uninstructed, of growing to be as much like other human beings as possible, and to accomplish this task according to a prearranged time schedule. For biosocial maturation, as we shall later describe it,[55] involves the acquisition of social conformity, a conformity that must shift progressively through infancy, childhood and adolescence, as the standards of socially acceptable performance shift. And even after adulthood has been reached, new organizations of behavior are demanded as one's status changes with the changing years.

A great deal of what has been said of learning communicative speech is true of learning to conform in other ways. The problem is more one of behavioral selection, than one of behavioral creation. And the selection, as indeed we should expect, turns out to be a product neither of the child alone, nor of the reactions of his elders, but of the social interaction of child and elders as they participate in some shared activity. It is always the dynamic field, established first by one's parents and later contributed to by oneself, that gives impetus and direction to the organization of one's social behavior.

We often describe human behavior as though it developed through a compounding of single, specific movements into coordinated skills; and we sometimes seem to imply that by multiplying together such individual skills, human beings produce an organized societal product. But we have already found, in relation to communicative speech, as well as in other overt behavior, that the acquisition of skill is primarily a process of selection, of exclusion as well as inclusion.[56] We do not ordinarily build up complex, sequential acts by fastening simple isolated acts in chains with associative links. Neither do we convert our biological neonates into biosocial infants, children and adults, by training them in solitary little tricks, and then pushing them out into society to perform them, meaninglessly, like animals performing in a circus. The human infant learns to play his part in context; he acquires conformity through acquiring social roles; he learns to be like other human beings by living among and interacting with other human beings.

Behavioral reciprocity

The basis of interindividual cooperation, and therefore of any cooperative society, is the reciprocal relationship in behavior. Ordinary conversation, as we have already indicated, depends upon behavioral reciprocity. One speaks

[54] See especially pages 55–63.   [55] Pages 132–143.   [56] Compare pages 74–75.

while the other listens, and listens while the other speaks. Reciprocal behavior is perhaps most clearly illustrated by mammalian sex activity. The parts played by male and by female differ profoundly from one another; but they complement each other and together constitute a unitary act.

In human society, sexual reciprocity is often indefinitely expanded into mutually complementary masculine and feminine biosocial roles. These reciprocal roles, taken together, form an organizational unit into which the biological neonate is introduced as a new variable. The family unit, thus conceived, is not a house, a home, or three persons, but a dynamic field whose organization is determined at any moment by the interactions of its members.

The newborn infant is biologically capable of few organized reactions in relation to his surroundings. Accordingly, he can at first develop little in the way of behavioral reciprocity. Indeed, for some time the only reciprocal relationship into which he enters is that of nursing.[57] Here the mother reacts, in terms of her learned maternal attitudes, by making the nipple easily and continuously accessible to the infant's mouth. The infant reciprocates by sucking and, as he learns to do so, by searching for, pursuing and holding the nipple until he has had his fill. Even so restricted an activity as this, however, includes a great deal of mutual reactivity and reciprocal learning — skilled holding and skilled being held, deft giving and adroit taking, recognizing the signs of need, satiation or discomfort, and gaining stability in making recognizable signs.[58]

None of this early infant reciprocity is deliberate, of course, and no young infant can identify, reflect upon or plan the things he does and the signs he makes. He nurses when he is hungry, and he quits when he has had enough of food and sucking exercise. But as time passes, the infant develops anticipant attitudes [59] in relation to his feeding which ultimately generalize to the mother and to the whole feeding situation. This generalization, as we shall later see,[60] is fundamental to the development of early affectional relationships. It is also basic to the infant's acquisition of his first social role.

The first social role the human infant acquires is the only one which he is prepared behaviorally to take — the role of the helpless baby. It is defined by the behavior of his parents and of other persons in his environment, and by his own level of biological development. In this role, he is for some time a relatively passive instrument, something that feeds when fed, something to be cleaned, kept warm, cared for and protected. Social conformity requires little but submission to routine, and cooperation in nursing. Gradually, however, the infant learns rudimentary techniques of environmental control — crying, breath-holding, regurgitation and the beginnings of muscular resistance. To

[57] A more detailed account of feeding, in relation to biosocial maturation, is given on pages 134–137.
[58] Compare the discussion of reciprocal need on pages 255–256.
[59] See pages 65–66.
[60] See pages 137–143.

these are added the more positive techniques of smiling, laughing, cooing, bab-bling and crowing. And eventually, reaching, grasping, holding and manipu-lative movements are utilized in social interaction with other persons. The once relatively passive, receptive infant role has grown now into an actively participative one.

Before going on to consider the inevitable multiplication of social roles, which every human being must develop, let us define the terms we have been using. By *role* we mean *a comprehensive and coherent organization in behavior of functionally related, interlocking attitudes and responses*. In human society, roles are always the result of social learning. They are delineated, as in the example we have just discussed, in part by the culturally determined behavior of other persons, and in part by the degree of conformity, reciprocity and resistance that one can manage.

Role-taking is the living out of a socially delineated or socially derived be-havioral organization.[61] This living-out can occur in any one of three ways. (*a*) *The role taken is one's own*. In this sense, role-taking means behaving as a particular social person, in relation to other persons, according to one's own status. Thus, the role of police officer is played in earnest by a uniformed policeman. (*b*) *The role taken is reciprocal to one's own*. A man wishing to evade the police, takes a policeman's part — typically in covert fantasy — and is thus better able to anticipate police attitudes. (*c*) *The role is neither one's own nor its reciprocal*. Either in play or in earnest, overtly or covertly, or both, a person takes another's role. This, as we shall see abundantly hereafter, is an essential component of nearly all fantasy and the greater part of self-com-munication. It makes effective story-telling possible, forms the basis of imaginative dreaming and daydreaming, enters actively into delusion and hallucination, and adds enormously to everyman's repertory of social roles.

The multiplication of social roles

Social roles, we have said, are culturally delineated by the behavior of other persons in a given individual's environment. Thus the human infant, in ac-quiring his initial role of baby of the family, does so in direct relation to the reciprocal behavior of his parents. As time goes on, and the infant develops increasingly effective behavioral discrimination, his interbehavior with his father becomes differentiated from his interbehavior with his mother. Their individually and culturally distinct behavior organizations are represented in his reactions by two corresponding social roles. As father's boy he reflects paternal individuality and the masculine subculture; and as mother's boy he reflects maternal individuality and the feminine subculture.[62]

---

[61] Cameron, N., "Role concepts in behavior pathology." *Amer. J. Sociol.*, 1950, vol. 55, pp. 450–463.

[62] Compare Sears, R. R., Pintler, M. H., and Sears, P. S., "Effect of father separation on preschool children's doll play aggression." *Child Develpm.*, 1946, vol. 17, pp. 219–243.

If a child has older siblings, his interplay with them eventually will differentiate, in his repertory, behavior that is clearly fraternal instead of filial. And to other relatives and to family friends who frequent his home he will learn to give reactions, neither filial nor fraternal, but still different from his behavior among strangers. When at last he goes out of his own home into the neighborhood alone he continues to acquire and practice new social roles, always in the dynamic field of personal interaction. Since infants and children have no special trade, belong to no profession, cannot function as business men or housewives, and do not run for public office, their status is determined chiefly by the direct personal interrelationships they establish, and by their identification with the family unit of which they are a part. It is upon the terms implied by their status, so defined, that children are received into the neighborhood community.

Infants and preschool children devote a large share of their waking life to the performance of unspecialized but often highly laborious and painstaking work. This work we adults call play, because we tend to regard only that which we are forced to do as "work." The earliest forms of play are solitary and parallel. In one, the child plays without another like-aged companion; in the other he shares the play space with another child but not the play. Such activity gives a child endless practice in manipulation, locomotory coordination and the precursors of communicative speech. But it is not until he reaches a phase of maturity which enables him to engage in associative and cooperative play that he begins to participate in simple forms of reciprocal role-taking with his peers.[63]

The earliest role-taking in participative games usually involves more subordination than equality. The child at home and in the neighborhood is smaller and less experienced than are those who introduce him to cooperative and competitive play. Accordingly he joins the others on sufferance and therefore on their terms rather than on his. But as he becomes more useful, and more adept in participation, he takes reciprocal roles of equality and superordination as well as subordinate ones.

Like all their other enterprises, children's games are patterned after the social role-taking of the adolescent and adult peer cultures. Little girls play mother to their dolls and to children smaller than themselves. They take the roles of teacher, nurse and housewife. In wartime they follow the cultural shift and play the part of WAC or WAVE, of lady bus-driver or factory worker. Boys tend more to take the roles of fireman and policeman, of robbers and gunmen, cowboys and soldiers, truckmen, steamboat captains, engineers and doctors. Both girls and boys pick up and act out social roles from their

[63] For accounts of the development of play in young children, see Parten, M. and Newhall, S. M., "Social behavior in preschool children." In Barker, R. G., Kounin, J. S., and Wright, H. F. (Eds.), *Child behavior and development*. New York: McGraw-Hill, 1943, pp. 509–526.

surroundings — their parents and their parents' friends, their companions' parents, workers who come into the home or neighborhood, clowns and riders in the circus, characters from comic strips, movies and the radio, adults they see in shops, in church, in school and on the street.

If child's play were as idle as most people seem to think it is, to talk about it further would be idle too. But children's play is children's work, and much of it resembles closely the social roles that adults live. A child's role-taking games are unplanned introductions to the business of his adult life. In them, he gains practice in being this or that grownup, with these or those social responsibilities and privileges; he enters into certain culturally defined interrelations with other social persons whom his play companions seek to represent. The little mother, nurse or teacher finds out in fact how unruly a youngster, a patient or a pupil can be. The child policeman discovers that child robbers and gunmen are bold, tricky and defiant; while child robbers and gunmen taste the arrogance and violence of the child police.

No adult can ever live out all the roles he plays in childhood; they are too numerous, and many are beyond him. But the comparatively few adult roles he does live are never lived by him in isolation. At work he has superiors and subordinates with whom he practices behavioral reciprocity, just as he did with his playmates. He comes into contact, at some time or other, with almost every working role that he has played or played against. At home, there is a grownup mother and real children to whom he, as husband and father, must behave in conformity with cultural prescriptions. The overwhelming majority of men do not learn marital and parental roles from books and lectures. They derive them from their childhood play, their identification with their own and others' parents, the radio and movie roles that other adults play for them, and their own discussions and imaginings in childhood and in young adulthood.

The grownup mother likewise plays her real-life role in terms of what she played, witnessed, fantasied and indirectly learned in childhood, in adolescence and young womanhood. Her small children and her babies behave in ways not unfamiliar to her, and she is already practiced in behavioral reciprocity as a mother. Men and women come to her home, and into the neighborhood, whose social roles she acted out as a child in her parental home — milkmen, plumbers, landlords, grocery boys, policemen, bill collectors, postmen, visiting nurses and women neighbors. She goes shopping for merchandise which she symbolized in childhood by her playthings; and the merchants she must deal with are the ones her playmates caricatured and mimicked. Her children go to school and bring back stories of their classmates and their teachers — classmates like the ones with whom she once attended school, and teachers like the ones she herself knew as a pupil.

Gaining social perspective

To gain social perspective, a person must be able to put himself realistically in another person's place, to have the other's attitudes and so be able to predict and understand what the other does. In childhood play this is achieved by actively playing out the part. If a child plays teacher to pretended pupils, and his play follows the adult pattern, he can come closer to having a teacher's attitudes than if he had only played pupil. If, then, he shifts to pupil and someone else plays teacher, he finds that he can now predict what she will say and do, and he can give better appraisals of her competence than before, and make more penetrating criticisms. If a child at play is at one time a gangster, and at another time the F.B.I., he can thereafter play a more successful gangster and federal agent than if he had played only one role. It is this endless practice in behavioral reciprocity, back and forth, that gives the child an almost endless repertory of adult role renditions. He learns to be hundreds of social persons, animals, and even spirits, long before he comes to adulthood.[64]

Play is not all overt action, and social perspective is not all gained in play. What overt play begins in childhood, communicative speech and fantasy continue. Role-taking in games becomes role-taking in stories, talk and self-communication. The use of language symbols now makes the task of playing social roles far less laborious; the play can go faster and be made richer and more varied. Roles that are played publicly in words can be replayed privately in covert fantasy, changed and reworked to meet new needs or to prepare for new exigencies. The person who acquires a large repertory of social roles, and learns to shift easily from one to another, can in earnest or for entertainment run swiftly through them in imagination.

Shifting perspectives

It is obvious that a child or an adult whose repertory is made up of a large variety of social roles, which are well-practiced and realistic, is better equipped behaviorally than is a child or adult whose repertory is relatively unpracticed, meager and unrealistic. The skilled role-taker, like the skilled motorist, is more likely than the unskilled to meet competently a sudden, unlooked-for stress, and to continue operating effectively in the face of protracted strain. Thus, one factor of importance in determining behavioral adequacy, under conditions of abruptly increased stress and prolonged strain, is that of the number of practiced, realistic social roles a person has already at his disposal.

To have many roles is to have many tools; but to have many tools in any

[64] Ames, L. B. and Learned, J., "Imaginary companions and related phenomena." *J. genet. Psychol.*, 1946, vol. 69, pp. 147–167; Havighurst, R. J., Robinson, M. Z., and Dorr, M., "The development of the ideal self in childhood and adolescence." *J. educ. Res.*, 1946, vol. 40, pp. 241–257; Radke, M., Trager, H. G., and Davis, H., "Social perceptions and attitudes of children." *Genet. Psychol. Monogr.*, 1949, vol. 40, pp. 327–447.

trade and be unable to shift quickly under changing conditions from one tool to another, is to be far below optimal adequacy. The same is true of the behavioral instruments which we call social roles. It is not enough to have a varied collection of social roles, and to be skilled in utilizing each. A person must also be adroit in shifting quickly in a critical moment, from one pattern of role behavior to another — whether this be done in terms of manipulative, verbal or imaginal operations. In cooperative and competitive activity, in public conversation and argument, in private reflection, soliloquy and debate, it is essential that a person be able to take, at least in some measure, the role of his co-workers, discussants and antagonists, as well as his own; and that he shift his perspective easily and realistically as he reflects, soliloquizes and debates in private.

To shift from one role to another, as we have already indicated, is to shift from one attitudinal organization to another or, more simply, to shift perspective.[65] Public cooperation, competition, conversation and argument all depend upon behavioral reciprocity; so also do private reflection, soliloquy and debate. And if behavioral reciprocity is to be anything more than a limited, specific, automatic trick — you jump this way and I jump that, you say this and I counter monotonously with that — it must involve actual sharing of appropriate attitudes. When you make a move, in a card game or a political discussion, I must be able imaginally to make the move with you and share your perspective, if I am to meet it with effective support, antagonism or reformulation.

Skill in shifting perspective is acquired, just as other skills are. One of the most important sources of this skill, of course, is the early participation in cooperative and competitive games. Children who engage continually in participative games with other children must inevitably take a large variety of roles, and learn to shift easily from one to its reciprocal, or from one role to another that is entirely unrelated. Most children's games include provisions for the exchange of roles, and many games place a high premium on swiftness and completeness in making the exchange. Adult games — football, card-playing, folk-dancing, charades — are also heavily dependent upon shifts and reciprocal exchange in role-play. Players, adult and child, are on the offensive at one moment, and the defensive the next, pursuing and then fleeing, leading and then following, paired with this one against those two, and then with a former opponent against a former partner, for a time acting the spectator and critic, and then suddenly being the watched and criticized.

A second and equally important source of skill in attitudinal shifting is that

<hr/>

[65] For an analysis of the shifting of perspectives in perceptual and attitudinal situations, see Frenkel-Brunswik, E., "Intolerance toward ambiguity as an emotional and perceptual variable." *J. Personality*, 1949, vol. 18, pp. 108–143; Adorno, T. W., Frenkel-Brunswik, E., Levinson, D. J., and Sanford, R. N. *The authoritarian personality.* New York: Harper, 1950, pp. 461–464.

of direct parental remonstrance and instruction. The small child is informed over and over, in numberless situations, that he must take into account "the way other people feel." [66] This is the behavioral context in which he learns not to tease the dog and hurt the cat, to be gentle with his baby sister and considerate of grandpa, to share things and space with other children, to be clean, neat, polite and quick. This whole business of how his behavior must seem to others is direct training in the practice of shifting roles, from his own to that of every person and animal with whom he comes in contact. Story-books and plays, proverbs and folk-sayings, the exchange of opinion with peers, and the acquisition of active curiosity about persons who seem quite different from himself, supplement the work of parental insistence and participative play. Given an adequate parental model and freedom to engage in participative play, a child in time will gain facility in shifting from one role to another, and so in having something like the attitude of others to play against or cooperate with his own.

The number of different real-life roles which any one person can live out, we have said, is narrowly restricted. The number of roles that can be rehearsed and acted through in fantasy, on the other hand, is almost infinite. This means, of course, that once a child has gained facility in shifting through a succession of social roles, he can gain endless practice in shifting perspective imaginally. The importance of imaginative role-taking becomes at once evident when we stop to consider how ordinary human beings operate in complex social situations. They commonly begin their organized behavior with an attempt to predict what will happen next, and after that, and what will then occur. The prediction is always a guess at how the other persons will react, and so we come once more to the question of anticipation — of being able to take the others' roles, to shift nimbly through probable perspectives and their probable consequences — and thus to be prepared for many developments and not for just one.

To gain and shift perspectives in imagination one must have already acquired reasonable facility in communication; and to keep imagined perspectives in harmony with those which other social persons hold, means that free communication must continue. Human social behavior is too complex, and human roles too intricately related, for inference to lead consistently to valid conclusion without corroboration. The simplest validating procedure is to share with other social persons one's suspicions and convictions with respect to others' behavior and one's own. This procedure allows one to discover and to incorporate modifications of *imagined* inference and conclusion in accordance

[66] For an account of the development of sympathy in young children, see Murphy, L. B., *Social behavior and child personality: an exploratory study of some roots of sympathy.* New York: Columbia University Press, 1937. For an analysis of the relationship between early family patterns and empathy in adults, see Dymond, R. F., "Personality and empathy." *J. consult. Psychol.*, 1950, vol. 14, pp. 343–350.

with the consensus, and thus to avoid the crystallization of mistake into delusion.[67]

Individual differences in the ease of adequate social communication appear to be great, even among children. Persons reared in a social atmosphere of free verbal interchange, whose friends are many and whose parents are warmly accepting and permissive, are likely to develop ease and skill in sharing inferences and conclusions. They master the techniques of social validation because they find communication safe and the interchange of perspective a rewarding game. The children of emotionally cold, restricting or rejecting parents, whose social atmosphere is one of taciturn concealment, who make few childhood friends and confidants, are likely to find dangers in communicative sharing. They tend to keep their inferences private and test out their conclusions by careful, furtive observation. These two contrasting kinds of children, grown to adolescence and adulthood, provide us with two extremes in susceptibility to behavior pathology under comparable conditions of emotional stress.

Emotional Reactions

Throughout our discussions of individual responsiveness, of need, stress and frustration, of the characteristics of learning, and the development of language, thinking and role-taking, we have repeatedly made reference to emotional behavior. As we turn, in the next chapter, to consider maturation and fixation, we shall find that affectional relationships are of prime importance — whether we deal with normal development or with developmental deviation. Indeed, one of the most significant trends among contemporary students of normal and pathological behavior is the rapidly increasing emphasis upon emotional components. We no longer, for example, oppose *intellect* and *emotion* as though one were the representative of civilization and the other of savagery. We recognize, instead, that any kind of behavior may have significant emotional components, whether the behavior be judged good or bad, organized or disorganized, simple or complex, overt or covert, symbolic or non-symbolic.

The characteristics of visceral activity

Emotional reactions are reactions in which visceral activity makes a significant contribution, even though their reference is not primarily visceral. Because most visceral changes are hidden from direct observation on the part of another person, they are often slighted and sometimes forgotten in discussions of social interaction. But there is no form of human behavior that excludes the possibility of visceral participation. The physiological and biochemical activities of the internal organs — the great systems of smooth and cardiac muscle,

[67] See Chapter 13.

of endocrines and of glands excreting to surfaces — throughout life, form a kinetic matrix of stimulation.

Muscular and secretory changes are occurring in the viscera constantly — whether we are working with our hands or walking empty-handed down the street, talking with someone or listening silently to the radio, remembering and pondering in symbolic thought or dreaming in our sleep. More than sixty times in every minute the heart contracts vigorously, relaxes and rests. The blood-pressure is forever moving up and down, stretching the vessels and stimulating them to respond. The lungs repeatedly expand with the expanding chest, and shrink again as the chest falls. With each breath many other internal organs are displaced and subjected to cycles of increased and decreased pressure; gastrointestinal and genitourinary systems of muscle and gland have their own rhythms and their own ebb and flow of changing contents. Glands of internal and external secretion add their activities and the products of their chemical elaboration to the ever shifting visceral background.

In speaking thus of visceral activity, we tend to think in terms of the contents of chest, pelvis and abdomen, since in these cavities are housed the large, well-defined organs. But blood-vessels are also viscera, and these, with their reactive smooth muscle walls, are virtually coextensive with the human body. So are the myriad glands which pour their secretions forth on to almost every outside and inside surface structure. Blood-vessels and glands are subject to the same kind of neural and humoral regulation as are other viscera, and they contribute directly or indirectly to the stimulation of the same coordinative central nervous system. We cannot begin to understand the diffuse, pervasive character of emotional behavior unless we recognize the pervasive diffusion of the internal organs whose activities underlie emotion.

Visceral performance tends to be not only diffuse and pervasive but also protracted. Smooth muscle is slower to contract than the striped muscle that moves the body about; and it is much slower in relaxing. It is also much less fatigable than the typical striped muscle; indeed, some of the smooth muscle sphincters of the body maintain contraction indefinitely. The glands, particularly the endocrines, produce stimulating chemical substances which are absorbed into the circulation; and here they may persist, as active stimulating agents, for some time before they are broken down or neutralized. The consequence of these physiological and biochemical properties of smooth muscle and gland is that visceral participation can have general behavioral effects which are prolonged, self-perpetuating and often cumulative.

Domestic and community functions

But even though all behavior has this shifting, kinetic background of internal organ activity, for us the visceral participation becomes important in only two general forms. One of these we may call the *visceral response to physiological change.* To this form belong visceral activities which are directly responsive to or regulated by an immediate, local visceral condition. To it belong also those visceral activities which are primarily related to a systemic physiological or biochemical reaction. Such normal physiological responses as profuse sweating in hot weather, and urinary frequency in cold, are specific physiological visceral responses. So also are elevated blood-pressure, increased pulse and respiration during vigorous exercise, vomiting and diarrhea in gastrointestinal irritation, dilated pupils in subdued light and a dry mouth when fluid intake is deficient.

The other form of importance to us we may designate, by way of contrast, as a *visceral response to behavioral change.* To this form belong visceral activities initiated or regulated by occurrences lying outside the strictly visceral functions — by occurrences which are in the field of shared behavior or in one's unshared thinking. Thus, we find profuse sweating and urinary frequency, developing often simultaneously, when neither is appropriate to the environmental temperature. Both are, however, appropriate as responses initiated by something feared, in the environment or in one's private fantasy. The same is true of increased blood-pressure, heart-rate and respiration when these are primarily related to interpersonal reactions or thinking.[68] And we are all familiar with the fact that frightened persons commonly develop a dry mouth and dilated pupils, and sometimes vomit and have diarrhea as well.

These non-specific visceral responses to behavioral change are the contributions which the internal organs make to emotional reactions. Let us now define *emotional reactions* as *reactions whose non-specific visceral contribution dominates or determines them, or colors them distinctively.* Thus, climbing a fence in the course of a cross-country hike, and climbing it to escape a charging bull, may both involve visceral change; but in one the visceral participation is likely to be negligible, while in the other it is clearly dominant. The same distinction holds between dispassionate discussion and angry argument, between picking up one's valise on arriving at the railroad station and picking up one's child, between breaking up a radio for its parts and breaking it up as a reaction to what it says.

In each of these paired examples, we designate one an emotional reaction because of the dominant, determinative or distinctive character of the visceral contribution. But it should clearly be understood that the characteristic we call emotional refers to the total reaction, not just to the visceral component, or just to the sympathetic and parasympathetic neural mechanisms, or to some diencephalic coordinating center. It is no more accurate to speak of emotion or emotional reactions as being in the viscera — or in this or that part of the

[68] See the discussion of anxiety in Chapter 10, especially pages 278–280; see also Edwards, A. S., "Involuntary movements following perceived and recalled emotional situations." *J. gen. Psychol.,* 1949, vol. 41, pp. 233–238.

autonomic or central nervous systems — than it is to speak of jumping as being in the quadriceps femoris muscles, in the spinal cord or in the precentral cortex. The emotional characteristic is always to be thought of as qualifying behavior; and the study of emotion is always a study of the reactions of the total organism, and not merely of some segment or some nucleus.

The physiological properties of the visceral contribution in emotional behavior are responsible for some of the most important phenomena in behavior pathology. The *diffuse* and *pervasive* character of visceral responses renders it always difficult, and sometimes impossible, to trace the origin and identify the referent of an emotional reaction.[69] Thus, the normal person frequently recognizes that he has suddenly become unhappy or distrustful, but cannot explain to himself or others what is wrong and how the change began. Under severe stress or strain, this vague reaction may be directly translated into specific worry or suspicion; and unless relief comes, or the person is behaviorally well-equipped to deal with unhappiness or distrust, he need take only a short step to the development of delusions and a pseudocommunity.[70]

Emotional displacement

The fact that visceral responses tend to be *protracted* and *self-perpetuating* also has special importance for behavior pathology. It means that visceral changes occurring appropriately, as part of one reaction, may easily persist and make their contribution inappropriately to a later reaction. Suppose a person to have been frightened, but not injured, by the collapse of a platform on which he had been standing. As he walks down the street afterwards, he is likely to overreact inappropriately to many potential threats [71] — approaching pedestrians, automobiles at street corners, a slammed door, even his name spoken unexpectedly — which on another day he would treat with indifference. The fear reaction, we say metaphorically, has been displaced from the platform to other, ordinarily ineffective sources of stimulation.

Displacement can be found in any kind of emotional behavior.[72] The office manager who is insulted on his way to work by a taxicab driver will make a great many decisions on the basis of his smouldering anger, rather than on the objective situations. Moreover, he will be critical and surly to his secretary, who may in turn find fault with a favorite office-boy, and develop indigestion

[69] Compare the discussion of displacement in anxiety reactions: pages 295–296 and 310–314.

[70] See Chapter 13. For an analysis of the effect of emotional reactions upon other behavior, see Bruner, J. S. and Postman, L., "Emotional selectivity in perception and reaction." *J. Personality*, 1947, vol. 16, pp. 69–77.

[71] Compare the discussion of the startle reaction in anxiety, on page 279.

[72] For an experimental analogue of displacement, using infrahuman subjects, see Miller, N. E., "Theory and experiment relating psychoanalytic displacement to stimulus-response generalization." *J. abn. soc. Psychol.*, 1948, vol. 43, pp. 155–178. For examples of displacement in experimentally-produced frustration with human subjects, see Zander, A. F., "A study of experimental frustration." *Psychol. Monogr.*, 1944, vol. 56, no. 3, pp. v–38.

following a harmless lunch. The same office manager, after a successful business deal, treats everyone around him with such unwonted kindness that they shake their heads in perplexity when he is out of sight. In both instances, the visceral contribution dominates, determines or colors distinctively a whole series of reactions which are not logically related to the original emotional reaction.

It is obvious that emotional displacement is responsible for much of the apparent illogicality of normal behavior. It is responsible also for a great deal of behavior pathology. If the original situation becomes for any reason self-inaccessible — because it passed unnoticed at the time, or is recalled but dismissed as trivial, or because it has been forgotten or repressed — the persistence or the continual rearousal may become a major problem. Frequently, under these circumstances, the individual grows so concerned over the now unintelligible reaction that it forms the chief complaint of his behavior disorder. This we shall see in pathological anxiety, in phobias, in compulsions and in delusional misinterpretations. We shall see it also in hysterical inactivation and autonomy where the symptom may be one isolated remnant of an emotional reaction which the patient can demonstrate.

Cumulative sequences and emotional decompensation

Because of their persistent, self-perpetuating visceral background, emotional reactions easily develop into cumulative sequences. The angry, frightened or unusually happy person remains for some time more susceptible to further stimulation in the same direction than he was before he was emotionally disturbed. A housewife whose husband angers her at breakfast is likely to be still more angry when her child soon after balks at going to school. Later in the morning, she surprises the milkman by her ill-mannered outburst when he states that he is out of butter; and, although she manages with effort to control herself at lunch, she has a furious outburst of temper in the grocery store because the clerk makes a mistake in adding. As she prepares dinner everything she does seems to go wrong to spite her; and by the time her husband gets home she is ready to burst out in rage at the first critical comment that leaves his lips, or, if he is quiet, she bursts out at his silence.

Fear sequences show similar progressions. The person frightened in one situation enters the next alerted to danger and already reaction-sensitive to fearsome stimulation.[73] If what he fears he meets, he reacts by being still more frightened until, if the succession of fear-provoking stimulation continues, he may develop acute anxiety, even to the point of panic.[74] Such cumulative sequences, whether in anger, fear or any other intense emotional reaction, may develop almost entirely within one's covert, unshared behavior. Thus a person

---

[73] See the discussion of anxiety sequences in Chapter 10.
[74] Panic reactions are defined on pages 306–310.

pursued by enemies, who never once sees or hears them, may through his own well-founded fantasies of pursuit and capture throw himself into mounting fear which culminates in panic. This occurs also, as we shall see, when the fear is wholly based upon delusional expectation and similarly nursed in the apprehensive patient's fantasy.

Everyone seems to have his limits of emotional tolerance. When these are passed, a person may react with *emotional decompensation*, that is, he reacts with a climactic outburst of rage, or with headlong flight, violent assault or sudden suicide. In some instances emotional decompensation takes the form of stupor; the individual ceases altogether to react in terms of the demands of his environment. We shall see emotional decompensation most dramatically in panic reactions,[75] which not uncommonly lead directly to behavioral disorganization.[76] The less dramatic, but no less challenging apathy we shall encounter in retarded depression [77] and schizophrenic desocialization.[78]

Emotional reactions and social conformity

In our discussion of the muting of communicative speech, we pointed out that a dichotomy normally develops between a child's public statement and his covert speech, between what he tells others and what he tells himself.[79] A corresponding dichotomy also appears in relation to emotional behavior. What a child is permitted in the way of overt emotional reactions is prescribed by his society and culture. He may laugh at some things and not at others; and even the same occurrence may properly be greeted with mirth in the street, but not in church or in school. Children are punished for temper outbursts and angry words; they are ridiculed or ostracized for showing signs of fear, and for too great affectional demonstration to the wrong person or object.

Through such prescriptions and such punishments, the child gradually learns to conform to the accepted social patterns, as far as his overt emotional behavior is concerned. However, just as in the case of communicative speech, he retains the privilege of responding with forbidden emotional reactions, provided that he does not make them public. In short, he practices behavioral duplicity.[80] Thus, a child may react covertly with joy over an opponent's ill fortune, as long as he appears to others impassive or overtly expresses sorrow. In similar vein, he learns to speak brave, defiant words to hide from his companions his covert fear; and if he does an exceptionally lifelike job of this, he may even persuade himself that he has not been afraid. As he grows older, and his affectional relationships spread to persons outside his immediate family, he will learn also to conceal his love for others, and to enjoy loving even though he continues to conceal it.

---

[75] See pages 306–310. [76] See pages 464–466. [77] See pages 321–327.
[78] See pages 494–515. [79] See pages 107–109.
[80] For a discussion of behavioral duplicity, see pages 109–112.

Unshared, covert emotional reactions have some of the advantages described for muted speech. They not only protect one from the consequences of others' disapproval; they also protect others from a great many of one's own unimportant and unwelcome emotional shifts. The individual who gives rein overtly to all his emotional behavior quickly becomes a public nuisance, in the same way that a person does who speaks out everything he thinks. Indignation, impatience, enthusiasm or disgust may seem justified at the moment, but thoroughly unwarranted later on; it is easier and less costly to retract or reverse oneself covertly than to eat one's words or apologize in public. The person who can preserve an appearance of equanimity in spite of inner turmoil is likely to deserve the confidence of others as well as to gain it. For the preservation of apparent calm under stress argues for self-control, and self-control can be extended to covert as well as to overt behavior.

What passes for self-control of emotional behavior, however, is often only denial and disowning. We all learn from others, when we are children, the public values placed upon the attitudes which we openly acknowledge. We are even told emphatically at times that we do not — indeed we cannot! — have this or that emotional attitude, when we have just given unmistakable evidence that indeed we can and we do. In consequence, we learn to hide our emotional reactions from others, to contradict our own covert behavior in what we say, and eventually to disavow the socially forbidden even in our unshared self-reactions. Thus, in the end, we accomplish the same sort of division of emotional behavior that we achieved in self-communication,[81] by means of the same behavioral duplicity. And we place ourselves in the same danger of disowning so completely, some day, that we attribute our attitudes to real or fictitious individuals in a pseudocommunity of our own construction.

A special problem is posed for behavior pathology and for therapy by the fact that emotional reactions are as a rule imperfectly communicable. This characteristic is to be explained in part on the basis of the diffuse and pervasive nature of the visceral contribution. Emotional behavior cannot be localized and it often cannot be satisfactorily identified or described. Language behavior, in contrast, is thoroughly social in origin and organization; it only becomes personal and individualistic secondarily. Emotional reactions are always personal and individualistic. To be shared completely, in the sense that language is shared, they would usually have to be formulated first in words; but when they are, they cease to be emotional reactions. By means of verbally formulating, "working through" or "acting through," an emotional situation, it is often possible to approximate emotional sharing. This can be achieved under special therapeutic conditions, with a highly trained therapist;[82] but it is rarely attained under the ordinary conditions of life, regardless of the individual's need.

---

[81] Compare the discussion of language and thinking on pages 88–122.
[82] See pages 617–620.

This relative incommunicability of emotional behavior is to some extent a product of early childhood training. As children, we are all given a great deal of practice in hiding and disowning forbidden emotional reactions long before we have acquired systematized communicative speech. Moreover, we are taught not to formulate, acknowledge or even recognize such reactions, when we have enough speech to be capable of doing so. In consequence, our early behavioral duplicity may never be symbolically expressed; and the ambivalent emotional attitudes we simultaneously or alternately hold cannot be described and shared with others when we need help. There is probably nothing more difficult to make self-accessible than emotional conflict which is operating in adolescence or adulthood at a non-language or prelanguage level of organization.[83]

The significance of communicability becomes still more evident when one realizes that in emotional behavior, as in all other behavior, standards of acceptability shift with age. Temper tantrums are appropriate in infancy; but they become punishable in childhood, and in adulthood they may lead an individual to lose his freedom. Everyone is expected, as a matter of course, to develop increasingly adequate self-regulation as he grows from infancy, through childhood and adolescence into adulthood, and on through middle life to old age. And it is in the areas of emotional behavior that we find the most surprising failures in biosocial maturity, and the most striking and often incongruous examples of pathological fixation.

[83] Compare pages 269–272.

5

Maturation and Fixation

Maturation

The task of developing into a biosocially mature adult is one that faces every human being during the first two or three decades of his life. It is not enough merely to grow large and strong and quick. One must also learn to adapt continually to a progressive upgrading of behavior standards. With increasing age, conduct that has previously been acceptable becomes outmoded; it must be replaced with new techniques and new relationships. The permitted and approved of last year may this year be derided and forbidden. Things which one's elders have all along declared absurd and inappropriate for a young child to do, or to demand, are one day expected of him as a matter of course, because now he is older.

Individuals vary widely in the rate and the completeness of their maturing.[1] Some proceed at a fairly even pace. Others lag well behind their contemporaries in one phase, only to catch up with or outstrip them in a succeeding phase. Some remain in most respects relatively immature throughout childhood and adolescence, when compared with other persons of their own age level. A few of these, as we shall see in the chapter on *developmental retardation*, continue indefinitely as generally immature adults.[2]

It is exceedingly common to find persons with persistent immaturity in some detail of behavior, or in a particular kind of interpersonal relationship, who are able in the rest of their biosocial maturation to meet satisfactorily the demands set up by their cultural norms. Such restricted failure to mature, if it persists, we call *fixation*, and its discussion will occupy the latter half of the present chapter. In the exceptional case, fixation appears to be central to the production of pathologically deviant social behavior; and this we shall take up when

[1] For a summary of studies on individual differences in growth careers, see Gesell, A. "The ontogenesis of infant behavior." In Carmichael, L. (Ed.), *Manual of child psychology.* New York: Wiley, 1946, pp. 322–329.
[2] See Chapter 6.

we come to the chapter on *selective biosocial immaturity*.[3] We turn now to a consideration of biological and biosocial maturation.

Biological maturation and learning

Under the conditions of everyday life, it is virtually impossible to distinguish between maturing and learning. As a child grows older he develops new biological potentialities; and some of these he is able to realize in acquiring new and more effective ways of dealing with his environment and himself. Without increasing biological maturity, a child would not develop the equipment necessary for learning more and more mature techniques. And without progressive learning, he could not make use of his increasing biological competence. Thus biological maturation and individual learning are ordinarily the inseparable components of a unified process.

In many psychological studies it is essential to do violence to this unity and attempt to isolate some of the components of human development by stressing one aspect and neglecting another.[4] Thus, for example, we may plot the increasing coordination in conjugate eye movements, which accompanies increasing age during infancy, without any reference to new learned behavior during the same time span. Or we may do the reverse of this, and plot progress in oculomotor learning, without reference to the known biological changes that make such learning possible. In the end, of course, analyses such as these serve to point up the very interdependence of one aspect of development upon the other which the artificially imposed breakdown at first seems to contradict.

The interdependence of biological maturation (*the growth of structures*) and learning (*the acquisition of new techniques*) becomes self-evident in the study of *maturity sequences*.[5] Certain activities must have become established before certain others can appear in behavior. Each development, from the biologically less mature to the more mature, requires the prior occurrence of specific growth changes and, in most cases, the achievement through practice of a minimal degree of coordination. For example, a child cannot stand until his musculature is strong enough, as well as sufficiently coordinated, to hold up his heavy head. He can then walk only after he has developed the postural mechanisms by means of which he may learn to maintain his equilibrium in spite of the locomotory movements in his limbs and trunk.[6]

The evolution of manipulatory and of linguistic skill illustrates the same point. The growing child, as we have already indicated, learns to fixate ob-

[3] See Chapter 7.
[4] For a review of representative studies, see McGraw, M. B., "Maturation of behavior." In Carmichael, L. (Ed.), *Manual of child psychology.* New York: Wiley, 1946, pp. 332–369.
[5] Shirley, M., *The first two years. A study of twenty-five babies.* (3 vols.) Minneapolis: University of Minnesota Press, 1931–1933.
[6] McGraw, M., *The neuro-muscular maturation of the human infant.* New York: Columbia University Press, 1942; Shirley, M., *The first two years:* vol. I. *Postural and locomotor development.* Minneapolis: University of Minnesota Press, 1931.

jects with his eyes when the oculomotor systems have sufficiently matured. And this ocular fixation, in turn, must be partially established before adequate eye-hand coordinations can be acquired through practice. Likewise, the development and use of thumb-finger apposition, a distinctively human achievement, is clearly the necessary antecedent to the complex manipulative habits that involve apposition.[7]

The child goes through still other inevitable maturity sequences in acquiring speech. As the organs of speech grow and change in shape, an increasing variety of sounds appears in the infant's repertory; and as the infant passes into childhood he shows a rapid development of more and more complex language habits.[8] The neuromuscular coordinations are made possible by the maturation of central and peripheral speech structures; and the modification of these structures by the occurrence of coordinated language behavior, in turn, lays the necessary foundation for the further maturation of speech. Learning and biological maturing are obviously interdependent variables in human development.[9]

Biosocial maturation

If we were to try describing human development in terms confined strictly to biological maturing and the mechanics of individual learning, the product would certainly be inadequate and incomplete. For such an account would neglect entirely the influence of the human organism's natural habitat — the environment of other persons, with its social organization and its cultural products. It is probably true that a human child, if he were protected, nourished and given enough freedom of action, would achieve biological maturity as an organism, even in the absence of contact with other human beings. If he succeeded in reaching biological maturity under these circumstances he would, of course, show progressive improvement in manipulating his society-less environment, as he grew, and in finding new ways of overcoming obstacles and circumventing frustration.[10]

But the maturity such an individual thus achieved alone, the complex manipulations he acquired, and the adjustive techniques he learned, would still not equip him to lead the life of a mature person in any contemporary society. Indeed, the pattern of his behavioral development would have omitted the

---

[7] Halverson, H., "Studies of the grasping responses of early infancy: I, II, III." *J. genet. Psychol.*, 1937, vol. 51, pp. 371–449.

[8] See McCarthy, D., "Language development in children." In Carmichael, L. (Ed.), *Manual of child psychology.* New York: Wiley, 1946, pp. 476–581.

[9] For a more extended discussion of language development, see pages 88–122.

[10] For studies of maturation with minimal social stimulation, see Dennis, W., "The effect of restricted practice upon the reaching, sitting and standing of two infants." *J. genet. Psychol.*, 1935, vol. 47, pp. 17–32; Dennis, W., "Infant development under conditions of restricted practice and of minimum social stimulation: A preliminary report." *J. genet. Psychol.*, 1938, vol. 53, pp. 149–158.

most necessary qualification for adequacy in normal human living — the acquisition of social skills in interpersonal behavior. In short, although this human being might be biologically mature, and skilled in coping individualistically with an impersonal environment, he would be biosocially immature and incompetent.

By *biosocial maturation* we mean *the progression from acquired reactions and relationships that are considered less appropriate and less adequate, to ones considered more appropriate and more adequate, with respect to the cultural norms accepted in a given individual's society for persons of his age, sex and status.* It is obvious that biosocial maturation, so defined, implies *biological maturation.* The demands made upon the growing individual by his elders and his contemporaries, for more and more adequate performance, cannot possibly be met unless there is also an increasing adequacy in the machinery of behavior. Biosocial maturation necessarily implies *learning* also. Indeed, the progressive acquisition of new behavior, in terms of the prevailing social organization, is itself a definition of human learning.[11]

One aspect of biosocial maturation, to which we shall now turn, is of prime importance for an understanding of behavior pathology. The child or adolescent, as he matures, is often compelled to modify profoundly an already familiar way of doing something, or a relationship which has become firmly established in his behavior. Sometimes he is required to abandon completely an accustomed way, or a settled relationship, and to replace it with a different and an unfamiliar one. If the new way, or the radically modified relationship, presents greater difficulties and yields smaller reward than the old, the child or adolescent is likely to find serious difficulty in making the transition from less to more mature.

Failure to make such transitions is nowhere more striking than in general *developmental retardation* [12] and in the complex syndromes of *selective biosocial immaturity.*[13] In the former, the individual suffers from a generally substandard ability to acquire new ways and establish new relationships, beyond a certain level of maturation. In the latter, the individual is not developmentally retarded in a general sense. But he nonetheless shows serious deficiencies in biosocial maturation with respect to certain areas of interpersonal behavior (*inadequate social deviant*); or he habitually utilizes techniques that are distortions or caricatures of adult social skills (*inept social deviant*). Both of these varieties of selective biosocial immaturity are, of course, special cases of pathological fixation.

Before taking up the general topic of fixation — the failure to effect a required transition from less to more mature behavior — we shall consider the normal course of biosocial maturation. Let us illustrate some of the shifts

---

[11] For a detailed discussion of learning in relation to behavior pathology, see Chapter 3.
[12] See Chapter 6.   [13] See Chapter 7.

involved in biosocially maturing by sketching briefly two progressions which are characteristic of our society: (1) the progression from infant sucking to adult communal eating and drinking, and (2) the progression from infantile to adult affectional relationships.

The maturation of feeding techniques

Weaning — the shift from food-getting by sucking to food-getting by drinking and eating — is one of the most illuminating examples of transition in biosocial maturation. In human beings, weaning typically involves a change in the character of the food obtained, a radical alteration of method in obtaining it, and profound modifications in the highly important interpersonal relationship between mother and child. The newborn infant feeds by sucking because his level of biological development necessitates it; but the machinery of sucking is not fully mature at birth. For example, the corners of the neonate's mouth usually spill milk, apparently because they are not as well supplied with nerve fibers, at first, as the medial lip regions are.[14]

The intricate interrelationship of biological maturing and learning is clear in the acquisition of skill in nutritive sucking. For, while the machinery is maturing, the coordinative integration of its activities is showing typical practice effects.[15] With biological growth and practice, nursing is soon worked into a smooth-running sequence, less and less air is swallowed as breathing is better regulated, and less and less milk dribbles out of the mouth. The infant eventually acquires an effective, skilled technique which permits him to satisfy his hunger need with ease and precision.

It is with this highly skilled satisfying act that weaning interferes. Of course, if the child is introduced to weaning gradually, and only after his oral structures have sufficiently matured, no great difficulty is likely to arise.[16] He may be given small amounts of semisolids in a spoon, and allowed to try drinking from a cup, provided always that little skill is expected of him and he is shown patient consideration. Such a procedure is then followed by the now completely familiar nursing, at the breast or the bottle, so that the infant satisfies his hunger in the accustomed way. If he still needs sucking exercise, after his hunger is gone, he can get all he needs from various non-nutritive oral manipulations — thumb-sucking, finger-sucking, object-sucking — which every infant carries on.[17] Weaning along this general line permits the infant

[14] For descriptions of the feeding response in newborn infants, see Pratt, K. C., "The neonate." In Carmichael, L. (Ed.), *Manual of child psychology.* New York: Wiley, 1946, pp. 226–228.

[15] See, for example, Halverson, H. M., "Infant sucking and tensional behavior." *J. genet. Psychol.*, 1938, vol 53, pp. 365–430.

[16] For a systematic study of the relationship between suddenness of weaning and ensuing frustration, see Sears, R. R. and Wise, G. W., "Relation of cup feeding in infancy to thumb-sucking and the oral drive." *Amer. J. Orthopsychiat.*, 1950, vol. 20, pp. 123–138.

[17] One investigator indicates, for example, that every one of 143 infants studied did some thumb- or finger-sucking during the first year of life. See Kunst, M. S., "A study of thumb- and finger-sucking in infants." *Psychol. Monogr.*, 1948, no. 3, vol. 62, vi–71.

to acquire the more mature techniques of eating and drinking without having to suffer any serious deprivation.

Unfortunately the change from sucking to eating and drinking is much too often introduced abruptly, dictated by an arbitrary maternal decision, or by some unexpected circumstance, such as the illness, absence or death of the mother.[18] The infant is suddenly barred from his well-learned path to hunger satisfaction, and forced to acquire rapidly an almost wholly new technique under the pressure of his feeder's insistence and of his own imperious hunger. The frustration resulting from forced learning under conditions of severe and sudden deprivation, such as this, is often obvious even at the level of visceral physiology. The infant's emotional reactions to the frustration engage his gastrointestinal system in activity which is incompatible with good digestion and assimilation, and may lead to regurgitation of the feeding after it has been swallowed.

The process of taking food is one of the basic activities around which the socialization of human beings is organized. The human child, of course, can survive only if he is fed by an older person, a person who has already been inducted into the society to which both belong. Thus the social environment comes to the infant in one of its most inescapable forms, as the biosocially organized behavior of his human feeder; in the process of receiving his nourishment, the infant also receives his culture.

Sudden weaning imposes a radical change in feeding method upon the infant, and with this there comes inevitably a profound modification in personal interaction.[19] In other words, sudden weaning represents an abrupt transition from one sort of human interbehavior to another. Spoon-feeding, compared with nursing, calls for a different technique and a different interpersonal relationship. In nursing, the food is made continuously available and its flow is regulated by the infant's own activities. The timing of lip and tongue movements, of swallowing and breathing, is a highly individualistic matter; its sources of stimulation lie almost wholly within the infant organism. But with weaning, the food comes intermittently in small loads, its approach is out of the infant's control, and its arrival at his mouth requires new kinds of cooperation with the adult who supplies it.

Even if the infant being weaned is still held while he is fed, the mother holding him cannot be as relaxed as in the nursing situation. She, too, must play an intermittently active part in the feeding, and her rhythms will reflect her own

[18] Berger, I. L., "Psychopathologic attitudes of frustrated previously employed mothers toward their offspring." *J. nerv. ment. Dis.*, 1948, vol. 108, pp. 241–249. There is some evidence also that the times and methods of weaning differ in different cultural subgroups. See, for example, Davis, A. and Havighurst, R. J., "Social class and color differences in child-rearing." *Amer. sociol. Rev.*, 1946, vol. 11, pp. 698–710.

[19] Some writers consider the changed personal interactions in sudden weaning so serious as to be considered traumatic. See, for example, Freud, S., *New introductory lectures on psychoanalysis.* New York: Norton, 1933, p. 166.

needs as well as his. Sooner or later — in abrupt weaning it may be at once —
the infant must exchange the warm intimacy of being mothered as he feeds for
a more business-like situation, involving the reciprocal activity of mother and
child in a face-to-face relationship. Neither the mother nor the food is any
longer an integral part of feeding. The food is now visible while it is not being
eaten; it can be seen approaching long before contact is possible; it is sometimes
withheld, dropped on the way, or hurried forward. Thus the food, as well as
the person providing it, is in a more detached, impersonal relationship to the
infant than in the nursing situation.

It is important to recognize that the reciprocal activity involved in spoon-
feeding provides the weaned child with new *privileges* as well as new tasks. For
while he must still depend upon his mother to feed him, she must also depend
upon him to accept the food she proffers. Sucking is a more or less automatic
affair; once it gets started it tends to go on. But in spoon-feeding, each approach of the food gives the child a new opportunity to refuse it, or to accept
it and then spit it out. If the weaned child has lost the direct control over his
food-intake, he has at the same time gained a new weapon for controlling his
human environment.[20] Having few duties, little responsibility and much
spare time, he can enter a contest for power, in the eating situation, with a
heavy advantage over any adult who cares to engage him. However, contest
or no contest, the child will ultimately acquire sufficient biological maturity,
technical skill and social self-control to qualify him for a seat at the family
table.

The shift from eating alone, or with a mother's help, to eating at the family
table, brings with it no radical changes in method. The new situation, however, is complexly structured. The child is no longer the focus of the feeding
situation or its principal actor. There is now the compound distraction of
many unfamiliar objects, of movements and noises unrelated to his own food-
getting, of interacting persons. The child sees and smells edibles which he is
denied but others are permitted to enjoy. He must acquire dexterity with the
tools of eating, and when he is finally allowed to eat what others do, he finds
that he must share with them, wait for his portion, and sometimes go without
because of a sibling's or a parent's priority.

The child joining the family table is likely to encounter another new element
in the feeding situation. In most homes, it is customary to utilize the granting
and withholding of food as reward and punishment for children. If a child
fails to do what is expected of him, breaks the rules or offends his parents, he
may be barred from further eating and perhaps banished from the communal

---

[20] That this weapon can be a powerful one is indicated by the fact that mothers of young
infants are more frequently concerned over their offspring's hunger, spitting and vomiting
than over other infant behavior. See Blum, L. H., "Some psychological and educational
aspects of pediatric practice: a study of well-baby clinics." *Genet. Psychol. Monogr.*, 1950,
vol. 41, pp. 3–98.

table. In this way, feeding comes to mean much more than just food-getting; it gains distinct ethical connotations. To be allowed to remain at the table and partake of the family food now means to be accepted and approved — an implication which carries over into religious ceremonies as well as into the behavior disorders.[21]

Indeed, a great deal of the practice that a young child needs in learning to conform to the ethics of cooperative and competitive behavior, of subordination and superordination, he gets at mealtimes. For it is then that his interactions with siblings, parents and visitors come under the critical scrutiny of the group to which he belongs. This intricate interrelationship between the processes of food-getting and questions of right and wrong — of good and evil, of social acceptance and social rejection, approval and condemnation — becomes most obvious in the confusions we encounter when we study behavior pathology. These we shall see particularly among the delusions of schizophrenia, paranoid disorders and depressions,[22] and as leading symptoms in the conflicts and substitutive complaints of hysterical and compulsive disorders.[23]

The general conversation that goes on at mealtime also plays an important role in the biosocial maturation of child and adolescent. Nowhere excepting at the dinner table do all members of the family come into prolonged face-to-face relationships at one time. Here the growing child hears and participates in talk about the activities of all members of the family group; he learns to exchange and share in attitude and opinion as he exchanges and shares in the food. With the discussions of topics that go beyond his individual experience, his horizons expand, and he learns something of the art of communicating in a group situation. In these ways, the feeding situation, which begins with the biological need of the infant organism, develops step-by-step into one of the most effective instruments in impelling the individual toward biosocial maturation.

Maturation in affectional relationships

The situation out of which affectional relationships ordinarily develop is that of the complete dependence of the human infant upon his parent or parent surrogate. The biosocial maturation of affectional relationships consists largely of a progression from this complete dependence toward reciprocal interdependence — first in relation to parents and siblings, and eventually in relation to persons of all ages. The earliest phases of this maturation are complicated by the fact that infantile dependence centers around direct body-care and feeding. Its later phases are complicated by the postpubescent appearance of specific procreative activities among the maturing reactions without, however, a reduction or loss in the non-procreative reciprocal attitudes.

[21] For a more extended discussion of this point, see Cameron, N., *The psychology of behavior disorders*. Boston: Houghton Mifflin, 1947, pp. 107–111.

[22] See pages 321–324.   [23] See pages 39–41, 358 and 369.

The derivation of adult affectional relationships from care and feeding during infancy and early childhood is dependent upon cultural transmission. The mother enters maternity with prefabricated affectional attitudes toward her infant. As a girl she has played mother to her dolls, and whenever possible she has watched and helped real mothers care for their real babies. She has identified with women in stories and plays, discussed feminine activities endlessly with other girls, and developed her own private fantasies of wifehood and motherhood.[24] Hence, when her first child is born to her, she is likely to have well-developed maternal role-taking already practiced in her behavior repertory. She is prepared to nurse and care for her infant in accordance with the cultural standards she has acquired in childhood and adolescence.

The infant begins postnatal life as an organism without social behavior. Because of his biological immaturity, he is at first a passive recipient rather than an active participant. He must be held, carried, shifted, fed, diapered, cleansed, covered and uncovered by his mother almost as though he were in reality a doll. When he responds to the stimulation of handling and body-care, his reactions at first tend to be relatively undifferentiated mass activities — not chaotic, since he is an organism, but without much specificity or localization of response. Nevertheless, the infant is immersed from the very start in an affectional field, set up by his mother's maternal behavior, long before he is capable of reciprocating with anything that resembles filial love.

As he matures biologically, the infant develops increasingly the ability to give specific organized reactions to the more stable, repeated patterns of stimulation to which he is exposed.[25] These patterns, of course, are the routines which his mother establishes — of shifting, carrying and holding, of feeding, cleansing and diapering, of dressing and undressing. It is obvious that the more consistent, smooth-running and predictable the maternal behavior is, the more successful the infant can be in developing anticipant attitudes which prepare him, during one phase of a maternal act, for his responses in the succeeding phase.[26] And the more effective and appropriate these anticipations become, the more numerous and varied will grow the opportunities that the infant finds for satisfying his multiple developing needs.

The infant establishes his earliest affectional relationship through developing his multiple need-satisfaction sequences, in the organized field of maternal behavior in which he is immersed.[27] He learns to respond specifically to recur-

[24] For a discussion of *identification*, see pages 60–63.

[25] This may be considered as an example of the general principle of *individuating maturation*. See Gesell, A., "The ontogenesis of infant behavior." In Carmichael, L. (Ed.), *Manual of child psychology*. New York: Wiley, 1946, pp. 313–314.

[26] For a discussion of anticipant attitudes, see pages 65–66.

[27] Some writers have emphasized "mothering" in the affectional development of infants almost to the exclusion of other factors. See, for example, Ribble, M. A., "Infantile experience in relation to personality development." In Hunt, J. McV. (Ed.), *Personality and the behavior disorders*. New York: Ronald, 1944, pp. 621–625. For a critique of this point

rent, stable elements of his routine life situations. His mother, of course, is a constant factor in all of the situations bringing him relief or satisfaction of his needs. She is, in other words, in the position of a multiply-reinforced agent of consummation for him. The infant ultimately gives adient, anticipating reactions to his mother — as to a specific object that occurs in, but is now separable from, the feeding and body-care routines. Thus, in developing consistent adience in relation to this consummating agent, his mother, the infant achieves his first stable affectional relationship.

Two things transform this originally one-sided situation into a genuinely reciprocal pattern of interpersonal behavior. One of these is the further development of *anticipant attitudes* in relation to the mother, so that she becomes more and more separable, in the infant's responses, from the situations of which originally she was an integral part. The other factor is the growth of *active participation* which, of course, depends upon effective anticipation.

This transformation brings with it distinct losses, as well as gains. The procedures involved in feeding, cleansing and body-care remain as important factors in the continued close interaction between mother and child. But as the child participates more and more actively, the techniques of interaction undergo a series of changes. And with changes in method come also changes in interpersonal relationships. The child begins to gain control over the impersonal objects in his environment, but with this gain he begins to lose the possession of his mother.

We have already pointed out that weaning terminates the phase of intimate mothering and passive receiving, in the feeding situation, at the same time that it brings an end to nutritive sucking. Similarly, at a somewhat later age, the introduction of toilet training terminates the phase of warm diapering and perineal irresponsibility, and replaces these eventually with the cold comfort of the toilet seat. And, just as arbitrary weaning requires a child to work cooperatively for his food in accordance with another person's timing, so strict toilet training stipulates that he shall void and evacuate on demand.[28]

Restraint and coercion now enter into eliminative activities for the first time. The child must earn his release by "doing his duty." He must learn to expect commendation or blame for his performance in this altogether unfamiliar situation. Ultimately the child must take over all responsibility for elimination, without maternal cooperation, just as he has previously taken over the task of feeding himself.[29] His mother, meanwhile, has passed through the

of view, see Orlansky, H., "Infant care and personality." *Psychol. Bull.*, 1949, vol. 46, pp. 1–48.

[28] The times of toilet training also differ in different cultural subgroups. See Davis, A. and Havighurst, R. J., "Social class and color differences in child-rearing." *Amer. sociol. Rev.*, 1946, vol. 11, pp. 698–710.

[29] There is some evidence that self-regulation in feeding and toilet behavior is related to realistic, as contrasted with fantasy, play in a standardized play interview. See Holway, A. R., "Early self-regulation of infants and later behavior in play interviews." *Amer. J. Orthopsychiat.*, 1949, vol. 19, pp. 612–623.

phases of satisfier, and of restrainer and coercer, to become a person who shows only an indirect, verbal interest in his eliminative welfare.

Affectional relationships grow increasingly complicated as the child's behavior becomes more complex. Improvement in strength, coordination and specific skill leads inevitably to more and more restraint and taboo from others. The more the child can do that he enjoys, the more he is expected to do that he does not enjoy. The greater his range of activity the more he comes into conflict with the established rights and the wishes of those around him, and the more he invites competition, interference and punishment.[30] His growing initiative and enterprise gradually shift the balance in his relationships with his mother, so that she may become more impressively his frustrator than his satisfier. This opposition of behavior carries still further the process by which a child's mother becomes objective and detached from him. It exerts an emancipating influence upon him, thus contributing to his affectional maturity by weakening the ties of his dependent attachment.

This complication of the mother-role, into a contradictory duality of attitude, makes it easier in yet another way for the child to achieve affectional maturity. Since the mother represents her culture in her own behavior, she introduces the still dependent child to the prevailing systems of ethics, through the permissions she dispenses and the taboos she erects.[31] Indeed, even early in life, a child's first exposure to judgments of good and evil, of right and wrong, is in relation to his mother's approval and disapproval of visceral function — feeding, elimination and cleanliness. His earliest ethical system is in fact a system of *visceral ethics*, a fact which Freudians were the first to emphasize.[32] But the appearance of locomotion and of skilled manipulation expands the ethical system indefinitely, just as it expands general activity. Finally, as language develops,[33] the ethics of action is supplemented, and to some extent replaced, by an ethics of precept, parable and opinion which every adult must have at his command.

Emancipation from dependence upon the mother is a necessary first step in affectional maturation. Without it, the child is hindered not only in develop-

[30] This sequence is reflected also in the characteristic play of children of different ages. See, for example, Murphy, L. B., *Social behavior and child personality: an exploratory study of some roots of sympathy.* New York: Columbia University Press, 1937; Parten, M. and Newhall, S. M., "Social behavior of preschool children." In Barker, R. G., Kounin, J. S., and Wright, H. F., *Child behavior and development.* New York: McGraw-Hill, 1943, pp. 509–526.

[31] The mother typically reflects her own early training in her attitudes toward her child. See Ingersoll, H. L., "A study of the transmission of authority patterns in the family." *Genet. Psychol. Monogr.*, 1948, vol. 38, pp. 225–302.

[32] Freud, S., "Character and anal erotism." *Collected Papers*, vol. 2. London: Hogarth Press, 1924; "The infantile genital reorganization of the libido." *Collected Papers*, vol. 2. London: Hogarth Press, 1924; "Three contributions to the theory of sex." *Nerv. ment. Dis. Monogr. Series*, 1930, no. 7; *New introductory lectures on psychoanalysis.* New York: Norton, 1933, pp. 135–140.

[33] For a discussion of language development, see pp. 88–105.

ing self-reliance but, what is still more important, in developing the variety of affectional relationships with other persons upon which his success as an adult will largely depend.[34]   Emancipation is facilitated by anything that obliges the child to share his mother's attention with others — with an affectionate or jealous father, a sibling rival, the mother's friends, and whatever interests take her outside the home.   It is facilitated also by the expansion of the child's life space, by his attachment to other members of the family and, when he is old enough to join the neighborhood community of children, by his contact with his peers at play.

Siblings and father offer the child, who is growing away from mother-dependence, new and different opportunities for need-satisfaction, and new occasions for mutual dependence.[35]   The expansion of affectional relationships to include several members of a family is an extremely important step in bio-social maturation.[36]   For in many ways the family is a small-scale model of the community outside.[37]   The manifold character of intrafamilial behavior gives the child essential practice in establishing and maintaining affectional contacts, not only with a greater number of separate individuals, but also with interacting constellations of interdependent persons.

With the family as his proving ground and the home as his base, the young child is prepared for the next important step — his emergence into the neighborhood community.   If his biosocial maturation has progressed satisfactorily up to this point, he is unlikely to encounter any lasting difficulty in gaining the acceptance of his peers.[38]   This acceptance is essential for the further development of his affectional relationships.   Eventually, if he is to become a competent, mature adult the child must acquire techniques of cooperating and competing with his contemporaries, of developing strong loyalties and antipathies unconnected with his parental home, and of learning to give and receive affection in participative activities with children who are not his relatives.

The friendships of childhood do not ordinarily interfere with or displace filial and fraternal affection; they tend rather to supplement than to supplant it.   The close *chumships* of the prepubertal and pubertal years, however, introduce new elements into maturation.   Chumships develop typically between persons of the same sex; but they display some of the most conspicuous features of adult heterosexual love.   Chums in this phase are for a time insep-

[34] For examples of retarded affectional development in dependent children, see Levy, D., *Maternal overprotection.*   New York: Columbia University Press, 1943.

[35] For a description of the father's role, as seen in retrospect by children, see Gardner, L. P., "A survey of the attitudes and activities of fathers." *J. genet. Psychol.*, 1943, vol. 63, pp. 15–53.

[36] The presence of more than one child in the family may even alter the relationship between the mother's adjustment to pregnancy and her child's adjustment. See Wallin, P. and Riley, R. P., "Reactions of mothers to pregnancy and adjustment of offspring in infancy." *Amer. J. Orthopsychiat.*, 1950, vol. 20, pp. 616–622.

[37] For a more detailed discussion of social communities, see pages 372–376 and 478–481.

[38] Compare the difficulty of Levy's overprotected children in making friends, pages 56–57.

arable, they overvalue each other, quarrel easily and are quick to be jealous. They resent and reject the least criticism of each other by their respective families; but they do not hesitate to make comparisons themselves in which members of their own family show up badly.[39]

Whether or not the chumship is biologically an inescapable phase of affectional maturation, it does seem to be almost inevitable in our culture. Undoubtedly it has its advantages as well as its hazards. For one thing it enables each participant to see his parental home in a new perspective, even though this be an unfavorable one. The critical attitudes toward parents and siblings, and the often greater sympathy for members of the chum's family and for their ways, advance the pubescent another step toward objectivity and affectional emancipation. At about the same period, or a little later, there develop "crushes" and attitudes of hero-worship toward adults of the same and the opposite sex. The behavioral ground by this time has been prepared for the serious adolescent business of learning the techniques of dealing with contemporaries of the opposite sex.

The critical attitudes toward home and family, which appear around puberty, may develop into derision, impatience and even downright antipathy during adolescence. This transition has two origins. One is the increasing biosocial aggression which accompanies sexual maturing and is heightened by parental attempts at continuing supervision and control.[40] The other is the influence of the adolescent peer culture,[41] which is intolerant of parental opinions and parental ways, but most intolerant of all when it comes to any disagreement with its prevailing attitudes.

The individual adolescent, standing as he does in the greatest need of acceptance by them, can scarcely be expected to hold out for long against his peers. Thus, under the pressure of these conflicting claims, he must make the critical choice: to give the ways and standards of his contemporaries preference over the approval of his parents. When he has taken this step he has finally emancipated himself from the family.

This progressive emancipation from emotional dependence upon the family, as we have indicated, is paralleled by the growth of increasingly mature affectional relationships with outsiders. Under the influence of biological changes and social pressures, the chumships and crushes of pubescence and early adolescence give way to heterosexual interests aimed more and more at specific procreative activities. In our culture, the biosocial maturation of affectional

[39] Tryon, C., "Evaluation of adolescent personality by adolescents." *Monogr. Soc. Res. Child Develpm.*, 1939, vol. 4, pp. 1–88; Tryon, C., "The adolescent peer culture." *Yearb. Nat. Soc. Stud. Educ.*, 1944, vol. 43, pp. 217–239.

[40] Stolz, H. and Stolz, L., "Adolescent problems related to somatic variations." *Yearb. Nat. Soc. Stud. Educ.*, 1944, vol. 43, pp. 80–99.

[41] Tryon, C., "The adolescent peer culture." *Yearb. Nat. Soc. Stud. Educ.*, 1944, vol. 43, pp. 217–239.

relationships is considered complete with the establishment of an adult hetero-sexual attachment which leads to marriage and parenthood.

Fixation

We have been stressing the fact that children, in the process of biosocially maturing, often find difficulty in passing from familiar to unfamiliar ways, and from established relationships to relationships that must be newly structured. One of the commonest indicators of such difficulty is the appearance of delay in making the transition. The child fails to give up or to modify his accustomed patterns of behavior, in the face of conditions calling for their abandonment or for fundamental changes in them. This delay or failure we call fixation.

We may define *fixation* as *the persistence of acquired behavior patterns until they have become biosocially immature, in terms of the cultural norms accepted in a given individual's society for persons of his age, sex and status.*[42] Fixation so conceived is clearly relativistic and contingent. Thus, for example, standards of maturity shift with increase in *chronological age.* That which the child may do, the adolescent must not; what is condoned in the adolescent is condemned in the adult; the behavior which in young adulthood meets with approval may earn only derision in old age. In each age group, the persistence of behavior accepted as characteristic of a younger phase of development should be regarded as presumptive evidence of fixation.

Comparable distinctions hold for differences in *sex, occupation, socio-economic level* and *place of residence.* Among adults of the same age, for example, we countenance and even applaud certain manifestations of dependence in women which are penalized as immature if they occur in men. On the other hand, we expect and encourage mature men to show relative incompetence and dependence in relation to domestic management and child care.[43] Obviously, in either case, we should do violence to the facts if we were to characterize the persistence of such dependent behavior as *fixation,* when it is socially approved.

Similarly, that which is accepted as normal adult behavior in a person holding a subordinate position — in business and industry, in the professions, in politics and in military service — may be considered irresponsible and immature in an executive or a superior. Standards of maturity, and therefore judgments as to what constitutes fixation, will also be found to fluctuate as one

[42] Compare this definition with that of Freud. See, for example, Freud, S., "Three contributions to the theory of sex." *Nerv. ment. Dis. Monogr. Series,* 1930, no. 7; Freud, S., "Instincts and their vicissitudes." *Collected Papers,* vol. 4, pp. 60–83. A discussion of various concepts of fixation may be found in Sears, R. R., "Survey of objective studies of psychoanalytic concepts." *Soc. Sci. Res. Council Bull. 51.* New York, 1943, pp. 78–89; and Sears, R. R., "Experimental analysis of psychoanalytic phenomena." In Hunt, J. McV. (Ed.), *Personality and the behavior disorders.* New York: Ronald, 1944, pp. 307–311.

[43] See the discussion of identification on pages 60–63, and of role-taking on pages 114–122.

shifts from a well-to-do neighborhood to the slums, from rural to urban areas, and even from one region of the country to another.[44] In short, before we can designate any sample of behavior as fixated, we must know whose behavior it is and under what conditions it has occurred.

Fixation varies greatly in *temporal span*. It may be brief, protracted or permanent; and this variation introduces further complexities into the recognition of fixated patterns. For, if biosocially immature behavior persists for a prolonged period, we should expect it to undergo some modification as a result of changes in an individual's general personality organization. And that is what we usually find. In exceptional instances, however, fixated reactions remain essentially unaltered in spite of the general biosocial maturation of a person. The clearest examples of this are to be found in *selective biosocial immaturity;* [45] but we shall have occasion to return to this important point also when we take up the topics of *repression* [46] and *disorganization*.[47]

Fixation and biosocial maturation

Individual differences in human beings are expressions of the multiform dissimilarities of environment to which different persons have been in the past exposed. They are expressions also of the fact that no two individuals are ever biologically identical — even identical twins — and of the cumulative effects of a person's earlier behavior upon what he later does. Thus, persons of the same sex and chronological age, living under comparable conditions, and faced with problems that seem to an observer to be objectively similar, may nevertheless vary widely in the degrees of maturity they exhibit in different areas of behavior. Fixation is often responsible for important components of such individual variation.

We are all familiar with the persistent immature behavior which shows up in group activities and defeats cooperative endeavors — not only among children but among adults also — in business and industry, in family life, in neighborhood and civic organizations, and even in national and international affairs. There is the man who seems never able to subordinate his demands to those of any group he joins. His way is the only way; he cannot take the role of others and gain their perspectives for his guidance. Another man can perform effectively in a group only if he remains in a subordinate relationship and receives expressions of approval from the others. He is always a dependent child among adults. A third shows exceptional initiative in lone enterprises but loses it the moment he finds himself at work with others. He has never abandoned the role of the only child or the child who is fearful of his siblings.

---

[44] The amount of freedom given prepubertal and pubertal children, and the degree of responsibility for contributing to the family income, for example, vary in different cultural subgroups. See Davis, A. and Havighurst, R. J., "Social class and color differences in child-rearing." *Amer. sociol. Rev.*, 1946, vol. 11, pp. 698–710.

[45] See Chapter 7.   [46] See pages 337–351.   [47] See pages 450–451.

A fourth cannot afford to leave group situations because to be alone is to be insecure and restless. Each of these individuals is paying with relative social incompetence for his failure to progress in some phase of biosocial maturation.

Differences in maturity between individuals are more than matched by the differences existing in the levels of maturity within the same individual's behavior. Biosocial maturation is a complex and uneven process.[48] In acquiring skills demanded of him in his culture, a person does not progress at a constant rate in everything. His behavioral growth never proceeds in all directions uniformly, like the growth of a vegetable, but always irregularly, in a developmental pattern whose design is highly individualistic. Even if a person is generally retarded in his behavioral maturation, he will not show exactly the same degree of retardation in everything he does at any given time.[49] Likewise, if he matures precociously, he cannot be expected to show equal precocity in everything at once.[50]

Some of this irregularity, and the individuality it confers, may result directly from *fixation* — that is, from a delay in the progression from less to more mature behavior. In the vast majority of instances, the delay need be of no lasting significance for the individual's further personality development. In other words, the infant or child can fail to progress in some respect for a considerable period, while his peers advance, without giving valid reason for maternal or professional concern. The same is true for adolescents. A child growing into adulthood often pauses for a time while his companions go on with the business of behaviorally maturing.[51] Then he enters a phase of rapid acceleration, and before long he has caught up with his like-aged peers or moved ahead of them.

Such hesitations in the process of ordinary maturation are examples of what we may call *normal fixations*. We reserve the designation *pathological fixation* for those more exceptional instances of the premature termination of some aspect of personality development, and for delay in one phase of maturation when the effect of the delay is to retard or to distort personality development in a subsequent phase.[52]

Premature termination. The premature termination of some aspect of biosocial maturing, we have said, is far less common than the retardation or

[48] Compare Gesell, A., "The ontogenesis of infant behavior." In Carmichael, L. (Ed.), *Manual of child psychology.* New York: Wiley, 1946, pp. 295–331.

[49] See pages 166–167.

[50] This is demonstrated particularly in studies of "gifted" individuals. See, for example, Terman, L. M. *et al.*, *Genetic studies of genius: Vol. I. The mental and physical traits of a thousand gifted children.* Stanford University, Calif.: Stanford University Press, 1925; Hollingworth, L. S., *Children above 180 IQ.* New York: World Book Co., 1942.

[51] That such hesitations in development may be disturbing to the adolescent is indicated by Stolz, H. and Stolz, L., "Adolescent problems related to somatic variations." *Yearb. Nat. Soc. Stud. Educ.*, 1944, vol. 43, pp. 80–99.

[52] This is closely related to the Freudian concept of fixation. Compare Freud, S., "Three contributions to the theory of sex." *Nerv. ment. Dis. Monogr. Series*, 1930, no. 7.

distortion of subsequent maturation. But when it does occur, it presents us with clinical pictures which are often dramatically clear, and hence lend themselves well to exposition. Occasionally we encounter obviously infantile or childish techniques which have persisted virtually unchanged into adulthood.

A sixty-two-year-old unmarried lawyer controlled his household, in which he lived with his less competent siblings, by the same kind of temper tantrums which he had used to control his parents. The siblings stated that he had never given up this technique. So infantile were his attacks of rage, when he was frustrated in a hospital to which he had come for treatment of an unrelated illness, that the nursing staff at first reported them as convulsions.

The temper tantrum, usually in a somewhat more modified form than this, is probably the commonest infantile technique to persist into adolescence and adulthood. However, it is by no means the only one. We find adult men and women who, whenever they are denied special privilege or attention, sulk until they have their way — sometimes even in public. We come across others who always vomit when they are faced with a distasteful choice, just as they did in infancy and childhood.[53] These, of course, are only samples from an almost endless list.

No less numerous are the fixations centering about some infantile, childish or adolescent *interest* which is carried over into succeeding phases of biosocial maturation, when it should have been replaced by other interests. Thus we find adult women who fail to relinquish their girlhood fascination for dolls, in human or animal form, and continue to lavish the attention upon them that is usually reserved for infants. Men sometimes exhibit comparable fixations in surrounding themselves with statuettes and figurines, usually of animals, toward which they evidence affectionate overevaluation. In an exceptional case, but by no means an unique one, a college man accidentally disclosed the fact, in action, that he could not go to sleep unless he had his childhood teddy-bear in his arms.

We see other examples of persistent immaturity in children who stick to solitary play and old familiar toys when their peers have graduated to companions and new toys. Even the child who is praised for sitting alone and reading "good literature" is, more often than not, one who sits alone and reads because he cannot adapt to the cooperative and competitive attitudes of his contemporaries. Likewise the child who prefers above all to stay with a parent — even though here he engages in activities which are unquestionably *more* mature than those of his peers — may well be a child who cannot succeed in establishing adequate social relationships with other children.[54] A girl may enjoy being a "little mother" to her younger siblings because she can-

---

[53] Compare the case described on pages 40–41.
[54] This was the case with some of the children studied in Levy, D., *Maternal overprotection.* New York: Columbia University Press, 1943.

not achieve equality with girls of her own age; and a boy may willingly help his father in business or with chores because it protects him from the effects of his failure to gain acceptance among his would-be playmates.

To all these should be added the adults who cling to boys' and girls' club activities, to fraternities and sororities after graduation, or to the social and athletic affairs of the grade school, high school or college of earlier days. We must include, also, adults who skip over the national and international news to bury themselves in the sport page, or in the fashion and "society" page, and those whose preoccupation with characters in so-called "comic strips" and "soap operas" takes precedence over that for the welfare of real men or women, and for the common good.

Delay and distortion. The commonest forms of fixation are those resulting from a delay in maturation, during one phase of personality development, which has led to delay or distortion in subsequent phases.[55] Oral fixation in nursing, for example, may leave no recognizable direct trace in later oral reactions. Nevertheless, the early persistent oral habit may retard a child's socialization during a critical period in his life, lead perhaps to habitual petulance as his reaction against the coercion he invites, and even result in his developing organized *self-attitudes* of inadequacy, as the reflections of *other's attitudes* toward persistent immature behavior. If, of course, he is indulged instead of coerced, and protected from derogatory attitudes, he is likely to exhibit habitual dependent affection, instead of petulance, and the self-attitudes of a person who has been encouraged rather to overvalue than to undervalue himself.[56]

Children who for any reason have been obliged to play alone for a long period of time sometimes find themselves unequal to the challenge of cooperative play when they are thrown among their peers. In other respects they may show satisfactory biosocial maturation, and progress materially in their general adaptations to interpersonal relationship. But in group situations that require cooperative interaction with contemporaries, particularly in social recreation, they may never succeed in advancing beyond a shy, reserved, awkward, defensive attitude. Thus the early enforced fixation in solitary play, prolonged into a phase which otherwise might have initiated the child

---

[55] This point has been investigated in a number of studies on infrahuman animals. See, for example, Hunt, J. McV., "The effects of infant-feeding frustration upon adult hoarding in the albino rat." *J. abn. soc. Psychol.*, 1941, vol. 36, pp. 338–360; Hunt, J. McV., Schlosberg, H., Solomon, R. L., and Stellar, E., "Studies of the effect of infantile experience on adult behavior in rats. I. Effects of infantile feeding frustration on adult hoarding." *J. comp. physiol. Psychol.*, 1947, vol. 40, pp. 291–304; Wolf, A., "The dynamics of the selective inhibition of specific functions in neurosis: a preliminary report." *Psychosom. Med.*, 1943, vol. 5, pp. 27–38.

[56] For discussions of the "oral character type," see Abraham, K., *Selected papers.* London: Hogarth Press, 1927, pp. 248–279, 370–417; Fenichel, O., *The psychoanalytic theory of neurosis.* New York: Norton, 1945, pp. 62–69, 278–284, 487–496; Sears, R. R., "Personality." In *Ann. Review Psychol.*, 1950, vol. I. Stanford University, Calif.: Annual Reviews, Inc. (C. P. Stone, Ed.), pp. 106–109; Orlansky, H., "Infant care and personality." *Psychol. Bull.*, 1949, vol. 46, pp. 3–12.

into associative and cooperative interrelationships with his peers, leaves its mark on later group behavior as relative social inadequacy in related interpersonal situations.[57]

The individual who in childhood has been fascinated or frightened by some sex experience may thereafter furtively seek to repeat it, or else to shun all situations which seem to lead toward further sex behavior. In the former case, the result is sometimes that the person shows a preference for, or a limitation to, relationships resembling the childhood one; and his adolescent and adult sex activities are thus distorted by the effects of the early fixation. This outcome is commonly referred to as sex deviation or perversion.[58] In the latter case, the individual may be unable to make any lasting adult heterosexual adaptation. A man, for example, may develop into a mature, competent business executive upon whose judgment his associates find they can safely depend, and yet be incapable of entering into an adult heterosexual relationship.

In much of the preceding discussion of fixation, the persistence of relative immaturity in interpersonal relationships is clearly implied. Human beings, throughout life, have few activities and few interests which do not include the behavior of other persons. From childhood on, if no other individual is included in relation to one's behavior, it is more than likely that important self-attitudes and self-responses are; and self-reactions, we know, are derived always from interpersonal activities in shared social operations.[59] Indeed, even were a person's behavior to involve no one else, and no important self-reactions, it would still be true that the very omission of social participation — if long continued — would certainly delay, distort or prevent the further maturation of biosocial personality.[60] Thus, as we shall find in reviewing some of the conditions favoring fixation, impersonal as well as personal interests and activities may indirectly result in persistent immaturity of interpersonal relationships.

Conditions favoring fixation

It is fair to assume that, given the necessary conditions, the development of any human behavior, during any phase of biosocial maturation, might be arrested or fixated. The possible variety of fixation, therefore, is practically without limit. However, the concept of fixation was evolved originally in the field of affectional relationships and, more specifically, in dealing clinically with sexual inadequacies and distortions.[61]

This origin was no historical accident. Intimate interpersonal behavior,

---

[57] Compare the discussion of Levy's overprotected children, pages 56–57.

[58] See pages 208–209.

[59] For a discussion of self-reactions, see pages 95–105.

[60] For the consequences of such a development in *desocialization*, see pages 484–491.

[61] Freud, S., "Three contributions to the theory of sex." *Nerv. ment. Dis. Monogr. Series,* 1930, no. 7.

and the sexual attitudes and responses that develop in it, provide us with some of our most important sources of behavior pathology, as we shall see demonstrated in our clinical cases.[62] Nevertheless, affectional relationships and sexual reactions are still parts of a more inclusive behavioral whole. Hence, in what follows, their discussion will be integrated with, rather than segregated from, the rest of personality organization.

As we have already indicated, fixations in relation to certain normal infantile activities and interests have been the subject of important speculations in the development of modern behavior pathology. It is generally believed today that many such fixations are the result in large part of undue parental emphases, anxieties and preoccupations.[63] Thus, so great an issue may be made of weaning, thumb-sucking or blanket-chewing, that a child's oral behavior is unintentionally elevated to the position of a symbol of resistance, and a war is begun which the child may never stop fighting. In this situation, parental restraint, nagging and punishment act as reinforcing agents instead of as corrective ones, and actually prevent the extinction of an otherwise useless habit.[64]

Toilet-training also has its casualties in persistent immaturity. A mother's inflexible insistence upon her child's evacuating, under conditions and at times which she arbitrarily predetermines, can become an effective call to battle. The outcome may then be an emotional over-emphasis upon the toilet situation, and the activities it includes, which in this way gain a significance they need never otherwise have had. Parental overevaluation of the quantity and regularity of bowel movements, for example, is a common source of childhood fixation.[65] Adults with such early training sometimes give evidence, in their outspoken pride, that they equate bowel function with good health, and regularity with virtue.

More important for behavior pathology, however, are those cases of adults whose fixation continues their childhood attitudes of anxiety and preoccupation in relation to gastrointestinal affairs. These attitudes they have usually adopted from their parents; later, as parents themselves, they are likely to pass similar anxieties and preoccupations on to their own children. Thus, we see one of the common conditions under which hypochondriacal concern may become the cultural heritage of a family line.[66] One generation trains the next in developing reaction-sensitivity to normal gastrointestinal activity, in the same general way that their neighbors may train succeeding generations in reaction-sensitivity to some religious or political belief.

Fixations involving genital function may also be related to parental over-

[62] See, for example, pages 407–411 and 497–500.   [63] Compare page 60.

[64] For a review of the literature on this point, see Lehman, E., "Feeding problems of psychogenic origin: a survey of the literature." In Freud, A. (Ed.), *The psychoanalytic study of the child*, vol. 3/4. New York: International Universities Press, 1949, pp. 461–488.

[65] For a review of the literature on the "anal character type," see Orlansky, H., "Infant care and personality." *Psychol. Bull.*, 1949, vol. 46, pp. 17–21.

[66] See the case example on page 58.

concern.[67]   Indeed, so nearly universal is the persistence in adults of childlike anxiety, fascination and misconception, when it comes to sexual matters, that some behavior pathologists have made this the keystone of their theoretical structure. As in the case of other forms of persistent immaturity, it is unusual for infantile or childish activities and interests to be preserved into adolescence and adulthood without modification. Examples of such fixations, however, are to be found in those persons who gain their chief or sole sexual satisfaction through the common childhood techniques of gazing, peeping, manipulating or exhibiting the genitals, or through making obscene remarks to strangers. Homosexual behavior, likewise, seems occasionally to represent the persistence into adulthood of immature sex attitudes growing out of otherwise normal childhood "crushes." [68]

The fixations just discussed are relatively simple in design, and sometimes their background is relatively simple too. Thus, for example, they may be an incidental component of a more *general retardation in development*.[69] A child's specific immaturity is then only a part of his total pattern of slow or incomplete biosocial maturation. In other instances, the fixation is brought out by a person's otherwise *precocious development*. The behavior in question is relatively immature and troublesome because the rest of the person's biosocial maturation has out-distanced it. Compared with the corresponding behavior of one's contemporaries, a given fixated pattern may be at an average level; but it is none the less out of step with the individual's own general biosocial organization. The more or less isolated fixations found in average children have been already sufficiently discussed in the preceding paragraphs.

Whenever we find such examples of comparatively simple fixation — whether they occur in retarded, precocious or average individuals — we can assume that we are dealing with the products of comparatively simple learning. It is our ultimate goal, of course, to be able to formulate the development of persistent, selective immaturity in terms of learning processes — of reward and punishment, of reinforcement and extinction, of transfer and generalization, of behavior organization, disorganization and deterioration, of need, satisfaction and frustration.[70]

A great many attempts are currently being made to lay the foundations for formulations of this nature.[71] Most of them, however, have been carried out

[67] Ramsey, G. V., "The sex information of younger boys." *Amer. J. Orthopsychiat.*, 1943, vol. 13, pp. 347–352; Spitz, R. A. and Wolf, K. M., "Autoerotism: some empirical findings and hypotheses on three of its manifestations in the first year of life." In Freud, A. (Ed.), *The psychoanalytic study of the child*, vol. 3/4. New York: International Universities Press, 1949, pp. 85–120.
[68] Compare pages 208–209.
[69] See pages 166–167.   [70] See Chapter 3.
[71] For reviews of relevant experiments, see Sears, R. R., "Survey of objective studies of psychoanalytic concepts." *Soc. Sci. Res. Council Bull. 51.* New York, 1943; Sears, R. R., "Experimental analysis of psychoanalytic phenomena." In Hunt, J. McV. (Ed.), *Person-*

through experimentation with lower mammals as their subjects, and of course these animals are reared under conditions that have little similarity to the conditions of human infancy and childhood. Moreover, the experimental formulations of fixation so far reached have omitted entirely the concept of relative biosocial immaturity, which for the human being is the chief reference point in judgments of fixation.[72] Hence it is that we have actually not yet begun the experimental analysis of the basic problems with which even simple cases of clinical fixation are concerned.

Unfortunately for behavior pathology, the fixations most commonly encountered are neither as simple in design nor as clear in origin as those we have been discussing. Their analysis undoubtedly belongs also in the field of learning, since they are all examples of acquired behavior patterns. But they have been evolved out of so complex a behavioral matrix, with such intricate social interaction and so much symbolic transmutation, that there is little likelihood of our ever being able to do them justice by means of a simple, direct formulation.

The principal reason for the complexity of fixations, of course, is that they tend to develop in relation to interpersonal behavior. The infant, as we have said, is inducted into human society through the care he receives from older human beings, and this usually means from his mother. It is obvious, for example, that the child who is breast-fed, or bottle-fed, long after the age at which other children have been completely weaned, is more likely than they to show a strong attachment to the mother who administers the bottle or the breast. As pressures are applied to him by other persons to relinquish sucking for eating and drinking, the child cannot help turning away from the other persons and toward his mother-protector. The more they scorn and belittle him, the more they become representatives of a hostile, threatening world from which his only shelter is his mother. Thus, he may remain for a long time diffident and silent with others, but secure and communicative when alone with her.

Some of the most consistent patterns of fixation in interpersonal relationships are the products of prolonged parental overprotection. A child with normally maturing biological machinery may show serious retardation in biosocial development, for example, because of the overwhelming domination or the tireless indulgence of an overprotective mother. In the cases studied by Levy,[73] it is especially interesting to discover that not one overprotected child was able to abandon his overlearned infantile techniques when he attempted to

ality and the behavior disorders. New York: Ronald, 1944; Sears, R. R., "Personality." In *Ann. Review Psychol.*, 1950, vol. I. Stanford University, Calif.: Annual Reviews, Inc. (C. P. Stone, Ed.), pp. 106–109; Orlansky, H., "Infant care and personality." *Psychol. Bull.*, 1949, vol. 46, pp. 1–48.

[72] See pages 225–226.

[73] Levy, D., *Maternal overprotection.* New York: Columbia University Press, 1943.

join other children in play outside the home. Even though their interpersonal behavior brought them only frustration and isolation, the overprotected children continued to perform in the ways they had long practiced with their mothers. The outcome was that they were permanently excluded from play-groups by their like-sexed peers, and left to play with younger and weaker children. Because of the tenacity of their immature techniques they were unable to avail themselves of the usual opportunities of childhood for personal interaction in subsequent phases of their development.

The biosocial immaturity of some overprotected children is so marked and so inclusive that they remain throughout life unfit for competition or coopera-tion on a level with their peers. Their chief social techniques, however thickly overlaid with apt verbalisms and good manners, are essentially infantile or juvenile in character. Indeed, it is often the discrepancy between their verbal aptness and their social ineptitude, between their good manners and their general interpersonal incompetence, that leads to their being adjudged in adulthood as unethical and unreliable. Their behavior cannot be confidently predicted, either by them or by their fellows, on the basis of the expected behavior of mature persons in adult situations.[74]

It would be a gross oversimplification, of course, to assume that persistent immaturity such as this comes always from parental overprotection, or that parental overprotection leads always to persistent immaturity of this exact pattern. Parental neglect, and parental inconsistency in affectional relation-ships, can equally well result in stable, complex patterns of fixation. In one, the child develops hostility, guilt and overcompensating attachments, which leave him unfit to meet the demands of adult life in the same ways that more fortu-nate persons do. In the other, the parents' inconsistent, and therefore unpre-dictable behavior, helps to organize inconsistent, unpredictable and dependent behavior in the child who must learn to be constantly alert to signals from his capricious patrons.[75] Sibling rivalry, chronic personal conflict, adolescent bio-social failures, and marital or premarital misfortunes are other important con-tributing influences that favor the persistence of relative immaturity.

The variation we find in complex patterns of fixation, regardless of their precise origin, is also great. It would be a serious mistake, for instance, to assume that biosocially immature persons are all delinquent, or unpredictable, or even unsuccessful. On the contrary, some of our best citizens, and some of our political leaders, industrialists, scientists and creative workers give unmis-takable signs of behavioral immaturity. We see the evidence of this in the excessive devotion an individual exhibits in relation to the parental home, with either comparative neglect of his own family, or an inability to leave his parents

---

[74] For a more extended discussion of selective biosocial immaturity, with illustrations from case material, see pages 203–211.

[75] For examples of such behavior, see pages 213–215.

and establish his own home at all. We see it in the otherwise inexplicable hostility to everything new or to anything characteristic of the parents' generation, in excessive caution or never ceasing rebellion — political, industrial, scientific, or artistic — in the life of devotion to mother surrogates and father symbols, and in the attempts to repeat a parental career or to negate it. The fixation may be pathological and the immaturity striking, but the resulting behavior frequently *supports*, instead of running contrary to, the prevailing mores.

With this background and these attitudes, we are now ready to consider in greater detail the behavior pathology to be found in two highly important kinds of immaturity. In the next chapter, we shall take up the problem of *developmental retardation*, or "feeble-mindedness" as it is often labelled. In the chapter following that, we shall discuss the complex and controversial subject of *selective biosocial immaturity*, including the behavior pathology of so-called *psychopathic* or *sociopathic personalities*.

6

Behavior Pathology in Biosocial Immaturity

I. DEVELOPMENTAL RETARDATION

Progressive maturation from infantile dependence to adult maturity is achieved by the many, denied to a few, and guaranteed for no one. Biosocial maturation, we have said, involves the progressive acquisition of social skills within a framework of increasing biological development. The successful learning of any skill — whether it be talking, roller-skating, eating with a spoon, or circumventing frustration by a variety of adjustive techniques — requires a certain minimal level of biological maturity. We have also seen, however, that biological readiness alone guarantees neither the acquisition nor the maintenance of the habits which define biosocial competence. Under conditions of frustration, increased stress, or lack of opportunity, anyone may fail to exchange his present patterns of response for more mature ones (*fixation*), or may behave in ways characteristic of earlier phases in maturation (*regression*). His behavior may then be considered socially immature, even though he is biologically an adult.

Some persons, however, exhibit socially immature behavior consistently throughout their lives, in the absence of those special conditions imposed by strain, frustration or lack of opportunity which may produce fixation or regression. They approach the levels of biological maturity slowly, and their acquisition of social skills is correspondingly delayed. Even when allowance is made for the wide individual differences in rates of growth to be found in the general population, these individuals still lag behind in biosocial development. At any age from infancy to adulthood their behavior seems much less mature than that of their contemporaries. It is as if, with short steps and at a slow pace, these persons linger along the path of development, and even in a lifetime fail to achieve the expected degree of maturity.

This failure to develop biosocially at the usual rate has two important consequences for the student of behavior pathology. The immaturity which results from developmental retardation constitutes in itself a problem for study. More significantly, however, immaturity exposes the retarded person to continuous competition with his more mature contemporaries, in which he cannot avoid being the loser. In a society whose customs, habits and expectations are developed for average persons, the retarded individual is vulnerable to a wide range of frustrations, while at the same time he lacks the necessary maturity to develop techniques of circumventing them. We shall see that not only the developmental retardation itself, but also the failures it makes inevitable, define behavior pathology in biosocial immaturity.

Biosocial immaturity resulting from developmental retardation is characterized by behavior which, even in the absence of special frustration or stress, is consistently more appropriate for younger age levels than for the individual's own chronological age. This developmental retardation must be distinguished, on the one hand, from the immature behavior which all of us display occasionally under stress and, on the other hand, from the relatively more stable patterns of immaturity which may be the end-product of fixation or regression, of social deviation, of schizophrenic disorganization and of cerebral incompetence.[1] Were we to restrict our study of behavior pathology to momentary cross-sectional samples, we would find evidence of biosocial immaturity in a good share of our material. But often it is only by examining the patient's life history that we can differentiate between the immaturity resulting from developmental retardation and that associated with other forms of behavior pathology. The continuous chronicle of slow progress, from infancy onward, characterizes developmental retardation and its consequent biosocial immaturity.

Developmental retardation has been recognized as a serious social and scientific problem for the past 150 years.[2] Prior to the nineteenth century, retarded persons were considered innately defective fools, social outcasts, or degenerates; but occasionally the occurrence of developmental retardation in a family line has been superstitiously thought to presage the appearance of genius. The systematic study of retardation began around 1800 with the work of Itard,[3] a French physician, who published an account of his attempts to train a boy who had presumably spent his life in isolation in a forest near Aveyron. Itard's persistent but eventually futile efforts to teach the boy,

---

[1] Fixation is discussed in detail on pages 143–153, regression on pages 217–230, social deviation on pages 187–216, schizophrenic disorganization on pages 494–515, and cerebral incompetence on pages 531–555.

[2] For reviews of the history of this problem, see Haskell, R. H., "Mental deficiency over a hundred years: a brief historical sketch of trends in this field." *Amer. J. Psychiat.*, 1944, vol. 100, pp. 107–118; Peterson, J., *Early conceptions and tests of intelligence.* New York: World Book Co., 1925, Chapter 2; Pintner, R., "The feeble-minded child." In Murchison, C. (Ed.), *A handbook of child psychology* (2nd ed., rev.). Worcester, Mass.: Clark University Press, 1933, pp. 802–841; Strauss, A. A. and Lehtinen, L. E., *Psychopathology and education of the brain-injured child.* New York: Grune and Stratton, 1948, pp. 7–17.

[3] Itard, J.-M.-G., *The wild boy of Aveyron* (Trans. by G. and M. Humphrey. Original in 1894). New York: Century, 1932.

stimulated an interest in the education of retarded persons — an interest which was perpetuated through the contributions of Itard's pupil, Seguin.[4] In the subsequent study of developmental retardation, two threads can be discerned: (1) the development of methods for training and caring for retarded persons in the community; and (2) the development of more and more precise methods of diagnosing retardation.

Throughout this history, the status of the retarded person has changed from that of a social outcast to that of an individual in need of special treatment. The change has been a slow one, the product of an almost fanatical fervor on the part of groups of physicians, welfare workers and legislators who preached the importance of training for the "unfortunates." These early reformers overlooked the failures of Itard and his associates to bring the performance of the retarded person up to the level of his contemporaries, and they maintained an optimistic view of the ultimate success of formal education in fitting all persons for a useful, independent life. Gradually, however, it was realized that, even with special training, a simplified environment was essential if the characteristic needs of developmentally retarded individuals were to be met. Such a program was facilitated by the construction and increasing use of standardized scales of intelligence, built upon the principles originally set forth by Alfred Binet.

As a legacy from this long history we have retained up to the present a variety of points of view toward developmental retardation, many of them outmoded or misleading. The undeniable limitations of the retarded person, for example, encourage some of us to emphasize his custodial care, even though less than 5 per cent of the total number of these individuals reside in institutions. The retarded person's obvious inadequacies in learning tempt us to explain retardation wholly in biological and hereditary terms, although our research results here are inadequate and conflicting. The widespread use of standardized intelligence scales in diagnosing developmental retardation often blinds us to more important aspects of the immature person's behavior.

Even the terms we use to designate retardation reflect our historical heritage. Most common among them are the labels "feeble-mindedness" and "mental deficiency"; these isolate and emphasize the inadequacies of the retarded person as demonstrated on intelligence tests. The general immaturity of the retarded person is acknowledged in the rarer terms "defectiveness" or "physical degeneracy"; and these carry with them the unfortunate misconception that retardation is the same thing as shameful inferiority. This error is perpetuated in the designation of "moral imbecility," which mistakenly brands the immature person as actually or imminently wayward.

---

[4] Seguin, E., *Idiocy: and its treatment by the physiological method.* (Reprint of 1866 ed. by Committee on Publication, Teachers College, Columbia University) Albany, N.Y.: Brandow Printing Co., 1907.

If we are to understand developmental retardation, we cannot single out intellect or emotion or anatomy or morals for isolated study, after the manner of nineteenth-century faculty psychologists. Neither can we begin by taking it for granted that retardation is shameful or degrading. Maturation, we have seen, is a complex and uneven process, which embraces the total behavior of the individual as he develops the skills required of him in his culture. Delay or failure in maturation is an equally complex and uneven process. The behavior characterizing developmental retardation is the behavior of a biosocially immature person whose attempts to master the techniques of his society fail oftener than they succeed.

Behavioral Characteristics of Developmental Retardation

Delay in maturation means delay in the acquisition of social skills. It means that the retarded person fails to achieve the level of biosocial competence shown by most others of his own age. To an untrained observer, the resulting behavior may appear peculiar, bizarre and even inexplicable. It is deceptively easy for the puzzled layman to conclude that the immature person *could* handle more complex situations if he only *would* — that his failure is a failure in effort or in training, rather than a genuine and pervasive developmental retardation. When consistent retardation is the basis for behavioral immaturity, we can best understand retarded behavior in terms of the characteristics of age groups younger than the one to which the person belongs. It is not sufficient, however, to be content with a description of such behavior as merely childlike. It is the discrepancy between the individual's level of performance and his own chronological age that gives developmental retardation its distinctive character.

Psychometric classifications

It is customary to describe retarded behavior in terms of achievement on standardized scales of intelligence. On many such scales, age is the measuring unit.[5] A test is located at a given point on the scale according to the chronological age of the representative children who succeed in passing it. Each test carries a value in terms of months, and the total score of all tests added together can then be expressed in years and months. This total score is called the *mental age* (MA). Whatever his own life age, the person who attains a mental age of, for example, seven years on such a scale is comparable at least in his level of test performance to an average seven-year-old child. The mental age signifies the *level* on the intelligence scale which the individual succeeds in reaching.

It is not enough, however, to describe performance on an intelligence scale

[5] This discussion follows the technique of scale construction employed by Terman, L. M. and Merrill, M. A., *Measuring intelligence.* Boston: Houghton Mifflin, 1937.

in terms of mental age alone.   There is clearly a vast difference between the child of seven years who earns a mental age of seven and an adult who earns a mental age of seven.   Hence, a more useful description of test performance is one that includes the individual's own *chronological age* (CA) in the statement of his final score.   The *intelligence quotient* (IQ), which is the ratio of attained mental age to chronological age,[6] is ordinarily employed for this purpose.   The IQ is interpreted as an indication of the *rate* of maturation at which the individual is progressing, according to the items which he passes on a particular intelligence scale.   When mental age and chronological age are equal, the value of the intelligence quotient is 100 and the rate of development, as defined by the test items, is average.   A child of seven whose mental age score is seven years thus achieves an intelligence quotient of 100, and this indicates that he is progressing at the usual rate.

An adult who attains a mental age score of seven years has obviously been progressing at a retarded rate.   The computation of the intelligence quotient for adults is complicated, however, by the fact that mental age scores on most of our tests do not continue to increase with age, in the general population, from a point somewhere between the ages of thirteen and eighteen.   Therefore, we cannot use the adult's own life age in calculating the IQ ratio.   In practice we ordinarily employ as the denominator in our IQ fraction the chronological age of fifteen for adult subjects.[7]   An adult with a mental age of seven would thus have an intelligence quotient of 47, which signifies a degree of retardation found in an exceedingly small proportion of the population.

It should be clearly understood, of course, that the scores derived from any standardized scale of intelligence reflect a person's achievement in only a very few selected samples of performance, carried out in restricted situations.   The items usually found on intelligence scales include such fragments of behavior as repeating digits, defining words, solving arithmetic problems, detecting absurdities and reproducing drawings.   The scores certainly provide us with an expedient, even though arbitrary scheme, but the scales themselves by no means encompass the scope of behavior which we have included in our definition of biosocial immaturity.   Indeed, performance on test items alone can no more define biosocial immaturity than can a refractive index define the complex process of seeing.

Developmental retardation gross enough to be considered pathological occurs in less than 2 per cent of the general population.[8]   This group includes

---

[6] The computing formula for the IQ is: $IQ = \dfrac{MA}{CA} \times 100$.

[7] The computing formula for the IQ for adult subjects is: $IQ = \dfrac{MA}{15} \times 100$.

[8] The exact percentage depends, of course, upon the definition of retardation which is used.   For discussions of this point, see Doll, E. A., "The feeble-minded child."   In Carmichael, L. (Ed.), *Manual of child psychology*.   New York: Wiley, 1946, pp. 863–867;

all those persons who score below IQ 70 on standardized intelligence scales. Since scores on these scales are assumed to occur in the population according to the normal distribution curve, the number of persons falling within the retarded group decreases with increasing severity of retardation. It is customary to subdivide pathological retardation further according to degree of severity — again on the basis of intelligence test performance.

We recognize three levels of increasingly severe retardation: *moron, imbecile* and *idiot*. Such levels, of course, do not represent discrete categories; they shade imperceptibly into one another. The line from the severe biosocial immaturity of profound idiocy to the maturity of the biosocially competent adult is a continuous one; we make our divisions arbitrarily and only for convenience. And while we can begin by classifying levels of retardation according to test score, we cannot arrive finally at an adequate understanding of immaturity in developmental retardation unless we also take into consideration each individual's behavior in all of its aspects.

Moron. The adult who on an intelligence scale, achieves a mental age of ten years and six months and an IQ of 70, shows developmental retardation gross enough to be considered pathological. He falls at the upper limit of the IQ range of 50 to 70 which defines the relatively mildly retarded *moron* group. Let us study the course of his maturation. We find him acquiring most of the skills which define maturity at much later ages than do most people. He learns toilet and feeding habits, walking and talking, eight or nine months later than is customary. When other children his own age are playing constructively and acquiring techniques of sharing in nursery school, he is still engaged in solitary, non-constructive play. He still needs constant parental supervision. He is still limited in his interpersonal relationships by immature speech and delayed motor development. At the age of five, when his contemporaries are entering kindergarten, he is ready only for play in nursery school with children much younger than he. He is eight and a half before he begins to acquire the preliminary skills necessary to learn to read and write. His maximum school achievement never goes beyond the sixth grade. As an adult in terms of his chronological age, he still shows the unmistakable signs of biosocial immaturity. He may hold a simple job within the security of continuous and sympathetic supervision. But in planning for his own future, in handling financial matters, in recreational choices and in interpersonal relationships, he still resembles persons of a much younger age than his own.

This is an example of immaturity resulting from consistent developmental retardation. Individuals who never exceed this level of maturity can and do become self-supporting, marry and rear families. They manage to maintain

Kanner, L., "Feeblemindedness: absolute, relative and apparent." *Nerv. Child*, 1949, vol. 7, pp. 365–397; Sarason, S. B., *Psychological problems in mental deficiency*. New York: Harper, 1949, pp. 1–42.

themselves in their society without such obvious difficulties that they incur legal punishment or require the simplified routine or protection of an institution. But these are hard-won gains. For a history of developmental retardation is typically a history of repeated failure in many of the most significant areas of life adjustment. We shall see that at this level of relatively mild retardation the immature person's attempts to achieve the expectations of his society are most likely to be rewarded only with increased frustration.

Imbecile. Let us compare the behavior of the adult described above with that of a more seriously retarded one — an adult who earns a mental age of six years and an IQ of 40 on a standardized intelligence scale. On the basis of his test performance, this person falls within the IQ range of 25 to 50, which defines the *imbecile* group. His developmental history is a story of severe delay and failure in biosocial maturation. He passes such milestones of development as talking and walking two or three years after most children do. Success at even the first grade of a conventionally organized school is difficult for him. As an adult he still lacks the basic skills of reading and writing, the techniques of effective interpersonal relationship and the vocational competence which would permit him to be self-sufficient in a job which the average person would consider undemanding. Under constant, direct, step-by-step supervision, he may complete simple tasks, follow uncomplicated patterns of recreation, care for himself, and even look after other persons less mature than he. Of course, these achievements are possible for an imbecile only within the carefully organized routine of simplified family or institutional living, where constant supervision can be adequately supplied.

Idiot. The most severe degree of developmental retardation is illustrated in the behavior of individuals who are designated as *idiots.* These are persons who never progress beyond the mental age of three, as defined on intelligence scales, and whose IQ is therefore below 25. Some idiots fail to achieve simple eye-hand coordinations; more fail to acquire bladder and bowel control or organized eating habits; and still more never, throughout their lives, learn walking and talking at the level where these skills can serve a useful purpose in biosocial interaction. Highly routinized environments may provide the behavior of individuals in this group with a certain degree of apparent organization; but for the most part the idiot is a completely dependent individual who requires unceasing custodial care.

Phases in biosocial maturation

Were we to stop, after merely cataloguing the performance of idiots, imbeciles and morons in test situations we would, in effect, be dismissing our problem of trying to understand developmental retardation before we had fairly confronted it. We cannot conclude simply that the person with a low MA score resembles the child of comparable chronological age. Indeed, even on the items which make up standardized intelligence scales, the achievement of the retarded individual differs markedly from that of the non-retarded.[9] When we look beyond the formal test situation, into areas which are significant in the maturing of any individual, we find again that the retarded person differs notably from the non-retarded child. Three examples, each representing an important aspect of biosocial maturation, will introduce us to these differences: (1) *play and role-taking;* (2) *behavioral rigidity;* and (3) *language and thinking.*

Play and the acquisition of role-taking skills. Play, whether spontaneous or organized, has consequences for maturation far beyond its superficial entertainment values. In his early solitary play, his increasing constructiveness in handling toys, his use of situations paralleling those of adult life — in activities shared with his peers from nursery school to adolescence — the child acquires techniques which help determine his level of behavioral maturity. He learns to organize his language and his thinking, and his anticipant attitudes and responses toward other persons, into interlocking systems of behavior, or *roles.*[10] The more practice he has in role-taking behavior the more easily can he anticipate the responses of others and his own, and come at last to share the perspectives common to his culture. In furnishing realistic practice in role-taking, play is an essential part of maturation. The child whose play is for any reason characteristically limited, stereotyped, or solitary, misses an important phase of biosocial development.

The developmentally retarded person, in his play as in his other activities, reveals his similarities to and his differences from the non-retarded child. Indeed, even grossly retarded idiots differ among themselves in their undirected activity. In one study of fifty-four adult idiots, for example,[11] at least thirteen different sorts of response were noted during a thirty-minute period of controlled observation. Generalized motor activity and repetitive mannerisms occurred most frequently, but instances of constructive use of toys and solitary talk and laughter were not uncommon.

When mildly retarded persons are compared with average children, both the individual differences in play preference and the differences between the immature and the non-retarded group appear still more clearly. In one such study,[12] fifty retarded children were compared with twenty-five non-retarded children of equal mental age. The investigators observed each child in his responses to sixteen different play materials. In much of their play behavior the two groups were similar. The immature girls, for example, reflected the

[9] Thompson, C. W. and Margaret, A., "Differential test responses of normals and mental defectives." *J. abn. soc. Psychol.,* 1947, vol. 42, pp. 285–293.

[10] See pages 114–118.

[11] Chipman, C. E., "Undirected activity of a group of adult idiots." *Amer. J. ment. Def.,* 1940, vol. 45, pp. 228–232.

[12] Horne, B. M. and Philleo, C. C., "A comparative study of the spontaneous play activities of normal and mentally deficient children." *J. genet. Psychol.,* 1942, vol. 61, pp. 33–46.

training and expectations of their culture as did average girls, by showing special interest in dolls and sewing materials. The retarded children differed from the non-retarded, however, in showing less preference for constructive toys and greater preference for materials demanding prescribed activities.

This tendency for the retarded person to adhere to routine and to non-imaginative activities in his play, appears even more strongly when creative fantasy is studied. The mildly retarded child, for example, may have his favorite movie star or his favorite character in fiction, but he seems to use these figures more as topics of conversation than as stimuli to new fantasy or as objects of genuine identification.[13] Retarded persons asked to make up stories about pictures are likely to give brief statements which stick closely to commonplace, everyday incidents, rather than to construct unusual or imaginative accounts.[14] The traditional myths and conventional fantasies, upon which young children in our culture are reared, seem to continue unchanged for longer periods of time in the behavior of the retarded person. One study revealed the persistence of belief in Santa Claus in a few retarded adult women whose mental ages were as high as eleven or twelve years.[15] In the play upon which maturation in part depends, the retarded person not only lags behind others of his own age, but is less constructive, less creative and less closely identified with his play objects than are comparable non-retarded children.

Rigidity of behavior. Practice in play and in role-taking skills, we have said, enables the child to shift his perspectives and thus share the viewpoints both of his contemporaries and of the adults in his society.[16] His flexibility in this regard is an important determiner of his maturity. Indeed, as we shall see, difficulty in establishing role-taking behavior may mean special vulnerability to behavior disorder.[17] Our description of the play and fantasy of retarded persons suggests that a restricted repertory of socially-defined roles, and an inability to shift easily from one situation to another, might prove to be characteristic of the biosocially immature. Perseveration and stereotyped behavior have long been considered the special mark of developmental retardation.[18] The research results, however, do not justify such a simple picture, as the following investigation demonstrates.

Kounin, starting with a specialized hypothesis regarding rigidity as a characteristic of personality organization, made a number of predictions as to the

---

[13] Abel, T. and Kinder, E., *The subnormal adolescent girl.* New York: Columbia University Press, 1942, pp. 20–21.

[14] Sarason, S. B., "The use of the Thematic Apperception Test with mentally defective children: I. A study of high grade girls." *Amer. J. ment. Def.*, 1943, vol. 47, pp. 414–421; "II. A study of high grade boys." *Amer. J. ment. Def.*, 1943, vol. 48, pp. 169–173.

[15] Ordahl, G., Keyt, N. L., and Wright, C., "The social competence of high-grade mental defectives as determined by self-report." *Amer. J. ment. Def.*, 1944, vol. 48, pp. 367–373.

[16] See pages 119–122.

[17] See pages 391–392, and 484–492.

[18] For a recent illustration, see Werner, H., "Abnormal and subnormal rigidity." *J. abn. soc. Psychol.*, 1946, vol. 41, pp. 15–24.

kinds of responses retarded persons would make in five experimental situations.[19] His subjects were three groups of individuals of equal mental age but varied chronological age — old retarded persons comprising one group, young retarded persons a second group, and non-retarded children a third group. By means of this experimental design, Kounin was able to assign any differences between the groups to the effect of chronological age and since mental age was constant, to the consequent effect of IQ. His five experimental tasks measured satiation in drawing activities, transfer of a learned motor skill from one situation to another, card sorting under simple and complex conditions, classification of objects into various categories, and shift from one principle of classifying objects to another. For each task he predicted that the retarded groups would respond in a characteristic way because of their greater rigidity.

Kounin's obtained results to a considerable degree verified his predictions. As contrasted with the non-retarded children, his retarded groups of equal mental age showed a greater willingness to keep on drawing simple figures, often continuing until the last of the pages on which they were working was filled. The retarded subjects classified cards according to the most obvious characteristics, and shifted to other categories of classification less often than did the average children. In the experiment requiring the transfer of motor response from one situation to another, however, the retarded groups made fewer errors than the non-retarded. This result Kounin interprets as demonstrating that the retarded person is less likely to be influenced by two situations simultaneously; he is, in other words, either entirely in one situation or entirely in the other.

It is obvious, from his behavior in these restricted laboratory tasks, that the retarded person is characteristically different from children of his own mental age. Having once started an activity, he continues working at it long after his non-retarded contemporaries are satiated. It is hard for him to change from one task to another, although after he has shifted he is unlikely to carry over his responses from the first situation into the second. Such laboratory findings as these reinforce the results of studies on play and fantasy. Both emphasize the fact that the retarded person is by no means an adult who behaves like a child. Instead, he is an adult who, partly because of limited facility in role-taking and in shifting perspectives, has special difficulty in establishing himself in his culture.

Language and thinking. There is no more critical phase in biosocial maturation than that involving language development.[20] Through the acquisition and use of the language symbols of his society, a child wins not only a means of

[19] Kounin, J. S., "Experimental studies of rigidity. I. The measurement of rigidity in normal and feeble-minded persons." *Char. and Pers.*, 1941, vol. 9, pp. 251–272; "II. The explanatory power of the concept of rigidity as applied to feeble-mindedness." *Char. and Pers.*, 1941, vol. 9, pp. 273–282.

[20] See pages 88–95.

communication with others, and a framework within which he organizes his interpersonal relationships. He earns also the tools by which are organized his reactions to himself, both in his public statements and in his private, unshared thinking.[21] Delay and failure in language development, therefore, mean delay and failure in an essential phase of behavioral maturation.

Developmental retardation, we have seen, carries with it retardation in the acquisition of language. The mildly retarded person is ordinarily slow in learning and using words; the grossly retarded idiot may never talk. One study of 2500 institutionalized immature persons indicated that only one-third of the group talked normally; moreover, the more severe was the retardation, the lower was the incidence of normal speech.[22] Both limitation in the extent of his vocabulary and special difficulty with abstract terms make language for the retarded person a troublesome tool.

The same immaturity which characterizes his language development describes also the acquisition of socially organized thinking. In the study of adult idiots mentioned earlier,[23] only twenty of the fifty-four subjects showed behavior from which the experimenter could infer the occurrence of thinking. In simple situations requiring the use of tools, in delayed responses and in detour behavior, however, a somewhat larger proportion of grossly retarded idiots succeeded in solving problems.[24]

Thinking which is organized through language behavior, on the other hand, seems to function in the *mildly* retarded person in ways that resemble the methods of the young child.[25] Many of the characteristics which Piaget [26] identified in the thinking of children can be found in the behavior of retarded adults. Because of his egocentric attitude, for example, the immature adult does not take account of the viewpoints of others around him. He has difficulty in integrating his detailed responses into a coherent organization. He is likely to attend to the immediate, concrete aspects of stimuli, at the expense of the more general.

We have seen, in discussing play and behavioral rigidity, that it is wholly inaccurate to picture the retarded individual as a childlike adult. The same is true of thinking. The differences between retarded adult and non-retarded child, as well as their implications for the achievement of maturity, become

[21] See pages 95–105.

[22] Sirkin, J. and Lyons, W. F., "A study of speech defects in mental deficiency." *Amer. J. ment. Def.,* 1941, vol. 46, pp. 74–80.

[23] Chipman, C. E., "Undirected activity of a group of adult idiots." *Amer. J. ment. Def.,* 1940, vol. 45, pp. 228–232.

[24] Aldrich, C. G. and Doll, E. A., "Problem solving among idiots: the use of implements." *J. soc. Psychol.,* 1931, vol. 2, pp. 306–336.

[25] For a summary of the characteristics of thinking in the mildly retarded person, see Abel, T. and Kinder, E., *The subnormal adolescent girl.* New York: Columbia University Press, 1942, pp. 11–17.

[26] Piaget, J., *The language and thought of the child* (2nd ed., trans. by M. Gabain). New York: Harcourt, Brace, 1932.

clear in studies of *animism* in thinking. Piaget early reported [27] that young children ascribed life to inanimate objects in attempting to account for everyday physical phenomena. The application of Piaget's techniques, in modified form, to retarded children yields evidence of similar animistic thinking in these subjects.[28] Retarded adults, however, show less childlike varieties of animism than do retarded children, even when mental age is held constant. Perhaps because he has lived longer among his contemporaries the immature adult is less susceptible to this distortion of thinking than are younger retarded persons. Nevertheless, he still resembles the non-retarded child more closely than he resembles the non-retarded adult.

What immature thinking means for the retarded person who confronts practical, everyday problems emerges most sharply in matters of ethical judgment. One investigator [29] told a group of mildly retarded girls a story in which a young girl, who had stolen a pie, fell through a bridge and into a stream while attempting to escape. The retarded girls were then asked to explain these two events. In a significantly large proportion of cases, the retarded subjects found a causal relationship between the theft of the pie and the collapse of the bridge: the girl fell into the water *because* she had stolen the pie. Examples of animism were also not uncommon: the bridge *knew* the girl had stolen the pie. It is such characteristically immature thinking as this that underlies the so-called poor judgment of the retarded person. Thus, his delay and failure in developing play and role-taking skills, his difficulty in shifting easily from one situation to another, and his immaturity in socially organized thinking, may transform commonplace events into special threats to him.

The levels of retardation which we have described carry with them immaturity in every area of biosocial development. The more extreme the behavioral immaturity, the more obvious it is to the casual observer. Paradoxically, the very conspicuousness of gross developmental retardation protects the most immature individual from many of the frustrations to which the more mildly retarded person is susceptible. For although he may lead a dependent, supervised existence, and become the target of pity, ridicule, contempt or hostility from his contemporaries, the severely retarded person is early recognized by those around him as one upon whom the usual demands of society cannot legitimately be made. Milder developmental retardation, on the other hand, is apt to be overlooked or misunderstood by others — a fact which helps determine, as we shall now see, the special vulnerability of mildly retarded persons to failure and frustration.

[27] Piaget, J., *The child's conception of physical causality* (Trans. by M. Gabain). New York: Harcourt, Brace, 1930.

[28] Russell, R. W., Dennis, W., and Ach, F. E., "Studies in animism: III. Animism in feebleminded subjects." *J. genet. Psychol.*, 1940, vol. 57, pp. 57–63; Werner, H. and Carrison, D., "Animistic thinking in brain-injured, mentally retarded children." *J. abn. soc. Psychol.*, 1944, vol. 39, pp. 43–62.

[29] Abel, T. M., "Moral judgments among subnormals." *J. abn. soc. Psychol.*, 1941, vol. 36, pp. 378–392.

Biosocial Matrix of Developmental Retardation

Maturation, whether delayed or accelerated, is always an irregular process. The rates of increase in height and weight never correlate perfectly with one another, nor with the rate of learning to grasp a cube, to climb stairs or to speak in sentences or to read.[30] This unevenness is at least as characteristic of retarded development as it is of normal growth. To be sure, there are instances of extreme immaturity where the person's bodily contours are as infantile as his behavior, just as there are examples of developmentally accelerated persons who exceed the statistical norms both in height and in weight. The idiot who spends his life in a crib, unable to support his head or focus his eyes, and unresponsive to light or sound, illustrates this dramatically pervasive retardation. But such examples of severe retardation are too rare to permit us to identify all immature individuals simply by their appearance. The "stupid look" supposedly typical of retarded persons is a fiction, perpetuated from an era when contemptuous attitudes made an understanding of biosocial immaturity impossible. This fiction played an important part in the problems presented by the following case.

A man, aged thirty-four years, came to the out-patient department of a large metropolitan hospital accompanied by his elder brother. The brother, after some hesitation, explained that the time had come to "make some plans" for the patient's future, and that the family was therefore seeking medical help. The patient himself was a friendly but rather diffident man who was dressed expensively, but unobtrusively, and in excellent taste. During physical, psychiatric and psychometric examinations he chatted pleasantly with the staff members, giving somewhat the impression of a quiet, considerate host at a party. He was meticulous in observing such social niceties as deferring to older persons, opening doors for others, and standing when a woman physician entered the room. He proved to be a well-developed man, in excellent health, but severely retarded in biosocial maturity. On standardized tests of intelligence, for example, his IQ was 66 and his mental age was nine years eleven months.

This patient was the youngest son of a socially prominent family in the community. His developmental history was one of consistent retardation. Because he was slow in walking and talking, and did not succeed in mastering the public school curriculum at the expected rate, he was early placed in a private training school, where social skills as well as school subjects were emphasized. He spent his vacation periods at home, and here every effort was made to help him play a significant role in the family circle. This arrangement continued until the patient was eighteen, after which time he lived permanently at home, where he was always included in every family activity. Large-scale social gatherings were frequent in the family, and at all these affairs the patient was present; he conversed with the guests and was accepted by them

[30] See pages 144–148.

on equal terms. Because his family considered it financially unnecessary, he had never been required to work or to learn a trade. The
result of his lifelong protection and his impractical social training was
that of providing him with an appearance of behavioral maturity so
deceptive as to raise an observer's expectations of the patient's behavior
far beyond what he could achieve. The patient's brother expressed
the situation nicely in his wry comment to the psychometrician when
he said, "He fooled you, didn't he?"

Shortly before this man came to the clinic, the artificial protection
which he had always received was suddenly interrupted by the death
of his father, and by the subsequent decision on the part of other family
members to make long-time plans for the patient's future. The financial
situation made expensive private care impossible, so it was decided
that he should enter a state-supported training school. When, however, this was suggested to the patient he wept, pleaded with the family,
and finally became so upset that he left the house and ran about the
neighborhood screaming in a severe temper outburst. This behavior
seemed to his relatives so unusual and inexplicable, and exposed them
so completely to the kind of neighborhood curiosity, gossip and hostility which they had thus far avoided by training and protecting the
patient, that they were driven to seek medical help. Even then, it
was only after months of discussion, argument, try-out and failure
that placement in a private nursing-home close to the patient's family
was finally agreed upon.

This case demonstrates the special problems faced by the individual
whose retardation is relatively mild and whose general appearance and
superficial behavior lead others to expect more of him than his level
of maturity permits. The inevitable change in living arrangements
necessitated by death in the family swept away the protection within
which this person's life had been organized, and represented to him a
wholesale rejection which he was unable to tolerate. His only techniques
for handling the threatening situation were those of weeping, pleading
and using simple, direct aggression — all characteristic of much younger
persons than he. His relatives' surprise, and their inability to understand his behavior, indicate clearly the unwarranted expectations to
which their own careful training and protection of the patient had led
them.

Social expectation

Parental attitudes. Long before most children are born, the web of expectations which they must meet is being woven by their parents. In talk, in private fantasy, in publicly communicated plans, the prospective parents define
the goals and the accomplishments, and even predict the appearance of their
unborn child. They watch for his first tooth, his first word, his first step, and
they report these achievements as proudly as they later report his school
grades, his playground victories and his first pay check. The exact nature of
these expectations differs widely in different families, but in general they are

based upon a conception — often inaccurate and inarticulate but none-the-less precise — of what most children should be like. The child for his part, early learns that if he meets the expectations of his parents he wins their approval and acceptance. If he achieves special success or developmental acceleration, as his parents define these, he may earn still further praise and more affection. If, on the other hand, he is slow in attaining maturity according to his parents' standards, he may become the focus of disappointment, a target for parental pressure, or an object of rejection and hostility.

The consistent failure of the retarded child to reach his parents' expectations constitutes one of the most serious sources of frustration for him.[31] To the parents it can mean only disappointment, embarrassment, anxiety and guilt. The reasons for these attitudes are deeply rooted in the fears and misconceptions about retardation still prevalent in our society. The birth of a retarded child represents to some persons proof of an hereditary "taint" in the family line even though, as we shall see, the evidence for hereditary causation of developmental retardation is far from convincing. Even the archaic fallacy that the pregnant mother's attitudes and behavior can influence her unborn child still persists in a variety of forms. The mother whose child is unwelcome to her, or is planned to be used as a weapon in marital battles, or comes to normal term despite her attempt at abortion, may interpret the retardation of her offspring as a punishment for her own feelings. The popular but inexact use of the term "moron" to designate antisocial behavior, and its supposed tie-up with violence and with sexual crimes, add to the parents' concern. Thus the weight of public ignorance and private guilt can make the burden borne by parents of a retarded child far heavier than the objective facts can ever justify.

The consequences of these parental attitudes are far-reaching. Not only does the retarded child fail to fit the pattern of his parents' expectations, but he is also in danger of becoming a symbol of hereditary defect and an instrument of reproach. The treatment he receives at home will depend upon his parents' flexibility in lowering their expectations of him and upon their understanding the significance of retardation as well as upon their own preferred patterns of adjustment. It is a rare parent who accepts as final even the most obvious signs of biosocial immaturity in his child. He is more apt to deny the possibility of retardation, to conceal it from himself and others, to watch for and overvalue the slightest indicators of increasing growth. He is likely to shop among practitioners for more optimistic diagnoses, and to undertake rigorous

---

[31] For a discussion of parental attitudes toward retarded children, see Sarason, S. B., *Psychological problems in mental deficiency.* New York: Harper, 1949, pp. 148–162; Rheingold, H. L., "Interpreting mental retardation to parents." *J. consult. Psychol.*, 1945, vol. 9, pp. 142–148; Stone, M. M., "Parental attitudes to retardation." *Amer. J. ment. Def.*, 1948, vol. 53, pp. 363–372. See especially the case cited in Merrill, M. A., *Problems of child delinquency.* Boston: Houghton Mifflin, 1947, pp. 177–179, summarized on pages 169–170.

but eventually hopeless programs of special training or medication. The resulting unrealistic atmosphere in which the child is reared provides a perfect formula for maladjustment, as the following case will demonstrate.

A large, physically mature boy of fourteen was brought to a juvenile court by police officers who reported that his theft of a bicycle was the latest in a long series of minor offenses. He had already been reprimanded for attempting to gain admission to theaters for a penny, for damaging trucks in his farm community, and for ordering and eating meals in restaurants without paying for them. His neighbors complained that he struck and injured other children, that he was noisy and disorderly in his general conduct, and that he seemed to be out of the control of his family.

In a routinized hospital environment, where he was placed for observation and further study, the boy was vigorous and energetic, seeking physical activity wherever he could find it. Left alone, he occupied himself by dismantling the furnishings of the room and then rearranging them. Whenever he associated with the other children in the hospital he became excited, dominated them by sheer size and strength, and had finally to be prevented from playing with them because of the very real possibility that he might injure them. Examinations indicated that he was taller and heavier than most fourteen-year-old boys, his muscular coordination was poor, and he was so severely retarded on standardized tests that he fell within the imbecile group.

It was impossible to obtain from the parents reliable evidence concerning this boy's early development. As the only son, he occupied the central position in a large family of girls. Consistently, in their reports, in their attitudes and in their general treatment of him, his parents and his sisters denied his retardation. Because the family was itinerant there were no school records available; but the parents reported that the boy had made steady school progress. The parents explained that their son was "just playing" when in his vigorous activity he knocked his mother down, or nearly choked to death another child. When court officers insisted that adequate plans be made for the boy, the family parried with the suggestion that he be sent on a short trip with an older sister. Over and over again the parents repeated their repudiation of their boy's diagnosis of retardation. His sister expressed the family attitude in her description of her brother: "He's so bright and so good — he's just like Jesus."

In this case are combined many of the factors which make the retarded person especially susceptible to maladjustment. The boy's general appearance and biological development were not inferior to those of most fourteen-year-olds. Other persons, therefore, expected him to demonstrate the biosocial maturity appropriate to his age and appearance. His failure to meet these expectations, obvious to most people, was completely overlooked by his parents. His vigorous, fumbling aggressive attempts to satisfy his needs won him consistent parental affection and approval, even when these attempts were recognized by others as signs of severe social maladjustment. Through his parents' mistaken attitude toward his retardation, the boy had acquired behavior which was almost certain to lead him into serious difficulty. The community, for its part, had no better solution to offer than that of institutionalizing him.

Expectations of others. Not only the parents, but also others associated with the retarded person, are likely to demand of him more than he can deliver. Those older brothers and sisters whose development proceeds at the usual rate serve as an ever-present standard for measuring his delayed growth. Younger siblings may surpass the retarded child in biosocial maturity and by their superiority provide a background against which his retardation is sharply silhouetted. Through expressed or implied comparisons with his brothers and sisters he gathers both what is expected of him, and the extent and importance of his own shortcomings.

When the retarded child begins playing with neighborhood children or starts school, we can rightly anticipate that demands will be made upon him which are as impossible for him to meet as those made upon him by his parents and his siblings. Unskilled in the techniques of playing, sharing and learning, which define mature competence at his age, he is apt to become both an unwelcome playmate and a troublesome student.[32] The story of his retardation usually precedes him into the neighborhood and the school, so that the labels "dull," "dumb" and "stupid," the vague, undeserved fears of other parents that he may harm their children, and the potential irritations of his teachers — all of these are there, ready and waiting for him. With failure once more guaranteed him, the child is likely to seek the companionship of children younger than himself, where competition is less threatening and at least some success can be attained. His strenuous attempts to meet his teachers' expectations are reflected in the occasional tendency of the retarded child to achieve more in classroom learning than would be predicted from his mental age scores. Regardless of his efforts, however, the retarded child in the conventionally organized schoolroom fights a losing battle. Increasingly often, as he grows older, he must bring home to his parents report cards that are poorer and poorer, and more announcements that he must repeat his school grade.

The demands of others that a retarded person live up to their expectations of him do not cease when his formal schooling is over. His employer is as likely to require too much of him as were his parents, his friends and his teachers.[33] His difficulty in learning vocational skills earns him at best the designation of "lazy" or "unreliable"; and if his employer's exasperation increases, he may become a convenient scapegoat who carries the blame for others' shortcomings as well as for his own. Rejection from military service,

[32] Abel, T. and Kinder, E., *The subnormal adolescent girl.* New York: Columbia University Press, 1942, pp. 48–74.
[33] Abel, T. and Kinder, E., *The subnormal adolescent girl.* New York: Columbia University Press, 1942, pp. 75–102.

inability to get and hold a job, economic and emotional failure in marriage, ineptness in caring for his children, misunderstanding and violation of minor legal regulations — these come to reinforce in adulthood the characterization of biosocial inadequacy which has long since been all too familiar to the retarded person.

Self-reactions in developmental retardation. Out of this matrix of expectation, comment and unspoken attitude, the characteristic self-reactions of the retarded person develop.[34] What others call him and expect of him he learns to call himself and to anticipate in his own behavior. A retarded man, for example, praised by an occupational therapist for his manual skill, replied simply, "Yes, we inferiors can do some things well." When the demands of his parents and his teachers are tinged with an obvious expectation of disappointment, his demands upon himself become equally pessimistic. Slowly, through the reactions of others to him, he builds up a picture of himself as a dull, incompetent, blameworthy individual for whom failure is almost a foregone conclusion. What then appears to the observer as unusual or peculiar behavior in the immature person may be only the techniques that he has developed for reducing his tensions of anticipated failure.

This point is made obvious by the studies of Sears [35] on the level of aspiration of academically unsuccessful children. Her subjects had already met consistent failure in reading and arithmetic for a three-year period. When, in an experimental situation, they were then required to state their goals — in terms of scores on achievement tests in reading and arithmetic — they responded by either sharply underestimating their level of attainment, or by unrealistically overestimating it. A control group of children, without a history of school retardation, characteristically set their goals close to their actual performance. The retarded children, well accustomed to failure on the tasks, protected themselves either by guaranteeing success through setting low goals, or by blunting the effect of failure through setting such high goals that success could not be expected of them.

It is the retarded person's superficial similarity to others, combined with his lifelong failure to achieve what society demands of him and his consequent self-reactions as an inadequate person, that makes his biosocial immaturity significant to the behavior pathologist. Delayed in biosocial development, but expected to behave in ways suitable for his age, he is in effect a member of two different groups at the same time. His appearance and casual behavior identify him with the statistical average and dictate the role which others require him to play. His consistent retardation, on the other hand, identifies him

---

[34] See pages 95–105.

[35] Sears, P. S., "Levels of aspiration in academically successful and unsuccessful children." *J. abn. soc. Psychol.*, 1940, vol. 35, pp. 498–536; "Levels of aspiration in relation to some variables of personality: clinical studies." *J. soc. Psychol.*, 1941, vol. 14, pp. 311–336.

with a younger, less mature group to which his actual behavior is more appropriate. The resulting conflict, between the socially expected and the individually possible roles, introduces the retarded person to endless possibilities of frustration.

Affectional Relationships and Emancipation

The path of behavioral maturation in our society carries all of us into certain situations which are likely to make special difficulty for everyone. When, in his slow progress along this path, the retarded person encounters these critical situations, he is apt still to be relatively unpracticed and incompetent in the skills he needs to be able to meet them successfully. Frustrations which no one can completely avoid are likely to present much graver problems to the biosocially immature individual than to the mature. The techniques which the retarded person uses in circumventing delay, thwarting and conflict in these areas represent his own, once learned and now preferred, patterns of adjustment. And these techniques, as we would expect, are usually more appropriate to his level of behavioral maturity than to his chronological age.[36] This is nowhere more clearly illustrated than in two examples of crucial points in biosocial maturation: (1) the development of affectional relationships; and (2) the development of an independent place among contemporaries.

Development of affectional relationships

Growth in affectional relationships, we have said,[37] depends upon progress from infantile dependence upon the mother, through extension of affectional attitudes outside the family, to adult heterosexuality culminating in marriage and parenthood. Severe retardation, sufficient to prevent the acquisition of eating and toilet habits, will obviously make impossible the development of those fundamental reciprocal relationships with others upon which affectional maturity is based. The grossly retarded idiot, for example, never advances beyond the phase of complete dependence upon others for the satisfaction of his simplest needs; consequently he can seldom if ever take genuinely reciprocal attitudes toward others. The less severely retarded person may acquire skills which permit friendship, chumship and heterosexual relationships; but his immature reactions and the unjustified expectations of his contemporaries reduce sharply his possibilities of success. For him, the affectional field within which these complex relationships develop is one of unrealized expectation, threatened rejection and impending failure.

---

[36] Lurie, L. A., "Conduct disorders of intellectually subnormal children: a study of correlations of intelligence levels of eighty to eighty-nine to behavior disorders of children." *Amer. J. Psychiat.*, 1937, vol. 93, pp. 1025–1038; Stogdill, R. M., "Some behavior adjustment techniques in use with mentally retarded children." *J. except. Child.*, 1938, vol. 5, pp. 25–30; Altus, W. D., "The adjustment of Army illiterates." *Psychol. Bull.*, 1945, vol. 42, pp. 461–476.
[37] See pages 137–143.

Delay in affectional development has this important consequence for the retarded person — that he is for a longer time than usual a recipient rather than a participant in social interaction. Prolonged dependence upon his parents for simple need-satisfaction postpones his adoption of a reciprocal role. His first steps in emancipation from the family lead him directly into contact with others, who are inevitably more practiced in social skills than he. To participate on equal terms with his nursery-school contemporaries in play, with his schoolmates in games and finally with his fellow-adolescents in the activities leading to adult heterosexual adjustment, demands greater maturity than he has achieved. Both his own immaturity and the pressures of his contemporaries prevent him from full participation in affectional relationships.

What the role of recipient means for the retarded person is clearly demonstrated in studies of friendship and chumship. Biosocially immature children are more likely to follow than to lead in organized play groups. Their schoolmates rarely choose them for participation in games, or single them out as possessing desirable or enviable traits. In restricted, institutionalized surroundings they are most effective when they can use their supervisors and teachers as parent-surrogates. There is some evidence that close partnerships between a younger and an older retarded person represent this same tendency to perpetuate the early role of dependence upon parents. Even at adolescence, the mildly retarded individual shows more concern over rules and regulations, and greater desire to conform, than do his contemporaries.[38]

The developmentally retarded person who arrives at the physiological maturity which helps define puberty does so with inadequate skill in taking reciprocal attitudes, an uncertain emancipation from his early affectional ties, and an exaggerated desire for conformity with his contemporaries. It is not surprising, therefore, that failure to progress from preparatory adolescent behavior to full heterosexual maturity is more common than success. A good many retarded persons remain in the parental home throughout their lives, dependent upon parents and siblings for affectional support.

Other retarded persons, like some persons who do not show developmental retardation, respond to the complexities of adolescence with techniques so inappropriate as to be considered antisocial. The variety of unsuitable techniques is wide, and each may represent in the retarded person, as well as in the non-retarded, a preferred pattern of adjustment. Because of his biological maturity, his suggestibility and his difficulty in anticipating the consequences of his behavior, however, the retarded adolescent is particularly susceptible to sex delinquency.[39] This susceptibility, far from being a sign of moral deprav-

[38] Abel, T. and Kinder, E., *The subnormal adolescent girl.* New York: Columbia University Press, 1942, pp. 22–26; Cummings, S. B., Jr., "The 'kid-friend' relationship." *Amer. J. Orthopsychiat.*, 1941, vol. 11, pp. 725–730.

[39] For discussions of this point, see Abel, T. and Kinder, E., *The subnormal adolescent girl.* New York: Columbia University Press, 1942, pp. 139–146; Merrill, M. A., *Problems of child delinquency.* Boston: Houghton Mifflin, 1947, pp. 158–180.

ity or degeneracy, is a consequence of the same discrepancy between expected and possible roles which characterize his behavior in other areas.

A relatively few retarded persons achieve adult heterosexuality which culminates in marriage and parenthood.[40] Their success in maintaining adequate affectional relationships at this level depends heavily upon the nature and complexity of the demands made upon them. Delay and failure in learning to take reciprocal attitudes and in achieving emancipation predispose them to a lifelong role of affectional immaturity. A level of maturity represented by successful marriage and parenthood is rarely attained by the developmentally retarded individual.

Development of emancipation

The same factors that prevent the retarded person from achieving affectional maturity prevent him likewise from establishing himself as an independent, contributing individual in the society of his contemporaries. Delay in emancipation from his family, failure to acquire the techniques necessary for mature self-determination, and the inevitable competition with others more advanced than he, make the role of participating member of his community exceedingly difficult. Indeed, a completely independent role may sometimes have disastrous results. Some idiots, for example, are so severely retarded that, left to themselves they cannot possibly defend themselves from the everyday hazards of rain and snow, of sharp knives and hot stoves, of steep stairways and oncoming automobiles. But even the mildly retarded person, who is able to protect himself from such dangers, cannot always protect himself from the consequences of unattainable demands in school and on the job.

The school is often the agent which confirms irrevocably both the immature person's self-reactions of inadequacy and his parents' unwelcome suspicions that he may be retarded. Through its clearcut standards of success and failure, its demands for even progress in academic subjects, and its insistence upon increasing independence — all based upon the hypothetical average child — the conventionally organized public school provides a scale from which anyone can read the degree of the retarded person's limitations.[41] The point at which the suggestion of retardation becomes a publicly demonstrated fact depends, of course, upon the degree of an individual's immaturity. The imbecile, we have said, rarely succeeds at first- or second-grade school work. Less severely retarded persons, on the other hand, may progress slowly through primary and elementary grades, and even into high school, before repeated failure results finally in the termination of their formal schooling.

[40] See, for example, Kaplan, O. J., "Marriage of mental defectives." *Amer. J. ment. Def.*, 1944, vol. 48, pp. 379–384; Mickelson, P., "The feeble-minded parent: a study of 90 cases." *Amer. J. ment. Def.*, 1947, vol. 51, pp. 644–653; Muench, G. A., "A follow-up of mental defectives after eighteen years." *J. abn. soc. Psychol.*, 1944, vol. 39, pp. 407–418.

[41] See Abel, T. and Kinder, E., *The subnormal adolescent girl.* New York: Columbia University Press, 1942, pp. 48–74.

The retarded person, in his school achievement as in many other areas of his life, resembles those who are younger than he. His educational age, derived from standardized tests of academic attainment, is characteristically closer to his mental age than to his chronological age.[42] Such formal testimony of educational retardation, however, has little meaning unless it is translated into a statement of competence in the social skills upon which an independent role in our society depends. An educational age of eight years in a retarded adult, for example, means severely limited facility with reading, writing, spelling and arithmetical operations, as these are taught in the conventional public school classroom. But it also means difficulty in making change on shopping trips, in following current happenings in newspapers and magazines, in writing social and business letters, and even in reading such essential labels as "danger," "beware" and "poison."

Furthermore, limitation in school achievement means spending school hours in the company of younger, smaller children, among whom the retarded child can often establish his independent role only through the dubious techniques of physical domination. If he succeeds in outgrowing the seats in his classroom, he may receive on this questionable basis a promotion to more and more severe competition, with children who have already outstripped him in biosocial maturation. Lacking many of the skills that are preliminary to normal social operations and interpersonal relationships, he is finally obliged to end his schooling without having securely established himself as an independent, contributing individual among his contemporaries. It is from this inadequate and uncertain base that he goes forth to find a job.

The success with which the retarded person learns and practices vocational skills that permit him to hold a job depends upon many factors. The appropriateness of his job to his developmental level, the extent of his immaturity, the protection and guidance which his employer can give him, and the attitudes of his family — as well as the meaning and importance of a vocation to him as an individual — all help determine his achievement of independent status as a wage earner. The jobs which can be successfully performed by retarded adults range from simple domestic tasks and freight-handling, which are suitable for the imbecile, to certain machine operations and sales activities which have proved suitable for the mildly retarded moron.[43]

But behavioral maturation to the level of vocational independence involves

[42] Bradway, K. P., "Academic achievement in a group of mentally retarded subjects." *Proc. Amer. Ass. ment. Def.*, 1939, vol. 44, pp. 154–162.

[43] For information concerning vocational possibilities for persons of varying degrees of developmental retardation see: Burr, E. T., "Adapting the feebleminded to industry." *Indust. Psychol.*, 1927, vol. 2, pp. 132–138; Burr, E. T., "How a thousand girls were trained for self-support." *Personnel J.*, 1932, vol. 10, pp. 344–346; Burr, E. T., "The vocational adjustment of mental defectives." *Psychol. Clinic*, 1931, vol. 20, pp. 55–63; Abel, T. and Kinder, E., *The subnormal adolescent girl*. New York: Columbia University Press, 1942, Chapter 4; Louttit, C. M., *Clinical psychology*. New York: Harper, 1947, pp. 226–227.

far more than a mechanical matching of IQ to job. A three-year study of eighty-four retarded adolescent girls from a New York City industrial school who were placed in the women's garment trades, for example, reports that only half the girls succeeded in working steadily for the first month. However, the proportion of successful adjustments increased steadily during the three-year period.[44] This study showed that job failures were related to degree of retardation, to lack of guidance by the employer in the initial adjustment to industry, to rejection of the retarded girl by her family, and to special rigidity and persistent effort, on the girl's part, toward an inappropriate vocation. Job failure, in other words, was the consequence of the complex pattern of limitation, expectation and special vulnerability to frustration which defines biosocial immaturity.

Although the pervasive effects of behavioral immaturity are the important obstacles to job independence, the particular social and economic milieu in which the retarded person seeks employment plays no small part in his success. Parents who consider simple jobs beneath their children's status, employers who regard the retarded adult as peculiar, and the unsympathetic competition of fellow-workers, reduce the chances of successful adjustment still further. Of course, when jobs are plentiful and help is badly needed, as in a national emergency, the retarded person stands a better chance than usual of attaining vocational independence.[45] Full participation as a contributing member of society, however, with all the hazards of solitary, independent living, of indifference and unconcern from one's contemporaries, and of complex, seemingly irrational networks of wage scales, piece rates, union rules and time clocks, often pushes the immature adult beyond the threshold of his frustration tolerance. The following case illustrates the consequence of repeated, unsuccessful efforts at achieving vocational independence in complex urban surroundings.

> An attractive young woman of twenty-four was brought to a state psychiatric hospital by members of a social agency who considered her seriously disturbed. The eldest of an impoverished rural family of six children, the patient had early showed indication of consistent developmental retardation. She had completed the eighth grade in her country school at the age of eighteen; standardized tests located her in the lower moron group. When her mother died, the patient was left without

[44] Abel, T. M., "A study of a group of subnormal girls successfully adjusted in industry and the community." *Amer. J. ment. Def.*, 1940, vol. 45, pp. 66–72.

[45] Butler, F. O., "Mental defectives in military service and wartime industries." *Amer. J. ment. Def.*, 1945, vol. 50, pp. 296–300; Haskell, R. H. and Strauss, A. A., "One hundred institutionalized mental defectives in the armed forces." *Amer. J. ment. Def.*, 1943, vol. 48, pp. 67–71; Hegge, T. G., "The occupational status of higher-grade mental defectives in the present emergency: a study of parolees from the Wayne County Training School at Northville, Michigan." *Amer. J. ment. Def.*, 1944, vol. 49, pp. 86–98; Weaver, T. R., "The incidence of maladjustment among mental defectives in military environment." *Amer. J. ment. Def.*, 1946, vol. 51, pp. 238–246.

supervision. She was, accordingly, placed in a state training school, but at the end of two years her father insisted upon her release. The girl tried to get and hold jobs which would enable her to contribute to the meager family income. Her vocational history, however, was characterized by frequent changes in job, irritability toward her employers, and increasing anxiety over her inability to help out at home. The housework and maid-service which she performed at tourist homes throughout the state brought her into contact with male guests, and their behavior toward her ranged from casual flirtation to open sexual advances. During this period the patient suffered from repeated gastrointestinal distress which her physicians were inclined to relate to the circumstances of her mother's death.

In a desperate attempt to achieve the vocational independence and security upon which her family's economic welfare largely depended, the patient went to a city, where she obtained a job as night waitress in a short-order restaurant, and took a room at a girls' boarding house. Here she found the pace of city life increasingly difficult. There were the responsibilities of saving her earnings to pay her rent, of providing herself with food and of contributing to her family's support, and the problems raised by the continued advances of some of her male customers at the restaurant.

She returned to her room alone early one morning and went to bed; but shortly afterward she became convinced that there was a man in her room. Her search failed to reveal anyone, but the conviction remained. Her loud complaints brought her neighbors, the proprietors of the boarding house, and finally the police, who could neither find the supposed intruder nor convince her that she was safe. She remained so excited and terrified that medical help was called for and she was hospitalized, still insisting that men were following her and that she could see them. In the hospital she became more calm; but it was agreed that she could not return to the complex urban setting. She was eventually returned to the simplified, protected environment of the training school, away from the demands of adult vocational independence, which had proved intolerable and damaging to her.

This case illustrates a degree of failure in achieving an independent status in an environment peopled by mature adults, which is not uncommon for developmentally retarded persons. Delay and ineptness in learning and maintaining the role of participator among contemporaries — from the first contacts with siblings and nursery school playmates to the competition with adults for jobs — make each new step toward independence a new threat of frustration. We have already seen the disturbing effects of necessary changes in living arrangements upon an overtrained, protected immature man.[46] The situation is further complicated by the unusually early decline in efficiency, as measured by standardized tests,[47] and by the premature signs of biological

[46] See pages 166–167.

[47] See, for example, Kaplan, O., "Mental decline in older morons." *Amer. J. ment. Def.*, 1943, vol. 47, pp. 277–285; Kuhlmann, F., "The results of repeated mental re-examinations of 639 feeble-minded over a period of ten years." *J. appl. Psychol.*, 1921, vol. 5, pp. 195–

ageing,[48] which characterize the developmentally retarded individual. And finally, the reduction in efficiency, the insecurity and the uncertainty which attend ageing and senility among non-retarded persons,[49] are intensified in the older retarded person who has never established himself firmly in his culture. It is clear that any problem of biosocial maturation for the non-retarded person presents exaggerated difficulties for the retarded one.

Determinants of Developmental Retardation

The intricate interweaving of biological growth, opportunity for learning, social expectation and personal frustration, which characterizes the process of biosocial maturation, makes it virtually impossible to identify some one exclusive determinant of developmental retardation. Because a certain level of biological development must precede the completion of many early maturity sequences, however, most students in this field have selected biological factors as a starting-point for investigation. The impressive finality of the retarded person's limitations — his apparent inability, even under the most favorable environmental circumstances, to learn as others of his age learn — has directed the search for causes of retardation toward the relatively stable biological properties of the organism.

The most popular starting-point, in the hunt for biological correlates, has been the gross structure of the central nervous system. For the past half-century, striking but relatively isolated examples of brain pathology in severely retarded persons have been energetically put forward as proof that developmental retardation is the result of cerebral maldevelopment. There are well-authenticated cases of severe immaturity in which post-mortem studies establish low brain weight, decrease in number of brain convolutions, absence of important brain structures, decreased number and incomplete development of neurons in the brain.[50] Unfortunately for the investigator seeking one hypothesis to cover all cases, however, these findings do not support a unified biological explanation of developmental retardation. Indeed, a nice correspondence between brain structure and biosocial maturity is the rare exception rather than the general rule. We find it occurring typically among the clinical types

224. That the early decline may be related to hospitalization is indicated by the findings of Cutts, R. A. and Lane, M. O'K., "The effect of hospitalization on Wechsler-Bellevue subtest scores by mental defectives." *Amer. J. ment. Def.*, 1947, vol. 51, pp. 391–393; Wright, C., "The nature of the decline of performance abilities in adult morons as compared with that of normal adults." Unpublished doctoral dissertation, Stanford University, 1943.

[48] For a review of studies on this point, see Kaplan, O. J., "The aged subnormal." In Kaplan, O. J. (Ed.), *Mental disorders in later life*. Stanford University, Calif.: Stanford University Press, 1945, pp. 333–347.

[49] See pages 546–555.

[50] For a review of these findings see Tredgold, A. F., *A textbook of mental deficiency*. Baltimore: Wm. Wood and Co., 1937, Chapter 6.

of severely retarded persons who constitute an exceedingly small minority of the total retarded group. To extend our search for the reasons underlying developmental retardation beyond the study of brain pathology is to open ourselves immediately to a consideration of complex and interrelated aspects of behavior which still elude analysis. This is nowhere more forcefully demonstrated than in the studies of hereditary factors in developmental retardation.

Heredity

The problem of the inheritance of developmental retardation is a part of the more inclusive problem of the relative importance of heredity and environment as determiners of human behavior. We have seen that maturation proceeds within an enormously complicated field of interacting persons and cultural objects, a field in which there is perpetually change — in attitude and fulfillment. An attempt to consider any one of these variables separately will be not only unrealistic but impossible. Consequently our evidence regarding the importance of hereditary factors in developmental retardation is presumptive rather than direct; and like all presumptive evidence it leaves the impartial student uncertain of his conclusions and compels him to suspend his judgment. It is generally accepted that developmental retardation to some extent "runs in families";[51] estimates of the frequency of familial retardation, however, range from 33 per cent to 75 per cent of all cases of developmental retardation.[52] Greater-than-chance frequency of retardation within a family does not, of course, establish an hereditary etiology, since the preferred patterns of behavior and techniques of teaching early skills, which are passed on through learning from generation to generation, also "run in families." We can be certain of the hereditary determination of developmental retardation, at most, only if the frequency of its actual occurrence in a family strain matches the theoretical frequency predicted from known genetic relationships.

The comparison of expected with observed frequencies of developmental retardation, within a given family line, has so far aroused more speculation than careful investigation. The hypothesis that retardation is genetically transmitted, as a recessive characteristic, is the one that has been most com-

[51] Goddard, H. H., *The Kallikak family: a study in the heredity of feeble-mindedness.* New York: Macmillan, 1912; Penrose, L. S., "A clinical and genetic study of 1280 cases of mental defect." *Privy Coun., Med. Res. Coun., Special Rep. Ser.,* no. 229. London: His Majesty's Stationery Office, 1938; Tredgold, A. F., *A textbook of mental deficiency.* Baltimore: Wm. Wood and Co., 1937; Town, C. H., *Familial feeble-mindedness: a study of one hundred and forty-one families.* Buffalo, N.Y.: Foster and Stewart, 1939.

[52] Myerson, A. (Chmn.), *Eugenical sterilization: a reorientation of the problem.* (By the Committee of the American Neurological Association for the Investigation of Eugenical Sterilization.) New York: Macmillan, 1936; Hopwood, A. T., Kirk, C. C., and Keiser, F. L., "The hereditary factor in mental deficiency." *Amer. J. Psychiat.,* 1941, vol. 98, pp. 22–28; Penrose, L. A., "A study of the inheritance of intelligence: the analysis of 100 families containing subcultural mental defectives." *Brit. J. Psychol.,* 1933, vol. 24, pp. 1–19.

monly entertained.[53] Evidence which tends to support this hypothesis is slight, however, and comes from studies of two extremely rare sorts of developmental retardation which are complicated by sensory and motor difficulties: *amaurotic family idiocy* [54] and *phenylpyruvic oligophrenia.*[55] Many geneticists deny the possibility that developmental rate in the human organism could be a unit character which follows the generally accepted patterns of transmission and compares with such familiar traits as eye color and albinism.[56] In the face of meager and conflicting evidence, we are obliged to conclude that although developmental retardation may "run in families," we are uncertain of the frequency with which familial retardation occurs; and, if it is genetically determined, we are ignorant of the mechanics of its determination.

Birth injury

In a small number of cases, complications and accidents during the birth process result in intracranial lesions which may be associated with developmental retardation.[57] Such conditions as cranial distortion, occurring when the infant is presented in unusual positions in the birth canal, the resulting gross and punctate cerebral hemorrhages and temporary cerebral anemia, are frequently cited as sources of retardation. As in the case of hereditary factors, however, no simple cause-effect relationship can be demonstrated here.

In a study of over 20,000 retarded children, for example, Dayton found that unusual conditions during labor and delivery were no more characteristic of developmentally retarded children than of the general Massachusetts population.[58] About 10 per cent of all developmentally retarded persons are classifiable as birth-injured, and among these such motor difficulties as spasticity

[53] See, for example, Davenport, C. B., "Causes of retarded and incomplete development." *Proc. Amer. Ass. ment. Def.*, 1936, vol. 60, pp. 208–214; and Jervis, G. A., "The genetics of phenylpyruvic oligophrenia." *J. ment. Sci.*, 1939, vol. 85, pp. 719–762. For a discussion of the Rh-factor as a determinant, see Cook, R. C., "The Rh gene as a cause of mental deficiency." *J. Hered.*, 1944, vol. 35, pp. 133–134; Snyder, L. H., Schonfeld, M. P., and Offerman, E. M., "The Rh factor and feeble-mindedness." *J. Hered.*, 1945, vol. 36, pp. 9–10.

[54] Sachs, B., "On arrested cerebral development with special reference to its cortical pathology." *J. nerv. ment. Dis.*, 1887, vol. 14, pp. 541–553; "A family form of idiocy." *N.Y. State J. Med.*, 1896, vol. 63, pp. 697–703.

[55] Frazier, R. L., "Phenylpyruvic amentia." *Amer. J. ment. Def.*, 1947, vol. 51, pp. 577–586; Jervis, G. A., "Phenylpyruvic oligophrenia." *Arch. Neurol. Psychiat.*, 1937, vol. 38, pp. 944–963.

[56] For a discussion of the problems involved here, see Morgan, T. H., "The mechanism and laws of heredity." In Murchison, C. (Ed.), *Handbook of general experimental psychology.* Worcester, Mass.: Clark University Press, 1934, pp. 109–154.

[57] For investigations of the characteristics of birth-injured retarded persons, see Doll, E. A., Phelps, W. M., and Melcher, R. T., *Mental deficiency due to birth injuries.* New York: Macmillan, 1932; Strauss, A. A. and Lehtinen, L. E., *Psychopathology and education of the brain-injured child.* New York: Grune and Stratton, 1948; Wallin, J. E. W., *Children with mental and physical handicaps.* New York: Prentice-Hall, 1949.

[58] Dayton, N. A., "Abnormal labor as an etiological factor in mental deficiency and other associated conditions: analysis of 20,473 cases." *New Eng. J. Med.*, 1930, vol. 203, pp. 398–413.

and athetosis ordinarily complicate the picture of retardation. Birth injury, with or without these motor signs, may be found in the histories of consistently and severely retarded persons. But birth injury is also found in individuals who do not begin to lag behind their contemporaries in development until late in childhood, and in average and even in developmentally accelerated adults.

Endocrine dysfunction

The complicated interrelationships of the various ductless glands in the human organism provide endless opportunities for speculation on the effect of endocrine dysfunction upon behavioral development. The demonstrated correspondence between the function of certain glands of internal secretion and physiological maturation has encouraged investigators to explain developmental retardation in terms of hypofunctioning of some part of the endocrine system. Endocrine dysfunction has been reported in 17 per cent of retarded children;[59] but the absence of comparable statistical data for a non-retarded group prevents adequate interpretation of these results.

The search for simple cause-effect relationships in this area has unearthed only one extremely rare form of retardation: *cretinism*. Occurring in perhaps 0.2 per cent to 0.3 per cent of all institutionalized retarded persons, this condition is associated with thyroid hypofunctioning; absence or severe atrophy of the thyroid gland has been verified by post-mortem examinations.[60] The typical cretin differs from other persons not only in his retardation to the idiot or imbecile level but also in gross anatomical ways. Coarse and scanty hair, an apparently low forehead, wide separation of the eyes, and somewhat infantile bodily proportions testify to the pervasive effect of low metabolic activity upon bodily growth. Although early and continued treatment with thyroid substance may produce progress in development, the over-all biosocial immaturity of the cretin ordinarily necessitates protection and supervision throughout his life.[61]

Prenatal and early infantile factors

During the approximately nine-month period of gestation, the prenatal organism is supported and maintained in physiological contact with the mother. This sustaining relationship, essential to the life of the unborn child, may also provide conditions for developmental retardation. Two easily identifiable but rare examples of retarded development are to be found in

[59] Kimball, O. P. and Marinus, J. C., "The relation of endemic goiter to mental deficiency." *Ann. Int. Med.*, 1930, vol. 4, pp. 569–577.

[60] Bronstein, I. P. and Milles, G., "Hypothyroidism and cretinism in childhood: IV. Post-mortem reports on two cretins." *Amer. J. Dis. Child.*, 1935, vol. 49, pp. 1564–1569.

[61] Gesell, A., Amatruda, C. S., and Culotta, C. S., "Effect of thyroid therapy on the mental and physical growth of cretinous infants." *Amer. J. Dis. Child.*, 1936, vol. 52, pp. 1117–1138.

hydrocephalus and *microcephalus;* these occur once in two or three hundred cases. In hydrocephalus there is increased production of cerebrospinal fluid which may result in increased intracranial pressure, and consequent diminution or destruction of cerebral cortex. Hydrocephalus, like many of the other anatomical conditions found in retarded persons, may occur in individuals classified as idiot, imbecile or moron; but it is also found in persons who are not retarded at all. In microcephalus, on the other hand, there is an apparent arrest of cerebral development at the level of the fourth or fifth intrauterine month, the cerebral hemispheres remain small and there is a correspondingly small cranium. The microcephalic person is typically severely retarded in biosocial maturation.

If the mother is suffering from syphilis and is not treated for it during pregnancy, the fetus may be infected *in utero,* and signs of lues (syphilis) may then be present at birth. Neither the frequency of congenital lues nor its relationship to developmental retardation is well understood. In a study of over 9,000 retarded school children, Dayton [62] found positive Wassermann reactions in only 5.4 per cent; a control group of over 16,000 non-retarded children included 4.3 per cent with positive Wassermann reactions. Moreover, an intensive study of a selected sample of the retarded persons with signs of lues suggested that in at least half the cases there were other factors which might account for the developmental retardation present. Juvenile paresis developed on the basis of congenital lues is generally regarded as closely related to developmental retardation; one study indicates [63] that about 40 per cent of a large group of juvenile paretics were retarded. This disease, however, appears in only 1.5 to 2 per cent of children with congenital lues.

Not only prenatal infection, but also infection of the central nervous system occurring early in infancy, may result in developmental retardation. Again, however, the extent and importance of these conditions is by no means perfectly understood. It has been estimated [64] that 11 per cent of institutionalized retarded persons have suffered brain infection. But there are difficulties in the way of obtaining accurate information concerning early infantile disease many years after its presumed onset; and the accuracy of such figures, therefore, is questionable. Meningococcal meningitis, polioencephalitis and epidemic encephalitis, in which the brain may be involved early in the course of development, are usually considered possible sources of consistent biosocial immaturity. In the presence of conflicting statistics, inadequate histories and alternative possibilities, it is safe to conclude only that prenatal and early

[62] Dayton, N. A., "Congenital syphilis as a cause of mental deficiency." *Boston Med. Surg. J.*, 1925, vol. 193, pp. 668–673.

[63] Menninger, W. C., "Juvenile paresis." *Menn. Clinic Monogr. Series*, no. 1. Baltimore: Williams and Wilkins, 1936.

[64] Tredgold, A. F., *A textbook of mental deficiency.* Baltimore: Wm. Wood and Co., 1937, p. 259.

infantile influences explain unequivocally an extremely small proportion of cases of developmental retardation.

The scarcity of information and the uncertainty of our knowledge concerning the hereditary, germinal, endocrine and infectious conditions associated with mental retardation, are demonstrated with especial emphasis in the clinical type of retardation known as *mongolism*. This condition occurs in perhaps 5 or 10 per cent of institutionalized retarded persons, and involves such characteristic anatomical features as apparently slanted, protruding eyes and unusual skull formation, as well as immaturity at the idiot or imbecile level. An extraordinary variety of attacks on the problem of the etiology of mongolism has so far yielded no clear-cut result.[65] Germ plasm defect, advanced age in the mother, anomalies of fertilization, decreased viability of the ovum, congenital syphilis, abnormalities of uterine structure, and multiple endocrine dysfunction have all been set forth as possible causes. Thus, even in the rare but relatively well described clinical types of developmental retardation, the successful isolation of etiological factors still eludes the careful investigator.

Lack of opportunity to learn. Biosocial maturation, we have emphasized, depends upon the progressive acquisition of the skills that prepare an individual to behave in ways appropriate to his age and culture. Our previous consideration of the biological factors which may retard learning makes it obvious that we cannot afford to ignore the factor of lack of opportunity for learning as a possible determinant of developmental retardation. It is conceivable, on hypothetical grounds, that special restriction and extreme overprotection during the early years of development might produce consistent delay and even failure in achieving biosocial maturity.[66] If a child were reared in rigidly circumscribed surroundings, isolated from other persons, prevented from walking and talking, and deprived of school opportunities and interpersonal relationships, he might well reach adulthood a retarded, immature individual. We know, however, that when conditions approaching deprivation of this severity are instituted temporarily, as a part of an experimental situation, the retardation which occurs will speedily disappear again after ordinary opportunities for learning are reinstated.[67]

Lifelong deprivation which is comparable with that temporarily created in the laboratory cannot, of course, be produced for experimental purposes. Hence, it is highly unlikely that we shall ever have a fair test of the hypothesis that persistent retardation results from unfavorable learning opportunities. Our information concerning the significance of opportunity in advancing or

[65] Sherman, M., *Intelligence and its deviations.* New York: Ronald, 1945, Chapter 10.
[66] See pages 151–152.
[67] See, for example, Dennis, W., "The effect of restricted practice upon the reaching, sitting and standing of two infants." *J. genet. Psychol.*, 1935, vol. 47, pp. 17–32; Dennis, W., "Infant development under conditions of restricted practice and of minimum social stimulation: a preliminary report." *J. genet. Psychol.*, 1938, vol. 53, pp. 149–158.

retarding biosocial maturation must accordingly come from two sources, neither of which is wholly satisfactory: (1) from studies of persons who, through some accident of environment, have lived long in extremely deprived circumstances; and (2) from studies of limited aspects of behavior in persons reared in both deprived and favorable atmospheres. Investigations of the first sort include studies of so-called "wolf children" who have presumably been reared in isolation, with a minimum of human contact.[68] Although descriptions of the few cases of such children on record suggest severe developmental retardation, it is unfortunate that there is complete absence of controls, and dependence is chiefly upon hearsay, anecdote and unsystematic observation. Hence, it is impossible for the critical investigator to arrive at any dependable conclusions.

Investigations of the second sort are best illustrated by comparisons of the measured IQ of children in impoverished surroundings with the IQ of children in average surroundings; or similar comparisons of the same group of children before and after exposure to stimulating nursery-school training. This approach depends heavily upon a restricted measure of intelligence as the criterion of maturity, requires elaborate experimental and statistical controls, and often leads to controversy over the constancy of the IQ, and over the unanswerable heredity-environment riddle. The most recent extensive studies on this point seem to demonstrate changes in measured IQ, and concomitant changes in interpersonal relationships which are related to differences in the child's surroundings.[69] The narrowness of the behavior studies, however, as well as the difficulty of evaluating the data,[70] prohibit our accepting the results as conclusively demonstrating the interdependence of lack of opportunity and biosocial immaturity. The hypothesis that long-continued deprivation results in consistent developmental retardation remains logically attractive but empirically unverified.

[68] Gesell, A., *Wolf child and human child*. New York: Harper, 1941; Zingg, R. M., "Feral man and extreme cases of isolation." *Amer. J. Psychol.*, 1940, vol. 53, pp. 487–517; Dennis, W., "The significance of feral man." *Amer. J. Psychol.*, 1941, vol. 54, pp. 425–432; Zingg, R. M., "Reply to Professor Dennis' 'The significance of feral man.'" *Amer. J. Psychol.*, 1941, vol. 54, pp. 432–435. See also Davis, K., "Final note on a case of extreme isolation." *Amer. J. Sociol.*, 1947, vol. 52, pp. 432–437.

[69] See, for example, Schmidt, B. G., "Changes in personal, social and intellectual behavior of children originally classified as feeble-minded." *Psychol. Monogr.*, 1946, vol. 60, no. 5; Skeels, H. M., Updegraff, R., Wellman, B. L., and Williams, H. M., "A study of environmental stimulation." *Univ. Iowa stud. Child Welf.*, 1938, vol. 15, no. 4; Skodak, M., "Children in foster homes: a study of mental development." *Univ. Iowa stud. Child Welf.*, 1939, vol. 16, no. 1; Skeels, H. M. and Dye, H. B., "A study of the effects of differential stimulation on mentally retarded children." *Proc. Amer. Assoc. ment. Def.*, 1939, vol. 44, no. 1, pp. 114–136.

[70] For criticisms of these studies, see Woodworth, R. S., "Heredity and environment." *Soc. Sci. Res. Council Bull. 47*. New York, 1941; Kirk, S. A., "An evaluation of the study by Bernadine G. Schmidt entitled: Changes in personal, social and intellectual behavior of children originally classified as feebleminded." *Psychol. Bull.*, 1948, vol. 45, pp. 321–333; Schmidt, B. G., "A reply." *Psychol. Bull.*, 1948, vol. 45, pp. 334–343; McNemar, Q., "A critical examination of the University of Iowa studies of environmental influences upon the IQ." *Psychol. Bull.*, 1940, vol. 37, pp. 63–92.

The attempts to identify positively the etiological factors in developmental retardation have been strenuous, persistent, often precise and systematic, but generally unsuccessful.   They have unearthed an occasional startling correspondence between biological conditions and social maturity, but all such correlations added together would account for only a small fraction of the total number of cases of retardation; and even this small fraction comprises the usual clinical types which are rarely, if ever, met outside of institutions.   A tendency has been identified for retardation to "run in families"; but the problem of frequency of familial retardation, and its relationship to genetic factors, has been left unsolved.   The highly important question of opportunity for learning has been raised; but it has not yet been provided with an answer. Biosocial immaturity resulting from developmental retardation remains at present a complex phenomenon to which any of the numerous conditions interfering with learning may be expected to contribute.

Developmental Retardation as a Social Problem

The developmentally retarded person, like the one suffering from behavior disorder, is in danger of ridicule, hostility, rejection, misunderstanding and even legal attack from his contemporaries in adult society.   The recognition that his limitations are permanent has come slowly in the history of behavior pathology, as it comes slowly in the life history of the immature person himself. A modern, enlightened view of retardation demands that we accept two general principles as governing our attitudes toward the developmentally retarded individual.   Both principles imply that the retarded person is one whose needs differ from those of his contemporaries only in the phase of maturity at which they arise, and within which they must be satisfied.

(1) *The retarded person should achieve his maximum level of biosocial maturity in ways suitable to his own society.*   Except in the rare instance of the grossly retarded, almost unreactive idiot, there are skills appropriate to his phase of maturity which the retarded person can acquire.   These may be as simple as feeding and toilet habits, self-help in dressing, and independence and self-entertainment in play; [71] or they may be as complex as reading for pleasure, making purchases alone, or getting and holding a job.   Often, however, the retarded person never exhausts the possibilities of adjustment at his own level, because those who feel responsible for him never permit him to do so.   Like the protected child of solicitous parents, the immature person is subjected to undue restrictions from others who fear the consequences of his behavior.   Lack of opportunity and absence of useful training thus keep him more dependent than his level of maturity necessitates or warrants.

(2) *The retarded person should obtain satisfaction for his own individual needs*

---

[71] See, for example, Deacon, K. F., "An experiment in the cottage training of low-grade defectives." *Amer. J. ment. Def.*, 1942, vol. 47, pp. 209–214.

in ways appropriate to his level of biosocial maturity. For the grossly retarded person, these needs may be only the simple ones of hunger and thirst, of elimination, and of protection from danger. For the mildly retarded person, however, the number and variety of need-satisfaction sequences may spread out to include affectional relationships, vocational security and social acceptance. When these needs, whether simple or complex, are met at the level of biosocial maturity at which they develop — through suckling or diaper-changing, through attachments to parent-surrogates, through supervised industrial jobs, or through marriage — the retarded person escapes undue delay and thwarting. When, however, appropriate satisfactions are lacking, we can expect the retarded individual, like the non-retarded one, to acquire adjustive techniques which are ineffectual and even harmful.

The successful application of these two principles depends largely upon closing the gap between the expected and the possible roles for a retarded person. Since the overwhelming majority of immature individuals spend their lives among relatives in their own homes, it is here that their needs must be met and their possibilities of maturation realized. The necessity for realistic expectations and suitable guidance, however, extends beyond the home — into the schools that provide special classes and individualized instruction, into industries that furnish on-the-job training and sympathetic supervision, and into courts that recognize the difference between biosocial immaturity and willful social irresponsibility. When we turn to the small minority of retarded persons who require the constant custody of a training school or colony, our principles remain the same. Temporary or permanent residence in a restricted environment, far from being considered a punitive measure, should be regarded as an opportunity for treatment appropriate to the retarded person's level of biosocial maturity.[72]

In his efforts to satisfy his needs in a social context too complicated for him, the immature person may develop behavior that is inept, inappropriate, sometimes bizarre and sometimes antisocial. We have seen that these reactions are best understood as the product of a long history of unattainable expectations, frustration and failure, in an individual who has consistently resembled those who are younger than he. Such behavior, of course, is by no means the necessary concomitant of developmental retardation, nor is it characteristic only of retarded persons. The adjustive techniques which carry an individual away from the accepted patterns of his society may be learned and practiced by anyone. They occur most frequently, however, in persons who are biosocially immature, not by reason of consistent developmental retardation, but as a consequence of fixation at certain phases of maturation. We shall consider next the behavior pathology occurring in this second variety of biosocial immaturity.

[72] For a summary of treatment procedures with retarded persons, see Sarason, S. B., *Psychological problems in mental deficiency.* New York: Harper, 1949, pp. 263–336.

7

Behavior Pathology in Biosocial Immaturity

II. SOCIAL DEVIATION

Progress from infantile immaturity to adult biosocial maturity is rarely steady and uniform for anyone. Delay in one phase of maturation may accompany acceleration in another, and both delay and acceleration may be brief or protracted, temporary or permanent.[1] For most persons, this irregularity in development is neither gross enough nor sufficiently prolonged to single them out for special notice. But some individuals undergo a *selective retardation* in their behavioral development which is so severe that their social behavior as adults is conspicuously inept or inappropriate. Such social deviants provide the behavior pathologist with an exceptionally difficult problem.

Selective retardation produces behavior which is almost endlessly diverse. Overtly aggressive or irresponsible actions, passive dependency, inadequacy, timidity and restless wandering may all be signs of selective immaturity. It is unfortunate, both for the social deviant and for the field of behavior pathology, that the characteristics of immaturity which have usually been most emphasized are those which have the greatest nuisance value. Behavior pathologists of the past, in focussing their attention upon the impressive antisocial aspects of biosocial immaturity, have erred in ignoring the less obvious but equally important passivity and inadequacy which also characterize it.

There are several reasons for this distortion in emphasis. In our everyday social contacts, we tend to stress that which stands out in human behavior, particularly if it is annoying or threatening to us. In the home, on the playground, in school and in adult society it is the active, outspoken, aggressive or rebellious person who calls forth retaliatory responses from others.[2] The withdrawn, passive or inadequate individual is likely to elicit from his con-

---

[1] See pages 144–148.

[2] Thompson, C. E., "The attitudes of various groups toward behavior problems of children." *J. abn. soc. Psychol.*, 1940, vol. 35, pp. 120–125.

temporaries only indifference or disregard. Through our own selective reactions to immature individuals, we single out the aggressive and irresponsible persons for special notice.

The complex framework of permission and prohibition which characterizes our society, of course, reinforces these selective reactions toward socially immature individuals. This framework, interpreted and transmitted by parents to their children, specifies the behavior which, in our particular culture, is prescribed, approved and therefore learned. The earliest rules by which we live, as we have seen, are the concrete demands and expectations of our own family.[3] In most families, however, these requirements support the prescriptions and proscriptions of wider social groups — the immediate neighborhood, the school, the local community, the nation. They support also the explicitly described behavior we call custom, and the rigidly codified regulations we call law.

Law and custom, inevitable components of social living, both draw an arbitrary line between social conformity and non-conformity. Whether codified as formal law, or crystallized as custom, the demands and expectations of a social group confer upon the behavior of a large share of the population a deceptive appearance of homogeneity. We may, for example, punish children for open aggressiveness, for overt sexual expression and for signs of irresponsibility toward other persons. If we are consistent and successful in such training, children may become adults who for the most part inhibit hostility, satisfy their sexual needs mainly in prescribed ways, and maintain overtly responsible relationships with their peers. When we see this result in adult behavior, however, we are likely to overlook the intervening years of training. As adults we interpret this uniformity as inherent in human nature, and segregate those who deviate from it as a class apart. In this way, explicitly understood law and custom serve to single out those persons who fail in some important respect to learn adherence to prescribed standards. But law and custom necessarily sort out chiefly those social deviants whose behavior is antisocial and unlawful, and tend to overlook those whose behavior, although inept and inappropriate, still remains within the bounds of the legal and the customary.

If we are to understand social deviation, we must extend our concept far beyond the small circle of those whom a society of rigid convention labels misfits. We must include the indecisive, ineffectual person whose search for security carries him repeatedly back to childlike dependence on others, and the pleasant, ingratiating, often successful adult whose interpersonal relationships are a chain of superficial contacts. We must include the nomad whose restless wandering seems never to bring him peace, and the sex deviant whose affectional development does not reach an adult level. And we must include the antisocial rebel who, through aggressive behavior, again and again provokes legal punishment which is powerless to deter him, and the timid, inadequate

[3] See pages 136–137.

person who never quite succeeds in achieving the vocational, economic, or marital status of the average adult. To the behavior pathologist, all of these persons illustrate social deviation, and they all show in their behavior the unmistakable signs of biosocial immaturity.

In many ways, the social ineptness we are here considering resembles that resulting from general developmental retardation, which we have been discussing in the previous chapter.[4] Failure to achieve the status of a responsible, participating member of a community, delay in attaining affectional maturity, and special vulnerability to frustration characterize the social deviant as well as the generally retarded individual. In the lifelong course of their maturation, however, the generally retarded and the selectively retarded persons differ. The individual who is selectively immature learns walking and talking at the expected times. His formal school achievement and his vocational aptitude are in line with those of his contemporaries. His performance on standardized scales of intelligence locates him in the average and sometimes in the accelerated ranges.[5] Through many aspects of maturation the social deviant progresses at the expected rate. It is in the development of his interpersonal relationships that he lags behind his contemporaries. The consequence of this developmental retardation is a persistent selective biosocial immaturity.

Biosocial immaturity resulting from selective developmental retardation is characterized by *interpersonal relationships which consistently deviate from the accepted norms of adult society in the direction of behavior appropriate to younger age levels, but which are not included in general developmental retardation.* Occasional deviation from conventional or expected behavior occurs, of course, in the behavioral repertory of us all. Under stressful or frustrating circumstances, or as the result of brief and temporary delays in maturation, anyone may behave toward others in dependent or aggressive ways, and anyone may seem inadequate, timid, antisocial or childlike.[6] For the social deviant, however, this sort of behavior is no transient adjustment to temporary frustration or stress; it is his way of life, evolved and practiced in childhood, and eventually overlearned. The course of his biosocial development brings him adult status in many other respects, but his interpersonal relationships identify him as immature. For in his ineptness, his inadequacy, or his open disavowal of the regulations of his society, he is a child who fights with adult weapons.

"Constitutional psychopathic inferiority"

The formal recognition of social deviation as a problem for the behavior pathologist is over a century old.[7] In 1835 the English psychiatrist Prich-

---

[4] See Chapter 6.
[5] Gurvitz, M. S., "The intelligence factor in psychopathic personality." *J. clin. Psychol.*, 1947, vol. 3, pp. 194–196.
[6] See pages 44–52 and 145–147.
[7] For an historical summary of this problem, see Preu, P. W., "The concept of psycho-

ard [8] described to his medical colleagues a type of behavior characterized, as he put it, by "emotional and volitional defects" which rendered the patient unable to conduct himself "with decency and propriety in the business of life." Since this behavior did not fit conveniently into the established psychiatric categories of his day, Prichard proposed the term "moral insanity" to describe it. It soon became evident that the deviant behavior included in Prichard's concept varied widely from patient to patient, and varied in the same patient from time to time. An attempt to make some order of this diversity was made by Koch toward the close of the century. Koch [9] coined the term "psychopathic inferiority," and used it to denote a special constitutional or hereditary weakness, which he thought predisposed certain individuals to socially deviant behavior. Armed with this concept, a great many behavior pathologists then attacked the problem of social deviation by classifying the observed varieties of deviant behavior under hypothetical hereditary predispositions.

This procedure inevitably led to the typing of socially deviant individuals in accordance with symptoms resembling those found in more highly systematized behavior disorders. Such men as Kraepelin [10] and Kahn [11] borrowed terms already well-established in psychiatric literature to classify deviant persons as *excitable, anxious, compulsive, hysterical* or *depressive*. Such categories, by accentuating the superficial similarities between "constitutional psychopathic inferiority" and certain neuroses and psychoses, raised the whole question of the relationship between social deviation and the major syndromes of behavior disorder. This question was answered in some quarters by postulating perversion as an escape from neurosis, in others by including psychopathic inferiority within the group of neuroses,[12] in still others by manufacturing the new term "sociopath" to distinguish the socially deviant patient from the neurotic one.[13] The concept of "constitutional psychopathic inferiority" was gradually stretched to cover all behavior pathology not otherwise easily categorized; and this has finally made the classification practically useless for definitive purposes. Today its status seems to be simply that of a convenient screen against which to project theoretical preconceptions current in behavior pathology.

The residue of this tortuous and perplexing historical development is unfortunately still with us.[14] For example, the popular label for social deviation

pathic personality." In Hunt, J. McV. (Ed.), *Personality and the behavior disorders.* New York: Ronald, 1944, Chapter 30; and Henderson, D. K., *Psychopathic states.* New York: Norton, 1939.

[8] Prichard, J. C., *Treatise on insanity.* London: Gilbert and Piper, 1835.

[9] Koch, J. L. A., *Die psychopathischen Minderwertigkeiten.* Ravensberg: Maier, 1891.

[10] Kraepelin, E., *Psychiatrie,* vol. 4 (8th ed.), Part 3. Leipzig: Barth, 1915.

[11] Kahn, E., *Psychopathic personalities.* New Haven: Yale University Press, 1931.

[12] Alexander, F., "The neurotic character." *Int. J. Psychoanal.*, 1930, vol. 2, pp. 292–311.

[13] Partridge, G. E., "Current conceptions of psychopathic personality." *Amer. J. Psychiat.*, 1930, vol. 10, pp. 53–99.

[14] See, for example, Curran, D. and Mallinson, P., "Psychopathic personality." *J. ment. Sci.*, 1944, vol. 90, pp. 266–286; Karpman, B., "The myth of the psychopathic per-

now is "psychopathic personality" or "psychopathic state"; but these terms seem merely to be a restatement of the outmoded category of "constitutional psychopathic inferiority." They do not refer to new concepts. Moreover, the accounts of psychopathic behavior given by present-day behavior pathologists are still likely to be accusations rather than descriptions. The evaluative attitudes of nineteenth-century psychiatry continue to tinge our modern classifications; and the psychopath stands accused of crime, of exploitation and of inability to profit from corrective procedures.

Even the early view that psychopathic personality is constitutionally determined has survived down to the present. Originally, this emphasis upon constitutional factors arose because of the chronic character of "psychopathic" behavior, and because of its stubborn resistance to therapeutic attack. Today, chronicity and therapeutic failure in social deviants are still explained away by reference to a hypothetical constitutional predisposition.[15] The observations that "psychopathic" behavior occurs among children, that it may appear among members of the same family strain,[16] and that "psychopaths" show an unexpectedly high percentage of abnormal electroencephalographic patterns,[17] are advanced as further support of the constitutional argument.

The background of "psychopathic personality" in nineteenth-century psychiatry, although relevant as past history, need not dictate the present and future development of the concept. If we are to understand the biosocial immaturity that results in social deviation, we must reject definitions which include all behavior pathology that does not fit elsewhere, as well as definitions that overemphasize aggressive, irresponsible behavior. Nor can we afford to perpetuate the implication that social deviation is morally bad, or the assumption that it is necessarily constitutional. We cannot ignore the effects of parental emphasis, of others' reactions and of self-reactions in training a growing child to socially deviant behavior. Let us then begin with the characteristic behavior of the social deviant, as it has been acquired within the enormously complicated context of other persons and cultural codes.

sonality." *Amer. J. Psychiat.*, 1948, vol. 104, pp. 523–534; Karpman, B., "Moral agenesis." *Psychiat. Quart.*, 1947, vol. 21, pp. 361–398; Cason, H., "The concept of the psychopath." *Amer. J. Orthopsychiat.*, 1948, vol. 18, pp. 297–308; Lindner, R. M., "A formulation of psychopathic personality." *Psychiatry*, 1944, vol. 7, pp. 59–63; Penrose, L. S., "Moral deficiency." *J. ment. Sci.*, 1947, vol. 93, pp. 273–277.

[15] Kahn, E., *Psychopathic personalities.* New Haven: Yale University Press, 1931; Sheldon, W. H., Hartl, E. M., and McDermott, E., *Varieties of delinquent youth.* New York: Harper, 1949.

[16] Slater, E. T. O., "Psychopathic personality as a genetical concept." *J. ment. Sci.*, 1948, vol. 94, pp. 277–282.

[17] See, for example, Hill, D. and Watterson, D., "Electro-encephalographic studies of psychopathic personalities." *J. neurol. Psychiat.*, 1942, vol. 5, pp. 47–65; Knott, J. R. and Gottlieb, J. S., "The electroencephalogram in psychopathic personality." *Psychosom. Med.*, 1943, vol. 5, pp. 139–142; Silverman, D., "Clinical and electroencephalographic studies on criminal psychopaths." *Arch. Neurol. Psychiat.*, 1943, vol. 50, pp. 18–33.

Behavioral Characteristics of Social Deviation

A list of the behavioral characteristics ascribed to social deviants is a catalog of contradiction.[18] In his day-to-day activities, the social deviant is frequently described as impulsive and aimless, a man who lives in the present without regard for the future; yet he is just as frequently said to be cunning and sly, a man who organizes his behavior in ways which obviously require planning and foresight. Deviants are considered incapable of learning from experience because they may repeat their behavior with almost monotonous regularity, despite failure and punishment. But there are many socially deviant persons who show distinct superiority in formal education, and who make important contributions to science, art and literature. Although the deviant is pictured as typically a shallow, superficial individual, whose affectional relationships never go beyond the point of fleeting contacts, there are many socially deviant persons whose close attachments to others resemble strikingly the relationship of an overdependent child to his parents. The very core of social deviation is commonly said to be a hostile rebellion against rules and regulations, but those persons illustrate social deviation equally well whose lifelong passive submission to authority has rendered them inadequate, ineffectual adults.

From this parade of contradictory characteristics stems the special difficulty which behavior pathologists have had in classifying and explaining social deviation. From it spring also the confusion and bewilderment which nonprofessional persons show in dealing with socially deviant individuals. For the social deviant, in his relationships with his contemporaries, appears to behave so capriciously that others tend to consider him wholly unpredictable. Even those who know him well are likely to complain that the social deviant perplexes them, that he is now affectionate, now cold, that he may be planful and aimless by turns, at one time engrossed in his own undertakings and at another unaccountably impulsive.

Were we to find this diversity of behavioral characteristics in a young child — open aggression toward authority, passive dependency upon others, impulsiveness, socially irresponsible intent, ineffectual submissiveness, and frequent indifference toward punishment — we should not be altogether surprised.[19] Neither would we consider it unusual if the course and outcome of a young

[18] For illustrations, see Caldwell, J. M., "The constitutional psychopathic state (psychopathic personality): I. Studies of soldiers in the U.S. Army." *J. crim. Psychopath.*, 1941, vol. 3, pp. 171–179; Cason, H., "The psychopath and the psychopathic." *J. crim. Psychopath.*, 1943, vol. 4, pp. 522–527.

[19] See, for example, Jersild, A. T., "Emotional development." In Carmichael, L. (Ed.), *Manual of child psychology.* New York: Wiley, 1946, pp. 769–773, 777–778; Murphy, L. B., *Social behavior and child personality.* New York: Columbia University Press, 1937; Murphy, L. B., "Childhood experience in relation to personality development." In Hunt, J. McV. (Ed.), *Personality and the behavior disorders.* New York: Ronald, 1944, pp. 652–690.

child's behavior seemed unpredictable as measured by adult standards. Such behavior is not only tolerated but expected in the immature individual who has not yet learned completely the social roles of adulthood; we should dismiss them without concern as appropriate to the level of maturity belonging to young children.[20] It is their inappropriateness in the behavioral repertory of the *adult* individual which singles out such characteristics for special study. This contradictory combination of adult and childlike behavior, produced by selective biosocial immaturity, is typical of social deviation, as the following case will show.

A young man of twenty-five, apprehended for forging a check, was brought by the sheriff, from the county jail in his home town, to a psychiatric hospital. Both officer and patient seemed equally puzzled by the behavior which had led to hospitalization. The sheriff kept reiterating that the young man came from an excellent family and had received the best of early training. He added that the patient had been quiet and unresisting when arrested, and in jail a model prisoner who enjoyed but did not abuse his privileges. The patient explained that when he cashed the forged check he still had plenty of his own money in the bank. His own behavior, he said, had convinced him that there must be something wrong with him, and he had therefore himself requested psychiatric study.

In the hospital the patient continued to show the quiet, cooperative, almost passive behavior which had perplexed his jailers. He earned special notice for his deference to ward attendants, his willingness to sweep and dust, and his assistance in caring for other patients. Casual conversation, as well as formal tests, suggested that he was highly intelligent, well-educated, and particularly adept at mechanical tasks. He had a serious, somewhat scholarly appearance. He described what he called his "psychotic symptoms" in polysyllabic, pseudomedical terms. The psychiatric study, which he had requested, unearthed a variety of complaints, all interpreted as proof of psychosis by the patient, although not by his physicians. He reported occasional precordial pain, dyspnea, left-sided headaches, "spells" in which he could not recall what he was doing, nightmares, suicidal thoughts and recurrent auditory hallucinations. Upon closer study, however, the pains could be related neither to particular events in the patient's life nor to organ or tissue pathology; the "spells" resembled his nightmares and were not invariably accompanied by amnesia; the suicidal thoughts turned out to have been expressed only in one hostile, threatening letter to the patient's wife; and the auditory hallucinations were found to be only vivid dreams, occurring always during sleep.

Toward the antisocial behavior which brought him to the county jail the patient showed a consistently moralistic attitude. He readily admitted the forgery, stated that he knew his behavior was wrong, and said that he was sorry. This same apparent concern with right and wrong characterized his performance on projective tests. The stories he told

[20] See pages 132–134.

in response to ambiguous pictures repeated again and again the theme of retributive justice triumphing over transgression. He pictured himself as a sober, hard-working, law-abiding citizen, who had suddenly and unaccountably resorted to behavior so unusual for him as to persuade him that he must be ill.

Lengthy interviews with the patient's wife and his mother, and a painstaking search of hospital and jail records, revealed at last that this man's behavior was by no means unusual for him. From the time of his early adolescence he had drifted from town to town, and from job to job, without ever establishing himself firmly as a member of any community. Forgery had for years been his means of getting enough money to travel to new communities, which seemed always to promise greater security for him. Indeed, neither county jails nor psychiatric hospitals were new to him. It was only the almost fierce protection of his reputation by his mother and his wife that had kept his behavior a secret from his acquaintances, and even from other members of his own family. The difficulty which brought the patient to the hospital, far from being unusual for him, was a combination of adult and childlike behavior that was actually characteristic of him — and, as we have already seen, characteristic of the biosocial immaturity of social deviants.

The background of this selective retardation in social development was one of early maternal overindulgence and general family protection.[21] The patient was the youngest of three children and an only son. His mother was said to be hypochondriacally concerned over her blood pressure, and his father was reported to have "upsets" if things did not go his way. The patient, in contrast to his two sisters, was precocious in the development of walking and talking, in toilet training, and in early school achievement. His mother and his sisters idolized him. In the fights, arguments and misunderstandings with peers and teachers — which are an inevitable part of the socialization of any child — the patient was consistently made to feel that his behavior was justifiable, and that others were always in the wrong. His father occasionally suggested that his son might be in error, and infrequently even attempted to punish him, but the weight of family opinion usually nullified his efforts. The patient for his part interpreted his father's disciplinary attempts as rejection, and complained that he had never attained the degree of closeness to his father that he had desired.[22] Relationships between the father and other family members became increasingly cool and indifferent, until finally mother and sisters united in keeping the patient's actions completely secret from his father.

When the patient was in the sixth grade, his teachers began sending home vague reports hinting that he might be untrustworthy. These reports were greeted by his mother and sisters with indignation and dismissed as false. Throughout high school his scholastic record grew increasingly poor, although his mother's insistence that he remain in school led finally to his graduation. Immediately after leaving high

---

[21] For a discussion of the relationship between parental indulgence and selective immaturity, see pages 213–215.

[22] For a discussion of parental identification in relation to maturation, see pages 60–63 and 138.

school, the patient ran away from home without warning, joined the merchant marine, and was enrolled in a special mechanical training course. His success in the course won him a high rating as a mechanic. Notwithstanding this, his career in the merchant marine was one of jumping ship, wandering from town to town, signing on to a new ship, again earning a high rating, and then jumping ship again. During this period he communicated with his mother only for the purpose of requesting money, which was invariably sent him without question. His father and his acquaintances in his small home town were kept in ignorance of his activities.

After three years in the merchant marine, the patient became attached to, and married, a woman older than he, a college graduate and former school teacher. During the early months of their marriage, the patient entertained his wife with detailed stories of his physical prowess, and of his accomplishments at sea. He also spoke with obvious pride of his elder brother, whose achievements were made to sound even more startling than the patient's. He represented himself to his wife as a former salesman who was now travelling about the country in the hope of finding a successful advertising agency which he might purchase. At this point he was discharged from the merchant marine as undesirable, and returned with his wife to his parental home. It was here that the wife discovered that the patient had no brother, that he was not a salesman, that his funds had for years come largely from his mother, and that his descriptions of his accomplishments were without basis in fact. Her only response to her discovery was to excuse his stories by calling them "slightly exaggerated."

The patient's wife was at first received by his mother and sisters with coolness and some hostility. She suggested and finally demanded that her husband find a home for her away from the parental home; but the patient insisted that he must first settle his current financial deals. In this atmosphere of tension, contradictory demand and unrest the patient had his first so-called "spell"; he left home without explanation for a three-month period. A private detective agency employed by his wife located the patient in jail in a nearby state, where he had forged checks to the amount of several thousand dollars. In this emergency, the patient's wife and mother joined forces and toured the country for four months, visiting every town the patient had visited, and making good every worthless check he had written. The patient was then released from jail and returned to his home town.

For the next six months the patient held jobs intermittently, supporting himself and his wife largely through his mother's contributions. His wife's pregnancy then raised again the question of quitting the parental home for an independent domicile. The patient at this point left home once more without explanation, and nothing was heard of him until a hospital in a distant state communicated with the family. After forging checks to travel from town to town, he had entered a hotel, announced that he was the public relations representative of a large corporation, staged a banquet for the local employees, and then forged a check on a nonexistent bank to pay for the entertainment. He was jailed and afterwards transferred to a state psychiatric hospital.

He could give no explanation for his behavior other than that he liked to be a "big shot." In the hospital he wrote the letter to his wife in which he threatened suicide. Here also he became friendly with a staff member, whom he assisted in routine professional work, and from whom he gained considerable information concerning psychiatric diagnosis, symptomatology and therapy. Upon the repeated requests of his family he was discharged, unimproved, with a diagnosis of "constitutional psychopathic inferiority," to return home.

The patient described the ensuing five months as a time of "floating around." He obtained various jobs, but held none of them for more than a few weeks. Shortly before his child was to be born, he forged a check in his own home town, in order that he might be able to leave home again. It was in the middle of his jail sentence for this offense that he had made the request for psychiatric study which brought him to the hospital. Since it proved virtually impossible to sort out fact from fabrication in his story, and his physicians could not obtain from his wife, his mother or the patient himself the cooperation necessary for effective treatment, the patient was finally transferred to a state psychiatric hospital near his home under long-time commitment.

This case demonstrates clearly the contradictory behavior which perplexes the behavior pathologist who handles social deviation. Our patient's unexplained truancies from home made him seem aimless and impulsive, but his forgeries and his business deals were planned and executed with care and foresight. His affectional relationships with his wife and child seemed fleeting and superficial, but his close dependence upon his mother and his sisters was consistent and enduring. He repeatedly violated the law, despite punishment, but in his reactions to the personalized authority of hospital staffs and police officers he was cooperative and obedient. The unpredictability of his behavior was reflected in the inability of those who knew him well either to understand him, or to behave consistently toward him. Indeed, the patient himself expressed these contradictory trends, not only in his everyday actions, but also in his own verbalized self-reactions: his behavior, he said, was inexplicable even to himself.

In this case we can identify the elements from which earlier behavior pathologists built their various concepts of constitutional psychopathic inferiority.[23] Our patient's reports of auditory hallucinations and of "spells," together with his suicidal threats, raise at once the suspicion of severe neurotic or psychotic disturbance. A nineteenth-century psychiatrist might well have classified him as hysterical or depressed. The apparent irresponsibility and illegality of the patient's behavior lends itself readily to a moralistic evaluation. His mother's hypochondriacal complaints, and his father's "upsets" might further mislead the behavior pathologist into emphasizing possible hereditary factors, to the exclusion of other determinants. And the repetitive nature of the patient's behavior, in addition to the failure of active psychotherapy,

23 See pages 189–191.

could easily earn for this patient the designation of "constitutional predisposition."

Neither a list of contradictions nor a return to nineteenth-century attitudes, however, will help us to understand this case. The distinguishing feature of our patient's behavior is the unmistakable evidence he gives of selective biosocial immaturity. Throughout his life, he showed a combination of mature and immature behavior which seems inexplicable unless we view it as the consequence of a selective developmental retardation. In his general intelligence, his school accomplishment, his superior achievement in mechanical vocations, and his relationship to those in authority over him in jail or in hospitals, he showed behavior appropriate to his age. In his dependence upon his mother and sisters, his exaggerated stories of his own ability, in his irresponsibility toward his wife and family, in his admitted desire to be a "big shot," and in his disavowal of law — even after repeated punishment — he demonstrated behavior appropriate to adolescent or infantile levels. He is the overprotected child who is continually evading adult responsibilities by means of well-learned dependent adjustive techniques, characteristic more of childhood than of full biosocial maturity.

When viewed in this way, the kaleidoscopic fragments of behavior, which the earlier behavior pathologists put side by side to produce a confused picture of psychopathic personality, fall into a more coherent pattern. It is undeniable that the varieties of behavior characterizing social deviation are many. But they are not more diverse, nor more incomprehensible, than the varieties of technique all of us acquire as we proceed from infantile immaturity to full adulthood. Any of these immature approaches may persist beyond childhood, and in so persisting may render the adult individual selectively immature.[24] It is now evident that the varieties of social deviation, to which we next turn, are actually varieties of selective biosocial immaturity.

Varieties of Social Deviation

Biosocial maturation in interpersonal relationships is a progression from close dependence upon others to relative independence.[25] In attaining biosocial maturity, the individual adds to the role of passive recipient that of active participant in a society of other persons. And in our culture, with its characteristic customs and laws, the role of active social participant demands of a mature individual both the suppression of overt aggression toward others, and the assumption of an increasing degree of responsibility in relation to them. Hence, we find two major varieties of biosocial immaturity in interpersonal relationships: (1) the failure to arrive at the status of an autonomous social

[24] See pages 143–148.
[25] See pages 132–134.

participant, and (2) the development of a participant role, but without the acquisition of those attitudes toward others which law and custom demand.

These two distinguishing marks of immature behavior define two major varieties of social deviation: the *inadequate* and the *inept*. (*a*) Socially deviant persons may be characterized by failure to develop and maintain effectively the role of social participant in their adult society. We classify such immature individuals as *inadequate*.[26] (*b*) Other socially deviant persons, while they succeed in becoming active social participants, show themselves to be incapable of playing the participant role in ways which are acceptable and appropriate to their adult society.[27] We classify these immature individuals as *inept*. In short, the *inadequate* social deviant lacks the techniques of social participation, whereas the *inept* social deviant, although he acquires these techniques, uses them inappropriately, in the light of the standards current in adult society.

Both these varieties of social deviation represent phases of maturation through which most persons progress in the course of attaining adulthood. The infant and young child are expected to be relatively passive, dependent recipients in interpersonal relationships.[28] Indeed, in our culture the early training of infant and child is in many ways directed toward prolonging a dependent, recipient role beyond the time that it is biologically essential. The half-grown child and the adolescent are expected to blunder occasionally in learning a relatively active, independent, participant role.[29] Often we recognize and even encourage, as indicators of increasing maturity, certain signs of aggressive or socially irresponsible behavior. It is only when a dependent, recipient role or an irresponsible participant role persists into the adult years that we can speak of social deviation.

Successful and unsuccessful social deviants

Selective developmental retardation which leads to inadequacy or ineptness in adult behavior does not necessarily lead to failure in adult achievement. Deviant behavior which, through fortunate circumstances, culminates in social benefit and recognition may, under less favorable conditions, end in unproductiveness and ostracism. The social demands and expectations which define successful or unsuccessful adult achievement are never abstract or general. They are always the concrete, specific demands and expectations of particular familial, social, occupational, religious, economic or geographic groups. Under certain circumstances, these groups may tolerate, require and

[26] Compare the classification of "immaturity reaction" employed by the Veterans Administration. "Nomenclature of psychiatric disorders and reactions." *Vet. Adm. Tech. Bull.*, United States Veterans Administration, 1947, TB10–A–78.

[27] Compare the common emphasis upon antisocial behavior in classifying social deviation, discussed on pages 187–189.

[28] See pages 135–136.   [29] See pages 141–143.

even reward behavior which by our definition is socially deviant. When this is so, actions which to the behavior pathologist signify a selective biosocial immaturity may, nevertheless, lead to successful accomplishment in adulthood.[30]

The *inadequate* social deviant, for example, often finds protective home surroundings, a subordinate vocational position or a dependent marital relationship within which he is able to maintain himself effectively. Compared with most adults of his own age and status he is immature, but within his own particular environmental context he is successful. Should this context change, so that greater independence and more aggressive participation are required of him, he is likely to become and to be recognized by others as unsuccessful. His success, in maintaining himself in his culture, has obviously been determined by the relatively simple demands made upon him.

In the same way, the *inept* social deviant may achieve success by seeking out situations which are loosely enough structured to provide a wide scope for his behavior. He may find a vocation which capitalizes upon his impulsiveness, his restless wandering, or his devious and imaginative planning. He may find friends who accept his fleeting attachments, his unpredictabilities and his pleasant, ingratiating ways, at best as signs of genius, and at worst as unimportant eccentricities. Compared to his peers, of course, the inept deviant is selectively immature, but he may still be successful and productive in adult life. It is only when his particular environmental context does not support or tolerate his immature behavior that he can be singled out as unsuccessful.

Inadequate Social Deviants

To the casual observer, those socially deviant persons whom we term *inadequate* seem forever on the verge of achieving biosocial adulthood. They are frequently described as "good," "nice," or "no trouble at all." Their failure to attain full adult status is often attributed by their associates to an unusually unfavorable or unsympathetic environment. It is only after their repeated attempts at school, vocational or marital adjustment have been uniformly unsuccessful that their social inadequacy begins to become apparent. Confronted by the complex adult demands of independence, self-determination and mature social participation, the inadequate social deviant seems almost — but not quite — able to qualify. The following case illustrates many of the characteristics of the *inadequate social deviant*.

A young man of twenty-three came to the out-patient clinic of a psychiatric hospital, accompanied by his mother. The patient's concern was directed toward gastrointestinal "attacks" which he inter-

---

[30] For examples of social deviants who achieved success in business, professional and social fields, see Cleckley, H., *The mask of sanity*. St. Louis: Mosby, 1941, pp. 139–174.

preted as symptoms of appendicitis. The mother, however, was chiefly worried over the patient's failure to hold a job, and over what she considered his inability to "settle down" and make plans for his future. The young man was admitted to the hospital for more extended study, which ruled out the possibility of gastrointestinal disease but disclosed that the patient was biosocially immature to a degree not suspected at the time of his admission.

In his general appearance, his manner of speaking and his rapport with the hospital staff, the patient was decidedly boyish. Although he was otherwise neat and clean, he gave the impression of being somewhat unkempt — an impression which was intensified by his unwillingness to shave because, he explained, he was trying to grow a moustache. He was shy, but tensely cooperative, in interviews and at staff conferences, and spoke with hesitancy and an occasional stammer. He had a grasp of general information and an attitude toward current problems more appropriate to an early adolescent than to a man of twenty-three. Indeed, his behavior reminded one more of a fourteen-year-old boy; and at first his behavior was thought to indicate general developmental retardation.[31]

A careful history, however, and the results of standardized tests, dispelled at once any suspicion of generalized retardation. His childhood development had proceeded at the usual rate, although he had been enuretic until five years of age, and he had stammered from the time he began to talk. He had succeeded in completing high school with an above-average record; he scored in the average range on intelligence scales; and he showed distinct superiority in clerical and arithmetical operations. But in developing and maintaining social relationships he showed distinctly the signs of selective retardation.

The patient was the eldest of a highly religious family of eight children. He had lived all his life in small towns situated in an agricultural area. Both he and his mother described the home situation as strictly disciplined. Both agreed that the father was rigid, and frequently unfair in his punishment of his children. The patient recalled that, as a child, he had been spanked for transgressions of which he was innocent, and reported that his father had more than once kicked him in the face because he could not talk plainly. Although in direct interview the patient described these incidents placidly, under sodium amytal narcosis[32] he expressed open hatred for his father. It is of especial interest, in view of the patient's presenting symptoms at the time of admission, that his father had suffered from recurrent gastrointestinal difficulties which were diagnosed at the time as chronic appendicitis. Toward his mother, the patient showed affectionate, immature dependence, but he was reported to have formed no close attachments to his siblings.

Outside the family circle, the patient had no friends and few acquaintances. He had gone out with girls only twice in his life, and his responses to questions about marital plans were dictated largely

[31] Compare the presenting symptoms of the case of general developmental retardation, pages 166–167.

[32] For a discussion of narcosis as a therapeutic procedure, see pages 592–594.

by what he thought his questioners expected of him. During his hospital stay, he gathered that he ought to be thinking about marriage and a family, but he volunteered that he could not consider this step seriously until he had a steady job. His only group activities and interests had been centered about his membership in a small religious sect, where he held a position of leadership. He was able to talk fluently and enthusiastically of his religious beliefs, and to quote at length from the Bible and his sectarian literature. Occasionally he spoke of becoming a missionary and of having prophetic powers. Further study of these religious attitudes, however, revealed that the patient's missionary plans were vague and unformulated, and that they changed from day to day, depending upon changes in his audience. It was possible to trace all of the prophetic powers that he claimed for himself to literal interpretations of the religious literature belonging to the cult in which he had been reared. They proved to have no really personal significance for him.

In his attempts to secure and hold jobs, this man had been uniformly unsuccessful. Although he had had special training and facility in bookkeeping, he seemed to lose jobs almost as soon as he had obtained them. Besides trying numerous office positions, he had worked in a restaurant, in a hospital, as dining-car waiter, and as machine operator in a paper mill and in a shoe factory — never keeping any job longer than a month. Several of his numerous, short-time employers confessed to staff psychiatrists their bewilderment over the patient's vocational difficulties. They agreed that at first he seemed skilled and competent on the job, but that as time went on he appeared increasingly ineffectual, absented himself more and more, and finally drifted away altogether. These employers all showed concern for the patient, and concluded by saying that he was good, a "nice kid," and no trouble.

From the patient's point of view, the most satisfying period of his life had been during his brief Army service, when he was trained as a medical corpsman. He explained that there he had always known exactly what was expected of him. He had enjoyed the routine nature of the work, and he "felt safe" in the military hospital environment. Indeed, initially his gastrointestinal distress had developed when his training period was almost over and he was being prepared for more strenuous and more independent overseas duty. His most concrete plans for the future involved a return to similar work in some hospital, although he was unclear as to how he might go about finding such a job. Even his present hospitalization seemed to be providing the safe surroundings he desired; his physicians agreed that if they were to tell the patient that he must remain in the hospital for twenty years, he would certainly raise mild objections but as certainly stay.

It was this conviction, that the hospital had come to signify for the patient the same sort of artificial protection which his home provided, that led the staff to terminate his hospital stay. After prolonged interviews with the patient and his mother, directed toward interpreting to them the necessity for an independent vocational adjustment, the staff arranged for the patient's placement, as orderly, in a hospital some distance from his home town. Confronted with this situation, the patient stated that he might be equally satisfied if he spent the rest of his life in his parental home. When given his choice of protective job or protective home, the patient elected to return to his home — for a visit before taking the job, he said. He became somewhat upset over the necessity for travelling alone on the train for a few hours; but eventually he got back to the sanctuary of his parental home. The hospital where he was to have worked as orderly reported that he never arrived to take the job.

This patient combines in his behavior some of the most outstanding characteristics of the *inadequate* social deviant. A protective relationship with his mother, rejection by his father, and two decades spent in an undemanding rural environment, had prevented him from acquiring many of the techniques of social participation that were demanded of him as an adult. At twenty-three, he was still behaving as an early adolescent, vacillating between the uncertain challenge of mature adulthood and the safe refuge of dependent childhood. His brief, sporadic attempts to live as an adult among adults made him seem always on the verge of achieving biosocial maturity. They served also to persuade his mother, his employers, and even some of his physicians that sooner or later — with the next girl, on the next job, in the next hospital — he would achieve adult status. But for this patient, as for most inadequate social deviants, the next attempt, like the preceding ones, brought him only another failure.

It is only in routinized, protective surroundings that a socially deviant young man such as this can possibly be successful. His own parental home seemed to represent completely the kind and the degree of security he needed. If this degree of protectiveness had been duplicated and maintained for him, in a job situation or in a marital relationship, the patient might well have become an effective member of his immediate social group. In all probability neither he nor his mother would then have found it necessary to seek psychiatric help. His success in Army medical corps training, his leadership within a rigidly structured religious group, and his admitted contentment in the psychiatric hospital, all suggest that for him, satisfactory adjustment was certain only within a wholly sheltered environmental context. Once this protection was threatened the patient promptly demonstrated his inadequacy, and was then easily singled out as selectively immature.

The signs of immaturity in this case are clear. The patient, in his speech and his appearance, resembled persons much younger than himself. He was shy and withdrawn in the company of his peers to a degree that prevented him from making friends among individuals of either sex. He sought to maintain and prolong a childlike dependence upon his mother, although she herself recognized this behavior as a mark of inadequacy. He was ostentatiously cooperative and readily suggestible toward those whom he considered his superiors; he agreed quickly to attitudes that he felt were expected of him, even though his actions did not support his words. In a job situation which demanded of him more than he could give, he grew increasingly ineffectual and finally stopped coming to work altogether. When he was faced with a threatening change in his Army training course, he developed bodily overconcern, on the basis of his father's symptoms of appendicitis. His own fumbling attempts at achieving biosocial adulthood were epitomized by his efforts to raise a moustache in order to appear older. His final decision to return home, instead of taking a job as hospital orderly, constituted for him a renunciation — in action as well as words — of independent adulthood. It is this failure to develop the mature role of social participant that defines, for us, the inadequate social deviant.

Inept Social Deviants

The *inept* social deviant has at his command a variety of learned social roles which bear the superficial marks of mature adulthood.[33] He is an active participant in his society. He may behave as charming raconteur, as mature lover or husband, as respectful son, as amusing "big shot," as conforming patient, as rebellious delinquent, or as model prisoner. His techniques of social participation, however, deviate from adult role-taking behavior in the direction of inept immaturity. He is socially deviant by reason of the inappropriateness of his behavior to the customs and laws of his society.

The social roles which the inept deviant has learned are, in a sense, caricatures of the behavioral systems learned by mature adults. They are products, as we shall see, of delay in early phases of personality development; and this delay has modified subsequent biosocial learning.[34] Moreover, the inept deviant is often capable of shifting readily and unexpectedly from one of these incompletely developed roles to another, divesting himself of a former role almost as easily as if he were changing his clothes. He seems so little involved in the roles he takes, that it would be more accurate to describe him as superficially playing the part of an adult than as genuinely taking the role of one. The following case illustrates many of these characteristics of *inept social deviants*.

A young man of twenty was referred to a psychiatric hospital by a social agency. For the first few hours after his admission he was angry and resentful. He kept repeating, "A hospital is better than jail, anyhow." When his initial hostility had diminished, he said by way of explanation, "I've come to get help for what is wrong with me. . . . I'm afraid I'll do something and harm somebody sometime." He concluded by stating that he knew the difference between right and wrong, but that he liked "to do the opposite of what society expects." The patient's account was amplified by reports from the referring agency, which disclosed among other things that the patient had sought financial aid for himself and his wife, and investigation had shown that he was at the time married to three different girls. His turbulent history and his present predicament led the agency to recommend immediate hospitalization.

On the hospital ward, the patient spent his time in what appeared to be a ceaseless variety of bids for the attention and approval of staff members. For a time he was affable, cheerful and quietly cooperative;

[33] See page 118. [34] Compare pages 147–148 and 211–213.

then he grew loud, boisterous and talkative until he was reprimanded, when he became apologetic, submissive and remorseful. His shifts in attitude were directly related to the immediate praise or reproof he obtained from the staff. He disregarded hospital regulations until he was admonished; next he persuaded his psychiatrist to give him special privileges; and then he extended the privileges to suit his own convenience. Frequently he seemed to seek out opportunities for breaking rules. When, for example, he was placed on a diet to lose weight, at his own request, he devised ingenious trading schemes through which he obtained additional food from other patients. It was finally pointed out to him that there was no need for him to go to the trouble of finding extra food, since he was free at any time to leave the diet table. Contritely, but rather petulantly, he gave up both the diet and the schemes for trading food.

The patient's discussion with the psychiatrist demonstrated the same rapid shifts in attitude, the same demands for attention, and the same personal irresponsibility which characterized his ward behavior. He announced repeatedly that he would "turn over a new leaf"; he said apologetically that he "couldn't hurt people"; he invented facile and everchanging explanations for his actions, and stated without hesitation that he would rather lie than tell the truth. He shrugged off the consequences of his own behavior in a characteristic tic-like gesture of head and right shoulder as well as in his words. His relationship toward his psychiatrist was one of close, childlike dependence, thinly disguised by an air of bravado and unconcern.

The background of this behavior was a family situation in which rejection and hostility were prominent. The senile father was described as hot-tempered and given to threats that he would get a gun and kill his family. The mother took little interest in the patient who believed that she had rejected her children from the time of their birth. The patient said that, according to family legend, he had been born "black"; and it was his conviction that he had been neglected as dead for a considerable time after his birth, while efforts were being made to revive his mother. Whether fact or fancy, the story emphasizes vividly the patient's feelings of being an unwanted child. His three siblings, all older than himself, he described as either hostile or indifferent toward him. The patient stated repeatedly that he had never felt loved or accepted by anyone.

For this patient, childhood seems to have consisted of a series of aggressive, irresponsible acts too long to catalog completely here. As a child, for example, he escaped from his locked room to attend all-night movies, peeked into windows at night to watch people undressing, stole money from home to buy presents for his friends, got into fights with younger, smaller children, and was repeatedly picked up by the police for truancy from school. His school achievement was poor, due largely to his frequent absences and his expulsions for misconduct; standardized tests of intelligence located him within the average range. He made no long-lasting friendships. By the time he had reached adolescence he was well known to school principals, guidance officers, and juvenile court authorities, all of whom seem to have considered him hopeless.

Adulthood brought no fundamental change in the patient's behavior. He continued the aggression and irresponsibility which had characterized his earlier years; but as an adult, of course, he had more powerful means of attack at his disposal. He forged checks against his father's account; he carried a gun because, he said, he liked to feel important; he served jail sentences for auto theft and for breaking and entering. All of his jobs were temporary, none lasting longer than a week, and most of them no more than one or two days. Usually, as soon as he had collected his wages, he would leave town and push on. His itinerant life, of course, brought him no close personal attachments.

It was in the course of his wandering from place to place that the patient met and married his first wife. When she was five months pregnant he left her, became involved with another girl, and married her. After a two-week period he left this second wife, resumed his travelling, persuaded a third girl to marry him, spent a few days with her, and then returned to his second wife. All three girls were considerably younger than the patient. When the patient discussed his marital ventures with the psychiatrist, he was intense in his assertions that he "couldn't hurt the girls" and in his insistence that to tell each of them about the other two would be unthinkable. He persisted unavailingly in attempting to persuade his psychiatrist to write the girls and explain for him the tangled situation.

Over a three-month period in the hospital, the patient showed no significant change in his behavior. For a short time he seemed interested in learning a trade; but he attended his vocational classes for only a brief period. He participated occasionally in athletic events; but he was awkward and poorly coordinated in comparison with other patients of his own age. He finally joined a hospital dramatic group, and practiced faithfully for two weeks. He was given a special free period for final rehearsal, and he promptly left the hospital without permission. He took with him some clothing belonging to another patient, and left behind him, in the safekeeping of the patient whose clothes he was stealing, a friendly note of gratitude to his physician.

This patient's aggressive, antisocial behavior is characteristic of inept selective immaturity. His persistent bids for attention, which developed out of dependent relationships, were more appropriate to childhood than to biosocial adulthood. His wheedling, ingratiating attitudes, aimed at gaining special privilege, resemble strongly the young child's manipulation of a vacillating or indulgent parent.[35] His resistance to authority is reminiscent both of the preschool years and of early adolescence.[36] His fleeting, irresponsible attachments to others — with or without sexual components — are comprehensible as an integral part of the developmental phases which precede mature heterosexuality. In his demands for attention, his resistance and his affectional irresponsibility, this inept social deviant continued, as an adult, to behave in ways in which he became practiced as a child and an adolescent.

[35] Compare the cases described in Levy, D., *Maternal overprotection.* New York: Columbia University Press, 1943.
[36] See pages 103–105.

It is conceivable that our patient, within a social context somewhat different from his own, even though he maintained the same selectively immature behavior, might have achieved acceptance and success instead of ostracism and legal punishment. Tolerant and indulgent associates might have found his childlike wheedling and his ingratiating manner entertaining and acceptable. It is possible that political or religious groups, with planned campaigns of reform, could have made use of his antipathy toward authority. As a reformer, he could have capitalized in socially effective ways upon attitudes which, in a different setting, led him into antisocial behavior. The selective immaturity characteristic of the inept social deviant, of course, does not necessarily end in imprisonment or hospitalization. The expectations, tolerances and regulations of his immediate social group may permit the immature person to gain instead some measure of adult success.[37]

The immature techniques which led this patient toward inacceptable and eventually illegal behavior illustrate some of the varieties of inept social deviation. The patient's easy rationalizations for his own behavior, as well as his statement that he would rather lie than tell the truth, characterize the immature reactions called *pathological lying*. His childhood practice of peering into bedroom windows, his choice of young girls as marital partners, and his irresponsible attitudes toward them, illustrate immaturities in the form of *sex deviation*. His stealing in childhood, and his adult offenses of forgery, theft, and burglary, fit the legal definition of *delinquency*.

Any one of these three manifestations of social ineptness — *pathological lying, sex deviation* or *delinquency* — may be conspicuously dominant in the behavior of a given patient. When this occurs, we are likely to attend exclusively to the obvious symptoms and to conclude mistakenly that we are dealing with discrete disorders. In so doing we are misled into the popular fallacy that the conspicuousness of behavior is a measure of its significance as behavior pathology. But, as we turn now to a consideration of each of these manifestations, we must not forget that none of them develops in isolation, as an exclusive sign of social ineptness. All arise and persist within the wider context of selective immaturity.

Pathological lying [38]

Some inept social deviants seem to falsify statements so easily, so habitually, and so convincingly, that they have been classified as "pathological liars." The observer who attempts to understand this deviant behavior is struck by the time and effort which a patient may invest in fabricating

[37] Cleckley, H., *The mask of sanity*. St. Louis: Mosby, 1941.
[38] For discussions of this behavior, see Healy, W. F., *Pathological lying, accusation and swindling*. Boston: Little, Brown, 1917; Louttit, C. M., *Clinical psychology* (Rev. ed.). New York: Harper, 1947, pp. 374–378.

stories, and in subsequently defending his fabrications. Often the stories are complex rationalizations which elaborate a theme of self-vindication. Sometimes they are so patently wish-fulfilling that we can consider them to be private fantasies translated into communicative speech. Occasionally the fabrications seem to take no consistent direction; a patient misrepresents capriciously, and falsely accuses others or himself without apparent reason. Like the inept deviants we have discussed above, the patient appears to fabricate when it would be simpler and more convenient to tell the truth.

The everyday use of fabrication common to normal childhood is the background of pathological lying. As every parent knows, children early have difficulty in distinguishing from one another the fairy tales they hear at home, the products of their own private fantasy, and what the adult world calls "reality." Most children under six confuse and intermingle these three sorts of stimulation.[39] The young child also learns, as soon as he has developed adequate communicative skills, that he can escape punishment by devising excuses for his own misdeeds.[40] If the threatened punishment is severe, and if it comes from his own self-reactions as well as from his parents, he may come at last to accept his fabricated excuses as truth — and as truth defend them against his elders' claim that he is lying.

The child who learns to quell his punishing self-reactions mainly by accepting his own invented excuses as true, has acquired a technique that predisposes him to pathological lying in adulthood. Whether he continues to generalize these techniques to each new situation, or whether — like most children — he learns the distinctions between fact, fancy and fabrication, depends upon a variety of factors. Punitive, rejecting reactions on the part of his parents, the intensity of his own guilty self-reactions, and the positive satisfactions he obtains — through attention from others, escape from guilt, or the rare reward of private fantasy which becomes translated into fact — all may serve to prolong the everyday fabrication of childhood into the adult years. When fabricating and misrepresenting become autonomous and self-perpetuating activities in adulthood, we may speak of pathological lying. It is clear, however, that what we are then describing is the persistence, into the adult years, of behavior which is more appropriate to childhood. The relative immaturity of pathological lying in adult behavior is illustrated by the following case.

> The patient, an eighteen-year-old boy, was brought to the hospital by a solicitous friend. From the age of six, according to his teachers and friends, the boy had been habitually falsifying. As a child, he had lied to escape responsibility for ordinary childish misdeeds, and had told "tall stories" woven around the theme of personal accomplishment and

[39] Murphy, L. B , "Childhood experience in relation to personality development." In Hunt, J. McV. (Ed.), *Personality and the behavior disorders.* New York: Ronald, 1944, p. 675.
[40] Pages 110–113 and 379–381.

courage. As an adolescent he had impressed his friends with stories of his adventurous life, his social position and his personal possessions. As a young adult, he was beginning to translate his extravagant tales into reality by stealing large sums of money and expensive cars, by borrowing airplanes and performing dangerous "stunts" in them, and by developing close, dependent relationships with older and more socially prominent persons. The boy was the only child of a widowed mother who had told him that she wished he had never been born. She never undertook to make a permanent home for him. During her periodic alcoholic excesses, however, she characteristically appealed to her son for support, embarrassing and frightening him by her behavior. It was clear, from a study of the case, that the patient's "pathological lying" began in the common fancies and rationalizations of childhood, and represented a translation into communicative speech of his compensatory, wish-fulfilling fantasies. The patient himself explained his habitual falsification as an attempt to "build himself up."

Sex deviation

The selective immaturity of some socially deviant persons is shown most clearly in their unskilled attempts at satisfying their sexual needs. In the human animal, as we have seen, sexual need-satisfaction sequences develop as intricately interrelated attitudes and responses, within a context of social permission and taboo.[41] Consequently, sexual behavior in all mature human beings is exceedingly complicated, and includes, in addition to the consummatory sex act, a wide variety of anticipant and substitute reactions. Those attitudes and responses which, for the mature adult, are preparatory or incidental parts of sex behavior may represent, for the selectively retarded person, his chief source of sexual gratification. We may then consider the sexual behavior of the immature person to be *deviant*.

The immaturity of sex deviation may be demonstrated in the *object* which the selectively retarded person needs as his source of satisfaction. In the course of exploring his body, the child inevitably learns to manipulate his own genitals (*masturbation*); and he often learns to obtain comfort and relief from such manipulation.[42] When this behavior persists into adulthood, and the grown individual finds his exclusive satisfaction likewise in masturbation, he may be considered sexually deviant. In a similar manner, the young adolescent often forms close attachments with individuals of his own sex.[43] When, in our culture, this behavior persists beyond adolescence, and the adult obtains his sexual gratification from persons of his own sex (*homosexuality*), he is showing sexually deviant behavior.[44]

[41] See pages 36–37.
[42] Spitz, R. A. and Wolf, K. M., "Autoerotism: some empirical findings and hypotheses on three of its manifestations in the first year of life." In Freud, A. (Ed.), *Psychoanalytic study of the child*. New York: International Universities Press, 1949, vol. 3/4, pp. 85–120.
[43] See pages 141–143.
[44] Henry, G. W., *Sex variants: a study of homosexual patterns*. New York: Hoeber, 1948;

In some instances, it is not the object chosen for sexual gratification, but the *attitude* supporting his sexual behavior, that characterizes the individual as an immature sex deviant. The normal exploratory behavior of the child who investigates, exhibits and comments upon the anatomical differences between himself, his friends and his parents, for example, may persist beyond childhood into the adult years. If this occurs, the adult may obtain sexual satisfaction chiefly from gazing at the body of a potential sex partner (*voyeurism*), or from exposing the genitals in the presence of another (*exhibitionism*).

A great many of the sexual activities we currently call deviant seem actually to be phases in the biosocial development of normal adult heterosexuality. Some of these persist into adulthood, and become part of normal foreplay. For the mature person, however, such behavior is merely preparatory or incidental to the consummatory sex act. But, for the selectively retarded person, this preparatory or incidental behavior may remain, as we have seen, the exclusive technique for achieving sexual satisfaction. Sex deviation, in these cases, can be interpreted as *fixation* — as the persistence into adulthood of exclusive attitudes and responses that are appropriate to an immature phase of development.[45]

Complete heterosexual behavior may also be supported by inappropriate or immature attitudes. The development of permanent attachments, within a context of social and personal responsibility for the marital partner and the offspring, is an expected accompaniment of adult heterosexuality in our culture. Irresponsible attitudes and impermanent attachments may therefore signify immaturity in the form of sexual deviation. Within this category belong the heterosexual assault (*rape*), and the repeated sexual relations with many different partners (*promiscuity*).[46] In contemporary Western society, most of these culturally deviant sexual manifestations are ordinarily considered so damaging, both personally and culturally, that they are punishable by law. Consequently, the social deviant whose selective retardation is manifest in his sexual behavior stands in danger of paying for his ineptness by imprisonment. If he escapes legal retaliation, he still runs the risk of ostracism by his associates, and of self-condemnation by his own culturally determined reactions of guilt and shame.[47]

Doshay, L. J., *The boy sex offender and his later career.* New York: Grune and Stratton, 1943.

[45] See pages 143–153.

[46] For a thoroughgoing study of promiscuity in women, see Lion, E. G., Jambor, H. M., Corrigan, H. G., and Bradway, K. P., *An experiment in the psychiatric treatment of promiscuous girls.* San Francisco: Dept. Public Health, 1945; Safier, B., Corrigan, H. G., Fein, E. J., and Bradway, K. P., *A psychiatric approach to the treatment of promiscuity.* New York: American Social Hygiene Association, 1949. For analyses of cases of unmarried mothers, see May, R., *The meaning of anxiety.* New York: Ronald, 1950, pp. 237–350.

[47] It should be noted that sexual activities permitted or encouraged in one culture may be strongly tabooed in another. Moreover, some of the more recent data concerning sexual behavior seem to indicate a wider range in our culture than had previously been supposed. See Kinsey, A. C., Pomeroy, W. B., and Martin, C. E., *Sexual behavior in the human male.* Philadelphia: Saunders, 1948.

Delinquency [48]

The inept techniques which some social deviants use in satisfying their needs bring them inevitably into conflict with the law. When an immature person violates the explicit regulations of his society and is discovered and punished for his violation, he is considered to be *delinquent*. Not all or even the majority of inept social deviants are delinquent, of course, just as not all antisocial persons are inept social deviants. For it is neither the aggressive character of his behavior, nor the immaturity from which it derives, that differentiates the delinquent deviant from the one who is not delinquent. It is the process of legal arrest and of ensuing punishment — and nothing else — which defines delinquency.

To list the varieties of immature behavior which we term delinquent, therefore, is only to record those inept techniques which happen to be prohibited by law. We have already seen some illustrations of delinquent behavior in cases of inept social deviants. The sailor-salesman who periodically left his wife and child, for example, had served repeated jail sentences for forgery. The patient who was simultaneously married to three girls had been apprehended, not only for bigamy, but also for carrying a gun, for forgery, for auto theft, and for breaking-and-entering. The young boy described as a pathological liar was known to juvenile court authorities as a member of an adolescent gang which stripped stolen cars and illegally sold the parts. We have also seen that sexually deviant persons stand in danger of legal punishment; and if their misdemeanor is discovered and they are arrested, they are also grouped with the delinquent.

For the most part, our statutes are set up to describe, regulate and punish behavior which is aggressive, irresponsible, or antisocial. Accordingly, the social deviant who is judged delinquent is the person whose inept techniques lead him into attacks upon other persons or upon their property. He does not proceed through the slow steps of job-training, promotion and increased wage-earning to financial security; he skips the intervening phases and forges or robs. He does not follow the usual pattern of courtship and marriage to achieve adult heterosexuality; he forms fleeting attachments, promiscuously, or he rapes. He does not employ the devious, indirect techniques of expressing aggression prescribed by his society; he assaults other persons directly. In all of these forms of deviant behavior, the delinquent reveals clearly his selective immaturity.

[48] For studies of this topic, see Aichhorn, A., *Wayward youth*. New York: Viking, 1935; Alexander, F. and Healy, W., *Roots of crime*. New York: Knopf, 1935; Glueck, S. and Glueck, E., *Criminal careers in retrospect*. New York: Commonwealth Fund, 1943; Healy, W. and Bronner, A. F., *New light on delinquency and its treatment*. New Haven: Yale University Press, 1936; Lindner, R. M. and Seliger, R. V., *Handbook of correctional psychology*. New York: Philosophical Library, 1947; Merrill, M. A., *Problems of child delinquency*. Boston: Houghton Mifflin, 1947; Metfessel, M. and Lovell, C., "Recent literature on individual correlates of crime." *Psychol. Bull.*, 1942, vol. 39, pp. 133–164.

The biosocially mature adult in our culture, we have said, learns to withstand delay in the satisfaction of his needs, in ways and to a degree which were impossible for him as a child. For the impulsive delinquent, in contrast to this, the need-satisfaction sequence is telescoped, until the delay between tension and its reduction is almost as brief as the delay between a hungry infant's wail and his mother's appearance to relieve his hunger. Much like the hungry infant in his earliest relationships with his mother, the delinquent social deviant in his relationships with other persons exhibits impatience, aggressiveness and impulsiveness. It is in his failure to tolerate delay in the satisfaction of his own imperious needs — for possessions, for money, for relief of the tensions of sexual need and aggression — that the delinquent reveals most impressively his biosocial immaturity.[49]

By now it has become clear that what we are describing as varieties of social deviation are varieties of selective retardation in behavioral development. Whether the deviant is so *inadequate* as never to achieve maturity, or so *inept* in his attempts to maintain himself as an adult that he incurs legal punishment, he is still behaving in ways that are not appropriate to his age. Whether his deviation appears most conspicuously as lying, as sexual immaturity, or as aggressive delinquency, he is still a biosocially immature adult. The background of this selective immaturity, to which we next turn, is a background of pathological fixation, to which parental training, defective role-taking skills, and the interplay of action and self-reaction may all contribute.

Biosocial Development of Social Deviation

Social immaturity of a temporary sort is characteristic of every maturing person. Even the normal adult who behaves appropriately for the most part may, in some special situation or at some particular time, act in ways that are more suitable to a young child. But not every growing person, or every grown adult, shows the persistence of immature behavior which characterizes the socially deviant individual. When selective immaturity persists into the adult years, and distinctively colors adult behavior, then some interruption or failure in the usual course of behavioral maturation has occurred. Socially deviant behavior, in other words, is the product of *pathological fixation*.

Socially deviant behavior as pathological fixation

Fixation, we have said,[50] involves the persistence of acquired behavior patterns after they have become biosocially immature — in terms of the cultural norms accepted in an individual's own society. We have further distinguished two varieties of pathological fixation: (1) a premature termination of some

[49] Lindner, R. M., *Rebel without a cause.* New York: Grune and Stratton, 1944.
[50] See pages 143–153.

aspect of personality development; and (2) a delay in one phase of biosocial maturation, the effect of which is to retard or distort personality development in a subsequent phase. These two varieties of fixation make intelligible the two major varieties of socially deviant behavior — the inadequate and the inept. Each represents a different form of the delay or termination in development which defines pathological fixation.

The *inadequate* social deviant, who never quite attains the degree of maturity reached by his adult contemporaries, illustrates the *premature termination* of personality development. In his behavior we find that some of the acquired behavior patterns which define personality persist long after they have become biosocially immature. For some deviants, it may be vocational adjustment that is never achieved, and for some it is the breaking of early attachments to parents and parent-surrogates. For others, it is failure to develop and maintain mature affectional relationships which demonstrates early termination of development. For a few inadequate deviants, like the medical corpsman described earlier,[51] practically all aspects of personality may remain permanently at an immature phase of development. The consequence of such premature termination of development, in a few or in many aspects of personality, is the persistence into adulthood of behavior which remains essentially childlike.

The *inept* social deviant uses his learned techniques of social participation in immature and inappropriate ways; and he exemplifies the second kind of pathological fixation. Like the inadequate deviant, he has undergone *delay* in some phase of biosocial maturation, but he has not suffered a premature termination of development. He is far from being an ineffectual, childlike adult. The biosocially immature behavior, which in the inept deviant persists into adulthood, has itself been modified and distorted. So also have those subsequent phases of his biosocial maturation which develop out of the areas wherein he has suffered delay. Thus, as a result of early but temporary delay in development, the inept social deviant is unprepared, at each succeeding phase of his behavioral maturation, for the acquisition of more mature techniques.

It is this modification and distortion of subsequent development, resulting from delay in an earlier phase, which accounts in large part for the apparent contradiction and unpredictability in the behavior of inept social deviants. The sailor-salesman,[52] for example, showed the consequences of his delayed emancipation from his mother by counting on maternal intervention. It was she who was expected to rescue him from jail, from hospital and from his own marital difficulties. His pattern was not that of remaining like a child in his childhood home. The bigamist[53] demonstrated his delay in achieving affectional maturity by multiplying his heterosexual relationships. He did this in ways which would be normal adult sex behavior for a non-social mammal, but

[51] See pages 199–203.   [52] See pages 193–196.   [53] See pages 203–205.

which for a human being were childlike in their irresponsibility. The habitual falsifier [54] had undergone delay in the area of distinguishing fact, fantasy and defensive rationalization; but this inability did not by any means persist unchanged into adulthood. As a young adult, the patient continued to fabricate; but he did it to achieve adult goals, and with full understanding of the character and even the significance of his own deception.

In all the behavior which characterizes the inept social deviant it is the same. We are not dealing here with the simple persistence into adulthood of childlike techniques. We are dealing rather with a delay in affectional maturity, or in the regulation of aggression toward others, which operates in such a way as to modify profoundly the later phases in the development of interpersonal relationships. The voyeur and the exhibitionist, for example, are employing childlike techniques, but they are using them with adult accents, in the service of adult need. The forger and the burglar, and even the man who attacks others violently, are showing the unreflective impulsiveness of childhood; but their weapons are the weapons of adults. These inept social deviants are selectively retarded by reason of pathological fixation; but for them developmental delay means progressive modification and distortion in behavior.

Conditions favoring social deviation

If socially deviant behavior is to be considered the result of pathological fixation, then we must seek the reasons for social deviation in those conditions which favor the persistence of behavior beyond the time it can be considered appropriate. We need not go outside of the facts of social learning — of overlearning, reward and punishment — in order to define the conditions under which immature behavior persists. The earliest, and many of the most significant, modifications of behavior occur within the context of the family, in relation to parental permission and taboo, and in connection with the relatively simple, concrete patterns of need-satisfaction sequence which constitute child training. This early learned behavior, as we have seen, may generalize to persons and objects outside the family, and it may undergo important modifications in a new social context.[55] Consequently, we shall begin by examining the conditions favoring the persistence or overlearning of behavior, first in parent-child relationships, and then in the reactions of others to the socially deviant person.

Parental emphases. Particular patterns of parent-child interrelationship may initiate much of the behavior we have called socially deviant. The child of an *overprotective* mother, for example, may become a child who is overtrained in dependent ways. If his mother is oversolicitous, he may learn to lean upon her for support in situations where most children are independent; if she is

---

[54] See pages 207–208.   [55] See pages 134–143.

domineering, he may learn to anticipate and to conform to her whims, as well as to her demands. If his mother is indulgently overprotective, and accepts from him overt hostility and aggressiveness, the child may learn that there is virtually no boundary to his field of activity. The interrelationships between overprotective mother and dependent or rebellious child constitute one social context within which the immature behavior of the social deviant may be overlearned. Maternal oversolicitousness or domination may be the start of adult *inadequacy;* and maternal indulgence may be the start of the irresponsible aggression of adult *ineptness.*

The child of cold, neglectful, *rejecting* parents, on the other hand, is a child deprived of his first lessons in affectional response. He may learn, in a setting of maternal rejection, the shallow and fleeting affectional attitudes, and the demanding, attention-getting, ingratiating responses, which characterize some socially deviant adults. The child of parents who are neither overprotective nor rejecting, but who show persistently *vacillating* attitudes, may also be overtrained in behavior which persists as selective immaturity. Such a child often learns to an unusual degree those techniques of minute-to-minute conformity with ever-changing demands which characterize the apparent inconsistency and unpredictability of the inept adult.

The four persons, cited earlier as examples of socially deviant behavior, all learned their earliest techniques of social interaction in relation to overprotective, rejecting or vacillating parents. The sailor-salesman was trained by his oversolicitous mother and sisters to expect protection for everything he did — even for those actions which were judged antisocial by the standards of his adult society. The medical corpsman was overtrained in the dependent ways of an inadequate social deviant by his oversolicitous mother who guarded him from his father's punishment. The bigamist was consistently rejected as a child — by his hostile, threatening father, by his ineffectual mother, and by his cold, indifferent siblings — until, he said, he felt that he had never been loved by anyone. The chronic prevaricator was reared by a rejecting mother who vacillated between open neglect of her son and dependent demands upon him. To these clinical examples may be added the classic case of antisocial behavior analyzed in detail by Lindner,[56] in which strong attachment to the protective mother, and hostility toward the rejecting father, provided a context for the overlearning and persistence of social ineptness.

The close relationship between parental emphases and socially deviant behavior is made clear in many studies of parent-child interaction. Levy's carefully controlled series of overprotected children, mentioned earlier, includes four cases in which the later adult behavior was so dependent, inept or antisocial as to be considered selectively immature.[57] Levy's observations

---

[56] Lindner, R. M., *Rebel without a cause.* New York: Grune and Stratton, 1944.
[57] Levy, D., *Maternal overprotection.* New York: Columbia University Press, 1943, Chapter 8.

point toward a relationship between childhood deprivation and the shallowness of adult affectional response. They support also the observation that childhood indulgence may be followed by free and antisocial aggressiveness in adult years.[58] Similar conclusions are reached by Greenacre [59] in an investigation of background factors in social deviation, and by Heaver [60] in a study of forty male social deviants. The implication of these studies is clear: parental overtraining in immature behavior provides the conditions for the development of pathological fixation.

Reactions of others and self-reactions. Most children whose parents are overprotective, rejecting or vacillating, have one safeguard against the development and persistence of pathological fixation. The reactions of their neighborhood contemporaries and of their teachers at school more often counteract than reinforce their continued use of immature techniques. The dependency or the irresponsible aggressiveness, the vacillation or the too ready conformity to demands of the moment, which a child may practice successfully at home, are frequently unsuccessful as adjustive techniques in the neighborhood or at school. The reactions of friends and teachers provide, for most children, an antidote to the persistence of inadequate or inept behavior outside. When, however, the parental pattern is duplicated or reinforced by the expectations of others in the child's social environment, we may expect selective immaturity to persist as adult social deviation.

The significance of others' reactions for training in persistent immaturity is clear in the case material cited earlier. Our sailor-salesman became involved in fights with his peers, struggles with his teachers, and conflict with the law. Had it not been for the energetic intervention of his mother and his wife, these reactions of others might eventually have ended his persistent inept techniques. Our medical corpsman was isolated, in his rural home, from any extensive contacts with contemporaries who could have trained him in more mature behavior. In addition, his religious activities, the jobs he preferred, and even the reactions of his employers toward him reinforced or duplicated, rather than offset, the protection he obtained from his mother. Our bigamist combined with his inept social skills a charming, ingratiating attitude, the practice of giving stolen gifts to his friends, and a dramatic acting-out of "big shot" behavior; and these protected him against the disapproval by others that might otherwise have served to alter his immature behavior.

From the reactions of others, we know, develop the spoken and unspoken evaluations of oneself which we call *self-reactions*.[61] The immature individual whose parents overvalue or overprotect him learns to overvalue his own behav-

[58] Levy, D., "Psychopathic personality and crime." *J. educ. Sociol.*, 1942, vol. 16, pp. 99–114.

[59] Greenacre, P., "Conscience in the psychopath." *Amer. J. Orthopsychiat.*, 1945, vol. 15, pp. 495–509.

[60] Heaver, W. L., "A study of forty male psychopathic personalities before, during and after hospitalization." *Amer. J. Psychiat.*, 1943, vol. 100, pp. 342–346.

[61] See pages 95–105.

ior and overprotect himself. When behavior which is inacceptable to his contemporaries is tolerated and indulged by his parents, the immature individual
comes to regard himself as immune to punishment.[62] The social deviant who
amuses and entertains his companions by his winning ways, or by his blasé
attitudes, learns to consider himself a charming sophisticate whose behavior is
beyond criticism.[63] When, on the other hand, other persons find his behavior
inconsistent and capricious, and respond to it in vacillating ways, a social
deviant learns to respond in the same manner until, as we saw in our case
material, his behavior may become unpredictable even to himself.

Self-reactions of this kind, like the reactions of others from which they are
derived, serve to perpetuate the inadequate or inept behavior of a social
deviant, and must therefore be included among the conditions favoring
pathological fixation. Of equal importance, however, is the fact that self-
regulation — what we popularly call *conscience* — develops from self-reactions
of disapproval or control.[64] The immature individual who fails to acquire such
self-reactions is able, therefore, to learn self-regulation only with difficulty or
not at all. Over-valuation of oneself, assumed immunity to punishment, and
conviction that one's own behavior is unpredictable, provide no basis for the
acquisition of effective self-control. So it is that the inept social deviant —
and to a lesser extent the inadequate one — are commonly described as "con-
scienceless," "without conflict" and "without guilt." In an earlier period,
such descriptions would have been used to justify "constitutional psychopathic inferiority." Today they point irresistibly toward ineffective socially
learned self-reactions.

The complex and uneven process of biosocial maturation, we have now
seen, may suffer retardation in two important ways, each of which results in
behavior pathology. When the course of maturation is slowed down generally, the result is adult behavior which we have described, in the previous
chapter, as *developmental retardation*. When, however, delay in maturation
occurs only in circumscribed aspects of personality development (pathological
fixation), the result is the selective retardation which we have described in the
present chapter as characteristic of *social deviation*. We turn now to a third
source of behavioral immaturity which has consequences that are no less fundamental in behavior pathology than general and selective retardation. This is
the failure to sustain behavior at a level of maturity that has already been
achieved, the return or the emergence of behavior appropriate to an earlier
phase of biosocial development, to which we apply the term *regression*.

[62] For an investigation of the attitudes toward paternal punishment characterizing
delinquent children, see Bach, G. R., and Bremer, G., "Projective father fantasies of pre-
adolescent, delinquent children." *J. Psychol.*, 1947, vol. 24, pp. 3–17.

[63] For examples of this behavior, see Thorne, F. C., "Etiological studies of psychopathic
personality: the ego-inflated, defectively-conditioned type." *J. consult. Psychol.*, 1947,
vol. 11, pp. 299–307.

[64] For a discussion of conscience, see pages 284–289.

Regression, Withdrawal and Invalidism

Regression

In our discussion of *maturation* and *fixation,* we have already pointed out that the process of acquiring biosocial maturity is never a smooth or completely homogeneous one.[1] We must expect that in the course of ordinary maturity, there will always be episodes of biosocial hesitation, which we have referred to as *normal fixations.* The designation *pathological fixation* we reserve for certain exceptional instances — the premature *termination* of some aspect of personality development, for example, and the *delay* in one phase of maturation which retards or distorts personality development in a subsequent phase.[2]

In pathological instances, the effects of fixation are commonly indirect, distorted, or greatly modified by the subsequent development of personality. When this is the case, it becomes always difficult, and frequently impossible, to demonstrate the actual fact of a specific fixation — and difficult or impossible also to trace its consequences in behavior organization. Sometimes such complex results can be successfully worked out through a prolonged and painstaking behavior analysis. But more often the fact of prior fixation, and the developmental modifications or distortions following early fixation, can only be *inferred.*

The *fixation-regression hypothesis,* one of the most important in behavior pathology, rests upon just such an inference.[3] It is that *regression* — the occurrence of relatively immature behavior in a situation previously met by more mature behavior — *is always an indication of an earlier fixation which had at some time in the past been given up.* The assumption usually made is

[1] See Chapter 5.   [2] See pages 145–148.

[3] Freud, S., "Instincts and their vicissitudes" (1915), in *Collected Papers,* vol. 4. London: Hogarth, 1948, pp. 60–83; Freud, S., *General introduction to psychoanalysis.* New York: Garden City Publishing Co., 1943, pp. 297–312.

that frustration becomes so severe, or the organism so incompetent, that the individual falls back upon a once preferred, but since abandoned, procedure or relationship. The appearance of regressive behavior, which we are about to discuss, is then accepted as *prima facie* evidence of preëxisting fixation.

Regression as recapitulation

The concept of regression, like many another fruitful concept, has undergone important changes since its adoption by behavior pathologists. The early writers on regression were still under the spell of the biological doctrine of recapitulation. This doctrine, in effect, stated that organisms tend to pass through successive stages in their embryonic development which correspond to successive stages in the evolution of their species ("ontogeny repeats phylogeny"). Individual organisms of any species that came to maturity with anatomical characteristics belonging to some earlier evolutionary stage were then called *atavistic*. They were said to show a "reversion to type," that is, a return in one respect or another to the structure of a primitive ancestor.

Genetic psychologists and behavior pathologists of four or five decades ago simply extended the doctrine of recapitulation to cover postnatal biosocial development. They said that infants and children, in becoming socialized, tend to repeat crucial stages in the development of human civilization.[4] Thus the infant was pictured as equivalent in his attitudes and responses to primitive, prehistoric man. To suffer *arrest* of biosocial progress, according to this hypothesis, was to be temporarily or permanently fixated at a primitive level. Similarly, to be unable to maintain oneself on a more advanced level, in childhood, adolescence or adulthood, was interpreted as meaning a reversion to one of the primitive stages of cultural evolution at which the individual had once supposedly been fixated. Such reversion to some primitive prototype was called *regression*.[5]

This was the general situation out of which came the original formulations of neuroses and psychoses as regressive disorders. Patients showing behavior pathology were said to have fixated at, advanced beyond, and then reverted to one or another infantile stage of development.[6] Since the socialization of every individual was supposed to repeat the process of mankind's civilization, these infantile stages in fixation and regression were also assumed to correspond to primitive stages in the infancy of the human race. Regression was thus equated with a return to human prehistory, at the same time that it was

---

[4] See, for example, Hall, G. S., *Adolescence: its psychology and its relations to physiology, anthropology, sociology, sex, crime, religion and education.* New York: Appleton, 1904, vol. 1, p. 2.

[5] For examples of this viewpoint, see Fenichel, O., *The psychoanalytic theory of neurosis.* New York: Norton, 1945, pp. 53, 65, 468.

[6] See, for example, Fenichel, O., *The psychoanalytic theory of neurosis.* New York: Norton, 1945, Chapters 17, 18, 20.

equated with a return to infantile levels in the individual patient's own developmental history. In this way arose the double-barrelled hypothesis, which still haunts us in behavior pathology, that regressive behavior is both childish and primitive.

Criticisms of regression as recapitulation

Objections to this deceptively simple account were raised by anthropologists, students of child development, and eventually by behavior pathologists themselves. The anthropologists asked, "Who was this primitive, original savage, the supposed prototype of our own uncivilized infants, and just what was he like?" Today, of course, the answer is that, since early prehistoric man has left us no record whatever of his behavior, we have nothing whatever upon which to base our behavioral parallels. We cannot reconstruct his thinking, his basic conflicts, and his ways of coping with frustration, from the scattered bony fragments and the few artifacts which are all the evidence we have.

The answer to the anthropological question several decades ago was quite different from today's answer. For it was confidently believed then that we could find out about primitive, aboriginal man simply by observing the contemporary inhabitants of central Africa or the natives living in the South Sea Islands. However, when these alleged "children of nature" were actually studied, they were all discovered to have developed complex cultures of their own. It is true that their cultures are in many respects quite different from those evolved in Western civilization, and are for the most part preliterate. Nevertheless, they are far too advanced to qualify as representatives of our own primitive predecessors. This discovery, of course, left us with no savage prototype at all for our uncivilized infants, or for our regressive patients either.

Students of child development found still other reasons for rejecting the application of the recapitulation doctrine to infant socialization. Since there is no single human society, but many different human societies, with different early phases and diverse developmental routes, there can be no single history of mankind's social evolution. In short, there is nothing for the child to recapitulate.

The child, of course, does tend to repeat in his own individual development many of the behavior sequences which his parents or parent-substitutes have gone through in theirs.[7] But this repetition is merely an expression of the fact that parent and child, or parent-substitute and child, are closely similar organisms which, during infancy and childhood, operate in similarly structured

[7] See, for example, Erikson, E. H., *Childhood and society.* New York: Norton, 1950, pp. 96–160; Mead, M., "Research on primitive children." In Carmichael, L. (Ed.), *Manual of child psychology.* New York: Wiley, 1946, pp. 667–706; Bateson, G., "Cultural determinants of personality." In Hunt, J. McV. (Ed.), *Personality and the behavior disorders.* New York: Ronald, 1944, pp. 714–735.

biosocial fields. This is biosocial maturation, not recapitulation; its basis is in human learning, not in racial memory.

A Chinese child, for example, reared from earliest infancy by American foster-parents — or an American child reared by Chinese foster-parents — does not repeat stages characteristic of his real parents, whom he cannot remember and may never have seen. Instead, he follows the general route of biosocial maturation that his adoptive parents traversed when they were infants and growing children (*cultural transmission*). For, of course, he must face the same general problems of socialization that were characteristic of the culture in which his foster-parents also were reared. It is obvious, therefore, that if such an adopted child were to regress, he would exhibit biosocially immature behavior in terms of the standards and the practices prevailing in the culture into which he had been inducted.

A biosocial definition of regression

From all that has been said, we should expect regression to exhibit the characteristics of a given individual's own personal development in his contemporary culture, and not those of a remote ancestor or a hypothetical savage. As a matter of fact, regressive behavior is sometimes little more than the reinstatement of a discarded or neglected technique, or the attempt to re-establish an interpersonal relationship which once had been abandoned. The clearest cut examples of such regression are to be found in young children whose earlier acquired patterns have as yet been neither replaced nor greatly modified by later and more mature reactions.

In most cases of regression, however, the situation involves more than a simple reinstatement of earlier relationships and techniques. Even the example most often cited in the literature on regression — the unhappy five-year-old who reverts to sucking and wetting when he finds himself competing with an infant sibling for his mother's affection — is not as clear as it may at first seem. It is true that the five-year-old sucked and wetted when he was an infant, and that in so behaving he received maternal attention. But it is equally true that his sibling rival also provides him with a current model of successful infant behavior which he may adopt.[8] To what degree one factor is responsible for the regressive action, and to what degree the other factor, is something that can be settled only through a study of the individual child, if at all. It cannot be decided *a priori*.

It is obvious now that we cannot take regression to previously fixated techniques and relationships as our one prototype, even though this variety undoubtedly occurs. We cannot even limit regression to those instances in which it can be demonstrated that we are dealing with reversion to a specific

---

[8] For a discussion of learning through the adoption of the prevailing pattern, see pages 59–63.

earlier behavior pattern, whether fixated or not. If our conception is to fit the facts, as we have them today, and serve as a basis for further advances in behavior pathology, it must be broader than either of these. It must be broad enough to include the innumerable cases in which relatively immature reactions appear that cannot be traced, with any degree of certainty, to an individual's own behavior during an earlier phase of his development.

Let us therefore define *regression* as *the recurrence, or new occurrence, of behavior which is considered biosocially immature, in terms of the cultural norms accepted in a given individual's society for persons of his age, sex and status.* Regression thus defined includes the cases in which an outgrown pattern of behavior reappears in one's repertory. It also includes the new occurrence of techniques and relationships which, although apparently novel in an individual's life history, are definitely inappropriate because they belong to a biosocially less mature phase of personality development.[9]

From a practical standpoint, what is perhaps most important about this definition is that it does not require one to demonstrate a specific relationship to the earlier activities and interests of a person, before a given sample of his behavior may be called regressive. Neither does it require that one take such a relationship for granted. All that is necessary is that the reactions be considered relatively immature in a person's own culture, and that they be absent from the repertory of his immediate past — since otherwise they would be called *fixations*.[10]

Regressive behavior may be transient in character or it may be indefinitely prolonged. Its duration, of course, will in part depend upon the persistence of the conditions that originally precipitated it. Thus, if a mother's absence from home induces regressive behavior in a young child, her prompt return may bring its quick recession.[11] The duration of regression is also related to the persistence or transience of secondary gains. For example, illness or injury that renders a person bedfast will lead in anyone to dependent childlike behavior. If, however, the special privileges accorded to disabled persons in our culture prove especially rewarding to an individual, he may attempt to perpetuate his dependent status long after his illness or injury has ceased to be otherwise disabling.[12]

Regressive behavior may last indefinitely if for any reason it has been over-practiced, if it becomes a protection against anxiety, or if it is encouraged by someone — for example, by an oversolicitous parent or an insecure physician — after the precipitating conditions have disappeared. Finally, regression

---

[9] This form of regression has also been called *primitivation*. See Barker, R. G., Dembo, T., and Lewin, K., "Frustration and regression: an experiment with young children." *Univ. Iowa stud. Child Welf.*, 1941, vol. 18, no. 1, p. 8.

[10] See pages 143–148.

[11] For a discussion of separation anxiety, see pages 290–293.

[12] This point is considered in greater detail on pages 232–238.

may persist and even widen its scope if a person grows relatively incompetent as a result of behavioral deterioration. This we see as part of a general desocialization in schizophrenic disorders, and as part of degenerative brain disease in pathological senility.[13] We shall return to some of these relationships when we discuss the conditions favoring regression, and to others when we take up disorganization and deterioration.

Regression and retrogression

In the literature on behavior pathology, it is customary to distinguish between regression and retrogression.[14] Regression we have already defined. By *retrogression* we mean *the recurrence of a technique or a relationship which had earlier been given up.* Retrogression thus includes some but not all regressive behavior; that is, it includes any actual recurrence of an outmoded, immature pattern (*retrogressive regression*). It does not include immature behavior which is new in an individual's life history. Retrogression also includes behavior which is not regressive because it is not biosocially immature. That is, it includes the recurrence of any earlier acquired techniques or relationships, in place of a later acquired one, without regard to their relative maturity.

An interesting attempt has been made by Sears to equate fixation with habit-strength, and retrogression with a return from a later to a strong earlier habit.[15] If these parallels are valid, then the factors responsible for fixation and retrogression (including *retrogressive regression*) will be those responsible for learned patterns of behavior in general. A great many experimental studies, most of them upon rats, have been aimed at clarifying this relationship.[16] They seek to set up situations in which the relative prepotencies of an old and a new habit are determined in accordance with some arbitrary standard adopted by the experimenter. The obtained results are then expressed in terms of "habit-fixation" and "habit-regression."

It is essential to recognize that such experimental studies do not bear directly upon the topic of fixation and regression as these are defined in behavior

[13] For a discussion of desocialization see pages 481–492; for a discussion of cerebral incompetence in senility, see pages 546–555.

[14] Barker, R. G., Dembo, T., and Lewin, K., "Frustration and regression: an experiment with young children." *Univ. Iowa stud. Child Welf.*, 1941, vol. 18, no. 1, pp. 7–11.

[15] Sears, R. R., "A survey of objective studies of psychoanalytic concepts." *Soc. Sci. Res. Council Bull. 51.* New York: 1943, pp. 78–81. "Fixation" here is described as a "superlatively strong habit." It should be noted that Sears' term for retrogression is *instrumental act regression.*

[16] For reviews of such studies, see Sears, R. R., "A survey of objective studies of psychoanalytic concepts." *Soc. Sci. Res. Council Bull. 51.* New York: 1943; Sears, R. R., "Experimental analysis of psychoanalytic phenomena." In Hunt, J. McV. (Ed.), *Personality and the behavior disorders.* New York: Ronald, 1944, pp. 306–332. For a recent example of this experimental approach, see Whiting, J. W. M., and Mowrer, O. H., "Habit progression and regression — a laboratory study of some factors relevant to human socialization." *J. comp. Psychol.*, 1943, vol. 36, pp. 229–253.

pathology — that is, in terms of relative maturity, adequacy and appropriateness in the individual's culture.   The fixation and retrogression with which they deal are defined simply in terms of failure to give up a habit learned earlier for one learned later, and the return to an earlier learned habit after another has once replaced it.   Moreover, the time elapsing between the earlier and later habits in experimental studies is characteristically short — often no more than a few days.   In behavior pathology, of course, the time lapses of any importance amount to a period of months for infants, of years for children, and sometimes of decades for adults.

The chief importance of such experiments lies in their relevance to a more general learning problem — the effect of an earlier habit upon a later one, and vice versa — without reference to biosocial maturation or cultural norms. The generalizations which may be derived from them can be expected to shed light upon the problem of how earlier and later learning interact when similar test situations are finally encountered.   It is difficult to predict their significance for the future of behavior pathology; for the clinical problems of fixation and regression are incomparably more complex, and the time-spans involved are incomparably greater, than in the deliberately simplified experimental situations.[17]

Object-regression, drive-regression and habit-regression

A further distinction which some behavior pathologists have found convenient in their descriptions is that between *object-regression, drive-regression* and *habit-regression.*[18]   These terms, of course, do not distinguish three different kinds of regression, but only three different emphases on the part of the behavior analyst who is studying regression.   Thus, when we speak of *object-regression*, we are calling attention primarily to the object (or person) which *instigates* the biosocially immature behavior, or around which the immature reaction is organized.   When we speak of *drive-regression* (Freud's "libidinal regression"),[19] we are focussing upon the *need* aspects of the immature behavior.   And when we talk about *habit-regressions*, we are referring directly to the biosocially immature *pattern* of the reaction.   In other words, the first emphasizes the stimulus-source, the second emphasizes the behavior disequilibrium, and the third emphasizes the act which has been instigated.

Individual variations in regressive behavior

Our definition of regression, like that of fixation, is couched in relativistic terms which refer directly to contemporary standards of biosocial maturity.[20]

[17] For a general critique of such experimental "analogues" in behavior pathology, see pages 18–19 and 54–55.

[18] Sears, R. R., "Experimental analysis of psychoanalytic phenomena." In Hunt, J. McV. (Ed.), *Personality and the behavior disorders.*   New York: Ronald, 1944, pp. 306–332.

[19] Freud, S., *A general introduction to psychoanalysis.*   New York: Garden City Publishing Co., 1943, pp. 297–302.

[20] See pages 143 and 221.

From this point of view, it is obvious that, under conditions of frustration, anxiety, behavior disorganization, enforced dependence or reduced competence, regressive behavior may develop at any age — from infancy through childhood, adolescence and adulthood, into old age and decline. We have already pointed out also the variations to be found in levels of maturity from person to person, and the diverse effects attributable to fixation. This should lead us to expect wide individual differences in the ease with which regression may be induced, in the degree to which it develops, and in its persistence as an habitual mode of reaction.

Thus, under objectively comparable circumstances, some individuals fall back *readily* upon biosocially immature techniques, while others, although perhaps equally unsuccessful in coping with their difficulties, show no recognizable regressive trends whatever. The same is true of the tenacity of regressive behavior, once it has been evoked. Suppose, for instance, that helpless dependence is forced upon two persons by strict disciplinary imprisonment for the same period of time. After release, one of them may continue indefinitely to look for guidance and initiative from those around him, while the other quickly regains his mature autonomy.[21]

We also find wide variations from person to person in the *inclusiveness* of regressive patterns, and in the age range to which these patterns are appropriate. In some cases, the regression may be restricted to a single kind of activity or relationship. A business man, for example, may react to a promotion, if this greatly increases both the range of his authority and the degree of his insecurity, by developing temper tantrums or demands for unusual attention and consideration, while otherwise discharging his functions as an executive in a thoroughly mature, dependable manner. In other cases, regression seems to involve most of a person's biosocial behavior. We see this occur when sudden, severe deprivation is forced upon an individual by the death of a love object. Indeed, it is the development and persistence of such sweeping regressive reactions that frequently leads over to depressive or schizophrenic disorders.[22]

Regression, regardless of whether its scope is limited or inclusive, may vary from person to person also in the *age range* that it represents. Thus, one adult may develop regressive behavior characteristic of adolescence, another

[21] For examples of individual differences in reactions to imprisonment, see Allport, G. W., Bruner, J. S., and Jandorf, E. M., "Personality under social catastrophe." *Char. and Pers.*, 1941, vol. 10, pp. 1–22; Curle, A., "Transitional communities and social re-connection: a follow-up study of the civil resettlement of British prisoners of war. Part I." *Hum. Relat.*, 1947, vol. 1, pp. 42–68; Curle, A., and Trist, E. L., "Transitional communities and social re-connection: a follow-up study of the civil resettlement of British prisoners of war. Part II." *Hum. Relat.*, 1947, vol. 1, pp. 240–288; Derrick, E., "Effects of evacuation on Japanese-American youth." *School Rev.*, 1947, vol. 55, pp. 356–362; Friedman, P., "Some aspects of concentration camp psychology." *Amer. J. Psychiat.*, 1949, vol. 105, pp. 601–605.

[22] Depressive disorders are discussed on pages 314–329; schizophrenic disorders are discussed on pages 494–515.

of childhood and a third of infancy. Moreover, the same adult may simultaneously exhibit infantile, childish and adolescent attitudes in relation to different aspects of a given situation.

Such variations in regression level within the same individual's behavior are related, of course, to the observed variations in biosocial maturation, discussed in an earlier chapter.[23] Human beings do not mature to the same level or at an equal pace in all things. Neither do they show, as a rule, the same susceptibility to regression in all their behavior. These intra-individual differences may be in part attributed to prior fixations, in part to the degree to which certain reactions have been shared with other persons — and therefore socialized — and in part to the specific character of the pressures, the frustrations, and the rewards to which a person is exposed.

The persistence of regressive behavior, once it has developed, will depend in part upon the persistence of the conditions precipitating it, and in part upon the degree to which it satisfies the individual as a way of life or leads to secondary gains. If the conditions responsible for regression last a long time, the regressive patterns are likely to become established through long practice and to be integrated with the rest of a person's organized habitual behavior. And even though these conditions disappear, there is always the possibility that regressive reactions may in themselves prove rewarding (functional autonomy).[24]

There is always the additional possibility that the regressive reactions which develop in a given person are behaviorally related to some earlier *fixation* which has long since been abandoned. For example, an adult situation of enforced dependence may rearouse childhood attitudes — originally given up with difficulty, a little late, and only because of strong pressure — now welcomed for the same general reasons that made them preferred attitudes in childhood. Regressive behavior, of course, may secondarily bring relief from anxieties not directly related to the precipitating conditions; and it may lead to incidental privileges and exemptions, which then operate to reinforce regression and to prevent its disappearing.[25]

The manifold inter- and intra-individual differences to be found in regressive trends help to account for the complex variability in the symptomatology of behavior disorders. For if all persons, under comparable stress, showed the same tendencies to regress, and to the same degree, we would need only to know the properties of the stress to be able to predict the character and severity of the resulting behavior disorders.[26] Likewise, if an individual were equally susceptible to regression in all of his behavior organization, we would need to

[23] See pages 144–148.   [24] See pages 38–42.

[25] See, for example, Schneider, D. M., "The social dynamics of physical disability in Army basic training." *Psychiatry*, 1947, vol. 10, pp. 323–333.

[26] For a discussion of stress in relation to behavior pathology, see pages 44–46.

know only the degree of his regression in one respect to be able to describe
it in all the rest.

Actually, of course, we can neither predict the character and severity of
behavior disorder from a knowledge of the stress alone, nor infer regression in
everything from the mere fact of regression in a single reaction. The unevenness and complexity of biosocial maturation which bestows a rich behavioral
variegation upon the human species, also burdens it with an infinitely varied
behavior pathology for which no simple formulas can be devised. The most
that we can do today is to indicate the conditions under which — given the
fact of frustration intolerance — regression is most likely to develop.

Conditions favoring regression

(1) *Fixation.* The *fixation-regression hypothesis,* stated in the opening
paragraphs of this chapter,[27] makes two fundamental assumptions. It assumes
that the mere fact of prior fixation, even though the fixation is subsequently
overcome, leaves one especially vulnerable to regression. It also assumes that
a vulnerable person, if he regresses, will revert to the previously fixated activity
or relationship. In other words, this hypothesis attempts to account both for
the general susceptibility of certain individuals to regression, and for the
specific regressive pattern which appears in their behavior.

Although the fixation-regression hypothesis was formulated originally in
terms of libidinous energy quanta,[28] it loses nothing in fruitfulness when it is
reformulated in terms of modern learning theory. Indeed, our definition of
fixation — as *the persistence of acquired behavior patterns until they have become
biosocially immature* [29] — clearly implies the factor of overlearning. Likewise,
in discussing our definition of *regression,* we included the reappearance in a
person's behavior repertory of patterns belonging to his own past which he
had once outgrown.[30] We may begin by saying, therefore, that fixation seems
to be one of the important conditions favoring regression, and that many of
the circumstances which originally resulted in fixation,[31] may also result in
regressive behavior that is specifically related to such fixation.

However, regression that can be thus specifically related to prior fixation
in an individual's own life history seems to be exceptional. Therefore, in
practice, regressive behavior is usually identified on a more general basis —
that, as behavior, it is considered to be immature in a person's culture, for
those of his own sex, age range and status, and that it has been absent from his
repertory in the immediate past.[32]

(2) *Deprivation.* Regressive behavior develops commonly under conditions

---

[27] See pages 217–218.
[28] Freud, S., "Instincts and their vicissitudes" (1915). In *Collected Papers,* vol. 4. London: Hogarth, 1948, p. 65.
[29] See pages 143–144.   [30] See pages 220–223.
[31] See pages 148–153.   [32] See pages 221–222.

which diminish or seriously threaten one's personal security. We know that security during infancy and early childhood is to a large extent based upon the affectional relationship with the mother. Anything which radically alters the character of this relationship is likely to precipitate anxiety and lead at once to regressive behavior.[33] One of the clearest examples of this appears in situations of sibling rivalry, to which we have already referred.[34] The infant sibling steals the show, takes maternal attention away from one who is used to getting all of it, and may be loved more intimately and more demonstratively than is the now more mature child. Regression under these circumstances amounts to maladaptive competition for the affectional security of which the older child has been deprived.

Regression occurring in other periods of life often has a similar origin in affectional deprivation with its attendant loss of security. Thus, a child made anxious by separation from his mother,[35] when he enters school, may react to this enforced isolation with sulking, whimpering, temper tantrums, or transient loss of sphincter control. Likewise, homesickness in adolescents and young adults, when they have had to go away from home to study, to work, or to give military service, is usually characterized by silent preoccupation with fantasies about home life and love, by tearfulness, malaise and dependent attitudes toward older persons in the new environment — and frequently terminates in an actual retreat to the parental home and parental care.[36] Newly married adults, whatever their age, if they find marital life insecure and unsatisfying, are apt to seize upon illness, financial distress or a quarrel as the occasion for a return to mother, which may also be terminal.

The loss of a love object, upon whom a person has depended, usually elicits reactions which are characteristic of earlier phases of maturity. The inconsolable grief of an adult mourner, as behavior, has many features in common with the reactions of a dependent child whose mother has left him for a week's vacation. In both, we may find crying, pounding with clenched fists, angry rejection of attempts at comforting by others, refusal to eat, and

[33] One early study, for example, indicates that a high percentage of college students who report frustration in their early parental relationships show regressive behavior. See Watson, G., "A comparison of the effects of lax versus strict home training." *J. soc. Psychol.*, 1934, vol. 5, pp. 102–115. More recently, Levy reports that when his overprotected children failed to achieve school stability they frequently resorted to an infantile pattern of adjustment. See Levy, D., *Maternal overprotection.* New York: Columbia University Press, 1943, p. 241.

[34] See page 220.

[35] Compare the reports of children separated from their mothers in Freud, A., and Burlingham, D. T., *War and children.* New York: Ernst Willard, 1943.

[36] In the study referred to earlier, twice as many "frustrated" as "non-frustrated" college students reported homesickness. Watson, G., "A comparison of the effects of lax versus strict home training." *J. soc. Psychol.*, 1934, vol. 5, pp. 102–115. See also Cammisa, J. J. V., and Moloney, J. C., "Separation anxiety." *Ment. Hyg.*, N.Y., 1947, vol. 31, pp. 229–236; Kaufman, M. R., "'Ill health' as an expression of anxiety in a combat unit." *Psychosom. Med.*, 1947, vol. 9, pp. 104–109.

refusal to consort or communicate with other persons. As a rule, the grief-stricken adult and the deserted child alike regain in time their previously more adequate and mature behavior patterns, and we speak of them as having "recovered" or "forgotten."

In exceptional cases, adult mourning may lead over into guilt reactions, a *crucial shift* occurs from resentment and self-pity to repentance and self-blame, and grief is transformed into a depressive illness.[37] Now the patient either takes the role of a threatening accuser toward himself, or else attributes threat and accusation to other persons or to God. In the one he may inflict punishment upon himself, behaving like an angry parent; in the other, he may live in fearful apprehension over the punishment he anticipates from whomever he has cast in the role of parent surrogate. Occasionally, a patient escapes depression by a manic illness.[38] In this he manages to fend off anxiety, and exculpate himself, by falling back upon behavior which on the surface resembles the irresponsible gaiety of a tense, excited child — gaiety in which elation and anxiety unite.

(3) *Disorganization.* Behavior disorganization, whether transient or lasting, and whether anxiety-provoked or not, nearly always includes reactions — ordinarily absent — which belong to some less mature phase of personality development.[39] Thus, if mourning leads to disorganization, instead of leading to the *crucial shift*, we are likely to witness the development of a schizophrenic illness in which regressive behavior is also manifest. The same is true of the disorganization accompanying acute cerebral incompetence — as in deliria of toxic or infectious origin, in brain injury, tumor, or cerebral accident — and in severe progressive cerebral incompetence such as one finds in chronic intoxication or infection, and in cerebral degeneration.[40]

(4) *Frustration.* Strong frustration — in the form of delay, thwarting or conflict — can at any age beyond earliest infancy lead to regression, when the frustrated individual passes the limits of his frustration tolerance.[41] Thus, the already weaned infant, if he is confined too long alone in his play pen, may resort to the old techniques of sucking, which quiet and comfort him again as they did in times past.[42] The child or adolescent, if he is rebuffed and rejected because of his clumsy attempts at social give-and-take with his contemporaries, may return to an affectionate dependence upon a parent whom he had lately been neglecting, or rejoin a play group from which he recently had been graduated.

---

[37] See pages 314–329.   [38] See pages 329–336.
[39] See pages 449–451.   [40] See pages 535–539.
[41] For a discussion of frustration and frustration tolerance, see pages 47–52.
[42] See, for example, Sears, R. R., and Wise, G. W., "Relation of cup feeding in infancy to thumb-sucking and the oral drive." *Amer. J. Orthopsychiat.*, 1950, vol. 20, pp. 123–138; Kunst, M. S., "A study of thumb- and finger-sucking in infants." *Psychol. Monogr.*, 1948, vol. 62, no. 3.

Similarly, an adult who fails in competition with his peers, or who finds the fruits of his success disappointing, may turn to some interest or activity identified with his childhood or adolescence. Frustrated, disappointed and disillusioned adults sometimes join an organized social group because it permits them to enjoy playing the role of dependent follower, or of big brother, in relationships that recapture to a certain degree the flavor of their childhood homes. The old man, finding the roads to his accustomed satisfactions blocked by his own infirmities and society's hostility toward the aged, may likewise seek to revive activities, interests and relationships belonging to his youth.[43]

(5) *Dependence.* Children, adolescents and adults typically develop regressive behavior when circumstances force them to play a dependent role. This is plainly evident in the bedridden person who is ill or injured. His actual helplessness compels him to adopt attitudes like those he once had in helpless infancy or early childhood, and the responses that such attitudes support are characteristically childlike. The chronic invalid and the convalescent both give many examples of regression in their daily behavior — crying, temper tantrums, breath-holding, pleading, clinging and sulking. Often their patterns of body concern suggest the rearousal of personal preoccupations characteristic of a child who is being trained in fundamental health habits. Obviously, if anxiety disorders, hysterical disorders or compulsions develop under these circumstances, they represent pathological outgrowths of regression.[44]

In prisons, concentration camps and disciplinary barracks, regressive behavior is engendered by the helplessness of the prisoner, who must depend for his every satisfaction and even for his life, upon the good will of persons whom he cannot control.[45] These situations also favor regression, in the severity of frustration which they are designed to provide. The biosocially immature behavior of indigent persons on relief is often itself a regressive product of the relief situation. For financial aid is usually made contingent upon helplessness and complete subordination, dependence is conferred upon the recipient without responsibility, and the indigent person is made to feel exceedingly insecure about his aid. The role that he may play within this situational frame virtually eliminates the possibility of self-reliance and self-respect, excepting perhaps in the form of a covert hostility which is hardly more mature than the dependence.

[43] Jones, H. E. and Kaplan, O. J., "Psychological aspects of mental disorders in later life." In Kaplan, O. J. (Ed.), *Mental disorders in later life.* Stanford University, Calif.: Stanford University Press, 1945, pp. 92–110; Gardner, L. P., "Attitudes and activities of the middle-aged and aged." *Geriatrics,* 1949, vol. 4, pp. 33–50.
[44] See Chapters 11 and 12.
[45] Allport, G. W., Bruner, J. S., and Jandorf, E. M., "Personality under social catastrophe." *Char. and Pers.,* 1941, vol. 10, pp. 1–22; Friedman, P., "Some aspects of concentration camp psychology." *Amer. J. Psychiat.,* 1949, vol. 105, pp. 601–605.

Regressive behavior, no matter what its sources, can under certain circumstances virtually replace the more mature behavior which an individual has previously succeeded in developing. Such a replacement frequently takes the form of a far-reaching withdrawal from almost all participation in the affairs of everyday life and the adoption of an invalid role. Indeed, we see some of the most interesting and important examples of regression and its related escape techniques in the maladaptive mode of living called invalidism, to a further consideration of which we now turn.

Withdrawal and Invalidism

Withdrawal, as an adjustive technique, is by no means necessarily pathological, or even undesirable. On the contrary, innumerable situations arise in everyday life for which withdrawal is both the simplest and the most appropriate reaction. Such is the case, for example, when a person is faced with overwhelming odds, and when to retire from the immediate scene of the struggle seems to hold the promise of a more successful defense elsewhere, or at another time. The same can be said of situations which — whether at the moment one is meeting defeat or meeting victory — appear almost certain to lead toward greater complexity, increased tension and ultimate failure. To withdraw, under these circumstances, is to escape the consequences of eventual defeat.

As compared with aggressive attack, withdrawal has some unquestionable advantages. It does not usually arouse hostile opposition, alienate sympathy, or invite retaliation. It protects the individual from fruitless expenditures of time and effort under conditions of unconquerable adversity and irresistible restraint. It shields him from humiliating defeat and personal injury, and if adroitly managed, it guards him from threats of damage to his social status. Those who, when they withdraw, find contentment and reward in solitude, may discover also that, in solitude, they run less risk of having to struggle against recurrent interference with their ongoing activities, than when they seek their satisfactions in the company of others.

Withdrawal has its dangers as well as its advantages. Continued aggression, for example, tends to become self-limiting because it inevitably arouses mounting counteraggression in other persons.[46] But the very protection from interference which withdrawal affords may operate in such a way as to prolong and increase withdrawing reactions indefinitely. For persistent withdrawal isolates a person from social participation, he suffers a reduction in his acquired social skills through lack of practice, and it may secondarily render him less and less able to derive satisfaction from competition and cooperation with other individuals.

[46] See the discussion of this point in connection with delusional developments, on pages 394–396.

Because of the isolation from socially shared behavior which it induces, withdrawal allows one's techniques, formulations and conclusions to drift farther and farther away from a necessary correspondence with the design of social operations. It sets the stage for a replacement of interest in others by an interest restricted to oneself, of public interbehavior by personal preoccupation, and of effort by passivity. One of the clearest illustrations of this shift in biosocial behavior is to be found in that form of withdrawal which we call *invalidism*.

Withdrawal into invalidism

Invalidism is the name commonly applied to a complex maladaptive way of living whose chief characteristic is withdrawal. At the same time, as everyone knows who has lived in its shadow, invalidism may be secondarily employed to threaten and control other persons. It is also sometimes used to take revenge upon others by limiting their freedom of action and making them anxious and self-punitive.

By *invalidism* we mean *a withdrawal reaction to need or anxiety, in which an individual takes the role of a sick or disabled person, to a degree or in a manner that is not justified by his biological status alone.* This definition includes exaggerated reactions of the chronically ill and handicapped to the behavioral consequences of their illness or their defect. It also includes many cases of incomplete and delayed recovery following illness, accident or operation. Less frequently, but sometimes more dramatically, one also finds invalidism complicating paranoid disorders, schizophrenia and depression.

Invalidism, it is clear, represents one of many patterns of attempted adaptation to personal difficulties that lead to the impoverishment or distortion of social role-taking. Invalidism is always the complex resultant of interactions between the individual's present behavior organization — with its developmental background — and the existing environmental factors and interpersonal relationships. It always involves important shifts or reversals in a person's dominant self-attitudes and self-responses.

On the other hand, there are wide variations in the *conditions favoring* invalidism; and some of these variations are reflected in the particular pattern of maladaptation that develops. Thus, invalidism growing out of serious permanent disability may throw into relief certain components of the invalid reaction; invalidism growing out of injury or illness without residual defect may emphasize different components; and invalidism arising without any immediately preceding injury or illness may bring out still others. Accordingly, in what follows, we shall present a few common varieties of the invalid reaction which, taken together, will give us a composite picture of *withdrawal into invalidism*.

Invalidism in the seriously handicapped and chronically ill

Persons in this group share an important characteristic in common: they can all show an undeniable defect. Some of them suffer from severe orthopedic disability — amputation, paralysis, or serious limitation of movement. Some have lost sight or hearing, with or without damage to the sense-organ, or have lost speech through surgery or cerebral accident. Others have been deprived of one or another part of gastrointestinal function — as in surgical removal of the esophagus, stomach or rectum — or of reproductive capacity, as in artificial sterilization. Still others suffer from cardiac damage and systemic disease, or are subject to recurrent attacks, as in convulsive disorders and migraine.[47]

It is essential to recognize from the start that these persons cannot possibly regain their premorbid level of functioning. Moreover, many of them must cope with the additional handicap of serious cosmetic defect, such as skeletal asymmetry, a distorted gait, a chronically haggard appearance or the obvious absence of a body part. For the individual who equates bodily integrity with personal status, and who is especially responsive to the opinions of others, the reactions which his cosmetic defect calls out in others may represent the greater burden.[48] Nevertheless, we must recognize the fact that neither cosmetic defect, nor tissue damage alone, nor a susceptibility to unpredictable, recurrent attacks of any kind, is in itself sufficient to prevent a reasonably good adaptation. Indeed, it is the very failure to achieve such an adaptive response to illness and handicap that constitutes the invalidism.

In our effort to construct a composite picture of *withdrawal into invalidism,* it will repay us to consider separately two varieties of unsuccessful reaction to serious disability. These differ from each other chiefly in their temporal relation to the original illness or trauma. In one, *the invalid reaction follows a period of relatively adequate adjustment.* In the other, *invalidism develops as a direct sequel to the original illness or trauma, with no intervening period of recovery.* Each, as we shall see, points up an important aspect of withdrawal into invalidism.

[47] For comprehensive discussions of the reactions of the chronically ill and handicapped, see Barker, R., Wright, B., and Gonick, M., "Adjustment to physical handicap: a survey of the social psychology of physique and disability." *Soc. Sci. Res. Council Bull. 55.* New York, 1946; Pintner, R., Eisenson, J., and Stanton, M., *The psychology of the physically handicapped.* New York: Appleton-Century-Crofts, 1941; Ruesch, J., "Mastery of long-term illness." *Med. Clin. N. Amer.,* 1949, vol. 33, pp. 435–446; Affleck, J. W., "Psychiatric disorders among the chronic sick in hospital." *J. ment. Sci.,* 1948, vol. 94, pp. 33–45.

[48] Studies of servicemen with visible injuries indicate that others' comments on the disability are frequent sources of concern and resentment. See, for example, Ladieu, G., Adler, D. L., and Dembo, T., "Studies in adjustment to visible injuries: social acceptance of the injured." *J. soc. Issues,* 1948, vol. 4, pp. 55–61; Ladieu, G., Hanfmann, E., and Dembo, T., "Studies in adjustment to visible injuries: evaluation of help by the injured." *J. abn. soc. Psychol.,* 1947, vol. 42, pp. 169–192; White, R. K., Wright, B. A., and Dembo, T., "Studies in adjustment to visible injuries: evaluation of curiosity by the injured." *J. abn. soc. Psychol.,* 1948, vol. 43, pp. 13–28.

(a) *Invalidism following relatively adequate adjustment.* Persons in this group, although seriously and permanently disabled, have at one time achieved an adaptive response which, in terms of their residual defect, is a good one. Subsequently, however, they have given up in the face of adverse conditions and withdrawn into invalidism. These patients, like all the others, are reacting primarily to personal difficulties. But because they are unquestionably disabled by chronic illness or grave handicap, and because they have already demonstrated their ability to cooperate and compete with others in spite of their disadvantages, they serve to illustrate most clearly of all the importance of the human environment — the concrete reactions of other persons — in producing invalidism.

The seriously handicapped and the chronically ill are faced with a peculiarly difficult situation. They must live by means of an environment whose design is based upon the needs and activities of the overwhelming majority, who are sound and healthy persons. Consequently, they are obliged to extract what satisfactions they can from surroundings that may be ill-adapted to their own needs and to the activities in which they are able to engage.[49]

In this disadvantageous situation, the chronically ill or permanently handicapped individual is never allowed to forget that he is considered fundamentally unlike other persons. He hears himself continually compared with his well and robust associates and competitors. In part, the comparisons are frankly pitying; in part, they imply a subtle disparagement in the overevaluation they bestow upon his achieving only what everyone else achieves.[50] Many important avenues of enterprise and gratification are closed to the disabled person, and his freedom to establish and maintain a variety of personal interrelationships is often seriously curtailed. Yet, in spite of this, he is expected to endure his disability and accept its consequences with uncomplaining fortitude, and even to rise above it.[51]

It is hardly surprising that, under such conditions, many disabled persons ultimately react to continued frustration and defeat by withdrawing — by restricting their activities and their human contacts well beyond the point made necessary by the disability alone. Of course, to withdraw from shared activities with others may greatly decrease a person's opportunities for satisfaction. But it also reduces greatly his burden of unrewarding cooperation and unsuccessful competition with more favored individuals. Thus, by the

[49] The special disabilities incident to *developmental retardation* are discussed in Chapter 6; and those resulting from *cerebral incompetence* on pages 531–555.

[50] There is some evidence of the existence of generalized attitudes or biases which result in a stereotype of the crippled person. See, for example, Mussen, P. H. and Barker, R. G., "Attitudes toward cripples." *J. abn. soc. Psychol.*, 1944, vol. 39, pp. 351–355.

[51] This expectation is not universal to all cultures. For a description of the variations in the social status of handicapped persons in different cultures, see Hanks, J. R. and Hanks, L. M., Jr., "The physically handicapped in certain non-Occidental societies." *J. soc. Issues*, 1948, vol. 4, pp. 11–20.

same withdrawing, insulating and negativistic maneuvers that deprive him of much liberty, the solitary invalid protects himself against the impact of intolerable anxieties and humiliations.

Many examples of such withdrawal into invalidism have been reported by Landis and Bolles.[52] The subjects of their study were one hundred disabled women who suffered from cardiac impairment, spastic paralysis, orthopedic disability or convulsive disorder. Withdrawal from socially shared activities was found to be one of the four principal kinds of adjustment developed by these persons. As might be expected, the particular mode of adjustment was not a function of the kind of illness or handicap present. It was related rather to the person's age — withdrawal into invalidism tended to be a last resort — and to her educational level and behavior organization. Thus, compared with the other three groups,[53] the withdrawing subjects were on the average older and had been ill or handicapped longer, they were somewhat lower in educational level and intelligence score, and they were all rated as being egocentric and preoccupied with personal problems.

These patients, then, begin with a serious disability which makes an invalid way of life culturally permissible. They ultimately develop an inability to continue with socially adequate adjustive reactions, which makes withdrawal into invalidism all but imperative. In these respects they superficially resemble the patients in our next subgroup; but there is an important difference between the two. The individuals just discussed have attempted to compete and to cooperate on equal terms with more favored persons, and have only later succumbed to prolonged frustration and repeated failure. Those in our next subgroup have from the start been unable — within the limits imposed by their impairment — to adapt sufficiently to bring attempted competition and cooperation even within their range. The former are defeated in the field, in a contest with other persons; the latter are defeated in a struggle with themselves.

(b) *Invalidism immediately following the acquisition of permanent disability.* Persons in this subgroup — after they have suffered irreparable tissue damage through accident, disease or surgery — fail for personal reasons to approximate the expected degree of recovery. They are able, like the patients we have just been discussing, to demonstrate objectively the presence of a biological deficit. They face the same general situation which those others managed to meet at first. Like them, also, they are required by the circumstances of their relative disability to accept loss, impairment and disfigurement as specific limitations

[52] Landis, C. and Bolles, M., *Personality and sexuality of the physically handicapped woman.* New York: Hoeber, 1942.

[53] The other groups were those adjusting (1) by "substitution," the acceptance of attainable goals for preferred but unattainable goals, (2) by "compensation," which varied from fatalistic acceptance to aggressive competition, and (3) by "obliteration," a refusal to admit handicap or incapacity.

which in part define their status. And, finally, in their social role-taking they are expected virtually to ignore the indisputable fact of their handicap.

On the other hand, patients in this subgroup are unlike those in the preceding one in that they *never* adequately meet the challenge of permanent disability. Thus, from the very start, they do not expose themselves to the full impact of the everyday human environment, but tend instead to minimize interpersonal contacts. Consequently, they do not have the experience of attempting to compete and to cooperate with more favored persons on terms of equality. It is, therefore, obvious that their response to disability cannot serve to illustrate the importance of the concrete reactions of other persons in the human environment in directly producing invalidism.

These persons do clearly illustrate two factors of significance in the genesis of invalidism. One is the part played by an individual's own *self-reactions* [54] to structural damage, dysfunction and disfigurement. The other is the role of an individual's acquired *reaction-sensitivity* to the anticipated attitudes of others toward him.[55]

The two factors cannot be separately discussed without doing some violence to their actual operation. For both *reaction-sensitivity* to the attitudes of other persons and one's own *self-reactions* are products of the same interpersonal behavior. In effect, patients belonging to this subgroup succeed in anticipating, in their self-reactions, the *kind* of treatment that patients in our first subgroup actually receive at the hands of the everyday human environment. However, it must be recognized that what they anticipate — and cannot bring themselves to face — will be primarily determined by their premorbid reaction-sensitivities, and only incidentally by what others say and do to them.

Cosmetic defect.[56] It is well known that wide individual variations can be found among normal, sound persons in the kind and the intensity of self-reaction given to the body's appearance and integrity, and to the adequacy of its functioning. These variations are especially evident in cases of acquired cosmetic defect, such as that resulting from mutilation and from the contracting scars of a severe burn. For the child or adult whose social status and emotional security seem to him to depend upon the impressions he makes on others, cosmetic damage may come as an insupportable catastrophe.

Such special premorbid reaction-sensitivity in a person commonly leads to prompt self-reactions of revulsion and rejection. The disfigured patient seeks at once to escape the reinforcement of *the behavior of others to him* which he anticipates in terms of *his own behavior* toward himself. Indeed, he is almost certain to exaggerate the signs of aversion that he sees in persons about him, and to misidentify surprise as horror, and pity as contempt. For in wheeling

---

[54] See pages 95–105.   [55] See pages 70–74.

[56] For a bibliography of studies on this point, see Barker, R. G., Wright, B., and Gonick, M., "Adjustment to physical handicap: a survey of the social psychology of physique and disability." *Soc. Sci. Res. Council Bull. 55.* New York: 1946, pp. 351–353.

down the hospital corridor, or in walking down the street, his chief preoccupation is likely to be one of furtively examining the responses of everyone he passes, and of building up from his observations a pseudocommunity of individuals who avoid him or despise him. It is from this pseudocommunity that he then withdraws into the protective custody of an invalid way of life.

Organismic integrity. Closely related to problems of cosmetic defect are those arising out of damage to the integrity of the organism. An amputation, for example, or the loss of an eye, is not alone disfiguring: it also destroys the body's completeness. There are patients for whom the latter effect arouses much more disturbing self-reactions than the former. Indeed, some persons regard even the break in skin-surface continuity made by a clean surgical scar, in an area covered by clothing, as a serious violation of the intactness of their body, which they cannot forget.[57]

The removal of part or all of an internal organ may introduce no cosmetic change of importance to the patient, and yet prove *fully* as inacceptable as a severe disfigurement might be. We find this most commonly in the removal of reproductive organs, and therefore much oftener in women than in men. A woman, for example, following hysterectomy or ovariectomy,[58] may look upon herself as no longer a complete woman. In her own eyes, she becomes a person of permanently reduced status who has lost her worth. If it be remembered that one's sex actually is a highly important determiner of one's social status, and that to most people sex means sexual functioning, it is not difficult to understand a person's self-evaluation in terms of the possession or lack of a complete set of sex organs. And even though sex organs may eventually lose their reproductive capacity entirely, they may still define sexual status for a person in his or her own self-attitudes.[59]

Surgery performed on the gastrointestinal tract frequently leads to personal crises that cannot possibly be accounted for merely on the basis of the consequent gastrointestinal dysfunction. One of our patients, a man fifty-two years of age, underwent an operation for suspected rectal carcinoma. It was found necessary to remove rectum and anus, and to make an artificial opening from the colon to the abdominal surface. When the patient discovered his loss, he begged to be killed and threatened to jump out of the hospital window.

---

[57] See, for example, Freud, S., "On narcissism: an introduction" (1914). In *Collected Papers*, vol. 4. London: Hogarth Press, 1948, pp. 30–59; Schilder, P., *The image and appearance of the human body*. London: Kegan Paul, 1935.

[58] The suffix *-ectomy* always refers to surgical removal of an organ. The organ is indicated by the prefix, in this instance *hyster-*, — meaning *uterus* or *womb*.

[59] This often becomes especially important in the changes of sexual functioning attendant upon ageing. See, for example, the discussion by Cameron, N., "Neuroses of later maturity." In Kaplan, O. (Ed.), *Mental disorders in later life*. Stanford University, Calif.: Stanford University Press, 1945, pp. 148–150. Note, also, that a study of 300 combat veterans indicated that 20% of the group had a special fear of being wounded in the genitals. Dollard, J., *Fear in battle*. New Haven: Yale University Institute of Human Relations, 1943, p 21.

He railed against his surgeon, even though he himself knew the diagnosis and its meaning for him. After leaving the hospital, he quit work, went on relief and devoted himself principally to self-care, living in semiseclusion. A follow-up report five years later indicated no essential change in this invalid solution.

Unlike the reproductive organs, such systems as the gastrointestinal, urinary and respiratory must continue to perform their functions if the individual is to survive. Therefore, major surgery must often include provisions for artificial diversion of intake or output, as we saw in the case just cited. Accident and disease of such systems may also lead to the production of sinuses and fistulas, through which products may leave the body in unusual places, and with relatively little control. In either instance, the results are likely to be that serious problems in interpersonal relationships will arise, that important reaction-sensitivities may develop, and that the patient's field of social operations may be organized in terms of his visceral dysfunction.

One of the most illuminating cases of this kind on record is that of the man, described by Wolf and Wolff,[60] whose esophagus had been destroyed in childhood by scalding. He found that the most satisfactory mode of eating for him was to chew his food well, and then to spit it into a funnel inserted directly into his stomach. As he grew up, he came to structure his whole social world in terms of the reactions given by other persons to his unesthetic feeding technique. The few who accepted him in the mealtime situation without disgust, he in turn accepted as his friends. To everyone else he remained an asocial, misanthropic recluse. Thus he withdrew from nearly all effective interaction with the human environment. His visceral defect, with its functional consequences, became the measure by which he gauged the worthiness of each potential human contact, and the chief determiner of the limits of his social interaction.

Reduction in energy and skill. Often less dramatic than the foregoing, but no less serious in outcome, is the situation faced by any patient who cannot successfully adapt to a permanent reduction in his general energy level, or to the partial loss of some specific coordinative skill. For the person who has all his life made strength or dexterity the basis of his personal worth, its loss must lead inevitably to the disappearance of his emotional security. In these circumstances, a common means of self-protection is that of never exposing oneself to the test. The threat of losing one's self-esteem is met by avoiding the possibility of a showdown.

Patients such as these, beginning with an indisputable and incurable disability, usually end up by superimposing upon it a hypochondriacal or hysterical disorder, which in turn constitutes their withdrawal into invalidism.[61]

---

[60] Wolf, S. and Wolff, H., *Human gastric function: an experimental study of a man and his stomach.* London: Oxford, 1943.

[61] For a discussion of hysterical disorders, see pages 359–371.

Thus, some persons develop progressive reaction-sensitization to signs of approaching fatigue or malaise. Others, instead, become progressively re-action-insensitive to stimulation that was once adequate to initiate their now impaired coordinated movements. This increased selective sensitivity or insensitivity then becomes, not only the chief factor in limiting the range of social interaction, but also the basis for the patient's explanation of his invalid non-participation — to himself as well as to others. In the end, his state is almost precisely like that of the patient *without significant residual defect* who adopts the role of a disabled person following operation, illness or injury. To this group we shall next turn.

Invalidism in persons without significant residual defects [62]

In this category belong those patients who were originally bedridden be-cause of systemic illness, accident or surgery, but whose invalidism is now no longer complicated by residual defects that call for special adaptation. In other words, we are here dealing with persons, forced for a time by circum-stances to accept the fact of being disabled, who subsequently continue in the invalid role when they could have been completely sound and well. In a sense, they are opportunists without realizing it. For the conditions of their temporary incapacitation have provided them with a behavior pattern, which they now unwittingly follow in reconstructing their dominant attitudes to-ward life.

The specific contribution of this group to our composite picture of *with-drawal into invalidism* is a most important one for behavior pathology. There is objectively present, we have said, no clear-cut systemic illness and no residual defect that will publicly support the patient's claim to an invalid role. Accordingly, the person who stakes out such a claim must build upon the signs and symptoms of his waning disability, or he must develop new signs and symptoms to replace those that disappear. This, of course, is not deliberately planned or executed. The patient must himself believe in the verity of his persistent or newly organized complaints; for to do otherwise would be to take the role of a malingerer, not an invalid.

We have already pointed out [63] that any incapacitated patient is obliged to live as a comparatively helpless individual while his incapacitation lasts. He is dependent for his security, and for the satisfaction of even his simplest needs, upon the helping hand of stronger and more competent persons.[64]

---

[62] For a bibliography of literature on this point, see Barker, R. G., Wright, B., and Gonick, M., "Adjustment to physical handicap: a survey of the social psychology of physique and disability." *Soc. Sci. Res. Council Bull. 55.* New York, 1946, pp. 244–245.

[63] See pages 229–230.

[64] Compare the findings of Ladieu, G., Hanfmann, E., and Dembo, T., "Studies in adjustment to visible injuries: evaluation of help by the injured." *J. abn. soc. Psychol.,* 1947, vol. 42, pp. 169–192.

This is essentially a repetition of the normal situation in infancy; and it tends to evoke infantile attitudes and responses from the relatively helpless adult. Some individuals discover a new and welcome satisfaction in their dependent status, and develop anxiety and insecurity when they face the necessity for regaining independence. Their reactions of anxiety and insecurity in convalescence may then contribute to the foundations of new complaints, or of an exaggeration of old complaints — which often increase, paradoxically, as the patient's general condition shows improvement.

Another potentially important factor in the development of invalidism is the *instruction* which most patients receive in the art of being ill or convalescent.[65] The temporarily disabled person, like the permanently disabled one, is usually taught to avoid doing certain things, to watch out for certain physiological changes, and to report these if he detects them. Under this regime, it is inevitable that every patient shall acquire new reaction-sensitivities to changes in the function or appearance of his body — whether these changes be normal or pathological. For the anxious, dependent or dissatisfied convalescent, the effect of this training is to provide a considerable matrix of reaction-sensitivity from which to organize new galaxies of complaint.

If personal insecurity increases, as convalescence proceeds and the prospect of independence grows imminent, the very absence of a significant residual defect might be expected to give a relatively free rein to the development of symptoms. The pattern is not tied to an objectively demonstrable impairment. This situation undoubtedly helps to account for the clinical finding that, in cases of delayed or incomplete recovery, the symptomatology tends to grow more varied as time goes on. To take head-injury as an example, it is reported that in late posttraumatic cases the patients with severe head injuries gave few complaints, while those with only mild injuries gave many. Moreover, the longer the posttraumatic complaint syndrome lasted, the more likely were the complaints to increase in number and to become diffuse in character.[66]

The diagnostic situation is often complicated by the presence of definite but non-significant residual defects. In the medical evaluation of such cases, the tendency is strong to attribute the many complaints to whatever tissue pathology can be demonstrated, even though the same pathology is also present in patients who lack the same complaints. Here, again, we find the

---

[65] For an analysis of the social situation in illness, with especial reference to medical procedures, see Barker, R. G., Wright, B., and Gonick, M., "Adjustment to physical handicap: a survey of the social psychology of physique and disability." *Soc. Sci. Res. Council Bull. 55.* New York, 1946, pp. 228–244.

[66] Ruesch, J., Harris, R., and Bowman, K., "Pre- and post-traumatic personality in head injuries." In *Trauma of the central nervous system.* Baltimore: Williams and Wilkins, 1945, vol. 24, pp. 507–544; Ruesch, J. and Bowman, K., "Prolonged post-traumatic syndromes following head injury." *Amer. J. Psychiat.,* 1945, vol. 102, pp. 145–163.

fact overlooked that the complaint is not alone the product of tissue pathology.[67]

In patients without significant residual defects, as in patients with them, the complaint always includes the individual's own reaction to illness, to the experience of being disabled, and to the behavior of others toward him as a disabled person. The complaint is in part the outcome of the patient's conception of his role as an incapacitated person and how that role should be played. It may also be an expression of his fundamental needs, his hopes, fears, and anticipations, or the vehicle by means of which he can now attain what has previously been denied him. Thus it is that eventually the complaint picture in delayed and incomplete recovery becomes indistinguishable from the picture found in invalidism that does *not* stem from accident, operation or systemic illness.

Invalidism in persons neither disabled nor convalescent

These patients differ from the seriously handicapped and chronically ill in that they do not have to cope with the grave problems of competition and cooperation as permanently disabled individuals in a world of sound and healthy persons. They differ from the patients we have just been discussing in that they lack an immediately preceding episode of helplessness and dependence. The importance of these differences for an understanding of *withdrawal into invalidism* is that here the complaints are neither supported by handicap and chronic illness, nor explicable in terms of prolonged convalescence. The symptomatology, in short, is derived neither from immediately present disability nor from immediately prior incapacitation.

The specific contribution of this group to our concept of invalidism is obvious. These persons, having themselves no recent or existing pattern of disability and dysfunction on which to base their complaints, must clearly derive them from other sources. A patient may utilize patterns of illness belonging to some earlier period of his own life or to the life of another individual, particularly one with whom he can easily identify.[68] He may take the role of an invalid about whom he has heard or read. He may build his own pattern of complaints out of the comments and suggestions of other persons — including medical personnel — out of the emotional components of his own reactions to stress and strain,[69] and out of the specific reaction-sensitivities which characterize his unique behavior organization. In the following case, we

[67] Ruesch, J., Harris, R. *et al.*, "Chronic disease and psychological invalidism, a psychosomatic study." *Psychosom. Med. Monogr.*, 1946. See especially Table XXIV, p. 38, of this reference.

[68] For a discussion of the development of behavior pathology through adoption of the prevailing pattern, see pages 59–63.

[69] For a discussion of the tendency to interpret anxiety symptoms as illness, see pages 311–312.

shall witness the operation of some of these factors in the development of
withdrawal into invalidism.

A thirty-year-old single woman was admitted to the surgical service
of a general hospital with complaints of rectal bleeding, recurrent attacks
of abdominal pain, rapid pulse and general weakness. Examinations
pointed to hemorrhoids as the source of the bleeding. Accordingly,
these were removed and the patient was discharged. She was readmitted
two months later because the attacks of abdominal pain, rapid pulse,
and general weakness still recurred. This time an exploratory abdominal
operation was performed, but no tissue pathology was found to account
for the symptoms. The patient was given positive reassurance to the
effect that the operation had revealed nothing abnormal, and she was
again discharged. When, after six weeks, she reappeared with the same
complaints, and the suggestion that another surgical exploration should
be made, a psychiatric consultation was requested.

The study of this patient as a person soon disclosed that her recorded
complaints were only fragments of a much more inclusive invalid pattern.
Her statements may be paraphrased as follows. When she was seven
years old, the patient had measles and scarlet fever which, according to
her report, the doctor said had settled in her stomach and destroyed her
pneumogastric nerve. For two years after this she never had enough
energy to play with other children and she frequently suffered from an
"all gone" feeling in her stomach. Her grandfather, who lived with her
parents, devoted himself to her care until, following a series of heart
attacks, he died. After his death, she gradually recovered her strength
and the stomach trouble disappeared.

At the age of sixteen, when the patient was in the eighth grade at
school, she began having "spells" in which her stomach "collapsed,"
her heart raced, and she could not get her breath. She was placed on
digitalis for a time and advised to give up school. For two years she
rested at home, either lying down and reading or sitting up and sewing.
Because of mounting criticism of her idleness from relatives, the patient
worked during the next four years, but she never managed to hold a
job more than a few months. Some jobs she left because she felt too
tired to work; from others she was discharged for absenteeism. At
twenty-two she took her complaints of fatigue and "spells" to a physician who, she said, admitted that he did not know what was the matter
with her. She thereupon decided to stop trying to work, and to devote
herself entirely to the task of keeping up her strength.

Throughout most of her life the patient had not been interested in
men. Marriage, she felt, was out of her reach because of her "spells."
When she was nineteen, she fell in love with a handsome foreigner who
left the country a few months later. In spite of the fact that this attachment lasted only a few months, and was apparently never an intimate
one, the patient found that she could not forget the man. She continued from then on to fantasy about him a great deal, and she was
unable to find other men in the least attractive. Tears came to her
eyes when she recounted this to the psychiatric consultant. She stated

that she had never had sex relations and that sex had never been a problem in her life.

For some months prior to her operations for rectal bleeding and abdominal pain, the patient had been exposed to sharply increasing anxiety over her personal security. Her parents, now in their sixties, were beginning themselves to complain of fatigue and poor health. In spite of her protests, they persisted in talking about ageing and the possibility of sudden death. They engaged in lengthy discussions of her precarious economic situation, emphasizing repeatedly the fact that they would not always be there to look after her and support her. It was in this setting that the attacks — which represented old patterns of anxiety in the patient's past — became severe enough to hold the center of the stage and lead to operative interference. The patient was discharged once more from surgery, and this time referred by the hospital to an out-patient psychiatric clinic in her home community for therapy and rehabilitation.

In this case, withdrawal into invalidism did not follow surgery but preceded it. Indeed, it was the trivial character of the tissue pathology (hemorrhoids), and the surgically unwarranted persistence of abdominal symptoms, that led eventually to a study of the patient as a person. It then appeared that this woman had as a child developed typical anxiety episodes and fatigue complaints, that she had ascribed these to previous measles and scarlet fever, and had for a time lived as an invalid in her grandfather's care. This early adoption of an invalid existence was terminated following his death. However, during adolescence and early adulthood, when the patient faced the advent of maturity, the fatigue and anxiety episodes ("spells") reappeared and again dominated her life pattern. Both the job record and the sex history in this case are characteristic for persons who fail to meet the challenge of biosocial maturation and remain in a dependent role under parental protection.

The parents themselves set the stage for the dramatic climax when they began harping upon the undeniable fact of their advancing age, and upon the increasing threat this represented to the patient's security. In the acute anxiety thus precipitated, the patient focussed upon her rectal bleeding as a danger signal. To this she quite understandably linked the abdominal components of her intense emotional reactions, and out of the combination of sign and symptom an abdominal syndrome was constructed that justified surgery. Here we see how the acquired reaction-sensitivities of childhood invalidism may be rearoused, by the anxieties incident to the unwelcome approach of adult life, to induce a second withdrawal into invalidism. Finally, we witness the fact that, in the face of new threats of impending insecurity, the patient misidentified sign and symptom in a direction that was again determined by the reaction-sensitivities of her childhood and by her conviction that she was a sick person.

Withdrawal as a reaction to delusional misinterpretation

All withdrawal, of course, is not withdrawal into invalidism; neither is every asocial recluse chronically fatigued, hypochondriacal or hysterical.

Retirement from social participation may be the product of any one of a variety of preconditions. Among these is the development of delusional misinterpretation and the organization of a pseudocommunity.[70]

Delusional misinterpretations, we know, are now and then a part of every normal person's behavior. For we must all proceed in the business of our daily living on the basis of much that is actually incomplete and uncertain. It is therefore inevitable that we occasionally come to conclusions which turn out to contradict the facts. When this happens, we are faced with a number of alternatives. We may, for example, simply shrug our shoulders over the discrepancy and dismiss the facts as inexplicable. We may, instead, reject our conclusions as unintelligible and seek to account for the facts in other ways. Or we may distort the facts, or our recall of what we had originally concluded — or both — and thus harmonize the discrepancy by an act of logical violence. We may do none of these, but rather lay the blame for our mistake upon the manipulations of fate, the deity, or an enemy, and then begin to look for signs that something in the nature of a plot is afoot.

If a person, in disowning responsibility for an important misinterpretation, attributes the unexplained event to someone's deliberate intent, he may be taking the first step toward organizing a pseudocommunity in his own behavior. If, having taken this step, he goes on to elaborate his pseudocommunity into a plan or plot of which he is the intended victim, his next move will be either to attack his supposed adversary or to flee. Withdrawal is one of the common and undramatic modes of escape to which paranoid persons have recourse, when their pseudocommunities seem to threaten their security or their existence. Thus we find, in most rural areas and urban neighborhoods, some individual who lives the life of a recluse, goes into hiding when visitors arrive and, if pressed too far, meets what to him seems a dangerous threat with counteraggression, even to the point of outright assault. Situations such as this are at the bottom of many an otherwise unintelligible act of intimidation and violence against neighbors, peddlers, minor officials and other innocent trespassers.

Withdrawal as a reaction to confusion

When overtaken by confusion, any social unit — a military outfit, a competing business group, a town hall meeting, or a gang — is likely to react by a withdrawal which may or may not be orderly, depending upon the goodness of internal organization present. The same can be said of individuals. The little child who finds the complexities of the neighborhood too much for him disappears into the house. His mother, confused by multiple responsibilities, takes refuge in the simpler activities of her domestic routine. Her husband, a business man who can see no way out of the intricate web of economic con-

[70] For a detailed discussion of the pseudocommunity, see pages 387-392.

tradictions in which he is caught, spends a weekend at manual labor in his garden, or takes a few days off to sit motionless, alone, fishing from a flat-bottomed boat. The tourist in foreign countries finds himself, after a time, unable to keep up any longer with the novelty of strange cultural patterns and unfamiliar places. He anticipates his original schedule, and returns to his native land to escape surroundings that confuse him.

Withdrawals from environmental complexities such as these are not always successful. The child may find indoors a nagging mother, the mother a pair of perpetually quarreling children, and her husband a home full of domestic crises, or a lake peopled by noisy adolescents. The returned traveller may discover that neighborhood improvements have destroyed familiar landmarks around his home, and new social regulations have changed the flavor of the cultural patterns to which he had been accustomed. If, under these circumstances, a person's preferred adjustive technique is still one of withdrawal, the next step away from the confusing surroundings is that of seclusion. And if seclusion cannot be achieved merely by moving out of the range of stimulation, then it must be done by inhibiting one's reactions to stimulation. The child, the mother, her husband and the traveller may still fall back upon fantasying — and this can be so intensively developed, by some individuals, as to shut out effectively the whole disorganizing environment, and substitute for it a satisfying inner order.[71]

Of course, what appears to the individual as environmental disorganization may be a function of personal disorganization.[72] There are wide variations from person to person in the degree to which fundamental change, sudden surprise or increasing complexity can be tolerated without serious confusion. Moreover, the same individual may undergo at different times marked shifts in his tolerance for change, surprise and complexity. These shifts may be related to alterations in a person's biological competence and his frustration tolerance, to his current success or failure in the satisfaction of insistent needs, and to changes in the severity of his anxieties and the character of his conflicts.

By far the commonest outcome is that the confused individual, if withdrawal effectively protects him from the impact of disintegrating stimulation, soon regains his ability to handle personal conflict and environmental complexity. It hardly needs saying that a successful withdrawal from environmental complexity is usually much less difficult than escape from conflict. This is just as true for conflict in which a possible solution seems too costly from the individual's point of view, as it is for conflict which seems to have no possible solution. It is as true for conflict in which dominant emotional components retard or prevent resolution as it is for conflict which actually cannot be resolved.

[71] See the discussion of desocialization in Chapter 16.
[72] For a discussion of disorganization see Chapter 15.

A person can often leave a situation which has given rise to severe conflict; but, in so doing, he does not necessarily eliminate the conflict. For, no matter what other activity he turns to, or where he goes, he always carries with him the ability to reconstruct the conflict situation in his symbolic behavior. And from this, we know, there is no final escape. Thus a person may not even succeed in reducing the anxiety from which he sought relief in flight. Indeed, because of the new deprivations which his new abstentions bring, he may actually heighten the intensity of his anxiety. It is because of these characteristic difficulties, as we shall see in the chapters immediately following, that human beings have developed elaborate techniques for handling anxieties which arise out of conflict, and that conflict and anxiety are now recognized as the cornerstones of behavior pathology.

9

Conflict

Conflict is an inescapable part of day-to-day existence. The infant, in developing an expanding repertory of behavior, inevitably develops mutually opposing responses. Likewise the growing child, as he learns new and increasingly complex techniques of satisfying need, learns also the contradictions among them. The maturing individual is provided with endless possibilities for conflict by the same framework of parental restriction and expectation, of social demand, of permission and taboo, which defines biosocial maturation.[1] And the adult who has firmly established himself in his society and culture still faces, in his everyday life, opposing demands from others, contradictions among his own self-reactions, discrepancies in his role-taking behavior, minor choices and major decisions. No one is immune; no one can escape the competing and contradictory responses which define conflict.

Any parent can observe a *conflict between simple responses* if he watches his child struggling to grasp one toy after another. An infant, in his crib, successfully takes a toy in one hand, and manages to retain it while he takes another toy in his other hand. If, however, a third attractive object is now dangled over the crib, by the parent, both the stimulating situation and the child's behavior change. For it turns out that the infant cannot relinquish either toy in order to take the third. Neither, of course, can he succeed in grasping the third while he still clutches a toy in each hand. To gain possession of the new object, the infant must give up one of the old; he cannot have them both. And to take this third object, he must let go his hold on the first or the second, for he cannot simultaneously grasp and relax. The child who remains in this situation shows clearly the consequences of conflict between incompatible reactions — in increased activity, heightened tension and a final outburst of crying.

[1] See pages 55–63, and pages 132–134.

This commonplace incident represents in elementary terms the contra-dictory reactions which define conflict for us all; but most conflicts are not as simple as this, as temporary, or as easily resolved. The growing child, as we have seen,[2] learns social roles which are complex, enduring, diverse and often discrepant. He lives out the roles of *baby* to his mother, *little man* to his father, and of *regular fellow* to his friends; and behavior which is appropriate to one role may bring him rejection or punishment in another. If he has younger siblings, he must one day exchange the role of dependent, protected baby of the family for the conflicting role of independent, protecting big boy. In adolescence he behaves now as a child and now as an adult, rejecting the guidance of his parents at the same time that he needs and invites it. It is evident that conflict among *contradictory and discrepant social roles* is an in-evitable part of maturation.

Later maturity represents to many persons an irreconcilable conflict among social roles.[3] The ageing adult finds retirement from his job both attractive and threatening. Retirement may bring him relief from the demands and responsibilities of his daily work, but the new freedom carries with it an un-welcome change of status. His role is likely to shift from principal breadwin-ner and head of his own household to that of dependent guest in his children's homes. The very deference and respect which others show him may reinforce his conviction that he is old, weak and worthless. Caught in this ambiguous situation where he must be at once a mature, emancipated adult, and a pas-sive, dependent child, the old person may demonstrate his conflicting reactions in a variety of ways. If he visits his place of work, he finds that his well-meaning suggestions to his successors are ignored. When he tries to par-ticipate in making domestic decisions, his opinions are at best only tolerated. If he seeks to develop new interests, the difficulty of learning unfamiliar skills may soon convince him once again that he is incompetent. In view of these ambiguities, it is not surprising that the conflicting roles which our society requires of its older members contribute sometimes to the development of frank behavior disorder. And to many an ageing adult, retirement from his job seems the first public step toward retirement from life itself.[4]

Reactions need not be publicly shared or socially valid in order to be con-flicting. A great many important and enduring conflicts occur in the indi-vidual's private behavior, among his own *competing self-reactions*.[5] This is particularly common when the contradictory reactions are directed toward forbidden topics. For example, a young man who must wait for years before he is financially in a position to marry may gain at once in fantasy the satis-

---

[2] See pages 114–118.   [3] See pages 553–555.

[4] For a discussion of the special problems of ageing, see Cameron, N., "Neuroses of later maturity." In Kaplan, O. (Ed.), *Mental disorders in later life*. Stanford University, Calif.: Stanford University Press, 1945, pp. 143–186.

[5] For a discussion of self-reactions, see pages 95–105.

factions he postpones in his everyday life. If fantasying on sexual themes violates his early training or his personal or religious code, he may show the contradictory reactions of conflict. He may begin by prohibiting, through his own self-reactions, the forbidden fantasying. If, however, during a period of relaxation or fatigue, he indulges in the forbidden thinking, he will then become guilty and anxious. Moreover, what he denies himself in day-dreaming he can achieve in night-dreaming, and his dreams may then be disturbing, erotic and guilt-ridden. He is thus encompassing, in his private unshared behavior, the discrepant self-reactions of indulgence and denial.

For many of us, the contradictions which define conflict are *inaccessible* even to our own self-reactions.[6] We may be able to report periods of inexplicable fatigue, malaise or tension; but only after prolonged behavior analysis, with the assistance of an impartial expert, can we identify the competing reactions which explain them. Consider, for example, the married woman who complains of tiredness, obscure and fleeting bodily symptoms, and sporadic attacks of anxiety and tension whenever she visits her unmarried sister. She reports that she and her sister have always been good friends, and there is nothing in the overt behavior of either to contradict her statement. Competent behavior analysis, however, reveals that when both were children, this patient failed more often than she succeeded in achieving the degree of closeness to her father which she desired. It indicates further that the married woman, insecure in her relationships with her husband, is still competing with her sister for the father's attention and love. The woman, whose overt behavior toward her sister is affectionate and accepting, entertains at the same time those attitudes of hostility and jealousy which she had developed years before in childhood rivalry with her sister. Her inability to identify and report these incompatible reactions, either to herself or to others, leads her to consider her tension and fatigue mysterious and incomprehensible. It is only when the competing reactions have been identified that her complaints can be seen as part of a once *inaccessible conflict*.

These examples illustrate the breadth and the diversity of competing reactions which we must consider if we are to understand conflict. Such reactions may range from the relatively simple grasping response of the young infant to the discrepant roles of child and adult, or the contradictory self-reactions of indulgence and denial. Conflicts may occur in overt behavior, in recall, in socially organized thinking, in covert fantasy or in night-dreaming. They may or may not be formulated in language. They may be shared or unshared, accessible to one's self-reactions and acknowledged, or inaccessible and denied. Since conflict is universal and inescapable in the daily lives of all of us, it is not surprising to find that it occupies a central place in behavior pathology. Indeed, if we are to understand the development of many behavior disorders,

[6] Self-inaccessible reactions are discussed on pages 79–83.

we must examine closely the ways in which conflict develops and the techniques which human beings employ for its resolution. To this task we bring the early clinical findings of Freud and his followers, and the data of modern experimental psychology.

The development of the concept of conflict in behavior pathology

The modern conception of conflict, and of its significance in human behavior, was stimulated by the nineteenth century trend toward "psychogenic" explanations in behavior pathology. That trend was both advanced by the clinical observations of Freud and elaborated in his writings. Freud's early use of free association as a method of treatment was itself the consequence of his conviction that behavior pathology was an outgrowth of "psychogenic" factors. Freud's patients, as they pursued in free association the steps which led them to recovery, guided Freud himself toward an understanding of the meaning of conflict. The patients characteristically reached a point where they could no longer free associate; they reported that they had forgotten what they were going to say, that "nothing came" when they tried to go on talking. Instead of concluding that his patients were just being uncooperative, Freud recognized in their resistance an indicator of conflict.[7] Moreover, he observed that the topics that his patients resisted in free association were those which, it seemed to him, were related to the reasons for the patients' difficulties. From Freud's keen clinical observations came first a description, and then a theory, of conflict.

The topics which his patients resisted, Freud believed, represented wishes that conflicted with the patients' other wishes. Typically, the opposition seemed to occur between strivings, which Freud considered instinctual, and the patients' ethical and moral principles. The longer and more carefully Freud listened to his patients free associate, the more firmly he became convinced that the important conflicts were basically those between infantile sexual strivings and adult standards. The conflicts occurred among the chaotic drives which Freud later called the *id*, the controlling, organizing drives he termed the *ego*, and the representation of social permission and taboo which he called the *super-ego*.[8] According to this viewpoint, conflict developed between two instinctual tendencies, one striving for discharge, the other striving to prevent discharge.

Freud restricted neither his observations nor his theorizing to his patients. He found in normal everyday slips of speech, in selective forgetting, in wit and fantasy, and in the dreams of healthy persons, additional examples of opposition between what is and what should be, of conflict between desire and pre-

[7] Freud, S., *An autobiographical study*. London: Hogarth Press, 1946, pp. 49–53.

[8] Freud, S., *The ego and the id* (4th ed.). London: Hogarth Press, 1947; Freud, S., *General introduction to psychoanalysis*. New York: Garden City Publishing Co., 1938, pp. 305–308; Fenichel, O., *The psychoanalytic theory of neurosis*. New York: Norton, 1945, p. 129.

tense, and of strife within the trio of id, ego and super-ego.[9] Through its many alterations and ramifications, his theory has consistently emphasized what Freud originally observed in his patients — the inevitability and universality of conflict in human existence.

In any scientific endeavor, the interpretations and theories advanced in one field are to a large extent originally derived from and dependent upon the viewpoints current in related fields. Because Freud wrote first in the late nineteenth and early twentieth centuries, his theoretical concepts necessarily reflected the notions then current in philosophy, psychology, biology and physics. Nineteenth-century philosophy and psychology were concerned with structural problems of mind, consciousness and the unconscious, and with the assimilation to these problems of the then current biological concept of instincts; nineteenth-century physics was a physics of static mechanics. It is largely for these reasons that Freud's theory originally pictured conflict as an opposition between instinctual drives located in different spheres of consciousness. Viewpoints in psychology, as well as in related fields, have changed markedly in the last fifty years; but Freud's theory of conflict has not undergone a corresponding change. His latest writings on the subject,[10] as well as the contributions of some of his present-day followers, adhere strongly to formulations of conflict which are difficult to integrate with contemporary psychological trends.

But whatever may be the shortcomings of Freud's theory of conflict, nothing can obscure the significance of his clinical observations. His emphasis upon the fact and the consequences of conflicting reactions, both in everyday life and in behavior disorder, provided hypotheses which have reoriented the entire field of behavior pathology. Few, indeed, are the behavior pathologists today who deny the central importance of conflict in initiating and prolonging maladaptive reactions. Many, however, would like to see the early psychoanalytic concepts of conflict reformulated so as to bring them in line with current findings in clinic and laboratory. These present-day pathologists differ from Freud most sharply in their description of the components which make up the opposing reactions we call conflict.

The work of Alexander and French [11] illustrates one effort of contemporary psychoanalysts to broaden the classical view of conflict. From their clinical work with patients, these writers conclude that conflict occurs between competition and cooperation, between social and antisocial trends, between "help-seeking dependence and self-assertive rivalry." Such conflict may or may not have its roots in infantile behavior. If the conflict is traceable to early infancy, its persistence into adulthood can be understood in terms of the familiar prin-

[9] Freud, S., *The psychopathology of everyday life.* London: Fisher and Unwin, 1914.

[10] Freud, S., "An outline of psychoanalysis." *Int. J. Psychoanal.*, 1940, vol. 21, pp. 28–30.

[11] Alexander, F. and French, T. M., *Psychoanalytic therapy.* New York: Ronald, 1946.

ciples of learning, rather than in the language of instincts and of dammed-up hypothetical impulses. In the same way, conflict resolution may be understood as relearning, rather than as a discharge of instinctual energy. Alexander and French retain the concept of conflict as central in theory and in therapy, but they define and describe it in contemporary terms.

Horney, also a contemporary psychoanalyst, recognizes the importance of the Freudian conflict between primitive drives and culturally determined prohibitions, but believes another conflict is still more basic in behavior pathology.[12] This is the conflict among contradictory attitudes which the young child develops toward other people. Conflicts among these trends mirror the contradictions of our society.[13] Conflicts between feelings of self-aggrandizement and personal helplessness, for example, reflect the cultural dilemma of individual freedom and social limitation. Opposing attitudes of aggression and yielding repeat a cultural contradiction between competition and altruism. Demand and fear-of-deprivation represent conflicting reactions in the individual; they reflect also an opposition, in current society, between the stimulation of our needs and our inability to attain complete satisfaction. Horney speaks of the satisfaction of need rather than of the primitive and instinctual impulses which Freud emphasized. In her formulation of conflict, the concepts of id, ego and super-ego are overshadowed by the hypothesized consequences of contradictory cultural demands.

To these alterations of Freudian doctrine by contemporary psychoanalysts we may add the efforts of experimentalists to reformulate the concept of conflict. In order to investigate conflict in the laboratory, of course, experimentalists must first have precise and straightforward definitions of the competing reactions involved. Unfortunately, many theories of conflict employ concepts which cannot yet be translated into the terms which the experimentalist needs for his work. The functions traditionally ascribed to ego, super-ego and id are difficult if not impossible to quantify and control sufficiently for adequate experimentation. Those of dependence, self-assertion and need are hardly less so. On the other hand, simple and usually temporary motor, verbal and autonomic responses can be observed, controlled and measured, with the precision which systematic investigation requires. Consequently, the present-day experimentalist has formulated conflict in terms of competing responses which he can conveniently handle in the laboratory.[14] If his experiments seem overrefined and artificial, it is because traditional laboratory methodology is still largely inappropriate to the problems of behavior pathology.[15]

[12] Horney, K., *Our inner conflicts*. New York: Norton, 1945, p. 40.
[13] Horney, K., *The neurotic personality of our time*. New York: Norton, 1937, Chapter 15.
[14] For summaries of such studies, see Miller, N. E., "Experimental studies of conflict." In Hunt, J. McV. (Ed.), *Personality and the behavior disorders*. New York: Ronald, 1944, pp. 431–465; Dollard, J. and Miller, N. E., *Personality and psychotherapy*. New York: McGraw-Hill, 1950, pp. 352–368.
[15] For a more detailed consideration of this point, see pages 18–19.

Even with this handicap of limited technique, however, the findings of modern experimentation, as we shall see, have contributed significantly to our understanding of conflict. For one thing, they have forced us to identify the competing components of conflict in the *behavior* of human beings, rather than in conceptualized areas of the mind, or in universal, abstract instincts. For another, they have demonstrated that many of our modern theories of learning can encompass, and even predict, the development and resolution of conflicts resembling those which the clinician identifies in his patient.[16] Finally, the shortcomings of our traditional experimental techniques in dealing with conflict have stimulated the development of new statistical and laboratory procedures, and these make it possible to increase the number of realistic investigations without sacrificing precision. In the study of conflict, the paths of clinical observation and of laboratory experiment are steadily converging.

If we are to understand the significance of conflict in behavior pathology, we cannot afford to ignore any aspect of this historical trend. We can begin, as late nineteenth-century behavior pathology began, with the rich and provocative clinical insights of Freud. At the same time we must follow, in our view of conflict, the emphasis of contemporary writers upon the cultural context within which conflicting reactions develop. We must include as well the findings of the laboratory, and the implications of current theories of learning. And most important of all, we need to remember that conflict can be found only where it develops, that is, in the behavior of human organisms operating in a social field — whether that behavior be simple or complex, overt or covert, relatively accessible or inaccessible.

A definition of conflict

By *conflict* we mean the *mutual interference of incompatible reactions*. The interference, as we have seen, may occur between simple responses, attitudes, roles, or self-reactions. The contradictory reactions may be overt or covert, easily identified or altogether inaccessible. They may be sharply circumscribed or widely inclusive. Whatever the character of the mutually interfering reactions, however, conflict has one necessary consequence: *it alters the smooth flow of ongoing behavior*.[17] When one reaction cannot develop, or reach consummation, unless it does so at the expense of a competing reaction, some change in the patterned sequence of behavior is inevitable.

The consequences of conflict in behavioral change are three-fold. (1) Mutual interference of two reactions is bound to develop *tension*, whether this be brief or prolonged, slight or severe. Tension, as a consequence of conflict, we saw in the behavior of the infant grasping the toys, of the young man struggling

---

[16] See, for example, Dollard, J. and Miller, N. E., *Personality and psychotherapy.* New York: McGraw-Hill, 1950, pp. 127–156; 331–383; and Guthrie, E. R., *The psychology of human conflict.* New York: Harper, 1938.

[17] For a discussion of the temporal character of behavior sequences, see pages 63–69.

with sexual fantasy, and of the married woman whose repressed hostility brought her anxiety and malaise.[18]   (2) The sacrifice of one competing reaction to another may create *impoverishment* of behavior.   The fatigue which the married woman reported, the suppression of sexual behavior which the young man occasionally achieved, and the reduction in ability to respond which Freud's patients showed, illustrate impoverishment of behavior as a consequence of conflict.   (3) Contradictory reactions are likely to produce *distortion* in the ongoing pattern of behavior.   This distortion may range from the facilitating responses of the infant grasping the toys, through the acquisition of substitute reactions, as shown by the fantasying young man, to the development of obvious behavior pathology, as in the case of the married woman with bodily complaints.   Tension, impoverishment and distortion are the common behavioral consequences of conflict.

Although conflict and its consequences are inescapable parts of human existence, individuals differ widely both in the ease with which they develop conflict, and in the nature and severity of its results.   To the person who, for example, sees in his biological need and erotic fantasy an irreconcilable conflict between good and evil, the acceptance and enjoyment of sex behavior by others is incomprehensible.   A woman may be guilty and anxious over her discrepant attitudes toward her sister, while the same sister never develops conflicting reactions toward her.   The man who in later maturity cannot retain consistently his earlier role of emancipated adult is bewildered when his friends make an easy transition from job to retirement.   This *individual susceptibility* to particular competing reactions is probably the consequence of individual differences in learned reaction-sensitivities.[19]

Individual susceptibility to conflict and to its consequences, however, is not entirely a matter of unique patterns of reaction-sensitivity.   Every individual is part of many different social groups, whose *contradictory demands and prohibitions* outline those aspects of behavior in which conflict is most frequent.[20] At least in current Western society, there are three common situations that represent conflicts to which we are all vulnerable.   It is seldom that an individual reaches the heterosexual maturity of marriage without conflict between his biological needs and the satisfactions which society permits.   The mature person is exceptional who establishes himself in his culture without at some time developing toward others aggressive attitudes which he knows are prohibited.   It is a rare person who proceeds through later maturity without assuming, at least for a time, the discrepant roles of child and adult.   Due largely to the particular pattern of permission and taboo in our society, we find our three most common examples of conflict in the competing reactions involved in *affectional relationships*, in *hostility*, and in *emancipation*.

[18] See pages 246–249.   [19] See pages 70–74.
[20] For a description of maturation as a function of social expectation, see pages 136–137.

By now it is clear that a complete description of conflict must include different varieties of competing reactions, different individual susceptibilities, and
different social patterns of permission and prohibition.   Contradictory reactions develop within a total biosocial field, where coordination of response is
as common as conflict.   If, in the interest of behavior analysis, we isolate reactions and identify them in competing pairs, we must still locate them within
the wide field of operations — verbal and non-verbal, private and social, brief
and protracted — which constitutes human behavior.   We cannot afford to
forget this point as we now turn to a consideration of the major types of conflict.

Varieties of conflict

One of the simplest ways of characterizing human reactions is to identify
the *direction* which the behavior takes.   Reactions directed *toward* a person,
object or situation we call *adient*.   The infant's approach to the dangling toy,
the adolescent's dreaming on erotic themes, the married woman's affectionate
and hostile attitudes toward her sister are all examples of adient behavior.
So also are the aggressive fantasies which a worker may develop toward his
hated employer; or the impatient criticism which a mother directs toward her
disobedient child.   Any reaction involving approach, whether overt or covert,
friendly or aggressive, is adient.

Reactions which are directed *away* from a person, object or situation, on the
other hand, we term *avoidant*.   They are particularly common in situations
involving fear or guilt,[21] as in the adolescent's forgetting of his erotic fantasying and his prohibition of such behavior in his self-reactions. The disobedient
child who disappears from home until his father's anger has cooled, the married woman who goes home to mother after a quarrel with her husband, the
aged man who prefers the solitude of his room to participation in domestic
matters over which he no longer has control, the stenographer who reacts to
her employer's criticism by quitting her job, all illustrate avoidant behavior.
Any reaction involving withdrawal, in shared or unshared behavior, is avoidant.   The concepts of adience and avoidance, both based solely on the direction
of behavior, permit the behavior pathologist to identify three major varieties
of conflict: *double-adient, double-avoidant,* and *adient-avoidant.*

Double-adient conflicts.   Two mutually incompatible reactions may be either
directed toward two *different* objects, persons or situations (*divergent adience*),
or toward the *same* object, person or situation (*convergent adience*).[22]   In either
case, if the reactions are contradictory, we speak of *double-adient* conflict.

Divergent adience.   The infant who cannot simultaneously retain one attrac-

---

[21] For a discussion of guilt, see pages 284–289.
[22] Compare the treatment of these points in Cameron, N., *The psychology of behavior disorders.*   Boston: Houghton Mifflin, 1947, p. 133.

tive toy, and grasp another which is equally attractive, illustrates *divergent adience*. The child who finds the safety of his own yard and the novelty of the kindergarten playground equally alluring, and the adolescent for whom the security of his parental home and the challenge of an independent existence are both compelling, also demonstrate the conflict between divergent adient reactions. An approach cannot be made in two opposite directions at once; in order to move toward one situation the individual must move away from another one which is also attractive. We shall see that conflicting adient reactions of the divergent sort are ordinarily resolved more easily, with less hesitation and distress, than are the other varieties. Even so, we shall occasionally find them contributing significantly to the development of behavior pathology.

Convergent adience. Where two incompatible reactions converge upon or are directed toward the same object, person or situation, the effect is more apt to be disruptive than in divergent adience. This is particularly true when the competing reactions are attitudes of affection and hostility pointed at the same person.

An illustration of such contradictory reactions is to be found in the behavior of a ten-year-old girl whose mother brought her to a child guidance clinic because she was enuretic, antagonistic at school, and generally unhappy. From the mother's story, it was evident that the child was particularly upset whenever her younger brother received special attention. If the boy had a cold and was permitted to share the mother's bed, for example, or if he was included in a family outing, the little girl was likely to have what her mother called a "stormy spell." She hid in a closet and cried, or announced that she would not go to school, or she played with her friends so roughly and aggressively that the neighbors complained. Toward her brother himself, however, she was overtly affectionate and protective.

It was only after prolonged behavior analysis, with the aid of indirect, projective devices, that the little girl displayed her adient hostile reactions to her brother. She told stories about boys who played the most exciting games, who were allowed to be untidy and to skip their nightly baths, but who "couldn't possibly have nice personalities." With her dolls she constructed dramatic scenes in which little boys were so much trouble that they were left outside and forgotten by their parents. It was clear that this little girl maintained overt adient attitudes of love and affection, simultaneously with covert attitudes of rivalry and hostility, toward her brother. The consequence of this conflict was a failure of both competing reactions to achieve consummation. The girl disowned her hostile reactions; and her overt affectionate reactions occurred within a context of displaced antagonism and unhappiness.

Double-adient conflicts of the convergent sort occur commonly in parent-child relationships as well as in situations of sibling rivalry. The same little girl, for example, maintained conflicting adient reactions toward her mother as well as toward her rival brother. She begged to be allowed to go with her mother on shopping trips, was homesick whenever she was away from her mother for even a brief time, and behaved protectively toward her, clutching her arm and warning her when the two crossed streets together.

Together with these adient affectionate reactions, however, the child demonstrated aggressive adient attitudes toward her mother. She made up a story about a mother who was killed while searching for her daughter; the daughter, she said, "wished she loved her mother but she didn't. She was very sorry that she didn't." In play she identified one doll as the mother, and then destroyed it, pulling it to pieces and finally trying to eat it. Her aggressive adience was frequently direct and overt. She called her mother names, stole money from her purse, and engaged her in rude arguments.

In convergent adient conflicts of this variety, the contradictory reactions of one individual are ordinarily reciprocated by the other person involved.[23] This little girl's mother, for example, described her daughter's reactions with a mixture of affectionate protectiveness and angry criticism. She behaved toward her child in the same contradictory way, first reassuring and then punishing her, now arguing with her and later giving her freedom and special privilege. It is the same in many sorts of parent-child relationship. The adolescent boy maintains toward his mother simultaneous attitudes of affection and rebellion; she responds with behavior toward him which is at once accepting and hostile. Parent and child are caught in a conflict between affectionate and aggressive adience which makes smooth-flowing behavior exceedingly difficult for both. The son can neither suppress his irritation at maternal restrictions nor can he sacrifice filial devotion to open revolt; the mother finds her affectionate attitudes intermingled with adient reactions of annoyance and criticism. The same situation may be found in the behavior of a father toward an infant who is unplanned and unwelcome; the expected paternal reactions of love and acceptance exist alongside reactions of hostility and rejection. In all such cases, the consequence in behavior of convergent adience is a parent-child relationship which is ambiguous and uneasy.

Double-avoidant conflicts. It is often the case that a person's reactions are simultaneously directed *away from* two competing situations. Such mutually incompatible avoidant reactions constitute a *double-avoidant conflict.* They are an exceedingly common development in early childhood, when unwelcome regulations are enforced by parental punishment. The child avoids going to bed on time, since this means interruption of his play or banishment from adult company. To ignore the appointed bedtime, however, is to invite retaliation, and this also provokes avoidant reactions. The alternative to a great many unpleasant prescriptions — eating vegetables before ice cream, putting toys where they belong, keeping quiet in adult company — is punishment as unwelcome as is the required behavior. The situation is often essentially the same in the

[23] For a discussion of reciprocity in behavior development, see pages 135–138.

early years of schooling. The child for whom the tasks of the conventional school have no appeal faces the dreary alternative, if he shirks, of still more unappealing tasks after school, imposed as punishment for inattention. Indeed, a good share of what is called "child training" goes on within the context of double-avoidant conflict.

The wider community enforces its regulations in much the same way as does the family — by exacting penalties for non-conformity with requirements which are often in themselves undesirable to the individual.[24] Double-avoidant conflict is therefore seldom absent from adult behavior. For the mature person, however, the punishment which is alternative to unwelcome behavior comes also from his own self-reactions. He faces daily a series of unpleasant requirements, boring routines or frightening responsibilities which evoke avoidant reactions. The office worker, for example, must arrive at work at eight o'clock, stay on the job until five, finish his letters and check his accounts. The executive must make decisions upon which the financial structure of his firm depends, and make them promptly and efficiently. But if office worker or executive escapes these tasks — by taking a day off, procrastinating, or shifting responsibility — he faces after-effects which go beyond loss of job or demotion. To violate the requirements, ignore the routines, or evade the responsibilities, is also to invite the self-reactions of remorse and loss of self-esteem.

The individual who acquires persistent, mutually incompatible avoidant reactions is the center of a threatening universe. Whichever direction he moves, in overt behavior or in covert fantasy, he faces pain, self-reproach or punishment. Ultimately it may seem to him that there is no possible course of action open to him. It is just such unresolved multiple-avoidant conflicts which seem to underlie the hopelessness and despair of many depressed patients.[25] The following case illustrates the gradual acquisition of avoidant reactions which culminated in agitated depression.

> An unmarried woman of thirty-seven entered a psychiatric hospital in a state of extreme agitation, weeping, moaning and wringing her hands. From her cousins who accompanied her, it was learned that the close-knit rural family to which the patient belonged had been recently and abruptly dissolved. The patient's brother, to whom she was strongly attached, had been killed in an accident; and shortly afterward, the patient's aged father and her ailing mother died within a week's time. For years the patient had carried the domestic responsibilities of her farm home, and had earned a wide reputation in the surrounding community as expert cook and efficient housekeeper. Her own satisfactions, however, came from serving her family rather than from her neighbors' approval. The sudden dissolution of the family left her over-

---

[24] Compare the discussion of inept social deviants on pages 203–211.
[25] Depressive disorders are discussed on pages 314–329.

whelmed with grief and unable to establish herself elsewhere. Trial visits at the homes of relatives seemed to make her more sorrowful and more agitated; she could not duplicate elsewhere the close personal relationships she had developed at home. Her avoidant reactions of grief and mourning gradually replaced her social behavior, until, in a state of confused agitation, she was brought to the hospital.

To this patient the hospital signified one more hopeless situation to be avoided. She expressed fear of contracting syphilis from the other patients, believed her hospitalization was punishment for her sins, and inquired anxiously what the staff was going to do with her. Discussion of her early life on the farm, of her parents and brother and cousins, or of her activities on the hospital ward all precipitated tears and moaning. Her covert reactions duplicated the despair she showed in overt behavior; in telling a story as part of a projective test of fantasy, for example, she said, "This lady has just had a sickness and the one that was sick had died and she's just closed the door. She seems in despair. She doesn't know which way to go; it seems that all doors are locked for her." Later she said, "I feel like I'm clinging to a string just before I sink under. . . . It's hard to explain. It's a quiet all your own, different from other people's. You see other people alone but that's different. This is a quiet that never ends." Multiple-avoidant reactions brought this patient despair and isolation, and from these she never fully recovered.

Adient-avoidant conflicts. The most common, and at the same time the most disrupting variety of conflict is one in which incompatible reactions of adience and avoidance develop in relation to the same object, person, or situation. The young child both welcomes and dreads his first day at school. The adolescent both seeks and avoids his parents' guidance. The adult man finds in a job promotion new responsibilities which are both challenging and frightening. The bride-to-be anticipates in marriage both new pleasures and new fears. The soldier in combat is caught between the adient reactions of performing his duty and the avoidant reactions of escaping bodily harm. The ageing person vacillates between the freedom of retirement and its unwelcome implication that he is no longer useful. These mutually incompatible reactions which develop in the same situation we designate as *adient-avoidant conflicts.*

Adient-avoidant conflicts often arise in situations where permission and taboo are enforced by the same individual. This means, of course, that we may expect to find our earliest illustrations of this type of conflict in relationships between the young child and the parent, who is at once the giver and the denier. In weaning her infant, for example, the mother replaces her accepting attitudes toward her child's adient reactions to the breast with denying, rejecting attitudes aimed at establishing avoidant reactions in her child. She interrupts his approaches to her breast by pushing away his hands, turning his head aside and placing the nipple of his bottle in his mouth. The adient reactions to the mother's breast, in consequence of this, become intermingled with avoidant reactions from it, and the infant participates for a time in an

adient-avoidant conflict.[26]   It is the same in many phases of biosocial maturation.   That which the parent formerly accepted he now prohibits; what he
once provided he now denies.   The inevitable consequence for the child, within
each phase of maturing, is a conflict, in his relations with his parent, between
adient and avoidant reactions.

For the older child and the adult, overt punishing or rejecting reactions from
a parent are no longer necessary to evoke an adient-avoidant conflict.   Adient
reactions toward a forbidden object compete rather with avoidant *self-reactions*. This is nowhere more clearly demonstrated than in the behavior of a preschool child in a permissive play situation who discovers, among the toys in the
playroom, a miniature nursing bottle.   He handles it hesitatingly, buries it
in the toy box only to rediscover it a moment later, turns his back on it, but
then cannot become involved in any other play.   He may put the bottle cautiously to his lips and then hastily reject it.   If the adult therapist suggests
that he may fill the bottle with water and suck on it, the child is likely to say
scornfully, "That's for babies."   He prohibits, in his avoidant self-reactions,
his adient reactions toward an attractive play object.

Adient-avoidant conflicts of this sort, in which punishing self-reactions are
the most conspicuous, provide endless possibilities for the development of
guilt.[27] The preschool child may eventually suck on the toy nipple, but in so
doing he courts self-reproach.   It is the same in many adient-avoidant conflicts: avoidant self-reactions prevent the development or consummation of
ongoing adient behavior.   Often the entire struggle is carried on in private
fantasy, with its only observable consequence the unverbalized tension of the
individual.   Largely because of their inaccessible character and their close
relationship to guilt and self-punishment, adient-avoidant conflicts lead relatively often to behavior pathology.

To analyze the three major varieties of conflict — double-adient, double-
avoidant, and adient-avoidant — in terms of *pairs* of interfering reactions is
to make everyday behavior far more simple than it really is.   Competing
reactions always develop within a wider context of concordant and discordant
behavior; and they rarely appear in neatly opposed couplets.   Frequently it
would be more accurate to speak of multiple-adient, multiple-avoidant, and
multiple-adient-avoidant conflicts than to imply that contradictory reactions
typically occur in simple opposition.   The behavior pathologist who abstracts
from a total behavior field such reactions as he can identify as contradictory,
emerges with classifications which are the product of his own operations in
behavior analysis.   These classifications provide, as we have seen, a basis for
the understanding of normal as well as pathological reactions.   They provide

[26] See pages 134–136.   It will be recalled that the conflict over weaning has been considered traumatic by some writers.   See, for example, Freud, S., *New introductory lectures
on psychoanalysis*.   New York: Norton, 1933, p. 166.
    [27] See pages 284–289.

also the clear-cut definitions of behavior which are necessary to controlled experimentation on conflict.

Experimental studies of conflict

The experimentalist who wishes to investigate conflict must first define precisely the reactions he proposes to study. His next task is to set up a controlled situation in which these reactions occur, in such a way that one reaction cannot be consummated except at the expense of another. Finally, he observes and records the behavior of his experimental subjects, and wherever possible he quantifies it.

The reactions which the behavior pathologist chooses to investigate may be brief and simple, or they may be prolonged and inclusive. The controlled situation may be restricted to the point of artificiality, or it may be a realistic model of a genuine everyday occurrence. The observations of the subject's behavior may be described in general terms, they may be classified, or they may be measured with greater or less precision. The possible variations in the design of studies on conflict are endless, but the basic pattern is always the same: *the experimental subject is required to respond in a situation where his reactions are mutually contradictory.*

This design can be applied most easily to experiments in which the subjects are infrahuman animals. A great many studies on conflict consequently employ contradictory learned reactions in cats, rats, sheep or goats.[28] Hungry rats, for example, are trained to run the length of an alley to secure food in a lighted compartment. When their acquired food-getting reactions are functioning smoothly, the animals are given an electric shock in the food box. Food as a stimulus now serves to elicit both adient and avoidant behavior; a conflict between contradictory reactions has therefore been produced. On subsequent trials, the hungry rats are observed to proceed part way down the alley and then stop, or vacillate between approaching the food box and retreating from it.[29] A somewhat different approach is illustrated by experiments in which rats learn to obtain food by going toward whichever end of a

[28] Summaries of such studies are to be found in Finger, F. W., "Experimental behavior disorders in the rat." In Hunt, J. McV. (Ed.), *Personality and the behavior disorders.* New York: Ronald, 1944, Chapter 13; Liddell, H. S., "Conditioned reflex method and experimental neurosis." In Hunt, J. McV. (Ed.), *Personality and the behavior disorders.* New York: Ronald, 1944, Chapter 12; Masserman, J., *Principles of dynamic psychiatry.* Philadelphia: Saunders, 1946. For examples of recent studies of conflict in infrahuman subjects, see Kaufman, E. L. and Miller, N. E., "Effect of number of reinforcements on strength of approach in an approach-avoidance conflict." *J. comp. physiol. Psychol.*, 1949, vol. 42, pp. 65–74; and Talcott, M. A., "Conflict: a study of some interactions between appetite and aversion in the white rat." *Genet. Psychol. Monogr.*, 1948, vol. 38, pp. 83–142.

[29] Miller, N. E., Brown, J. S., and Lipofsky, H., "A theoretical and experimental analysis of conflict behavior: III. Approach-avoidance conflict as a function of strength of drive and strength of shock." (Unpublished paper.) A description of this study is to be found in Hunt, J. McV. (Ed.), *Personality and the behavior disorders.* New York: Ronald, 1944, p. 437.

maze is lighted. The experimenter then lights *both* ends of the maze at once and observes the evidence of conflict in the vacillation, approach or retreat of his experimental subjects.[30]

Studies such as these — and there are many of them in the literature of conflict — are relatively easy to execute, since they employ simple animal subjects, rigidly controlled experimental conditions, and easily quantified measures. Their application to conflict in behavior pathology, however, is somewhat indirect. As analogues of human conflict, these experiments on infrahuman animals occasionally provide hypotheses which may be used in designing experiments with human subjects. Vacillation and blocking, for example, characterize the behavior of rats in a simple conflict situation. If we devise a correspondingly simple human conflict situation in the laboratory, we can see whether vacillation and blocking occur also in the reactions of human subjects.

The conflicts which concern the behavior pathologist, however, have characteristics which are neither derived from, nor easily studied through, animal experimentation. Human conflict does sometimes occur between simple responses; but even simple responses are more likely to reflect a lifetime of social learning than a month of daily trials in the laboratory. Human conflict typically involves discrepant social roles and competing self-reactions which have no close parallel in animal behavior. Those human conflicts which are accessible may be communicated — and even prolonged and intensified — by language systems which have no counterpart in the behavior of infrahuman animals. Many of the competing reactions that have special significance for behavior pathology are unshared and inaccessible. Consequently, the behavior pathologist is likely to profit more from experimental studies of human conflict than from investigations of laboratory animals. In what follows we shall classify the studies of human conflict according to the sort of contradictory reactions which are experimentally induced: (1) studies involving simple motor responses; (2) studies involving more inclusive reactions; and (3) studies of inaccessible reactions.

Conflict between simple motor responses. One of the earliest systematic attempts to investigate human conflict in the laboratory is that of the Russian psychologist Luria.[31] Between 1923 and 1930, Luria carried out a series of experiments aimed at deriving laws regarding the regulation and disorganization of human behavior. In his search for general principles which would explain equally well a variety of phenomena — such as emotional behavior, reaction to trauma, and neurosis — Luria was obliged to devise methods for creating conflict artificially in the laboratory. He employed a great many in-

[30] Klebanoff, S. F., "An experimental analysis of approach-approach and avoidance-avoidance conflict." (Dissertation.) New Haven: Yale University, 1939.
[31] Luria, A. R., *The nature of human conflicts* (Trans. by W. H. Gantt). New York: Liveright, 1932.

genious techniques, among them the use of mutually contradictory simple motor responses. The following two examples will serve to illustrate Luria's approach.

The subject is seated in a chair before a table, his hands resting lightly on a special device in such a way that his finger-tips can compress a pneumatic bulb. He is instructed to say rhythmically every word that occurs to him, and to depress the bulb with his right hand each time he speaks a word. He is told to leave his left hand passive. The time elapsing between the words the subject speaks is recorded on a revolving drum, and so also is the slightest movement of either hand. When he has learned to perform smoothly and at a constant rate this combined task of speaking a word and pressing the bulb with his right hand, the subject is unexpectedly required to slow down the *tempo* of his reactions. Here, according to Luria, is an artificial conflict between mutually contradictory motor reactions — between speaking and pressing at one rate, and speaking and pressing at a slower rate. The subject shows, in this conflict situation, disturbance of the chain word association and irregular movement of pressing, with diffuse hand tremor — in the *passive left* hand as well as in the more *active right*.

In a similarly designed experiment, Luria selected subjects who knew a foreign language well, in addition to their native Russian. These subjects were given a series of stimulus words in which both languages were represented. They were instructed to respond to each word with the first word that occurred to them, but always in the *same* language as the stimulus-word. After they had responded consecutively in Russian to a number of Russian words, the subjects were unexpectedly given a word from the other language. Here again, according to Luria, is an artificially created conflict — between responding in one language and responding in another language. Again the subjects demonstrated in their behavior the consequences of conflict. They responded more slowly, pressed the bulb irregularly, and showed diffuse tremor in both hands. Furthermore, the subjects in responding to the foreign stimulus-words stumbled in their speech, started to answer in Russian, and even reported occasionally that they could not hear the experimenter. In both these illustrative studies, experimentally-created conflicts between relatively simple motor reactions evoked definite disturbances of behavior.[32]

Analogous to the early studies of Luria are the more recent experiments on motor conflict carried on at Yale.[33] Both human and infrahuman animals have been used in the Yale studies. In those investigations which employ

---

[32] For a recent application of this technique in the study of conflict, see Albino, R. C., "The stable and labile personality types of Luria in clinically normal individuals." *Brit. J. Psychol.*, 1948, vol. 39, pp. 54–60.

[33] A number of these studies are summarized in Miller, N. E., "Experimental studies of conflict." In Hunt, J. McV. (Ed.), *Personality and the behavior disorders*. New York: Ronald, 1944, pp. 431–465.

human subjects, the responses are restricted to simple hand movements in one direction or another; no language reactions are included. The experiments are designed to verify certain principles regarding behavior in the three major types of conflict situation we have earlier discussed: (1) double-adient; (2) double-avoidant; and (3) adient-avoidant.[34]

(1) *Double-adient conflicts.* In one of several studies designed to investigate mutually contradictory adient reactions, the subjects sat at a table on which was a square piece of paper, held in place by brass strips.[35] At each of the two far corners of the paper was a light which could be turned on or off by the experimenter. The subjects were instructed to draw with their pencils, as quickly as possible, a diagonal line *toward* whichever light the experimenter turned on. After participating in several practice trials, in which the two signals were lighted in random order, the subjects were unexpectedly confronted with *both* lights turned on simultaneously. This, of course, is a simple example of divergent double-adient conflict: moving the pencil toward one light cannot be accomplished except by moving the pencil away from the other light which, by virtue of the experimental instructions, also requires an adient reaction. In this simple double-adient conflict situation, only 9 per cent of the human subjects were unable, in the time allowed, to make either of the two possible motor reactions.

(2) *Double-avoidant conflicts.* The same technique was employed by the Yale investigators in creating a double-avoidant conflict. Seated before the same apparatus, human subjects were instructed to draw a line as quickly as possible *away* from the lighted signal. After a series of practice trials, with the two signals lighted randomly, the experimenter flashed *both* lights at once. The subjects were caught in a simple double-avoidant conflict situation: to move their pencils away from one light they were compelled to move toward a light which also required an avoidant response. In this simple double-avoidant situation, 46 per cent of the human subjects were unable to make one avoidant motor reaction at the expense of the competing one.[36]

The greater frequency of blocking in double-avoidant conflicts, as compared with double-adient conflicts, verifies certain hypotheses of conflict-resolution set up by the Yale experimenters. *Double-adient conflict,* according to their hypotheses, is a situation of *unstable equilibrium.* Once the subject begins to

[34] In their reports, the Yale investigators employ the terms approach-approach, avoidant-avoidant, and approach-avoidant to designate these three varieties of conflict.

[35] Hovland, C. I. and Sears, R. R., "Experiments on motor conflict: I. Types of conflict and their modes of resolution." *J. exper. Psychol.,* 1938, vol. 23, pp. 477–493.

[36] Similar results have been obtained in an experimentally induced conflict situation involving the choice of liquids by ten-year-old boys. See Barker, R. G., "An experimental study of the resolution of conflict by children: time elapsing and amount of vicarious trial-and-error behavior occurring." In McNemar, Q. and Merrill, M. A. (Eds.), *Studies in personality (Contributed in honor of L. M. Terman).* New York: McGraw-Hill, 1942, pp. 13–34.

move toward one of two equally attractive alternatives, his adient reaction becomes stronger and stronger the closer he approaches the chosen alternative. The situation is analogous to that of the baton balanced on end in the hand of a juggler; once it starts falling, it continues to fall. Neither the experimental subject nor the baton reverses direction. This is the reason given for the fact that double-adient conflicts are resolved with ease and produce few instances of blocking in an experimental situation.

Double-avoidant conflict, on the other hand, represents a situation of *stable equilibrium*. The subject who moves *away from* one of two alternatives, because it is unattractive, necessarily moves *toward* the other alternative which, in this situation, is equally unattractive. Thus, avoidance of one alternative can be achieved only through movement nearer the other, and movement nearer the other means an increase in avoidance response. Here the situation is analogous to the arc described by a child's swing: the farther from the center the swing moves in either direction, the greater its tendency to return. The possibilities of vacillation and delay in reaction, according to this hypothesis, are therefore much greater in double-avoidant than in double-adient conflict. This is the reason advanced to account for the fact that subjects in double-avoidant conflict situations show a higher frequency of blocking than those who face double-adient conflicts.

(3) *Adient-avoidant conflicts.* A simplified example of mutually incompatible adient and avoidant reactions is to be found in a situation where the subject must *relinquish* one of two attractive objects in order to *secure* the other. Reluctance to abandon either object makes the subject unable to decide to take either one. The consequence of this situation is a conflict between an *adient reaction* (securing) and an *avoidant reaction* (relinquishing) in relation to each of the two objects. One of the Yale experimenters [37] investigated this third variety of conflict in young children. The child sat before two glass windows which were covered by tin shutters. The experimenter was able to lift either of these tin shutters and reveal a piece of candy, behind the glass window. Before the experiment began, the child learned to secure the candy quickly by pushing a handle forward toward it. Both the movements of the handle and the child's eye movements were recorded.

The experiment was carried out in three ways. In one of these, only one window was exposed at a time; in another, the two windows were unshuttered at once, but the child was assured that he could have the candy behind both of them. There was little conflict in the responses of the children to either of these procedures. In a third procedure, however, both windows were uncovered simultaneously, and the experimenter told the child that as soon as he selected one reward the other window would be covered by the shutter. This situation

[37] Godbeer, E., "Factors introducing conflict in the choice of behavior of children." (Dissertation.) New Haven: Yale University, 1940.

required the subject to accompany each adient reaction (securing one reward) with an avoidant reaction (relinquishing the other reward). The children responded by moving the handle, first toward the window they chose, and then quickly away from it and toward the window they relinquished; and their eyes vacillated back and forth from one window to the other. Moreover, they spent more time in making their choice than in the first two experiments. The necessity for relinquishing one reward, in other words, evoked reactions toward the chosen window which were both adient and avoidant. From this and other similar studies, the Yale experimenters concluded that adient-avoidant conflict, like double-avoidant, is characterized by vacillation and blocking.

These two groups of experiments on *conflict between simple motor responses* demonstrate, in a somewhat limited way, three behavioral consequences of contradictory reactions: tension, impoverishment and distortion. (1) The subjects in all experiments showed increased *tension* — in hand tremor and vacillation — when they were called upon to make two incompatible responses. (2) They also showed *impoverishment* of behavior — in blocking, failing to hear the experimenter, and slowing down their responses. (3) Finally, the disturbed and stumbling associations that Luria's subjects produced illustrate the *distortion* of behavior which is a common outcome of conflict. Thus we see that, even under rigidly-controlled, artificial laboratory conditions, the consequences of competing reactions show a remarkably close resemblance to those found in more complex clinical situations.

Conflict-resolution. Most of these experimental conflicts restrict the subjects to such circumscribed reactions that they yield little information regarding individual modes of *conflict-resolution.* It is important for the behavior pathologist to know, for example, *why* some subjects blocked while others did not, in the Yale experiments; and whether the subjects who in Luria's studies could not hear the experimenter were those who in other conflict situations also typically employed techniques of inattention, inactivation and withdrawal.[38] Crucial though it is, such information is rarely gained from experiments on simple motor conflicts. There has been one attempt, made by the Yale group, to identify the conditions favoring a variety of techniques of conflict-resolution.

In this experiment,[39] the subject held a vertical lever which could be moved in any direction. All movements were recorded by a concealed mechanism. (a) *One control group* of subjects was trained only to move the lever away from whichever one of two signal lights was flashed. (b) *Another control group*

[38] One recent study employing the Luria technique indicates that the magnitude of the disturbance of the subject's left hand is related to the number of neurotic symptoms he claims on a personality inventory. See Albino, R. C., "The stable and labile personality types of Luria in clinically normal individuals." *Brit. J. Psychol.*, 1948, vol. 39, pp. 54–60.

[39] Hovland, C. I. and Sears, R. R., "Experiments on motor conflict: III. The influence of previous training upon mode of resolution." (Unpublished paper.) A summary of this study is to be found in Hunt, J. McV. (Ed.), *Personality and the behavior disorders.* New York: Ronald, 1944, p. 445.

of subjects practiced moving the lever directly to the right-hand light whenever a buzzer sounded. (*c*) *The experimental groups* of subjects were trained to swing the lever at different angles when they heard the buzzer. The experimenter then induced conflict between the lever-moving responses by flashing both lights at once. In the conflict situation, the experimental subjects who were trained to move the lever at various angles showed more compromise reactions — more varied attempts at conflict-resolution — than did subjects trained in only one response. These results indicate that a person's ability to make compromise responses in conflict may be closely related to his previous training.[40]

Like the studies employing infrahuman subjects, these experiments on the production and resolution of simple motor conflict are more useful as analogues than as direct representations of everyday behavior. Nevertheless, they provide the behavior pathologist with information concerning three important aspects of conflict: (1) Subjects show behavioral tension, impoverishment and distortion when they are required to make mutually incompatible reactions. (2) The degree of disorganization, vacillation and blocking they exhibit is related to the type of conflict situation that is set up: double-adient conflicts evoke less behavioral disturbance than do double-avoidant or adient-avoidant conflicts. (3) Resolution of conflict seems to be determined at least in part by the variety of previously acquired reactions of the experimental subjects. We shall need to remember these three findings as we turn now to experiments involving conflict between incompatible reactions which are more inclusive, and therefore resemble somewhat more closely the conflicts we deal with in behavior pathology.

Conflict between inclusive reactions. A common experimental procedure for studying conflict in which the competing reactions are more inclusive, is to demand of a subject that he succeed at a task which is impossible. Of course, such a procedure must necessarily be much more complicated than the simple ones just described. Instead of the two-pronged conflicts studied by the Yale group, for example, we deal here with reactions characterized by multiple conflicts. The experimental subject is caught in a situation in which complex adient reactions develop alongside complex avoidant reactions. Among the adient may be counted those of accomplishing the task, cooperating in the experiment, seeking to impress the experimenter, or showing hostility toward him, and preserving self-reactions of approval. Among the avoidant reactions are those of attempting to leave the situation, admitting failure and surrendering to self-depreciation and even self-reproach.

Moreover, these conflicting reactions are not only multiple. They involve

---

[40] For a theoretical analysis of the learning of conflicts in the social situation of the family, see Dollard, J. and Miller, N. E., *Personality and psychotherapy.* New York: McGraw-Hill, 1950, pp. 127–156.

wide segments of behavior, which range from temporary responses, specifically evoked by the experimental procedure, to more permanent reactions which are characteristic for the individual subject. They include behavior which is shared and behavior which is private. In short, the reactions about to be discussed are closely similar to those defining the everyday conflicts which confront each one of us.

Lewin [41] and his students have been instrumental in bringing this realistic sort of conflict situation into the psychological laboratory. In one of their early experiments,[42] the subject was instructed to secure from a gymnasium "horse" an object which was just out of reach. She was allowed to secure it twice by whatever solution she devised. Thereafter every attempt the subject made to solve the problem was rejected, but the experimenter continued to insist upon a third solution and refused to permit the subject to leave the experimental room. The intensity of the subjects' anger, their hostility toward the experimenter, their occasional outburst of crying and the vigor of their search for alternative solutions left no doubt as to the genuineness of this experimentally-created conflict.

A similar but more restricted approach to the study of conflict between inclusive reactions was made by Luria.[43] He asked his subjects to respond to a list of stimulus-words according to a "whole-part" relationship (for example: house — family), but he included in the list an occasional word to which no "part" response could be given (for example: flour, pain). His subjects responded to this impossible task with increased reaction times, hand tremors and generally disorganized behavior.

A thoroughgoing and carefully controlled experiment involving inclusive and realistic competing reactions was carried out by Barker, Dembo and Lewin.[44] These investigators placed nursery-school children in a multiple-conflict situation by means of a threefold experimental procedure.

I. They first observed each child for thirty minutes in a free-play situation with a number of simple toys, making stenographic records of everything the child did, and rating his play on a five-point scale of constructiveness.

II. On the following day they brought the child back into the same playroom, but the room had meanwhile been extended to include play materials which were vastly superior to the ones he had played with during the first period. The child was now permitted to play with these attractive toys until he was thoroughly involved.

[41] Lewin, K., *A dynamic theory of personality.* New York: McGraw-Hill, 1935.

[42] Dembo, T., "Der Ärger als dynamisches Problem." *Psychol. Forsch,* 1931, vol. 15, pp. 1–144.

[43] Luria, A., *The nature of human conflicts* (Trans. by W. H. Gantt). New York: Liveright, 1932, pp. 224–232.

[44] Barker, R. G., Dembo, T., and Lewin, K., "Frustration and regression: an experiment with young children." *Univ. Iowa stud. Child Welf.,* 1941, vol. 18, no. 1, pp. 1–315.

III. As soon as the child had become completely engrossed in his play, the experimenters required him to leave the superior toys and return to his former play space, where he found the original inferior play materials. A wire mesh barrier prevented him from returning to the attractive toys, but did not prevent him from looking at them. The child was required to remain for another thirty-minute period in the original play situation.

The conflicting reactions in this experiment were numerous and for the nursery-school child severe. His adient reactions toward the superior toys, intensified by the sight of the attractive playroom through the wire mesh, were counteracted by the avoidant reactions evoked by the impassable barrier. His avoidant reactions of leaving the experimental room altogether were prevented by locked doors and the experimenter's insistence that he stay for the full thirty minutes. Moreover, the experimenter himself met adient reactions toward him with silence and apparent indifference. What this multiple-conflict situation meant for the child came out clearly in a comparison of the child's behavior in period I as contrasted with period III.

One outstanding result of this comparison was the unmistakable evidence of wide individual differences, among the thirty children, in their conflict reactions. Some tried to push through the barrier or force open the locked doors. Some attacked the experimenter, verbally or bodily; others appealed to him for escape; a few ignored him. A number of the children stated in words, or implied by gesture and general behavior, that the inferior toys were better than the more attractive but unobtainable ones. Many of the children acted out fantasies in which they pretended to use the toys on the other side of the wire fence. A few children rejected all the toys — both the available inferior and the unavailable superior ones — and sat in quiet isolation during the thirty-minute period. In general, the children showed a decrease in the maturity of their play in period III. In terms of the rating scale of play-constructiveness, they showed on the average a decrease of 17.3 months in their reactions — to the same play materials — in period III as compared with period I.[45] A great many additional findings were reported by these experimenters which are important for the general understanding of personality and of frustration following conflict.

For the behavior pathologist this investigation has a most significant implication. It shows that, when conflicting reactions of an inclusive sort are studied experimentally, subjects show wide individual differences in their modes of response. This finding reminds us of the relationship between number of solutions and previous training which was demonstrated, in a more closely restricted situation, by the Yale studies.[46] It is possible that the nursery school children in the Barker, Dembo, and Lewin experiments utilized com-

[45] For a discussion of the definitions of *regression* underlying this result, see page 221.
[46] See pages 265–266.

promise solutions in a conflict situation which had previously "worked" for them in their dealings with parents and siblings at home.[47] Such a relationship, if borne out by further study, would be a significant one for the behavior pathologist who deals daily with persons who either lack a variety of approaches to conflict, or who use ineptly the compromise solutions they have acquired.

Thus, this study offers the clinician an hypothesis regarding individual differences in techniques of conflict-resolution which may help him to understand the development of behavior pathology. It shows also that conflict situations of a genuine sort can be studied under controlled laboratory conditions. It demonstrates once again that reactions in conflict are comprehensible within the context of current theories of learning and of personality development. From this point of view, the experiment represents one more strand in the cable which ties together psychological theory, laboratory experimentation and clinical investigation.

Conflict between inaccessible reactions. The competing reactions which spell conflict in normal and pathological behavior, we have said, are frequently neither organized in language nor accessible to one's own self-reactions. The married woman whom we saw competing with her sister for her father's affection,[48] as well as the little girl who was covertly hostile toward her rival brother and her mother,[49] illustrated conflicts among inaccessible reactions. Indeed, the conflicts which Freud early emphasized as fundamental to the development of pathological behavior were those which he called "unconscious" and which we would designate as *self-inaccessible*. It is essential that the study of conflicts such as these be brought under controlled experimental conditions if we are ever to utilize laboratory procedures for the investigation of clinical problems. This is no easy task. Up to the present, we find two general approaches to the laboratory study of covert or inaccessible conflict: (1) the use of *subliminal conditioned reactions;* and (2) the use of *hypnotically-induced conflict.*

(1) *Subliminal conditioned reactions.* One variety of inaccessible reaction is the response which the subject learns to make consistently to a conditioned stimulus, but which he neither communicates in language nor organizes in his own self-reactions. This has been suggested in studies of conditioned pupillary and vasomotor responses.[50] A number of subjects in these experi-

---

[47] Some evidence for such an interpretation is to be found in the tendency of overprotected children to employ, in relationships with peers and teachers, the techniques which they overlearned at home, even though these techniques were unsuccessful. See Levy, D., *Maternal overprotection.* New York: Columbia University Press, 1943, pp. 101–111; 161–184.

[48] See page 248.   [49] See pages 255–256.

[50] See, for example, Cason, H., "Conditioned pupillary reactions." *J. exper. Psychol.,* 1922, vol. 5, pp. 108–146; Menzies, R., "Conditioned vasomotor responses in human subjects." *J. Psychol.,* 1937, vol. 4, pp. 75–120. For a critique of such experiments, see pages 80–82.

ments learned to make such autonomic responses to a conditioned stimulus, but were unaware that they were so responding. In at least one of these investigations,[51] the experimenter reported that the subjects were conditioned to make pupillary responses to stimuli that were below their threshold — to a sound they reported they did not hear, or to an electric shock they said they did not feel.

These experimental techniques suggest a tool for the investigation of inaccessible conflicting reactions; but as yet its application to the problem of conflict is exceedingly limited. An experiment by Diven [52] will serve as an example of the attempts being made in this direction. Diven's subjects were strapped into an apparatus that looked frightening but was actually harmless. They were then instructed to respond to each of a series of stimulus-words by continuing to speak all the words which occurred to them until they were told to stop. At the end of some of these chains of associated words, the subjects received an electric shock. The subjects were, thus, in a situation where (a) adient reactions toward cooperating in the experiment, by continuing to associate, were occasionally and unexpectedly brought into conflict with (b) avoidant reactions evoked by the shock.

One measure of the subject's behavior in this experimentally-induced conflict was the galvanic skin response. As contrasted with the response to non-shock words, the subject's galvanic skin response gave a significantly *higher* reading when the experimenter presented a stimulus-word which had previously been followed by shock. More significant for our present purpose, however, was the evidence that the adient-avoidant conflict was inaccessible to the subject's self-reactions. Almost half the subjects reported, at the end of the experiment, that they did not know which stimulus-word had been consistently followed by shock. Thus, even though the stimulus which evoked avoidant reactions in this experiment was self-inaccessible ("unconscious"), the subjects still showed in their responses the unmistakable evidence of conflicting reactions.[53]

(2) *Hypnotically-induced conflict.* Even closer to inaccessible conflicting reactions, which are central to the development of the science of behavior pathology, are those which experimenters have induced in hypnotized subjects.

---

[51] Baker, L. E., "The pupillary response conditioned to subliminal auditory stimuli." *Psychol. Monogr.*, 1938, vol. 50, no. 3. It should be noted that the interpretation of studies on the conditioned pupillary response have been called into question by the recent negative findings of Hilgard. See Hilgard, E. R., Dutton, C. E., and Helmick, J. S., "Attempted pupillary conditioning at four stimulus intervals." *J. exper. Psychol.*, 1949, vol. 39, pp. 683–689.

[52] Diven, K., "Certain determinants in the conditioning of anxiety reactions." *J. Psychol.*, 1937, vol. 3, pp. 291–308.

[53] Similar results are reported in a differently-designed study by McGinnies, in which subjects made galvanic skin responses to emotionally-loaded words which were below the perceptual threshold. See McGinnies, E., "Emotionality and perceptual defense." *Psychol. Rev.*, 1949, vol. 56, pp. 244–251.

Here the general procedure is to place the subject under deep hypnosis,[54] suggest to him some comprehensive role or attitude which is contradictory to his everyday behavior, and instruct him that when he awakens he will be unable to recall the suggested reaction. The hypnotic state is then terminated and the subject is placed in a situation tending to call forth the reactions suggested to him under hypnosis which, as we have said, conflict sharply with his customary reactions.

Luria included among his extensive studies of human conflict a number of such experiments.[55] He suggested to his hypnotized subjects that they had behaved in ways repulsive to them. To a medical student, for example, he suggested that she had performed an illegal abortion. To another subject he suggested that he had stolen some money from a close friend, and to still another subject that, in a temper outburst, he had beaten and injured a young child. When these subjects emerged from the hypnotic state they could not report the suggestions which had been made to them, but they gave indisputable evidence of self-inaccessible conflict. To crucial stimulus-words presented to them after hypnosis they gave unusual associations and long reaction times. The pneumatic bulb record indicated tremors and disorganization of response.

A series of similarly designed experiments employing hypnotic techniques have been reported by Erickson.[56] In these studies, however, the subject's post-hypnotic behavior has been studied in a realistic social situation rather than by means of restricted motor reactions such as those measured by Luria. On one occasion, for example, a young man was told under hypnosis that upon awakening he would become involved in a lengthy and boring conversation with the experimenter, that he would endure it politely, but that he would try to escape from the situation. The subject's behavior after hypnosis illustrated nicely his attempts to handle the conflicting reactions of overt courtesy and covert aggression. For he was excessively polite, he rationalized his glances and his approaches toward the exit as the result of a draft in the room. Finally he shut the door. When the experimenter then asked him what he was doing, he replied, "Why, I just shut the bore." Realizing at once what he had said, the subject became greatly embarrassed, denied that he had meant what he had just said, and offered profuse apologies to the experimenter.[57]

Studies such as these would be of sharply limited value if they did not go

---

[54] The technique of hypnosis is an extremely valuable one for the investigation of inaccessible reactions, but it is by no means an easy one to control to the degree necessary for precise experimentation. Individual differences in hypnotizability, as well as the ever-present danger of suggesting the desired responses to the subject in the waking state, make studies in this area difficult to perform and even more difficult to interpret.

[55] For a brief statement of his procedure, see pages 261–262.

[56] Erickson, M. H., "Experimental demonstrations of the psychopathology of everyday life." *Psychoanal. Quart.*, 1939, vol. 8, pp. 338–353.

[57] Slips of speech were among the phenomena early considered by Freud as indicators of unconscious conflict. See Freud, S., *The psychopathology of everyday life.* London: Fisher and Unwin, 1914.

well beyond the simple demonstration that reactions unidentified by the subject can be acquired under the conditions of laboratory experiment, and that they can contribute to inaccessible conflict. But they suggest further that when an experimental subject is caught between two mutually incompatible social roles, one of which is inaccessible to his self-reactions and therefore unrecognized by him, his general behavior includes a variety of disguised and compromise reactions which reveal clearly to others the conflict he himself denies. This is a highly significant finding for behavior pathology. Overemphasis, rationalization, slips of speech and rejection of one's own verbalized attitudes occur in these experiments as part of an inaccessible conflict. The situation is closely analogous to that which confronts anyone — whether normal subject or psychiatric patient — who, because of attitudes and responses acquired early in life, is caught in a self-inaccessible conflict between two social roles.

Much remains to be done in the experimental investigation of human conflict. Up to the present, certain of the phenomena observed by behavior pathologists in their patients have been reproduced in the laboratory, and a beginning has been made toward identifying the conditions under which conflicting reactions occur and are resolved. The results obtained so far point in the direction of the eventual possibility of accounting for the development and resolution of conflict in terms of hypotheses which can be applied to normal as well as to abnormal human reactions. Our greatest need now is for additional experimentation that will deal with the inclusive and the inaccessible covert reactions which, when conflict arises in them, are the ones most central to behavior pathology.

Conflict in behavior pathology

From the early writings of Freud to the present day, conflict has been considered a central factor in the development of behavior pathology. By now it is clear, however, that the mutual interference of competing reactions which defines conflict is inevitably part of the behavior organization of every person, whether he develops behavior which is pathological or not. The presence of conflicting reactions alone, therefore, is not sufficient to account for the development of behavior pathology. It is when conflict *persists or repeatedly recurs without satisfactory resolution* that it is most likely to lead to behavior disorder.

The relationship between persistent or recurrent conflict and behavior pathology becomes clear if we recall the behavioral consequences of conflicting reactions. In clinical and experimental studies alike, we have identified three general outcomes of conflict: *increased tension, impoverishment of reactions and distortion of behavior*. When conflict persists unresolved, then behavioral tension, impoverishment and distortion persist as well; and when these persist, the person suffering from them is in danger of developing, as a way of life, behavior which is personally unsatisfying and socially invalid — behavior which must then be called pathological. Thus, to trace the connections between conflict and behavior pathology it is not enough to ask how conflict develops. We must ask also the more significant question: *what conditions make contradictory reactions irreconcilable and therefore favor the persistence and recurrence of conflict?*

Conditions favoring persistence and recurrence of conflict. There are at least five conditions which render conflict difficult or impossible to resolve. All five, however, must be included within the context of individual susceptibilities and of social permissions and taboos. We have seen that, because of differences in acquired reaction-sensitivities, contradictory reactions which spell irreconcilable conflict for one person may be ignored or resolved with ease by another. We have seen also that, for members of contemporary Western society, certain reactions — those involved in affectional relationships, emancipation and hostility, for example — are bound to produce multiple conflicts.[58] Therefore, as we turn now to the five conditions favoring the persistence and recurrence of conflict, we cannot afford to forget the importance of personal susceptibility and cultural expectation.

(1) *Inclusiveness of competing reactions.* The more widespread and inclusive the contradictory reactions involved in conflict, the more difficult becomes its satisfactory resolution. This is clear from the facts of behavioral organization as well as from the experiments and clinical studies described earlier. From conflicting reactions which are brief and circumscribed — as in simple motor conflict — there is at least some temporary relief and escape. When, however, the conflicting reactions are as broad as organized *self-reactions*, or as comprehensive as *social roles*, relief or escape is much more difficult. If the conflicting reactions are widely inclusive, they are inevitably involved in practically any situation which the individual enters; he is then always to some extent participating in a conflict. This means, of course, not only that the consequences of conflict are continually reinstated, but also that the conflicting reactions may acquire more new excitants, so that conflict both persists and spreads. We shall see, in pathological behavior, the end result of inclusive conflicting reactions when we consider the rituals of compulsive disorder, the fugues and multiple personalities of hysterical autonomy,[59] and the disorganization and desocialization of schizophrenia.[60]

(2) *Kind of conflict situation.* Of the three major varieties of conflict situation, *double-avoidant* and *adient-avoidant* seem to be the most difficult to resolve. Except in those instances of convergent adience where reactions of love and hostility are pointed toward the same object, double-adient conflicts are

---

[58] See pages 252–254.
[59] Compulsive and hysterical disorders are discussed on pages 354–371.
[60] Schizophrenic disorders are discussed on pages 494–515.

resolved with relative ease. These differences in difficulty of conflict-resolution can be clearly inferred from the differences in tension, vacillation and blocking which occur under conditions of experimentally-induced conflict.[61] However, they also bear a significant relationship to the development of behavior pathology. We have seen, for example, that in one patient the irreconcilability of multiple-avoidant conflicts ended in the development of depressive disorder.[62] We have noted also that adient-avoidant conflicts develop commonly in a setting of guilt and self-punishment, and that consequently they not only resist resolution but may lead to severe behavior disorganization.

(3) *Inaccessibility of competing reactions.* The greater the degree to which the reactions in conflict are private, unshared or inaccessible to the individual's own self-reactions, the more likely is the conflict to persist unresolved. As we have seen, it is the inaccessible conflict which Freud early singled out for special attention as a precursor of behavior disorder. Competing reactions may remain self-inaccessible for many different reasons: (a) because they have never been organized in language; (b) because they occur in fantasy which the individual cannot recall; (c) because of their emotional components; or (d) because of prior punishment or threat.[63] But whatever may be the reason, the *consequence* of inaccessible conflict in the behavior of the individual remains essentially the same. Because the person is unable to identify some or all of the components of his conflict, he is in a poor position to acquire self-control over the competing reactions. Consequently, the conflicting reactions tend to generalize and spread to include a wider and wider organization of behavior [64] — and this, as we have seen, reinforces the irreconcilability of the conflict. At the same time, the individual himself may grow bewildered and mystified by his own behavior. The end results of conflict which persists because it is inaccessible are to be found in the bodily complaints of chronic invalidism and of anxiety disorder,[65] in the indecisions and ruminations of compulsive disorder, and in the anesthesias and paralyses of hysterical inactivation.[66]

(4) *Overlearning of contradictory reactions.* If the competing reactions involved in conflict are for any reason overlearned, they cannot be readily changed, and the resolution of conflict is therefore delayed or prevented. There are a great many factors which contribute to the overlearning of reactions. Some of these we have already considered in our discussion of fixation — parental overconcern or overprotection, excessive reward or punishment, and secondary gain.[67] Overlearning may occur in only one trial, as in the case

---

[61] See pages 260–272.   [62] See pages 257–258.

[63] For a more extended discussion of these points, see Cameron, N., *The psychology of behavior disorders.* Boston: Houghton Mifflin, 1947, pp. 137–139.

[64] This generalization was observed by Diven in his experiment, and by him termed "incubation." For a discussion of this point in relation to the Diven study, see pages 297–298.

[65] See pages 311–312.   [66] See pages 354–371.   [67] See pages 148–153.

of the hypnotized subject who, under conditions of special suggestibility, acquired an organization of behavior as the result of the explicit instructions of the hypnotist.[68] Because overlearned reactions do not yield easily to competing reactions, they may prolong and even intensify the tension, impoverishment and distortion of behavior which conflict induces. Indeed, it is the fixated reactions in many conflicts which render the individual incapable of shifting his perspectives, and lead him, in extreme cases, to develop the pathology of paranoid disorder.[69]

(5) *Repertory of techniques for conflict-resolution.* The greater the variety of techniques of handling conflict that an individual has acquired, the more likely he is to resolve conflict successfully. Laboratory experiments and clinical observations, as we have seen,[70] indicate that individuals differ markedly in the number and diversity of techniques they employ in conflict-resolution. The ability to use a variety of compromise solutions, we have also said,[71] is related in part to specific prior learning. Some persons attempt many different solutions to conflict, while others restrict their efforts to a few well-practiced but often inappropriate reactions. The occasional individual persists in using the same, unchanging and unsuccessful technique of conflict-resolution; this is what is called a "persistent non-adjustive reaction." [72] We see the consequences of a meager repertory of methods of handling conflict in the inflexibility, perseveration and stereotypy of behavior which seem to predispose certain individuals to behavior disorder.

These five conditions — (1) *inclusiveness of competing reactions;* (2) *variety of conflict situation;* (3) *inaccessibility of reactions;* (4) *overlearning of reactions;* and (5) *inadequate repertory of techniques of conflict-resolution* — contribute importantly to the persistence and recurrence of conflict. They serve to perpetuate and intensify the tension, the impoverishment and the distortion of social behavior which are the consequences of conflict. Perhaps the most common — and certainly the most immediate and pervasive — outcome of unresolved conflict is the organization of covert skeletal and visceral reactions we call *anxiety.* To this topic, which is in many ways pivotal to our understanding of behavior pathology, we next turn.

---

[68] See pages 270–272.
[69] An extended discussion of paranoid disorders is given on pages 405–413.
[70] See pages 265–269.   [71] See pages 268–269.
[72] Hamilton, G. V., "A study of perseverance reactions in primates and rodents." *Behav. Monogr.*, 1916, vol. 3, p. 2.

10

Anxiety in Normal Behavior

The problem of anxiety and of its relation to the development of pathological behavior is old in the history of psychiatry. It was a crucial problem for Freud, who believed that a syndrome of "primal anxiety," established by early traumata affecting the helpless infant, was reinstated later in the behavior of the neurotic adult.[1] Freud was not altogether satisfied with this interpretation, and neither were those who came after him. Consequently, there have been many attempts to reformulate the concept of anxiety and, particularly in recent years, to bring it within the framework of the general psychology of learning. It is generally agreed, however, that most of the behavior disorders either include among their symptoms the reactions of anxiety, or represent acquired techniques of minimizing or avoiding anxieties which might otherwise become intolerable. It is for this reason that the determinants and consequences of anxiety occupy a prominent place in the science of behavior pathology.

Anxiety is important in behavior pathology largely because it is an exceedingly common reaction in everyday life. A great many ongoing sequences of behavior are never carried through to consummation. From childhood on, parental control, social prohibition, and one's own self-reactions may interrupt or deflect the course of patterned behavior or alter its character. We have seen, in our discussion of frustration,[2] and of its predisposing conditions in delay, thwarting and conflict,[3] that amputated, unconsummated reactions are an inevitable part of human existence. We have also seen that the interrupted reactions are frequently those we call *emotional*, in which visceral participation is large.[4] When such reactions fail to reach consummation, the consequence

---

[1] Freud, S., *The problem of anxiety.* New York: The Psychoanalytic Quarterly Press and Norton, 1936, p. 100.

[2] See pages 47–52.   [3] See pages 252–254.   [4] See pages 122–129.

may be a persistence of the preliminary visceral responses and skeletal tensions which were initiated in the original situation. It is this amputated reaction, a preliminary phase of emotional excitement, which we shall designate as *anxiety*.

Let us begin with a simple example, one which in our culture is almost a stereotype.

Suppose that a young man has just taken his wife to the hospital for the birth of their first child. Banished to the waiting room with routine assurances that he will be notified when he is needed, the husband enters upon a long period of enforced waiting, during which he can do nothing constructive for his wife or child. He may begin by settling down with the appearance of calmness; but soon he becomes tense, restless and overactive. He may smoke incessantly, pace the floor, select a magazine only to reject it, or enter into half-preoccupied conversation with other equally anxious prospective fathers. His reading, his conversation and his thinking seem to be selective for the frightening aspects of his environment. Stories of pain and accident, rumors of medical mistakes, statistics regarding mortality and mutilation command his attention. He may interpret the most impersonal expressions on the faces of passing nurses as malicious or, at best, pitying. His heart pounds, he is short of breath, the palms of his hands grow moist, and his mouth becomes dry. If he dozes, his dreams are disturbed and horrible. If he attempts serious reading, he finds he cannot concentrate. If he goes on an errand, his motor coordinations are poor; he makes unwise decisions, or he cannot bring himself to decide at all.

It is useless to try to persuade this young man that his reactions are unjustified. He knows that his anxiety may be disproportionate to the probabilities of catastrophe involved; but he knows also the frightening statistical and medical evidence, all of it selected, that supports his fears. In his anxiety, he emphasizes the threatening elements of the situation and cannot accept completely any kind of reassurance. Sometimes behavior pathologists are inclined to look upon such intense, intractable anxiety as indicating latent wishes of hostility or death directed by the prospective father toward wife and unborn child. Sometimes it is construed to mean that the birth situation represents for the father a restatement of his own traumatic birth, with its consequent "primal anxiety." [5] If, however, we examine the total situation as it must be lived through by the young man, we shall find that these reactions are entirely comprehensible as normal anxiety.

The prospective father undergoes certain skeletal and visceral changes which are part of any reaction of emotional excitement. Under ordinary circumstances, these changes might be consummated in overt, directed activity. For the waiting husband, however, constructive activity is out of the question. The behavior for which his organism is prepared cannot be carried through.

---

[5] See, for example, Fenichel, O., *The psychoanalytic theory of neurosis.* New York: Norton, 1945, p. 42.

He cannot share his wife's labor, or give her direct assistance, care or comfort. Therefore, any activity he undertakes is bound to be incidental or even irrelevant to the emergency. In a literal sense he is helpless to consummate the patterned sequence of emotional behavior which his arrival at the hospital initiated. It is this abortive reaction of emotional excitement which we term anxiety.

Definition

We may now define *anxiety* as the *predominantly covert skeletal and visceral reaction which constitutes the unconsummated, preliminary phase of emotional excitement.*[6] Like most covert reactions, anxiety typically remains unshared, unverbalized, and often inaccessible to one's own self-reactions. For this reason, as we shall see, the individual commonly misinterprets his own anxiety reactions, misidentifies their excitants, or rationalizes their occurrence in socially invalid ways.

The visceral and skeletal reactions of anxiety seem most often to occur in fearsome situations, and to be interpreted by those reporting them as signs of fright or dread. Anxiety has therefore frequently been linked closely to fear. Indeed, anxiety is sometimes distinguished from fear only on the basis of the clarity with which its excitants may be identified, and its appropriateness as a response to these. *Fear*, it is said, represents a preparatory flight from a "real" danger; *anxiety* represents preparatory flight from a danger which is not identified, is no longer present, or seems not to demand so intense a reaction. From this point of view, anxiety is a preparatory and unconsummated reaction of escape or withdrawal in a fear-provoking situation.[7]

It is true that persons suffering from extreme anxiety typically report their feelings as fear, fright or dread. Because the verbal reports of his subjects are always significant data for the behavior pathologist, his first procedure, when his patient says he is afraid, is to search for fear excitants — in present situation and past history. Usually, the search is rewarded. Punitive self-reactions, or adient-avoidant conflicts involving the anticipation of punishment, are frequently discovered in the covert, unshared behavior of anxious persons.

It is equally true, on the other hand, that the skeletal and visceral reactions which a person interprets as fear cannot be precisely distinguished from those which occur when he is hostile or sexually aroused. At least in the present state of our knowledge, we are unable to define patterns of emotional response that are clearly different in situations which our subjects tell us are fearful, sexually arousing or anger-provoking.[8] Indeed, the most reliable distinction

[6] For a comprehensive and critical discussion of alternative theories and interpretations of anxiety, see May, R., *The meaning of anxiety.* New York: Ronald, 1950.

[7] See, for example, May, R., *The meaning of anxiety.* New York: Ronald, 1950, pp. 190–210; 331–334.

[8] Landis, C., "The interpretation of facial expression in emotion." *J. gen. Psychol.*, 1929, vol. 2, pp. 59–72; Sherman, M., "The differentiation of emotional responses in infants:

we can make is a much more general one — the antithesis between the bodily changes in *excitement* and those in *relaxation*.[9] Hostility and sexual arousal, as well as fear, are skeletal and visceral reactions of excitement.[10] To define anxiety in terms of abortive flight, therefore, is to restrict the concept in an unrealistic way. Although we recognize the central importance of *unconsummated escape*, we shall include as well among our anxiety reactions *unconsummated hostility* and *sex arousal*.

Behavioral characteristics of anxiety

By now it is clear that the reactions which constitute anxiety are those which characterize the preliminary phase of any emotional excitement, although they are most likely to be interpreted by the subject as fear. They include increased pulse rate, elevated blood pressure and changes in the functioning of the gastrointestinal and genitourinary systems and of the endocrines. Breathing may be shallow and rapid, the pupils dilate, excessive sweating occurs along with excessive dryness of the mouth. Tensions of the skeletal musculature are frequent, appearing in the subject's behavior as tremors, rigidities, and a tendency to jump or start at mild, unexpected stimuli. The chronically anxious person is preoccupied and restless; he complains of forgetfulness, of difficulty in concentrating, of disturbances in appetite and sleep. Because many of his reactions are selective for fear-inducing stimuli, he may misinterpret as threatening the most innocuous aspects of his environment.

The character of these reactions seems almost designed to trick and mislead the person who seeks to identify and interpret his own anxieties. For example, the visceral reactions in anxiety involve predominantly smooth muscle and gland activity.[11] Smooth muscle, we know, is slow to contract and slow to relax; and the endocrines empty their product into the blood stream where it may not be immediately metabolized. Thus visceral reactions tend to persist for some time after the instigating stimuli are no longer directly effective. This means that anxiety reactions easily spread, and acquire new excitants which bear no logical relationship to the original stimuli other than that found in chance concomitance. Moreover, the smooth and skeletal muscles participating in emotional excitement extend throughout the entire body. The

I. Judgments of emotional responses from motion picture views and from actual observation." *J. comp. Psychol.*, 1927, vol. 7, pp. 265–284; Pratt, K. C., Nelson, A. K., and Sun, K. H., "The behavior of the newborn infant." *Ohio State Univ. Stud., Contr. Psychol.*, 1930, no. 10.

[9] Bridges, K. M. B., "Emotional development in early infancy." *Child Develpm.*, 1932, vol. 3, pp. 324–334.

[10] This view is in harmony with the classical psychoanalytic interpretation of hostility and sex arousal. See, for example, Fenichel, O., *The psychoanalytic theory of neurosis.* New York: Norton, 1945, p. 42.

[11] See pages 122–123.

changes which occur in anxiety are consequently often diffuse and unlocalized. They also vary in intensity from time to time, and this variability may be importantly determined by the individual's self-reactions to them.

The persistence and diffuseness of these reactions have important consequences in the development of pathological exaggerations and distortions of normal anxiety. We shall find overgeneralization of anxiety reactions in the behavior of chronically anxious patients. We shall see the products of learning by chance concomitance in the development of phobias. Patients differ from one another in the particular aspects of their own anxiety reactions which seem conspicuous to them;[12] some acquire specific reaction-sensitivity to the gastrointestinal symptoms, for example, while others become concerned over their cardiac function. When to these facts we add the further one that emotional reactions are predominantly covert, unshared and inaccessible, we can see how great is the possibility that the patient will misidentify and misinterpret his own anxiety.

Conditions Favoring the Development of Anxiety

Normal anxiety reactions may develop, we have said, whenever emotional excitement cannot reach consummation. A complete list of the circumstances that prevent an individual from carrying through emotional reactions, of course, would be endless. It would certainly include the factors of delay, thwarting and conflict dealt with in our discussion of frustration,[13] and a great many more besides. From among the conditions favoring the development of anxiety, let us consider four. All four are unavoidable parts of normal social existence, and they provide us with a basis for the understanding of the exaggerated and distorted anxiety reactions we call pathological. Anxiety, we shall see, is most likely to develop (1) *when overt escape is impossible;* (2) *when anticipation of unwelcome punishment is strong;* (3) *when opportunity to carry through an adient reaction is absent;* and (4) *when separation from needed emotional support is imminent or has occurred.*

Impossibility of overt escape

When ongoing emotional excitement would ordinarily culminate in overt flight, but flight is for any reason impossible, the abortive reaction of anxiety is likely to develop. The most clear-cut, and at the same time most dramatic examples of this condition are to be found among combat personnel. Indeed, a great deal of our information regarding anxiety reactions in normal persons

---

[12] For a description of complaints commonly given by anxious patients, see Cameron, D. E., "Observations on the pattern of anxiety." *Amer. J. Psychiat.*, 1944, vol. 101, pp. 36–41.

[13] See pages 47–52.

has been obtained from observations made in wartime.[14] Active military combat inevitably places the soldier repeatedly in situations which jeopardize his life, and from which he cannot escape. The bomber pilot who brings his plane in on the target cannot deviate from his course, regardless of flak and direct enemy attack. Ground personnel in the air forces have no choice but to remain in the target area, where they are exposed to frequent, unexpected enemy bombing against which most of them are defenseless. Infantrymen may be overwhelmed and cut off from retreat, caught in crossfire, or surprised by an assault in force on an isolated island from which there are no means of escape. The anxiety that develops under all these circumstances may go beyond the predominantly covert visceral and skeletal reactions, as we earlier described them, and spiral up into panic which seriously disorganizes both the military unit and the patterned behavior of its individual members.

Most persons are metaphorically in the target area, without hope of escape, at one time or another in their everyday lives. To be sure, it is more commonly one's comfort or status than one's life which is threatened; but the impossibility of escape still favors the development of anxiety. The unwilling patient sweats and trembles in the dentist's chair or the doctor's consulting-room. The inexperienced person making his first appearance as a public speaker goes dry-mouthed, stammers before his audience, feels his lips tremble and his heart pound. For the growing child, flight from parental punishment and the avoidance of unpleasant duties are alike impossible. For the mature individual, to shrug off worrisome responsibilities is to invite reproachful self-reactions — and from self-reactions there is no escape. The ageing person can neither avoid the inevitability of death nor flee from the signs of humiliation and lowered status which punctuate his life. In all these situations we can recognize multiple-avoidant conflicts in which overt flight is impossible. The appropriate reaction of withdrawal cannot be consummated; the individual is helpless.

The very *helplessness* of the individual intensifies the anxiety which arises when escape is denied. This fact was early recognized by Freud, who considered the possibility that "primal anxiety" might be an infantile reaction to helplessness in the traumatic birth situation.[15] While we are less likely today to interpret anxiety in just this way, we cannot ignore the contribution of personal helplessness to the intensification and persistence of anxiety reactions. Restraint imposed on infants early in their lives, for example, particularly if

---

[14] For a consideration of these phenomena as they were observed in World War II, see Grinker, R. R. and Spiegel, J. P., *Men under stress*. Philadelphia: Blakiston, 1945; Sturdevant, C. O., "Residuals of combat induced anxiety." *Amer. J. Psychiat.*, 1946, vol. 103, pp. 55–59; Wright, D. G., "Anxiety in aerial combat." In *Military neuropsychiatry, Proc. Assn. Res. Nerv. Ment. Dis.*, Baltimore: Williams and Wilkins, 1946, vol. 25, pp. 116–124.

[15] Freud, S., *The problem of anxiety*. New York: The Psychoanalytic Quarterly Press and Norton, 1936, pp. 101; 150.

it is inflicted suddenly, seems often to initiate reactions of anxiety.[16] Restraint has similar implications for adults. Bomber pilots, who cannot maneuver their planes on the target-run, become anxious more readily than do fighter pilots, who are free to defend themselves. In the same way, members of ground forces who are relatively undefended from attack more frequently develop anxiety than do flying personnel.[17]

To these observations may be added evidence from experimentation on infrahuman animals. One study will serve as an example.[18] Laboratory rats were placed individually in a rectangular cage, which was floored with an electrified metal grill. After a twenty-minute interval, the experimenter offered the animal a bit of moist food, inserted upward through the grill on the end of a stick. Ten seconds later, electric shock was administered to the rat's feet. For half the animals, the shock was left on for a standard period of time; for the other half the shock was terminated whenever the rat, in the course of its general activity, leaped vertically into the air. Thus half the animals suffered uncontrollable shock for an arbitrary interval; while half could control the shock by a vertical leap which terminated it. In other words, half the animals were *helpless* to avoid the shock, and half could acquire a technique of escaping it.

The measure of anticipatory fear reactions employed in this investigation was the *delay* before the rat ate the food — an act which, under the conditions of this experiment, was always followed by electric shock. Rats who failed to eat at all in the time allowed, or who delayed in eating, were considered to have more intense anticipatory fear reactions than animals who ate promptly. The results indicate clearly that the helpless animals, for whom the shock-duration was uncontrollable, showed more delay and inhibition in eating than did the animals who could terminate the shock by a vertical leap. From these findings, the experimenters conclude that, at least in these laboratory animals, helplessness intensifies anticipatory fear reactions.[19] Such a study, of course, provides a close analogy to the clinical observation that anxiety increases when escape is denied.

[16] Greenacre, P., "Infant reactions to restraint: problems in the fate of infantile aggression." *Amer. J. Orthopsychiat.*, 1944, vol. 14, pp. 204–218.

[17] Wright, D. G., "Anxiety in aerial combat." In *Military neuropsychiatry, Proc. Assn. Res. Nerv. Ment. Dis.*, Baltimore: Williams and Wilkins, 1946, vol. 25, p. 118. For other studies indicating a relationship between helplessness and anxiety in combat situations, see Glavis, L. R., Jr., "Bombing mission number fifteen." *J. abn. soc. Psychol.*, 1946, vol. 41, pp. 189–198; Rees, J. R., "Neurosis on active service in the British Army." *Inter-Allied Conf. War Med.* (1942–1945), 1947, vol. 1, pp. 224–225; Shaffer, L. F., "Fear and courage in aerial combat." *J. consult. Psychol.*, 1947, vol. 11, pp. 137–143.

[18] Mowrer, O. H. and Viek, P., "An experimental analogue of fear from a sense of helplessness." *J. abn. soc. Psychol.*, 1948, vol. 43, pp. 193–200.

[19] For similar experiments on the role of subject-controlled stimuli in reducing "neurotic" behavior in infrahuman animals, see Griffiths, W. J., Jr., "The production of convulsions in the white rat." *Comp. Psychol. Monogr.*, 1942, vol. 17, no. 8; Masserman, J. H., *Behavior and neurosis.* Chicago: University of Chicago Press, 1943.

We shall find a similar phenomenon in the behavior of patients who suffer from pathological anxiety. Often such patients are unable to identify, and therefore unable to avoid, the excitants of their own unconsummated emotional excitement. Consequently, they are as helpless to control the onset of their anxiety reactions as are the restrained infant, the defenseless bomber pilot, and the laboratory rat. Indeed, as we shall see, one of the goals in treating anxious patients is to assist them in making the excitants of their own anxiety accessible to their self-reactions.[20] When bewilderment and helplessness give way to insight and control, anxiety reactions tend to become less frequent and less intense.

Anticipation of unwelcome punishment

Anxiety is likely to develop as the preliminary phase of emotional excitement in a behavioral sequence whose end-stage is unwelcome punishment. This is equally true whether punishment comes from the reactions of others or from one's own self-reactions. A simple illustration of this condition is to be found in the behavior of the nursery-school child who, for research purposes, is placed in a permissive environment and invited by the adult experimenter to engage in destructive behavior.[21] The child is given an inflated toy balloon and a pin, and is encouraged to go ahead and break the balloon. Many nursery-school children reach toward the balloon, hesitate, reach again, watch the adult for signs of oncoming displeasure, and ask repeatedly whether it is really all right to break the balloon. They show, in tense posture and vacillating approach-avoidance-approach, the unconsummated reaction of anxiety.

In this situation, of course, the anxious child is participating in an adient-avoidant conflict in which the avoidant component arises from his own self-reactions. The fact that the adult experimenter assures him that he may be destructive, and even presses him to go ahead, does not eliminate the avoidant character of his behavior. What the child hears the experimenter say is counteracted by his own self-reactions of avoidance, derived from prior punishment by other adults for destructive activity. Consequently, he responds in the early phases of his act as he would to a later phase, in which he believes punishment is sure to occur. This backward displacement in time of the end-reaction in a behavioral sequence we have called an *anticipant attitude*.[22] When the anticipant attitude is one of avoidance, derived from prior unwelcome punishment, the child is likely to develop anxiety.

This illustration, with its analysis, enables us to characterize still further the reactions we call anxiety. Because prior unwelcome punishment favors antici-

[20] See pages 617–620.
[21] Fisher, M. S., Stone, L. J., and Bucher, J., "Balloons: demonstration of a projective technique for the study of aggression and destruction in young children." New York: New York University Film Library, 1941.
[22] See pages 65–66.

pant attitudes of avoidance, we may expect to find anxiety developing in relation to reactions for which parents in our culture typically punish their children. It should not surprise us, for example, to find reactions of anxiety in situations of overt hostility. Indeed, as we shall see later, there is ample experimental evidence [23] that anxiety is common in children who have attacked their siblings or parents — even though the attack is indirect, and the siblings or parents are present only as doll figures in a free play situation. Similar results are found in projective tests with young children; the most frequent stimuli to anxiety are pictures involving child-child relationships in which the child is either the object of aggression or an attacker.[24] Nor should it surprise us to find anxiety developing in relation to sex activity, since the child in our culture is ordinarily punished severely and early for any behavior which adults might regard as sexual. Thus, it is often neither sex activity nor hostility as such, but their consequences in punishment, that favor the development of anxiety.

From our illustration of the child with the balloon, it must also be clear that anxiety often appears in relation to what are popularly called *conscience* and *guilt*. Indeed, if we were not particularly concerned with precision of statement, we would probably interpret the child's hesitancy in the experimental situation as the sign of a "guilty conscience." We would say that the child "knows it is bad" to break toys, and therefore refrains from puncturing the balloon. And because guilt and conscience have strong ethical and moral implications for most people, we might well applaud the child's inhibition of his own destructive behavior as "good," even though his attempts at self-control bring him vacillation and anxiety. Like many other household terms, the concepts of conscience and guilt — and the behavior they connote — are well embedded in the literature of behavior pathology. Accordingly, it will repay us to consider them more precisely.

Conscience and guilt

In the course of his biosocial maturation, we have said,[25] the child is subjected repeatedly to restriction, thwarting and control by those who interpret his culture — his parents, other adults and his own peers. Feeding routines, toilet training, schedules of naps and play, and zones of restricted and unrestricted territory, are instrumental in changing infantile irresponsibility into

---

[23] See pages 287–289.

[24] Temple, R. and Amen, E. W., "A study of anxiety reactions in young children by means of a projective technique." *Genet. Psychol. Monogr.*, 1944, vol. 30, pp. 59–114; Dorkey, M. and Amen, E. W., "A continuation study of anxiety reactions in young children by means of a projective technique." *Genet. Psychol. Monogr.*, 1947, vol. 35, pp. 139–183. For additional evidence from projective methods of a relationship between hostility and anxiety, see Korner, A. F., *Some aspects of hostility in young children.* New York: Grune and Stratton, 1949, pp. 32–33; 131–132; 141.

[25] See pages 47–48, and pages 136–141.

culturally patterned behavior. Through the uniform temporal sequences of *permitted act-approval* and *forbidden act-disapproval*, the child learns what he may do freely, and what he may do only at a price or not at all. His first lessons in ethics are thus mastered in reference to concrete objects and daily events, and not through the abstract principles of good and evil which adults specify as their own rules of conduct.

We have also seen [26] that the child comes to react to himself as a social object, and to comment upon, evaluate and punish his own behavior in much the same way that his parents earlier approved or disapproved what he did. When he eats well, performs well at toilet, or takes a long nap, he calls himself "good," proudly invites attention to his accomplishments, and shows other signs of self-evaluation. When the sequence *forbidden act-disapproval* begins, he can deflect its course by his own self-reactions: the child, we say, has acquired self-control. If, on the other hand, he privately completes the sequence of forbidden behavior, a child can also administer the punishment his parents once gave him, but now in the form of self-reactions of reproach. Self-evaluation, self-control and self-reproach are all constituents of *conscience*, and all are derived from prior approval or prior punishment of permitted or forbidden acts.

By *conscience* we shall mean *a person's reactions of self-evaluation, self-control, and self-reproach in relation to his ethical and moral conduct and to its effects.* Such a definition places conscience within the broad context of self-reaction which constitutes a substantial share of human behavior. Human beings, however, react to many diverse aspects of themselves as social objects. They comment upon their clothing, and upon the size, shape and appearance of their bodies; they evaluate the success of their social interbehavior and criticize their vocational competence; they control their own eating, drinking, sleeping and sex behavior. All these acts, and many more, are self-reactions. We reserve the term conscience for self-reactions made in reference to conduct which, for a given individual, has ethical and moral connotations.

From this analysis it should be clear that the self-reactions we call conscience may differ widely from one person to the next. The behavior which one man views within an ethical context of "right" and "wrong" may be for his neighbor a matter of expediency, taste or arbitrary cultural control. Some individuals find ethical overtones in everything they do; for them life may become an endless, private struggle between good and evil. Other persons restrict their ethical interpretations to a few situations; for them, good and evil wrestle only in certain arenas — in relation to filial obedience, sex and religion, for example. For the most part, these differences are the product of early parental approval and punishment, whether direct or incidental, which has tinged particular acts with the color of virtue or wickedness. We shall see in

[26] See pages 95–105.

many of our cases of behavior disorder the consequences of widespread and inflexible reactions of conscience.[27] We shall also find examples of behavior which, because of parental training or emotional displacement, has acquired ethical connotations for the patient that are not shared by other persons.

Conscience in everyday behavior is never the unitary regulator it seems to be in abstract writings. Like other human behavior, reactions of self-control and self-criticism are often consummated; but they are as often interrupted and deflected. We saw in the behavior of the child with the balloon, for example, incipient approaches and avoidances, hesitancies and vacillations, prior to his destructive act.[28] The uneven outline of such a child's self-reactions of control is highly characteristic of conscience in its developing stages. For some adults, self-regulation in relation to important areas of behavior continues equally uncertain and unpredictable. Caught in a permanent adient-avoidant conflict, such people remain in a state of indecision and ambivalence, unable either to relinquish or to implement their own evaluative and controlling reactions toward themselves. We shall find striking examples of anxious indecision and of alternating self-indulgence and self-denial, when we consider compulsive disorders.[29]

One further characteristic of conscience deserves our attention here, because of its close relationship to ordinary anxiety. The child who has been repeatedly punished for an act often learns not to initiate it at all; or, if he does begin it, he deflects the course of his own behavior through his self-reactions of control. For this control he receives praise and approval, first from his parents and later from his own self-reactions; and the praise and approval terminate the behavioral sequence. To put it in terms of our earlier formula, *forbidden act-disapproval* becomes *forbidden act — self-control — approval*. When, however, the child proceeds with his disapproved behavior, until the forbidden deed is done, one of two general outcomes may follow. The first of these is simple and straightforward. If the child's transgression is public, parental disapproval or punishment will sooner or later occur. This consequence, it should be noted, although it may be uncomfortable or unpleasant, still terminates or consummates the disapproved sequence of behavior.

The second outcome of performing a prohibited act is less simple than the first, but it is more closely related to the development of anxiety. Let us suppose that a child's transgression is private and known only to himself. He now escapes parental disfavor, but he does not succeed in escaping his own self-reactions of reproach. Occasionally, self-reproach is as effective as parental punishment in terminating the behavioral sequence. Much more commonly, however, self-reproach is not sufficient to provide the anticipated punishment and terminate the sequence *forbidden act-disapproval*. This is particularly the

[27] See, for example, the discussion of compulsive disorders on pages 354–359.
[28] See page 283.   [29] See pages 358–359.

case when a child has been rigidly trained in "good" behavior and made dependent upon signs of parental pleasure and displeasure. The child continues to reproach himself privately, avoids his parents, or seeks more and more reassurance from them — through protesting his innocence or demanding to know whether he is "good" — until his parents are likely to conclude that he must be *guilty*.

In this commonplace example, guilt is seen to be the product of the parents' analysis of their child's continuing reactions of self-reproach, their characterization of the child's obvious anxiety. So it is in other, more complex instances of guilt. When self-reactions of reproach and disapproval are not sufficient to terminate an ongoing behavioral sequence, the individual remains tense, insecure and intropunitive. He continues to seek reassurance from himself and others for unshared misdeeds. To the adult observer, as to the individual himself, these reactions are commonly taken to be signs of guilt. In short, in our own reactions as well as in those of others, we designate as *guilty* any *behavior in which self-reproach is prominent, but not sufficiently effective to terminate the behavioral sequence.*

From this point of view, guilty behavior is the resultant of prior punishment or the anticipation of punishment. It can occur only in individuals who have acquired the self-reactions we call conscience.[30] It develops in relation to behavior which is predominantly covert and unshared. Finally, it appears typically in a setting of behavior which is unconsummated. Neither the observer nor the individual himself can therefore distinguish the covert skeletal and visceral reactions of the person we call guilty from those of the anxious individual. We differentiate guilt from other preliminary reactions of emotional excitement only by analyzing the direction which the guilty person's behavior subsequently takes.

These points become clear if we take as an example David Levy's research on sibling rivalry in young children.[31] A number of children, all of them known clinically to be in severe competition with their siblings, were placed individually in a free play situation. The experimenter provided each child subject with dolls representing a mother, an infant, and an older child of the same sex as the subject. The infant doll was put into the mother doll's arms in a nursing position, and the subject was asked what the older doll child then would do. After considerable persuasion, most of the subjects showed hostility toward the infant or the mother — either directly or through the older doll — by attack or rough words. A great deal of important information concerning the patterns of sibling rivalry in young children was obtained in this indirect fashion.

[30] For a discussion of conscience in relation to antisocial behavior, see pages 215–216.
[31] Levy, D. M., "Studies in sibling rivalry." *Res. Monogr. Amer. Orthopsychiat. Assn.*, 1937, no. 2.

More relevant to our present point, however, is the behavior of the experimental subjects *after* the infant or mother doll had been attacked. Because hostility toward members of one's own family is forbidden and punished in our society, we would expect the child's subsequent behavior to include the self-reproach from which we infer guilt. In many cases this was true. Some of the children, for example, showed a group of reactions which we may call *restitution*. They asked the experimenter to put the smashed infant together again, promised him that they would repair it, or reassured both the experimenter and themselves that the situation was only play and the real baby was unharmed. Such attempts to make things right again, we may designate as indications of guilt. We see similar efforts at restitution in the overprotective reactions of mothers who reject their children, and in the reactions of over-friendliness and overpoliteness of adults toward persons they believe they have harmed. We shall find restitution in exaggerated and distorted forms in the ritualistic acts of patients suffering from compulsive disorders.[32]

Another reaction which followed hostility in these children was *self-punishment*. Some of the subjects caused the older doll to be destroyed after the older doll had been made to attack the infant doll. Others called the aggressive doll "bad" or "naughty," and threatened him with dragons, witches and bogeymen.[33] To the extent that the older doll was accepted by the child as himself, these reactions can be considered intropunitive. From them, as from attempted restitution, the observer infers the continuing self-reproach we specify as guilt.[34] We see similar guilty trends in the fears of anxious children that something will "get" them, in the behavior of certain normal individuals who seem to invite and even to welcome hostility from others, and in the self-flagellation of some religious devotees. Our most extreme examples of intropunitive reactions, however, will be found in patients suffering from depressive disorders.[35] Such patients often mistakenly conclude that they are responsible for horrible crimes, hallucinate reproachful and threatening voices, and expect to be beaten or executed. Occasionally their own self-punishing attitudes reach a tragic climax in the act of suicide.

To restitution and self-punishment, which were clear in Levy's study, we

[32] See pages 354–359.
[33] Compare the observations of Freud and Burlingham that many evacuated children reacted with anxiety to enemy attacks as if bombs and sirens had replaced the ghosts and bogeys they had earlier feared. Freud, A. and Burlingham, D. T., *War and children*. New York: Ernst Willard, 1943, pp. 30–31. For a psychoanalytic interpretation of fears of bogeymen as evidence of "externalized pre-superego," see Fenichel, O., *The psychoanalytic theory of neurosis*. New York: Norton, 1945, p. 103. In one study of hostility in preschool children, it is noted that fears, including nightmares, are frequent in hostile children. See Korner, A. F., *Some aspects of hostility in young children*. New York: Grune and Stratton, 1949, p. 141.
[34] Similar observations are reported by Korner, A. F., *Some aspects of hostility in young children*. New York: Grune and Stratton, 1949, pp. 32–33.
[35] For a discussion of depressive disorders, see pages 314–329.

may add other reactions which to the behavior analyst spell guilt. Expiation through confession, intense protestations of innocence, avoidance of situations in talk and thinking, denial of responsibility, and repression, may all indicate relentless self-blame. It is as if the individual, tormented by self-reproach which offers no relief, seeks either assurance that he is blameless or confirmation of his blame by overt punishment.[36] Thus until the sequence of *forbidden act-disapproval* is somehow consummated, he remains tense, apprehensive and anxious.

Absence of opportunity to carry through an adient reaction

When, due to lack of opportunity, an adient reaction involving emotional excitement cannot be consummated, anxiety may develop. The excitement involved in sexual behavior and in direct aggression is typically adient in character. It is common for sexual and aggressive acts to be punished in our society, and consequently for anxiety to develop because of the anticipation of punishment. However, there are in normal behavior many instances of interrupted, incomplete sexual arousal or hostile excitement to which conflict and prior punishment make only a minimal contribution. In these cases it is not parental disfavor or punitive self-reactions that induce anxiety, but rather the lack of opportunity to carry an adient emotional reaction through to consummation.

Perhaps the commonest example of this condition, as an antecedent of anxiety, is to be found in emotional reactions which arise in fantasy. Let us suppose that a young man with strong sexual needs, which he has no hope of fulfilling in the foreseeable future, resorts to fantasying on sexual themes. He follows out repeatedly, in his autistic behavior, the steps of courtship, marriage and procreation with his imaginary mate, and his fantasy includes the particulars of sexual intercourse as well as its more romantic setting. The inevitable consequence of such fantasy, once it has become well-practiced, is the arousal of sexual excitement which cannot then be consummated. This emotional reaction, in common with others, is likely to persist and become cumulative, until the young man may show, in many phases of his behavior, a pervasive anxiety reaction. Here it is not conflict, guilt or anticipated punishment that favors anxiety, but only the absence of opportunity to carry through realistically an adient emotional reaction.

The same rise and persistence of anxiety may stem from recurring fantasy themes of aggression. The worker who is subordinated to a foreman whom he can neither tolerate nor overtly attack, for example, may spend his lunch hour in fantasying a battle with his superior. He combats his foreman in imagina-

---

[36] Korner notes that some children in her study appeared to employ hostility as a punishment-provoking device to relieve anxiety. Korner, A. F., *Some aspects of hostility in young children.* New York: Grune and Stratton, 1949, pp. 131–132. For a discussion of the relation of this behavior to the development of the pseudocommunity, see pages 387–392.

tion with angry words, wrestles with him hand to hand, and demonstrates his opponent's incompetence as a leader and his ineffectuality as a fighting male. The worker's fantasied attack brings him the visceral and skeletal changes which would prepare him for direct aggression were the foreman within his reach. But the end of the lunch hour finds the would-be aggressor back with his hated but still inaccessible foreman, with persisting emotional excitement that cannot be consummated. If the worker values his job, he waits for the next noon hour and again confines his aggression to his autistic behavior. Thus the person whose fantasy is largely confined to attacks on others beyond his reach trains himself in the development of emotional excitement that cannot be consummated in overt behavior. In this way, unresolved aggression often persists as anxiety behavior.

Not only fantasy, but also artificial environmental restriction, may prevent an individual from consummating his emotional excitement. This is often the case when, for example, mature men and women accustomed to heterosexual behavior are segregated from one another. Imprisonment or separation because of military exigency, may render an individual unable to carry through the sexual activities to which he is habituated; and he then develops recurrently the reactions of anxiety. Likewise, combat troops whipped into enthusiasm for battle, by training and inflammatory propaganda, may become casualties to anxiety when unforeseen events deprive them of the opportunity to fight. In these instances, as in those we earlier discussed, conflict is minimally involved, but anxiety still persists.

Separation from needed support

Anxiety reactions are likely to develop whenever an individual is separated from support to which he has been accustomed. As a rule, the support which is withdrawn is that provided by the behavior of another person. The young child parted from his parents, for example, or the adult separated from a marital partner upon whom he has been dependent, is particularly vulnerable to the development of anxiety. The individual who has become an integral part of a structured group — his family, his military outfit, or a closely-knit clique of intimates — becomes tense and anxious when the group is dissolved. Indeed, so common and well recognized is this consequence of separation that behavior pathologists have long referred to it as *separation anxiety*.[37]

Any clinician who has worked with young children in free play can testify to the frequency and intensity of the anxiety reactions which develop in this setting. The child is separated from his mother and taken to a playroom equipped

[37] Freud's "primal anxiety," following "loss of the love object" is similar in general outline to this concept. See, for example, Freud, S., *The problem of anxiety*. New York: The Psychoanalytic Quarterly Press and Norton, 1936, p. 99. For a study of separation anxiety in military personnel, see Cammisa, J. J. V. and Moloney, J. C., "Separation anxiety." *Ment. Hyg.*, 1947, vol. 31, pp. 229–236.

with toys, where he is told simply that he may do whatever he likes. For many children, this combination of a lack of accustomed maternal support and the presence of a neutral environment that is unfamiliar and has no apparent boundaries, is sufficient to induce anxiety. The child may first try to escape or call for his mother; but eventually he stands wide-eyed, tense and trembling in the center of the room, unable to talk and sometimes even to move. If, after a time, he becomes involved with the toys, his play is likely to be restricted and disrupted. His tension and the disorganization of his behavior alike indicate the intense anxiety which has been aroused.

One of our best sources of information concerning anxiety in young children who are separated from their parents is to be found in the studies of Freud and Burlingham.[38] These investigators observed and described with care the behavior of English children who were evacuated from cities to rural areas because of the dangers of enemy bombing. For the most part, the children had witnessed air raids and had fled to underground shelter in the midst of falling bombs. Many of them had seen their own houses demolished. Many had lost one or both parents in the war. The anxieties which these children developed, however, were less often related to the danger of enemy attack than to the separation from parental support which resulted from their evacuation.

Some of the youngest children, for example, refused to eat or sleep after their mothers had left them in the country. Some clung for a day or two to some parting gift from the mother, or to a piece of bedding or clothing brought from home. An occasional child repeated, continuously and monotonously, the name of his mother. A good share of the children seemed to interpret their life in a strange nursery among unfamiliar adults as a sign that their own parents had abandoned them. Hostility toward the parent was then mixed with despair and loneliness. The children showed, in aggressive play, in disturbing dreams and nightmares, in indifference toward their own visiting parents, and in violent scenes of affection after these visitors had left, reactions from which the adult observer infers self-reproach and guilt. These children seemed to interpret separation as abandonment, and abandonment as punishment.

Similar reactions of anxiety upon separation from the mother occur when the young child must be hospitalized. Edelston has described a series of over forty cases of children referred to a child guidance clinic, in whom behavior problems were either initiated or intensified by anxiety arising from hospitalization.[39] Here again, it was not the pain, discomfort or strangeness of hospital procedures which aroused anxiety as much as separation from the family. This was particularly apparent when the child was isolated because of contagious disease and could be "visited" by his parents only while separated from them

[38] Freud, A. and Burlingham, D. T., *War and children.* New York: Ernst Willard, 1943.
[39] Edelston, M., "Separation anxiety in young children: a study of hospital cases." *Genet. Psychol. Monogr.*, 1943, vol. 28, pp. 3-95.

by a glass window. Like the evacuated English children, these hospitalized ones often interpreted separation as punishment. In both studies, it is the separation from needed support, and the child's interpretation of it, which provide the conditions for anxiety.

In the course of biosocial maturation, support, not only from others but also from one's own self-reactions, contributes to the organization of one's behavior. Consequently, when the accustomed pattern of self-reaction changes for any reason, the individual is likely to develop tension which is closely similar to separation anxiety. Traumatic events, or undue personal stress and strain, for example, may produce behavior which is foreign to the individual under ordinary circumstances. Recall of unpleasant events long forgotten — the return of the repressed — may provide a mirror in which the person sees a reflection which seems distorted but must still be his.[40] He views himself in a different light, and recognizes that he may be unpredictable even to himself. Similar disturbances in self-reaction often attend states of delirium or intoxication, in which cerebral competence is impaired. The consequence of this loss of support by one's own customary self-reactions is likely to be intense anxiety which, as we shall see, may initiate severe behavioral disorganization.[41]

One aspect of separation anxiety remains for our consideration. The individual who loses the support of others, or of his own self-reactions, finds himself in a situation which is for him unfamiliar and unstructured. The child in free play at the clinic, children in war nurseries or hospitals, and adults who see themselves behaving in unaccustomed ways, are alike unable to predict what they or others will do. The *unpredictability* of the situation is therefore at least as important as absence of needed support in favoring the development of anxiety. When events in an unstructured situation are unpredictable, the patterned consummation of emotional excitement becomes difficult and often impossible.

Partly because of their anxiety-provoking character, unstructured situations are frequently utilized by clinicians for diagnostic purposes. Indeed, this is one rationale for the *projective* methods of studying individual personality, in which the subject is given an opportunity to respond freely to a neutral or meaningless stimulus.[42] What he does with clay or with finger-paints, what he interprets in ink blots or in pictures, and what he hears in meaningless syllables, give clues both to his readiness to develop anxiety and his habitual techniques for handling it. Free association, whether used for diagnostic or for

[40] Compare the discussions of repression on pages 79–83, pages 337–351, and pages 617–620.

[41] See pages 464–466.

[42] For summaries of this technique, see Bell, J. E., *Projective techniques: a dynamic approach to the study of personality.* New York: Longmans, 1948; Sargent, H., "Projective methods." In Pennington, L. A. and Berg, I. A. (Eds.), *An introduction to clinical psychology.* New York: Ronald, 1948, pp. 416–439; Sargent, H., "Projective methods: their origins, theory and application in personality research." *Psychol. Bull.*, 1945, vol. 42, pp. 257–293.

therapeutic purposes, depends upon the same rationale. The patient who has been trained in the technique of free associating must speak without the support of his therapist or of his own accustomed reactions of self-criticism. As might be expected, however, individuals who are deprived of support, and placed in an unpredictable environment, differ widely from one another in their tendency to develop anxiety, and in their capacity to tolerate and to minimize it.

Individual Differences in Anxiety-Readiness

Some normal persons seem to develop reactions of emotional excitement readily, while others seem phlegmatic and unresponsive. Among those who initiate emotional behavior easily, some appear able to carry through the reactions without interruption; they rarely develop the preliminary, aborted behavior we call anxiety. Other normal persons, however, seem able to consummate emotional excitement only with difficulty or not at all. They easily develop anxiety reactions which then persist and cumulate. In some of these individuals, anxiety increases pathologically and grows chronic, until they appear to spend their lives in a state of readiness to react, tensely poised for action which somehow they never take.

The reasons for wide individual differences in readiness to develop anxiety must certainly be complex and interrelated. If we are to identify them at all, we must consider with equal care the biological properties of the human organism and the network of social expectation which together define biosocial maturation. Young infants, we have seen,[43] differ discernibly from one another in the ease and intensity with which they respond to stimulation. It is altogether possible that infantile responsiveness in part provides a predisposition toward ready arousal of emotional excitement in adulthood.

Of equal importance with biological responsiveness, however, are three further conditions which contribute to individual differences in anxiety-readiness. The character of others' reactions to an infant, for example, is importantly related to the development and persistence of his anxiety. Likewise, the behavior of other persons in a child's surroundings, even though it may not be directed toward the child, often renders him susceptible to anxiety. Finally, minimal anxiety reactions may increase sharply and even grow into an anxiety disorder if an individual, for any reason, cannot identify the excitants to his own anxiety. Thus, in order to account for individual differences in anxiety-readiness, we must turn now to a discussion of *parental training, adoption of the prevailing pattern,* and *the inaccessibility of excitants to anxiety.*

[43] See pages 22–26.

Parental training

The child receives his earliest instruction in anxiety at the hands of his parents. They may provide a setting for unconsummated emotional excitement by creating or reinforcing any of the conditions favoring anxiety which we have been discussing.[44] By repeatedly frustrating his ongoing behavior, for example, parents may train their child in incomplete, unsatisfied reactions which persist as anxiety. An extreme example of such training has been reported in the techniques which the Balinese mother characteristically employs to prompt her child to respond. By teasing or affectionate advance, she elicits temper or affection in her child, but having done this, she then fails to respond to the behavior she has elicited herself. Balinese child training, therefore, is in part training in emotional excitement that is aroused but not consummated. For the Balinese, this early training in anxiety during childhood apparently leads to dullness and indifference to personal relationships in the adult years.[45]

Parents in contemporary Western society often interrupt and frustrate their children's behavior in similar ways. An overrestrictive mother may interrupt any new behavioral sequence which her offspring undertakes — by darting forward, giving little warning cries or removing the child bodily from the scene — until the child himself becomes helpless to carry through his own behavior. Typically, the mother intercedes in situations which appear to her to be exciting or threatening for the child, and in which the child's behavior, consequently, is often emotional. The mother relieves her own tension by terminating the child's sequence of behavior; but she leaves her child tense and anxious.

Frequent, rejecting punishment, or threat of punishment which is not confirmed, may also predispose a child to the ready development of anxiety. Parents often keep their offspring in prolonged adient-avoidant conflict which, as we have seen, underlies much anxious behavior.[46] The child who is trained in reaction-sensitivity to punishment, who learns through his parents' cross-examinations to search his every act for signs of guilt, is on the way to becoming a chronically anxious adult. So also is the child whose parents, by repelling his confidences or ignoring his long periods of silent isolation, encourage him in the overdevelopment of covert fantasy. Children who are overtrained in fantasy are exposed to the recurrent anxiety which results when fearful, hostile and erotic reactions cannot be consummated.

One of the most important origins of susceptibility to separation anxiety lies in the failure of parents to provide consistently, through their own behavior, the support which their child needs. We have already seen [47] that whether or not separation from the parents induces anxiety depends heavily upon the

[44] See pages 280–293.
[45] Bateson, G., "The frustration-aggression hypothesis." *Psychol. Rev.*, 1941, vol. 48, pp. 350–355.
[46] See pages 258–259.   [47] See pages 290–293.

child's interpretation of the event. Hospitalization or evacuation to a secure area, even though these be essential to his life, may still be taken to be signs of rejection and abandonment by the child. In the same way, a child who is sent to live with grandparents when his mother has a baby, or is placed in nursery school because his mother must work, may conclude that he is unloved. When such separations from parental support are frequent and prolonged, a child is likely to become persistently tense and anxious. We shall later see the consequence of repeated separations in one of our cases of anxiety disorder.[48]

Occasionally a parent trains his child in anxiety, not so much by providing the proper conditions for it, as by direct tuition. One of the mothers described by Freud and Burlingham, for example, had fled with her son to a shelter during a daytime air raid.[49] Mother and child listened for a while to the exploding bombs; then the boy became involved in a book he had brought with him. The frightened mother, however, continued to take note of each bomb, frequently interrupting her child's reading with anxious cries. The child always returned at once to his book, until at length the adult said angrily, "Drop your book and attend to the air-raid!" Not very different from this terrified mother are parents who cover their children's ears against the crash of thunder, snatch their children away from windows during lightning bursts, or threaten them with dragons and ghosts if they misbehave. All these parents are providing direct instruction in anxiety which may persist throughout their children's lives.

Adoption of the prevailing pattern

By no means all the training in anxiety which individuals receive falls within the category of direct tuition, nor is it all confined to childhood. The person, whether child or adult, living among people who are themselves anxious, may develop the prevailing pattern of anxiety-readiness without being trained directly in it. At one time it was felt that infants as well as adults, perhaps through empathy, took over the tensions of other persons in their environment and responded anxiously in terms of them. Bodily posture, facial expression and muscular change, for example, were presumed to furnish the individual with subtle cues, often unrecognized and unverbalized, to the emotional state of others in his environment.[50] This would be an exceedingly important phenomenon for the behavior pathologist, if it were verified, but the evidence favoring it at present is ambiguous.[51] It seems undeniable, however, that anxious persons are likely to arouse anxiety in others.

---

[48] See pages 307–310.

[49] Freud, A. and Burlingham, D. T., *War and children.* New York: Ernst Willard, 1943, pp. 26–27.

[50] See, for example, Dunbar, F., "Effect of the mother's emotional attitude on the infant." *Psychosom. Med.,* 1944, vol. 6, pp. 156–159; Escalona, S. K., "Feeding disturbances in very young children." *Amer. J. Orthopsychiat.,* 1945, vol. 15, pp. 76–80. For a general discussion of this point, see also pages 59–60.

[51] For a critical review of the evidence, see Orlansky, H., "Infant care and personality." *Psychol. Bull.,* 1949, vol. 46, pp. 1–48.

Some of the mothers in the Freud and Burlingham study [52] refrained from snatching their children from place to place, or talking about the dangers of air raids, but could not control their own trembling and agitation. Anxious maternal behavior was thus not directed toward the child, but it still occurred in his immediate surroundings. Many of the children of these mothers developed anxieties which persisted long after they had been evacuated to safer areas. In the same way, the squadron leader who is himself terrified in battle finds his men more anxious and susceptible to panic than does the officer who handles his own inevitable anxiety effectively. The arousal of anxiety in individuals who are closely associated with the anxious persons may be partly accounted for through *identification*.[53] We would expect individuals to react anxiously to the same excitants that arouse anxiety in persons with whom they are strongly identified, whether parent, squadron leader, spouse or intimate friend.

Anxious people also tend to utilize others in their environment as foci for their own intolerable anxiety. Often this is no more than a reaching out for comfort and reassurance; the anxious individual clutches the arm of his friend, invites a smile or a nod, or, like the child, asks whether he has done well. Sometimes, however, the casual comfort thus obtained is not enough. The anxious person may then try to include others in his discomfort, asking them whether they are not frightened or upset, and implying that they should be. Occasionally, as in cases of pathologically exaggerated anxiety, the patient rails at those about him for not taking steps to alleviate his intolerable stress. Few people who are subjected, day after day, to any of these appeals can escape developing anxiety-readiness themselves.

Moreover, the unconsummated character of anxiety reactions stimulates the anxious individual to complete, or "close," his own behavior.[54] He acts as if he were seeking an explanation for his persistent visceral and skeletal reactions. And in his search he is bound, sooner or later, to hit upon the behavior of his close associates as a possible reason for his own inexplicable discomfort. Thus he blames others for his reactions, accuses them of upsetting him, and by means of these methods may come to exert unwitting control over their behavior. Through *emotional displacement* [55] and the adjustive technique of *projection*,[56] which may render his own anxiety tolerable to him, he arouses anxiety and self-reproach in his associates. Such a development, which is almost certain to increase the level of anxiety in other people, is particularly common when the excitants to anxiety are inaccessible to an individual's self-reactions.

[52] Freud, A. and Burlingham, D. T., *War and children*. New York: Ernst Willard, 1943, pp. 34 ff.

[53] See pages 60–63.   [54] See pages 75–79 and 302–303.

[55] See pages 125–126.   [56] See pages 381–387.

Inaccessibility of anxiety excitants

Not only susceptibility to the development of anxiety, but also the ease with which anxiety reactions, once initiated, persist and spread, contributes to individual differences in anxiety-readiness. Indeed, our most extreme examples of anxious behavior are to be found in persons whose anxiety reactions generalize to a great many excitants in their everyday lives, or are displaced to excitants which seem irrelevant. These reactions we shall see later when we consider the pathological developments of *chronic anxiety* and *phobias*.[57] In anxious patient and normal person alike, anxiety most easily cumulates and persists when the excitants to anxiety are inaccessible to the individual's self-reactions.

The relationship between inaccessibility of excitants and generalization of anxiety reactions is clearly indicated by the experiment of Diven,[58] which we considered in the previous chapter. In this study, it will be recalled, the subjects were required to produce a chain of associated words to each of a series of stimulus words. To most of the stimuli, the subject continued associating for a twelve-second interval, after which the experimenter presented the next stimulus word in the list and the process was repeated. One deviation from this procedure, however, was introduced. Whenever, in the list, the word *red* was followed by the word *barn*, the experimenter terminated the subject's associations to *barn* — after the standard twelve-second interval — by administering a mild but startling electric shock. This variation occurred six times in the list for each subject. When the word list was completed once, the entire procedure was repeated without the use of electric shock. Two different time-intervals were employed. For some subjects, the second session occurred five minutes after the first one. For others, the second session was delayed twenty-four or forty-eight hours.

Diven defined "anxiety" in his experiment in a somewhat restricted way, in terms of changes in the galvanic skin response (GSR). Each of his subjects kept one hand in liquid electrodes which picked up any shifts in electrical potential from the subject's skin. The excursions of a pointer on a kymograph drum recorded any change. Thus it was possible to obtain a quantitative measure of galvanic skin response throughout the experimental sessions. The amount of GSR activity was taken to be an indication of the subject's emotional upsetness — or, as Diven would put it, of his "anxiety." Although GSR change is only one component of the total pattern of preliminary reactions we call anxiety, it is a widely accepted indicator of emotional excitement.

For these subjects, as might be expected, the largest GSR's occurred on the word *barn*, which was always followed, after twelve seconds, by shock. Signifi-

---

[57] See pages 305 and 312–314.

[58] Diven, K., "Certain determinants in the conditioning of anxiety reactions." *J. Psychol.*, 1937, vol. 3, pp. 291–308.

cantly increased response also occurred, however, to the word *red*, which always preceded *barn*, and to whatever words followed *barn* in the list. Moreover, above-average GSR's occurred to all words in the list which had a rural flavor — *sheep, plow, pasture*, for example. In this way the anxiety reaction, as measured by the galvanic skin response, generalized from the original word that brought the subject electric shock, to words close to it in time, and to words apparently related to it in meaning. We shall find clinical examples of this sort of generalization when we consider phobias.[59]

Even more important for our present point, however, are the results obtained from those subjects who could not identify the excitants which elicited their own anxiety. It will be recalled that half the experimental subjects were unable, at the end of the experiment, to state which word had been followed by shock. For these subjects, the excitant to anxiety was inaccessible to their own self-reactions. Nevertheless, these subjects showed the same generalization of galvanic skin response to contiguous and related words as did the subjects who knew that shock followed *barn*. Thus the inaccessibility of the excitants in no way defended the subject against the spread of his anxiety reactions.

This finding has its close parallels in the susceptibility of certain persons to an overgeneralization of anxiety reactions. We have already seen [60] that the person who is unable to identify the excitants to his anxiety is literally helpless to control his reactions. He cannot escape from disturbing situations because he cannot say what it is that makes him anxious. He remains confused and bewildered, sometimes half-suspecting that mysterious forces beyond his control are responsible for his behavior. To his anxiety reactions, elicited by unidentified excitants, the patient now adds his own unconsummated self-reactions of avoidance. His anxieties increase and multiply until, as we shall see, they become not only cumulative but self-perpetuating. And cumulative and self-perpetuating anxiety reactions have important consequences, both in the subsequent behavior of normal persons, and in the disorders to which anxiety may lead.

Behavioral Consequences of Anxiety

Normal anxiety reactions, we have said, are emotional, which means that *visceral* participation is large; they involve *excitement*, as opposed to relaxation; and they are typically preliminary and *unconsummated*. From these three characteristics of normal anxiety stem three behavioral consequences, a discussion of which will serve both as a summary of what has gone before, and as an introduction to the pathological anxiety reactions to which we shall next turn. Accordingly, let us now consider (1) the consequence of persistent

[59] See pages 312–314.   [60] See pages 279–280.

visceral response in the production of organ pathology; (2) the consequence of reactions of *excitement* in reinforcing and fixating learned behavior; and (3) the consequence of *unconsummated* behavior in encouraging the individual to bring his own reactions to completion.

Visceral response and organ pathology

The visceral components in anxiety reactions, as we have seen, are diffuse and unlocalized; and, as in all smooth muscle and glandular activity, they are characteristically persistent. Consequently, the anxious person has ample opportunity to react to his own visceral activity; and his self-reactions, particularly if they are unshared, often perpetuate and intensify his anxieties. A great many behavior pathologists today have come to believe that the visceral changes of anxiety may persist and increase in this way, until the organs and tissues which participate in the reaction undergo extensive changes leading to organ pathology.[61] Disorders which are presumed to develop in this way are currently called *psychosomatic*.

So far, our best evidence concerning the relationship between persistent anxiety and consequent organ pathology comes from studies by Wolf and Wolff on the gastric mucosa of one subject.[62] The patient studied had suffered in childhood an injury which necessitated the production of a fistula in the stomach wall. This surgical procedure, as we have seen, had profound effects upon the patient's self-reactions and his organization of social interbehavior. However, it permitted Wolf and Wolff to make regular observations of the lining of the stomach in a living person, and to discern what visceral changes accompanied shifts in the patient's total behavior. Among many other significant results, the investigators found that when their patient was fearful, excited or resentful, the gastric mucosa became pale, or red and engorged. If, now, the engorged mucosa was experimentally abraded, the consequence was a small mucosal lesion which tended to persist.

Without generalizing unduly, the behavior pathologist can see in this result an analogue of the development of gastric ulcer in an anxious person. Let us suppose that an anxious individual suffers from gastrointestinal distress as part of his normal anxiety reaction, and that this visceral activity persists. His own self-reactions to his persistent gastrointestinal distress will almost certainly increase his anxiety reactions — particularly if he considers his visceral activity inexplicable, or misinterprets it as a sign of grave illness.[63] The cumulative and persistent gastrointestinal components of his anxiety reaction

[61] For a summary of this point of view, see Alexander, F. and French, T. M. (Eds.), *Studies in psychosomatic medicine.* New York: Ronald, 1948.

[62] Wolf, S. and Wolff, H., "Evidence on the genesis of peptic ulcer in man." *J. Amer. med. Assn.*, 1942, vol. 120, pp. 670–675; Wolf, S. and Wolff, H., *Human gastric function: an experimental study of a man and his stomach.* London: Oxford Univ. Press, 1943.

[63] For a case illustrating such a reaction, see pages 311–312.

may conceivably keep his gastric mucosa engorged and friable for long periods of time, and thus render it readily susceptible to abrasion. With this visceral background, it would not be surprising if the individual developed a persistent gastric ulcer.

Other pathological changes in organs and tissues may possibly follow upon the persisting visceral activity which characterizes anxiety and the person's self-reactions to it. Indeed, a convincing case can be made for a relationship between persistent emotional excitement and enduring cardiovascular disturbances — a relationship which has long been appreciated by the cardiologist who seeks to guard his patient from undue excitement. Respiratory disorders and certain skin diseases have also been interpreted as the consequence of bodily changes which begin as normal anxiety and become cumulative and self-perpetuating through the individual's reactions to them.

Emotional excitement and reinforcement in learning

Excitement, as opposed to relaxation, characterizes the reactions of anxiety. His bodily changes, we have said, keep the anxious person in a state of readiness-to-react, in which persistent skeletal and visceral tensions are prominent. When anxiety is intense and enduring, these tensions may disrupt an individual's patterned behavior and lead to temporary or permanent behavioral disorganization.[64] We shall see this consequence in the extreme anxiety of the *panic reaction*.[65] In milder degree, it can be demonstrated when an anxious person is required to perform simple learning tasks. Anxious patients, for example, often do poorly in serial rote learning experiments, apparently because the intensity of their anxiety increases the interference between the correct response and irrelevant, incorrect responses.[66] Such "anxiety-produced interference" may be a contributing factor, both to the anxious person's forgetfulness, and to the behavioral disorganization to which intense anxiety may lead.

It is a common observation, however, that mild muscular tension often facilitates learning.[67] The student who is moderately tense over an impending examination, and the laboratory subject who clenches his fist or exerts moderate pressure upon a spring dynamometer while he is memorizing nonsense syllables, may find the efficiency of their learning increased. Such facilitation through tension has been demonstrated even in the conditioning of autonomic responses. In one experiment, for example, subjects suffering from different intensities of anxiety were placed in a classical conditioning situation. The

[64] See pages 449–451 and 458–469.   [65] See page 306.

[66] For a study on this point, see Malmo, R. B. and Amsel, A., "Anxiety produced interference in serial rote learning, with observations on rote learning after partial frontal lobectomy." *J. exper. Psychol.*, 1948, vol. 38, pp. 440–454.

[67] See, for example, Courts, F. A., "Relations between experimentally-induced muscular tension and memorization." *J. exper. Psychol.*, 1939, vol. 25, pp. 235–256.

conditioned stimulus was a startlingly loud buzzer, and the response recorded was a change in galvanic skin response.[68] The most anxious subjects acquired a conditioned galvanic skin response to syllable-without-buzzer significantly sooner than did the least anxious. Moreover, with declining anxiety there was a systematic decline in the efficiency of conditioning.

Even more conspicuous is the increased efficiency of learning when the consequence of performing the learned act is a *reduction* in anxiety. Most of our evidence on this point comes from experiments on avoidance conditioning in infrahuman animals. In one typical study, laboratory rats were placed in a circular cage floored with separate segments of an electrified grill.[69] The experimenter sounded a tone and then administered electric shock, *which could be avoided* if the animal ran at once to another section of the cage. When the combination tone-shock occurred regularly, the rat soon learned to avoid the shock by running as soon as the tone sounded. A second group of animals was shocked at regular intervals between paired presentations of tone and shock; and from these interpolated shocks the rats *could not escape*. The second group of animals learned much more slowly than the first to run at the sound of the tone. Here the reduction of anxiety, by avoidance of shock, favored rapid acquisition of the conditioned response of running.[70]

Such experiments as these support what is commonly found in clinical material. Intense anxiety may produce interference with learning and introduce behavioral disorganization; but the tensions of mild anxiety may facilitate learning. Furthermore, behavior which is anxiety-reducing is typically learned more promptly and efficiently than behavior which does not have anxiety-reducing properties. This last finding has particular relevance for the acquisition of symptoms in cases of phobic and compulsive disorder. Often by chance, the intensely anxious patient hits upon a reaction which, perhaps only because it is distracting, serves to reduce his anxiety. But precisely because the reaction happens to be anxiety-reducing, the patient may learn it promptly, and retain it so successfully that it becomes a persistent symptom. We see instances of the reinforcement of chance acts, and their persistence as pathological symptoms, in the rituals of many compulsive patients.

---

[68] Welch, L. and Kubis, J., "Conditioned PGR in states of pathological anxiety." *J. nerv. ment. Dis.*, 1947, vol. 105, pp. 372–381; Welch, L. and Kubis, J., "The effect of anxiety on the conditioning rate and stability of the PGR." *J. Psychol.*, 1947, vol. 23, pp. 83–91.

[69] Mowrer, O. H., "Anxiety-reduction and learning." *J. exper. Psychol.*, 1940, vol. 27, pp. 497–516.

[70] For other examples of experiments bearing on these points, see Farber, I. E., "Response fixation under anxiety and non-anxiety conditions." *J. exper. Psychol.*, 1948, vol. 38, pp. 111–131; Miller, N. E., "Studies of fear as an acquirable drive: I. Fear as motivation and fear-reduction as reinforcement in the learning of new responses." *J. exper. Psychol.*, 1948, vol. 38, pp. 89–101; Mowrer, O. H., "A stimulus-response analysis of anxiety and its role as a reinforcing agent." *Psychol. Rev.*, 1939, vol. 46, pp. 553–565; Mowrer, O. H. and Lamoreaux, R. R., "Avoidance conditioning and signal duration: a study of secondary motivation and reward." *Psychol. Monogr.*, 1942, vol. 54, no. 5.

Unconsummated reactions and the completion of behavioral sequences

The preliminary, unconsummated nature of the emotional excitement we call anxiety encourages the anxious person to bring his own incomplete behavior to consummation. Partly because they are abortive sequences of emotional behavior, anxiety reactions often seem mysterious and inexplicable to the person participating in them. His own unconsummated skeletal and visceral reactions consequently provide him with an unstructured situation, a projective stimulus, which he is free to interpret as he will. That he will make some interpretations we may be sure. We have already seen, in our discussion of *closure*,[71] that human beings tend to complete an incomplete situation, and to organize one that is unstructured.

Anxious persons are particularly likely to interpret mild or innocuous stimuli as threatening or terrifying.[72] For some individuals, the bodily changes in anxiety are taken to be signs of fatal illness. Other persons — usually those well-trained in self-criticism — interpret their own anxiety as evidence of personal blame. They typically show the continuing self-reproach and self-punishment which leads their associates to conclude that these persons must be guilty. Still others, as we shall see, find reasons for their own anxieties in the behavior of other persons; such misuse of the adjustive technique of projection appears in the *sudden clarification* of paranoid patients.[73] These patients often spend long periods in unshared, silent searching for interpretations of their own unconsummated reactions. They come at last to the delusional conviction that other persons, by attacking them or plotting against them, are responsible for their intolerable anxieties.

The anxious person's interpretation of his own anxiety, although it may be wrong and even delusional, still seems to provide him with relief. Occasionally a patient gives us a glimpse into this consequence of anxiety. One woman, for example, who was depressed as well as anxious, said to her psychiatrist, "If I could only break my leg or something, then I'd have a reason for the way I feel." Such attitudes suggest, of course, that even misinterpretations may be anxiety-reducing. And if they are anxiety-reducing, we should expect these mistaken conclusions to be reinforced and to persist in the total behavior of anxious individuals.

The characteristics of normal anxiety provide us with a background for the study of the exaggerations and distortions of anxiety which we call *pathological*. We shall need to remember that anxiety reactions are likely to appear when a person cannot escape a threatening situation, when he anticipates punishment,

---

[71] See pages 75–79.

[72] For an experimental investigation supporting this point, see Murray, H. A., "The effect of fear upon estimates of the maliciousness of other personalities." *J. soc. Psychol.*, 1933, vol. 4, pp. 310–329.

[73] See pages 411–413.

when his ongoing adient reactions are interrupted, and when he is deprived of the support of others or of his own self-reactions. We shall need also to recall the significance of early responsiveness and of parental training in rendering individuals susceptible to the development of anxious behavior, and the significance of the prevailing pattern, and of the inaccessibility of anxiety excitants.[74]

In the next chapter, we shall consider three common forms of pathological anxiety. *Anxiety disorders* represent the most direct exaggeration of the normal anxiety reaction. In *depressive disorders* we shall find anxiety expressed through intropunitive reactions which are themselves magnifications of the anticipation of punishment and consequent self-reproach that we saw in normal anxiety. *Manic disorders* can also be interpreted as modes of escape from anxiety. But here the technique seems to be one of overt denial, either of mounting anxiety, or of the depressive reactions which anxiety is likely to induce. In all three of these disorders, unconsummated reactions of intense anxiety are basic to the patient's behavior.

[74] See the discussion on pages 293–298.

11

Anxiety in Behavior Pathology

Anxiety reactions, and the techniques which human beings acquire for coping with them, constitute a major span in the bridge between normal and pathological behavior. In some behavior disorders, anxiety is minimized so effectively that anxiety reactions seem to be altogether absent from a patient's behavior. To be sure, the patient shows the price he has paid for anxiety-reduction, in the restriction and distortion of his reactions; but it is only after prolonged and painstaking behavior analysis that some of his anxieties can be identified. Such an outcome is often found where *repression* plays a large part in mitigating anxiety, as in hysterical inactivation and autonomy.[1] In other behavior disorders, however, the techniques of handling anxiety are usually less complete, and anxiety reactions retain a prominent place in the patient's behavior. This situation characterizes *anxiety disorders*, and the related disorders which we call *depressive* and *manic*.

Anxiety Disorders

The patient suffering from *anxiety disorder* shows in his behavior a direct exaggeration of the normal anxiety reaction.[2] Such heightening of normal anxiety to a pathological level occurs typically in two general ways. (1) The anxiety reactions cumulate, *generalize* and spread to more and more excitants, until the patient seems habitually and chronically anxious in everything he does. (2) The anxiety reactions are *displaced* to specific excitants which the patient can identify, but which he often considers inexplicable. Both exaggerations are comprehensible in terms of the characteristics of anxiety behavior which normal persons inevitably exhibit in their everyday lives.

---

[1] See pages 359–371.
[2] For a description of normal anxiety reactions, see pages 276–280.

Overgeneralization of anxiety reactions

Among anxiety reactions which spread to include a major share of the patient's total behavior we may distinguish three grades of intensity. (a) In the *chronic anxiety reaction*, the patient maintains a persistent attitude of anxious anticipation, which keeps him in a state of habitually exaggerated readiness-to-react. (b) Against this background of chronic anxiety may occur brief episodes of acute anxiety, which we designate as *anxiety attacks*. (c) Persistent chronic anxiety, occasionally accentuated by anxiety attacks, may for some patients mount to the maximal and often disorganizing emotional excitement of *panic*.

(a) The *chronic anxiety reaction* is characterized by *the persistent, exaggerated skeletal and visceral tensions of preliminary, unconsummated emotional excitement*. To the patient, and often to his observer, the indicators of chronic anxiety present a heterogeneous and sometimes confusing picture. The patient shows, in tense posture, strained facial expression, brisk skeletal reflexes and occasional tremor, the effects of sustained muscular contraction. He may report that his legs ache or feel weak, that pain which starts in his neck and shoulders seems to shoot down his arm, that his head aches, feels constricted, or appears too heavy for his neck to support. His stomach feels upset and he may become nauseated. His hands and feet are cold and clammy, he sweats easily, and readily becomes dizzy.[3]

These complaints are all indicators of sustained skeletal and visceral tension, and they all have their consequences in the patient's total behavior. The chronically anxious person is likely to describe himself as "shaky" or "jittery" or about to "go to pieces." He jumps when someone strikes a match or slams a door. Slight noises disturb his sleep, and once awakened he may be unable to fall asleep again. He may complain that he has no appetite, that food has not appealed to him for months or even years, or that he eats too often and still remains unsatisfied. Anxious patients have trouble in concentrating and in remembering; and this difficulty often intensifies their anxiety.[4] Many patients suffering from chronic anxiety characterize their reactions as fear or dread, although they may be wholly unable to say what it is that so persistently frightens them.[5]

(b) The *anxiety attack* is an *acute episode of unconsummated emotional excite-*

[3] Common complaints given by anxious patients are described by Cameron, D. E., "Observations on the patterns of anxiety." *Amer. J. Psychiat.*, 1944, vol. 101, pp. 36–41. There is some evidence that degree of physiological distress, including reaction to painful stimulation, is positively correlated with degree of anxiety. See, for example, Malmo, R. B. and Shagass, C., "Physiologic studies of reaction to stress in anxiety and early schizophrenia." *Psychosom. Med.*, 1949, vol. 11, pp. 9–24.

[4] Malmo, R. B. and Amsel, A., "Anxiety-produced interference in serial rote learning, with observations on rote learning after partial frontal lobectomy." *J. exper. Psychol.*, 1948, vol. 38, pp. 440–454.

[5] Compare the tendency of normal persons to report anxiety as fear. See page 278.

ment, which exhibits to an exaggerated degree the characteristics of normal human fright. Anxiety attacks usually occur in a setting of chronic anxiety, and seem to represent the culmination of mounting anxiety reactions to the point of an uncontrolled emotional outburst. Such cumulative emotional reactions, which at last exceed the patient's self-control, we have earlier described as *emotional decompensation.*[6] The patient is helpless and terrified, overwhelmed by a nameless dread.

Because it resembles closely the picture of normal intense fright, the anxiety attack is easy to identify. The patient is agitated, trembling and terror-stricken. He may vomit and have urinary incontinence or diarrhea. His pupils dilate and his heart pounds, thumps or seems to skip beats. He feels as if he is choking and cannot get his breath. Many patients interpret these signs as portents of approaching death. "It's as if I'm dying," one patient recounted. "Everything gets black. I feel like I'm going to faint. It's terrible, so terrible." Another patient, a child, ran to his mother and cried over and over, "I'm going to choke! I'm going to die! Mother, I'm going to choke!" Other patients fear that they will lose control completely, that they will scream, make a spectacle of themselves in public, or commit suicide. In most cases, the attack subsides in a few minutes or an hour; and it is sometimes followed by crying spells or feelings of depression. Occasionally, however, the patient's fear of losing control is realized, and his anxiety attack spirals up into the disorganizing reaction of panic.

(c) *The panic reaction is a maximal episode of unconsummated emotional excitement.* It is an anxiety attack of extreme severity which may end in violent aggression, headlong flight or suicide. Like other anxiety attacks, the panic reaction occurs typically against a background of chronic tension.

> An adolescent boy, for example, who had acquired ambivalent self-attitudes toward obvious indications of his oncoming maturity,[7] developed severe chronic anxiety which was punctuated by frequent anxiety attacks. Late one night, after his parents and his friends had commented upon and ridiculed his physique, his appearance, and his ineptness with girls, his tension mounted further and further, as he ruminated over the situation alone, until he ran wildly from the house, raced down the street and broke into a nearby shop. There he climbed to the rafters in the basement and clung, trembling and terrified, refusing to speak or to move. Eventually he was rescued from his place of sanctuary, but not from the schizophrenic disorganization which his panic reaction ushered in.[8]

[6] See pages 126–127.

[7] For a general discussion of the problems of adolescent development, see pages 104–105, and 141–143. See also Milner, E., "Effects of sex role and social status on the early adolescent personality." *Genet. Psychol. Monogr.*, 1949, vol. 40, pp. 231–325.

[8] For a discussion of the relationship between panic and disorganization, see pages 464–466.

Most persons are able to endure chronic anxiety and occasional anxiety attacks without suffering panic or behavioral disorganization. Often they successfully compensate for chronic tensions, so that only those who know them well can identify their enthusiasms, their irritabilities and their spells of moodiness as indicators of anxiety. Sometimes, however, the cumulative tensions and recurrent episodes of heightened anxiety serve at length to restrict and distort the person's social interbehavior until he becomes seriously disabled. The following case illustrates such a typical, severe anxiety disorder.

> The twenty-six-year-old wife of a successful lawyer came to a psychiatric clinic with the complaint that she had "the jitters." She said she felt that she was going to pieces. She had fears of being alone, of screaming, of running away, and of committing suicide. These fears were all intensified when she came near an open window. She suffered from constant headache, fatigue and nervousness, from episodes of abdominal cramps and diarrhea. Twice in the past year there had been "attacks," in which she had become dizzy and had broken out into a cold sweat. Her hands and feet became clammy, her heart pounded, her head seemed tight, she had a lump in her throat and could not get her breath. One of these attacks occurred in the middle of the night when her husband was out of town. She awoke crying and shaking violently, and remembered thinking in terror, "I'm sick here alone and my husband is away and nobody knows who I am." As she related her symptoms at the clinic, the patient kept reiterating that her behavior was foolish. "I make such a fuss, but I can't help it," she said. "I scare *myself* as much as anything."
>
> Although the patient interpreted her difficulties as the consequence of the birth of her child, two years before, it soon became clear that she had been tense, insecure and anxious throughout much of her life. The responsibilities of her first pregnancy undoubtedly intensified, but certainly did not initiate, the difficulties which brought her to the clinic. The patient described the first five years of her life as lonely and isolated. In infancy she was sickly and irritable, and cried a great deal; as a child she was timid, afraid of the dark, and quiet and retiring among strangers. All her life she had made friends slowly; and she preferred the make-believe playmates she created in her vivid fantasy to those she might have found among her peers. Throughout childhood and adolescence she always became upset and unhappy when she was separated from her family.[9]
>
> Separation from her parents was a recurring event during the patient's early years. Because of chronic systemic illness, her father, a tense, moody man, was isolated from his wife and six children much of the time. The energetic but worrisome mother held a job teaching school, which scarcely enabled her to support the family, and which kept her away from home during the day. At the age of eight years, the patient was transferred from her public school to a private boarding school where she could obtain the sort of religious instruction that her father consid-

[9] For a discussion of separation anxiety, see pages 290–293.

ered necessary. Here she was unhappy and homesick, and had many crying spells in the evening when the sun went down. The following year, she returned to public school and lived at home. However, her father soon decided that she was having too gay a social life and, when the family finances permitted it, she was sent back to parochial boarding school. Until she was graduated from high school, she alternated between living at this school and living at home. Each separation from her home spelled misery, and each return to it was a happy reunion.

After a year at a state university, and a year at a religious teachers' college, the patient obtained a position teaching school. In her third year of teaching, she met and married a law student. Because of religious differences between the patient's family and her husband, the patient's father never wholly accepted his daughter's decision to marry. Indeed, it was only after considerable pleading and maneuvering that he was persuaded to give his consent to the marriage. With this beginning, it is not surprising that the patient developed ambivalent attitudes toward her marriage. Due largely to her persistent tension, she was unable to make a satisfactory sexual adjustment, although both she and her husband wanted to have children. She quickly became dependent upon her husband, although at the same time she said she preferred to stand on her own feet. It was clear from her resentful description of her husband, as "so self-sufficient that nothing bothers him," that she could not completely accept her own dependent needs.

Shortly after their marriage, the husband completed his law studies and took a position in a city near his father-in-law's home. Here the patient was able to visit her parents frequently, and to them she seemed happy and satisfied. She soon became pregnant, and almost immediately thereafter her husband found a job in a distant city to which they had to move. This new position was superior to his former one, but it carried with it new social responsibilities for his wife. The patient had never felt easy in social situations. Now she found herself called upon to arrange and carry through dinner parties for guests whom she scarcely knew and who seemed far beyond her in social sophistication. In this setting, she became "trembly," felt exhausted, lost weight, and showed increasing concern over her social duties. "If I have to look forward to things," she said, "I get so that by the time I have to do them I feel that I can't. I've lost practically all confidence in myself." It was in this setting that, tense and frightened, she gave birth to her child.

The patient's delivery was long and difficult, and her recovery from it was much slower than either she or her physicians expected. She complained of constant fatigue and nervousness, and refused to stay alone. She required the help of her mother, her mother-in-law, and finally her sister in caring for the baby. Although up to this time she had been making a few friends in the new city, she now began refusing to go out to social gatherings for fear, she said, that she would "go to pieces" and make a spectacle of herself. Medical examinations failed to reveal organic pathology sufficient to account for her complaints. Her physician told her she was "nervous," but this explanation she found impossible to accept.

Gradually the patient became more secure in her new responsibilities; but just as she began to feel better, her husband again received an offer of a position in a new locality. Although she encouraged him to accept the job, which he did, she was filled with dread at the thought of having to move again. The next two years were punctuated by three more changes of residence, each taking the husband to a better position, and each bringing the wife new and more demanding social responsibilities. The tension, fatigue and crying spells returned, and with them came, as we have seen, episodes of sharply increased anxiety. These difficulties were intensified whenever the patient was alone. "When my husband comes, I feel better immediately," she said. "If I'm alone, it's terrible."

The dreaded responsibility of caring for her growing child now increased to include the duties of his religious training, and the patient developed worries over her obligations in this direction. Although there had been no disagreement between husband and wife in relation to religious matters, the patient found herself becoming tense and concerned over her responsibility to her father's faith, and the one in which she herself had been reared. She reproached herself, saying, "I've fallen down on my end of it. I feel at a loss. I'm mixed up about the whole thing." Finally her fears became so insistent, her conflict so overwhelming, and her social activities so narrowed that she sought help in the psychiatric clinic.

In the clinic, where she stayed for a month, the patient was at first languid, apathetic and unsociable. For some time she remained anxious, and thought often of running away — probably to her husband's office, she said. From the beginning, however, she was able to discuss her fears with her psychiatrist and to understand in a limited way why certain situations seemed to intensify them. "When I try to put my best foot forward," she said, "my nerves take it out on me. My husband is very ambitious and I'm not. Things have gone a little too fast for me, and I've been lonely and missed the home folks." Only after she had come to accept also her ambivalence toward marriage, her dependent attitudes, and her own religious conflicts — all of them related to her childlike attachment to her father — did she become less anxious. Toward the end of her stay on the clinic ward she was able to find satisfaction in working in one of the hospital libraries. She left the hospital considerably improved, but still with the persistent attitude of chronic anxiety which had always been her characteristic way of life.

This case illustrates a lifelong pattern of anxiety reactions which increased sharply whenever circumstances became unduly stressful. From her earliest childhood, our patient had shown, in her fears of the dark and of strangers, and her general apprehensiveness, the symptoms of *chronic anxiety*. In her adult years, this persistent attitude of skeletal and visceral tension brought her fatigue, malaise, headache and gastrointestinal distress. Moreover, her anxiety reactions generalized to a wide range of excitants: she became afraid of open windows, of running away, of screaming and of committing suicide. Her discomforts subsided when she was protected by her parents or her husband; but they increased whenever she was defenseless against demands which seemed to her too great for her to meet. More and more often, as the obligations of adult life pressed in upon her, she developed the acute episodes of increased tension which we have termed *anxiety attacks*.

The conditions which favored the development of anxiety in this woman are no different from those which, as we have seen,[10] favor normal anxiety reactions. The patient was unusually responsive and irritable as an infant. She was reared in an atmosphere of anxious uncertainty by a tense father and a worrisome mother. Repeated separations from her family throughout childhood and adolescence brought her tension and unhappiness. Marriage, with its religious problems, created a conflict which brought out clearly her ambivalent attitudes of immature dependence upon her father, and her ultimate rebellion against his stated wishes. In adulthood, separation from her husband intensified her anxieties; while new social obligations and the unfamiliar responsibilities of child-rearing introduced her to situations which were unstructured and unpredictable. When she was planning her child's religious instruction, a resurgence of self-reproach intensified her chronic anxiety to the point of anxiety attacks.

Overgeneralization of this patient's anxiety was further encouraged by her own self-reactions. It was not alone the *overt act* of entertaining strangers, or of caring for her infant, that frightened her; the *anticipation* of either act and of her reaction to it was sufficient. In thinking and fantasying about an oncoming event, she pictured herself as a timid, shy ineffectual woman, totally unable to meet her obligations. Her own *anticipant attitudes* of anxiety and fear occurred earlier and earlier in each new sequence of behavior, so that eventually she was seldom without apprehension.[11] The patient recognized what she was doing when she said, "I scare myself as much as anything"; but she was powerless to control her reactions. It is largely for this reason that exaggerated anxiety reactions, such as these, once initiated, tend to persist and cumulate, until the tense and weary patient can find no respite from them. Under these circumstances, the patient often seems — by responding selectively to some chance excitant — to displace his anxiety reactions to stimuli that are irrelevant to the original situation.

Displacement of anxiety reactions to irrelevant stimuli [12]

The intensification and spread of anxiety reactions, which we have just considered, are the commonest pathological exaggerations of normal anxiety, but not the only ones. Severe anxiety also develops in response to specific excitants that seem remote from, or unrelated to, the situation in which it originally appeared. We may distinguish at least two ways in which such a displacement of anxiety reactions occurs. (*a*) A part or all of the pattern of *skeletal and visceral tension*, which itself constitutes the anxiety reaction, may become an excitant to further anxiety. (*b*) A *chance or incidental stimulus*,

---

[10] See pages 280–293.
[11] For a discussion of anticipant attitudes, see pages 65–66.
[12] See pages 125–126.

which is present when anxiety develops for any reason, may become an excitant to further anxiety through mere concomitance in time or space. Both sorts of displacement occur to some extent in normal anxiety reactions, and both are comprehensible in terms of the contemporary psychology of learning.

(a) *Displacement to the skeletal and visceral reactions of anxiety.* Unconsummated emotional excitement, we have said, involves severe and pervasive bodily changes which, to the person participating in them, seem often dramatic and threatening.[13] Indeed, we have already described sufferers from acute anxiety who, at the moment of an attack, believe they are about to faint or choke to death. For some patients, this temporary fear of what the anxiety reaction may mean is dispelled when the attack has subsided. Other patients, however, brood in retrospect over the possible significance of shortness of breath, pounding of the heart, or sudden vomiting. If they do not share with others their frightened search for explanations of their symptoms, such patients are likely to conclude at length that they are dying of cardiac or gastric disease. Misinterpretations of this kind are exceedingly common among anxious people, whose distressing and distracting symptoms effectively prevent them from making an impartial analysis of their own behavior. The visceral components of their anxiety reactions then become excitants to further and more intolerable anxiety.

> An ambitious but overdependent patient, for example, developed typical anxiety attacks in which gastrointestinal symptoms were prominent. One day at work, just after his convalescence from a severe attack of "grippe," he learned that he had not been granted an expected salary increase. To this information, which he angrily considered evidence of unfair discrimination, he reacted characteristically with nausea and diarrhea. Shortly afterward he had another attack of nausea and diarrhea, which he attributed to food poisoning; and because of his heightened anxiety level, the gastrointestinal symptoms persisted. The patient then became greatly concerned over the possibility that he had a gastric ulcer, or perhaps cancer of the stomach. He consulted one physician after another, tried innumerable sorts of medication, and insisted upon repeated gastrointestinal investigations, in spite of the discomfort they entailed. The consistent medical reassurances he received that there was no evidence of organ pathology gave him no lasting relief. Finally, he left work and stayed at home in bed for a period of nine weeks, convinced that he was suffering from an obscure but fatal illness.
>
> This man, of course, had misinterpreted the visceral reactions of his own anxiety as signs of organ pathology. To these signs, which to him meant invalidism and death for him, and poverty and disaster for his family, he reacted with intensified anxiety. But the intensified anxiety brought him more intense and more frequent gastrointestinal distress,[14]

[13] See pages 278–280.

[14] Compare the discussion of development of gastric ulcer as a consequence of persistent anxiety reactions, reinforced by the patient's self-reactions to bodily changes. See pages 299–300.

and this only served to reinforce his conviction that he was dying. When he finally appealed for psychiatric help, he reported that during the past ten years he had spent a total of eight thousand dollars for medical aid to combat his gastrointestinal symptoms. Therapy aimed, not at the symptoms of anxiety, but at the conflict between passive and aggressive reactions which had induced them, brought him eventually to full social recovery.

The character of the skeletal and visceral changes in emotional excitement is such that a patient's conviction of illness or impending death is altogether understandable.[15] Most people know that persistent nausea and diarrhea, or sudden vomiting, may presage severe gastrointestinal disorders. Anyone who reads the daily newspapers and popular magazines learns that difficulty in breathing, changes in heart rate, dizziness, and pains in the chest and arm may be signs of cardiac dysfunction. Indeed, these symptoms of anxiety so closely resemble the *angina pectoris* associated with heart disease that they have been called *pseudo-angina*. The anxious patient's conclusion that he has cardiac disease, gastric ulcer or cancer of the stomach, therefore, is neither fantastic nor bizarre. On the other hand, such symptoms cannot be cursorily dismissed as necessarily the products of anxiety alone by a responsible physician. For anxiety reactions, of course, do not immunize a patient from the gastrointestinal or cardiac diseases whose symptoms they so strongly resemble.

(b) *Displacement to an incidental or chance excitant.* The persistence of smooth muscle contraction and of endocrine substances in the blood, we have said,[16] guarantees that the unconsummated visceral reactions of anxiety will continue long after the original excitants have ceased to be effective. This characteristic of anxiety opens the way to displacement of anxiety reactions to *any* stimuli, no matter how incidental or irrelevant, to which an anxious person may be responsive. A good many of the aspects of learning which we considered earlier are involved in this second variety of displacement. The principles of simultaneity and contiguity, the phenomena of redintegration and equivalence of stimuli,[17] and the reinforcement of acquired responses through anxiety-reduction,[18] can all account in some degree for the fact that incidental stimuli, operating at a time when visceral reactions are occurring, may serve later to evoke the same reactions. The clearest example of displacement of anxiety reactions to incidental or chance excitants, of course, is to be found in the anxiety disorder we call *phobia*.

Phobias are anxiety disorders in which the specific anxiety excitants can be

---

[15] For a study of the frequency with which anxious combat veterans consider themselves in poor health, see Kaufman, M. R. "'Ill health' as an expression of anxiety in a combat unit." *Psychosom. Med.*, 1947, vol. 9, pp. 104–109. See also Bettelheim, B. and Sylvester, E., "Physical symptoms in emotionally disturbed children." In Freud, A. (Ed.), *The psychoanalytic study of the child.* New York: International Universities Press, 1949, vol. 3/4, pp. 353–390.

[16] See pages 122–125.   [17] See pages 66–69.   [18] See pages 75–79.

identified by the patient, but are usually considered by him to be inexplicable. One of the patients described earlier, it will be recalled, had a specific fear of the dark as a child, and an equally specific fear of open windows as an adult. The patient with prominent gastrointestinal symptoms of anxiety also feared dogs, thunderstorms and red skies at evening. Neither patient could explain his phobias, and both soon learned that to discuss their fears with others brought them only embarrassment, ridicule, humiliation — and further anxiety.

Because any chance or incidental stimulus may come to evoke anxiety reactions, a list of the fears of phobic patients would be a catalog of all the excitants to which human beings can respond. At one time, behavior pathologists tried to deal with phobias, by classifying the excitants according to the frequency of their occurrence in anxiety disorders, and giving to each a specific name.[19] At present, however, we recognize that ongoing reactions which are unconsummated can be displaced to any effective stimulus. Consequently, we have exchanged our concern with the static classification of phobias for an interest in the conditions under which phobic behavior develops.

Let us take, as an example of the contemporary approach to an understanding of phobias, the behavior of the man who feared red skies at evening. Like most phobic persons, this patient was unable to explain why red skies had come to be anxiety-provoking for him. Only after expert behavior analysis did he recall that as a boy he had been terrified at the red flames of a tenement fire in which, he had thought at the time, his mother was being burned to death. Clearly, the red sky of sunset had become for the patient equivalent to red flames which might devour his supporting mother. His *displacement* of anxiety reactions to a logically irrelevant excitant is closely analogous, of course, to the behavior of certain subjects in Diven's experiment,[20] who responded to the rural word *sheep* as if it were equivalent to the sequence *red-barn-shock*, which originally evoked a heightened galvanic skin response. Neither the patient nor the subject could explain logically the equivalent stimulus.

It is not infrequently possible to identify, through behavior analysis, some relationship between the anxiety excitant in a phobia and an earlier anxiety-provoking stimulus. This does not mean, however, that *all* phobic excitants have similar specific significance for the patient. Many specific anxiety-excitants undoubtedly do have personal meaning for the individual, even though he may not recognize their significance. Many other phobic excitants, however, seem merely to be stimuli which were operative at a time when anxiety reactions were occurring; they are related to earlier anxiety excitants only by way of chance concomitance.[21] In both instances, the excitant of a

---

[19] Among the common phobias were listed *acrophobia*, fear of high places; *agoraphobia*, fear of open spaces; *claustrophobia*, fear of closed places; and *phobophobia*, fear of being afraid.

[20] Diven, K., "Certain determinants in the conditioning of anxiety reactions." *J. Psychol.*, 1937, vol. 3, pp. 291–308. See pages 297–298.

[21] For a general discussion of learning through temporal contiguity, see pages 63–69.

phobic response is bound to the original anxiety-provoking stimulus in terms of the patient's total reactions. For the patient, the excitants are *equivalent,* since for him they initiate the unconsummated emotional excitement of anxiety.

By now it should be clear that the displacement of anxiety reactions to incidental or irrelevant stimuli depends in large part upon the persistence of visceral reactions. In this respect it resembles the overgeneralization of excitants that we considered as our first variety of anxiety disorder. In another important respect, however, displacement of anxiety to specific excitants differs from overgeneralization. The patient who fears he is ill or dying, or fears heights or storms or red skies, is in a sense defended against the stimuli which first initiated his anxiety, and he is prevented from identifying, comprehending or controlling them. To the behavior pathologist, this inability to identify and control the excitants of anxiety reactions suggests strongly that the patient is practiced in the techniques of *repression.*[22] The patient for his part, however, is like an amateur navigator armed with the wrong map; he avoids reefs that are marked on his chart, but remains unaware of the ones that threaten his safety. In this, however, the patient is often spared a further intensification of anxiety reactions which, in some persons, introduces the crucial shift characteristic of *depressive disorder.*

Depressive Disorders

The pathological exaggeration of normal anxiety, through overgeneralization or displacement, which we have just discussed, is but one of three behavior disorders in which anxiety is prominent. A second variety of pathological anxiety is the tense and often despairing reaction of *depressive disorder.* Between 10 and 14 per cent of all patients who enter psychiatric hospitals each year suffer from disorders of this kind. This figure seriously underestimates the frequency of depressive disorders. It is probable that there are at least an equal number of depressed patients who are cared for by their relatives at home, or carried in office practice without hospitalization.[23] Depression, sadness and hopelessness are fairly common reactions to prolonged tension, whether or not they so disable the individual that he requires expert help.

The depressed patient exhibits in exaggerated form the behavior of the normal person who is grief-stricken and hopeless. We shall therefore employ, as a

---

[22] See pages 337–351.

[23] Paskind, H., "Manic-depressive psychosis as seen in private practice: sex distribution and age incidence of first attacks." *Arch. Neurol. Psychiat.,* 1930, vol. 23, pp. 152–158; "Manic-depressive psychosis in private practice: length of the attack and length of the interval." *Arch. Neurol. Psychiat.,* 1930, vol. 23, pp. 789–794; "Hereditary factors in manic-depressive psychosis: a comparison of institutional and extramural cases." *Arch. Neurol. Psychiat.,* 1930, vol. 23, pp. 747–752.

useful starting-point for the understanding of pathological depression, an illustration taken from everyday normal grief. Let us suppose that a young wife has just received a telegram informing her of the sudden, accidental death of her husband. Her shocking, overwhelming loss affects not alone her immediate behavior; it also disrupts her fantasied future, and puts an end to the plans she has consistently entertained of a lifetime together with her husband. The widow now faces, without preparation or warning, a permanent separation, an irrevocable loss of support, and the widespread disorganization of her accustomed routines of living.

If we look closely at such a woman's behavior, we shall see in it most of the characteristics which are common to *normal intense grief* and *pathological depression.* The grieving wife will be at first agitated and restless; she will weep, moan, pace, rock back and forth, wring her hands and cling to other persons. This much of her behavior, of course, is strongly reminiscent of that shown by a person suffering from acute anxiety. There is also the possibility that she may deny the tragedy to herself by insisting that it could not have happened, that there is some mistake, that her husband must certainly return, and prove that this is all unreal. In spite of this denial, the mourner may go on to insist that the tragedy should never have occurred. Defensive denial then alternates with defensive attack; and the wife begins to rail at others who might have prevented the accident, at those who have escaped death, at fate, and even at herself.[24]

Eventually, as a result of fatigue, as well as of the inevitable acceptance of death, she becomes less agitated. For a long time, however, she is likely to remain quiet and unreactive. She eats and sleeps poorly. Her friends find her remote and preoccupied; she prefers seclusion to the well-intentioned social distractions which they try to provide. Indeed, attempts to cheer up a mourner may evoke greater sorrowing, or even anger and resentment. From the widow's point of view, it seems incredible that others' lives can be proceeding as usual, while her own is empty and barren.

Most people who have suffered deep personal loss respond to the passage of time, to social distractions and new interests, by slowly relinquishing their direct reactions of grief. Some components of mourning behavior, however, may persist in indirect and substitute ways.[25] In fantasy the widow may center her thoughts around her dead husband; she may in fantasy complete the

[24] A good many of these reactions have been formalized as parts of the conventional mourning and funeral ceremonies of various national and ethnic groups. Compare, for example, the rocking back and forth ("keening") and the wails of vengeance as well as grief, which are carried out by relatives and paid mourners in some subcultures. Note also the self-depreciatory character of traditional mourning garments — black clothing, sackcloth and ashes.

[25] Freud recognized the defense character of these reactions in normal grief and referred to them as the "work of mourning." See Freud, S., "Mourning and melancholia" (1919). In *Collected Papers*, vol. 4. London: Hogarth Press, 1948, pp. 152–170.

future plans which his death permanently interrupted. In overt talk, as well as in covert fantasy, she may find herself returning again and again to stories of her husband, and to past incidents, which at the time seemed trivial, but which now gain significance because they once involved him. Often the details of these events seem to lead the wife to recall occasions on which she had somehow failed her husband or hurt him, and she is apt then to add to her sorrow by berating herself. The husband's possessions and his photographs may come to occupy a conspicuous place in the household, both as decorations and as topics of conversation. The denial of his death, which was first made openly, may be maintained in the wife's faith that their separation is temporary. For some persons, the comfort of this conviction is increased by the belief that communication with dead persons can be established. Occasionally, these substitute reactions grow so prominent that each conversation ends in self-abnegation or in eulogy, and the home becomes a shrine.

All these characteristics are so common, as reactions to personal loss, that we have come to accept them as the inevitable components of normal grief. Even when the mourner seems for a time to organize his life around objects which preserve and stimulate his recall of a dead person, we still do not speak of pathological depression. At most, we say he "takes it too hard," and we expect him ultimately to "come out of it." Largely because the excitants to grief can be identified, and because the grieving reaction is appropriate to them, we consider a mourner's behavior normal. We reserve the diagnosis of *depressive disorder* for behavior which resembles that of the grief-stricken person, but in which the excitants are not identified, or seem not to deserve so intense a reaction, and in which guilt and self-reproach assume a prominent place. This distinction, it will be recalled, is similar to one made earlier between fear and anxiety,[26] and points once more to the close affiliation between anxiety and the depressive disorders.[27]

Varieties of Depressive Disorder

Depressive disorders, we have said, represent one variety of pathological anxiety. Most if not all depressions begin with a period of acute anxiety and tension,[28] although this often goes clinically unrecognized — partly because it may be brief, and partly because the patient successfully masks it. Even when despair and despondency dominate the picture, anxiety reactions continue to participate, to a greater or lesser degree, in the patient's behavior. Indeed, we may conveniently group depressive disorders according to the

---

[26] See pages 278–279.
[27] Cameron, D. E., "Some relationships between excitement, depression and anxiety." *Amer. J. Psychiat.*, 1945, vol. 102, pp. 385–394.
[28] It is reported that depressions developing under combat conditions are *always* preceded by anxiety. Grinker, R. R. and Spiegel, J. P., *Men under stress*. New York: Blakiston, 1945, p. 112.

extent to which anxiety reactions are prominent in them, as *agitated* or *re-tarded*. In agitated depression, anxiety reactions are an obvious part of the patient's behavior; he is exceedingly tense, fearful and apprehensive, as well as sad. In retarded depression, the anxiety reactions are less apparent. The patient is despondent, slowed down, and may even seem to be relaxed. It is only necessary to have brief contact with him, however, to find abundant evidence, in his visceral and skeletal tension, of the presence of unmistakable anxiety.

Agitated depression

The agitated depression is an anxiety disorder characterized by restlessness, tension, despair, and apprehensive or self-condemnatory delusions. Although agitated depression typically develops in a setting of personal strain, and against a background of persistent anxiety, it typically neither includes nor leads to serious behavioral disorganization. The patient remains tense and desperate, and shows in exaggerated form an admixture of anxiety and grief such as we saw in the normal mourning behavior of the young wife immediately after she learned of her husband's death.[29] The following case illustrates most of the characteristic features of agitated depression.

> The patient, an unmarried man of twenty-nine, came to the clinic complaining that he had lost his enthusiasm, was taking things too seriously, and was thinking about suicide. "My spirits are pretty low," he said. "I feel sort of all hopeless." His parents stated that at home he was excited, agitated and sleepless, that he occasionally talked in a confused and rambling way, and made rapid changes in decision without adequate cause. Although both the patient and his parents believed the trouble had begun three months before, when he had been in an automobile accident, it soon became clear that he had been unusually tense and restless for at least a year. He had begun, a year before coming to the clinic, to worry about his job, his physical condition, and religious differences with his fiancée. He became increasingly seclusive and believed that people looked at him contemptuously.
>
> The illness which brought him to the clinic seemed to represent the culmination of lifelong anxiety, intensified by job demands that he could not meet. Even as a young child he had been chronically anxious, and he retained in adulthood his early fears of dogs and of high places. He was the third of five children, and the only son. The family was a closely-knit one in which all the children were strongly attached to the mother.
>
> Our patient did poorly in school. He led a miserable existence there, because others teased him, picked on him and considered him stupid. He attempted college, but after two years of failure left to take a job in his father's factory. Here he felt that he was an annoyance to the employees who, he thought, seemed to tolerate him only because he was

[29] See pages 315–316.

the boss's son. He held a number of different positions in his father's establishment, in preparation for taking over the business when his father retired. Although he worried over his accomplishments, and felt he was not doing all he should, he also resented being kept in a subordinate position and felt he deserved more responsibility. When, however, he went on a six-week trip for the firm with a high-pressure salesman, he became tense and unhappy, and returned home more agitated and fatigued than before. He suspected that he was ill, but medical examinations failed to disclose any signs of organ pathology.

At about this time, the patient fell in love with a girl whose religious beliefs differed from his own. He was not himself a regular churchgoer; and, after a few weeks, he appeared to have reached a satisfactory understanding with the girl, and the two became engaged. However, the patient found he could not banish the religious problem from his thinking. He felt more and more need to discuss it with his father. In these discussions he insisted upon complete privacy, and his talk seemed to his father vague and rambling. He became increasingly restless. He grieved over the religious difficulty; and he cut down his social contacts until he was seeing no one but his family and his fiancée. He felt that people regarded him as "just a little fellow, insignificant and immature-looking." One afternoon, while the patient was driving home from work, his car was sideswiped by a large truck, and wrecked when it turned over in a ditch. At the time he gave no evidence of serious injury; but after he was brought home he collapsed and talked incoherently. Careful medical examination, however, disclosed only a few severe bruises about the body and no evidence of head trauma.

Back at work the patient's restlessness increased until he was unable to sit at his desk; he frequently got up and paced the floor. His appetite failed, his sleep became extremely poor, and he lost so much weight that he consulted his physician, who hospitalized him for a five-week rest. During this rest he at first felt better; but when his night nurse was discharged he again became restless and sleepless. He felt the need of greater guidance and support from his parents and from God. At times he thought he could see his parents and converse with them when they were absent. They seemed to tell him that he must get well, that he had been unfair, and that they would do all they could if only he would do his part. He left the hospital with increased weight, but the restlessness and agitation persisted, and were unaffected by brief vacations which he was told to take in the country. At length he came to the psychiatric clinic where he was admitted at once as an in-patient, and remained there for four months.

The patient was at first tense and restless, but after a week of full ward routine and therapeutic talks, he at first improved markedly. Soon, however, his behavior became distractible and capricious. He said he was in high spirits, and demonstrated this by singing, by skipping down the hall like a child, sitting on the floor, and putting ice down another patient's back. This period of tense gaiety was followed by a period of sadness and tearfulness, during which the patient became slow and hesitant. He said he was thinking of his fiancée and the mess he had made of things. Although there were other periods of mild elation followed by depression, he continued to improve. He never managed to develop self-confidence, however, and remained throughout his stay inept and apprehensive in social contacts with the other patients. His religious concern gradually assumed a less prominent place in his thinking. He was discharged from the clinic, almost free of his depressive symptoms, but with only superficial insight into the difficulties that had made him ill.

This patient's behavior illustrates most of the characteristics of agitated depression. The restlessness, tension, fatigue and bodily concern, which we found typical of anxiety reactions, occur here in a setting of despair and self-depreciation; and the patient ultimately concludes that through his own mistaken efforts he has brought himself to a hopeless predicament. Agitated depressed patients state these attitudes in different ways, and in their total behavior sharpen one or another part of the picture which this patient presented. For some patients, their own bodily changes become the most compelling feature of their anxiety. Sometimes their apprehension and terror over the cardiac and respiratory changes in anxiety become a conviction of bodily weakness or change which is so persistent and inappropriate that we can justifiably call it delusional.[30] For other patients, the most striking symptom is agitated fearfulness which continually disrupts the patient's overt and covert behavior until everything seems confused. As one patient put it, "My mind goes blank all the time. I can't get my mind together."

By far the most typical focus of the agitated depressed patient's anxiety, however, is his own guilty self.[31] Our patient, it will be recalled, believed that people regarded him contemptuously and tolerated him only because of his father's position. He said repeatedly that he had made a mess of things, and he frequently entertained suicidal thoughts. In his own guilty self-reactions, he believed he heard his parents reproaching him.

Many patients in agitated depression go farther than this. Their self-depreciatory attitude increases until they mistakenly conclude that they are personally responsible for most of the misery they see in the world. One patient, for example, considered herself to blame for the illness of all the other patients on her ward. Another harped on his guilt for stealing five torn towels from a laundry; and he copied and recopied lists of other articles which he claimed to have appropriated. A third insisted that he was responsible for a kidnapping which had been widely publicized at the time of his hospitalization.[32]

Such delusions of self-depreciation and guilt are not without their legal aspects. Often it is difficult for officials to demonstrate the innocence of de-

[30] For a discussion of delusional reactions, see pages 392–405.
[31] Guilt is discussed on pages 284–289.
[32] For a discussion of self-punitive reactions, see Levy, D. M., "Studies in sibling rivalry." *Res. Monogr. Amer. Ortho. Assn.*, 1937, no. 2; Korner, A. F., *Some aspects of hostility in young children.* New York: Grune and Stratton, 1949, pp. 131–132. See also pages 95–96, in this text.

pressed patients who have made insistent, public protestations of their own guilt. The legal problem, however, is a minor one when it is compared with the ever-present danger of suicide in agitated depressed patients. Our patient's suicidal thoughts become, in some cases, suicidal threats and attempts, which for a few patients culminate in tragic self-destruction.[33] The person who considers himself guilty, damned and hopelessly lost may allow neither personal scruples nor religious convictions to stand in the way of suicide. Only the most rigid, alert and expert supervision may then be able to prevent him from taking his own life.

The slow and gradual onset of depressive reactions, against a background of chronic anxiety which has been increased by personal stress, is common to most sufferers from agitated depression. To an inexpert observer, the patient seems to have attacks of tenseness and low spirits in response to particular personal problems, while between the attacks he seems relatively well. To the agitated depressed patient, however, it seems as if he is able to fend off tension and sadness only with increasing effort and, even then, for briefer and briefer periods of time. He grows to fear the emergence of his own depressive reactions, and eventually he becomes submerged by them. Now it is not only the frustrations of his daily life that arouse anxiety and despair; events long past, problems once settled, old conflicts and old ambivalences return and increase his agitation. Thus, in his illness, our patient found himself once more struggling with the problem of religious differences with his fiancée, which had formerly appeared to have been resolved, and then blaming himself for the "mess" he had made of his engagement. Through such intermingling of current with past excitants to anxiety and despair, the patient accomplishes the *crucial shift*[34] to the self-punitive attitudes of depressive disorder.

In his early social development, both in the home and outside of it, our patient is also representative of many persons who develop agitated depression. Like most anxious adults, he had been shy, timid and fearful as a child, and strongly dependent upon others for support. Instead of support, however, he had received only teasing and ridicule because of his social and academic ineffectuality. From others' depreciation of him and his accomplishments he acquired the attitudes of self-depreciation which made each new situation a threat of failure, and which later became a prominent part of his depressive disorder.

[33] In one study of suicidal patients, it appeared that patients who made *threats* of suicide were more seriously disturbed than those who had actually *attempted* it. This finding is interpreted as indicating that a suicidal attempt may provide some tension-reduction. See Farberow, N. L., "Personality patterns of suicidal mental hospital patients." *Genet. Psychol. Monogr.*, 1950, vol. 42, pp. 3–80. For additional discussions of suicide, see Fox, H., "Dynamic factors in the affective psychoses." *Amer. J. Psychiat.*, 1942, vol. 98, pp. 684–689; Wall, J., "Psychiatric problems of suicide." *Amer. J. Psychiat.*, 1944, vol. 101, pp. 404–406.

[34] Cameron, N., *The psychology of behavior disorders.* Boston: Houghton Mifflin, 1947, pp. 527–530.

One final point regarding our patient must be mentioned, because of its historical and theoretical importance. In his adult relationship with his father, the patient was at once accepting and resentful. He organized his vocational goals in accordance with his father's plans but resented his subordinate position and the fact that he was tolerated only as his father's son. Such ambivalent reactions [35] toward persons who are close to the patient are frequently found in the behavior of depressed persons. Often the patient has developed ambivalence toward a punitive parent, or toward a spouse who evokes both dependent and aggressive behavior. It was such clinical findings as these that originally led Karl Abraham to construct a highly important formulation of depressive disorders.[36] According to Abraham's hypothesis, depressive reactions are likely to develop whenever the person maintains attitudes of hostility toward some one whom he also loves, or believes he should love. It is the feelings of hatred, more often repressed than overt, that call forth the guilty and self-punitive reactions [37] which characteristically flavor depressive disorders. We shall see that ambivalence is prominent not only in agitated depression, but also in the retarded depressions to which we now turn.

Retarded depression

The retarded depression is an anxiety disorder characterized by general slowing and restriction of activity, with sadness, despondency and self-depreciatory delusions. Like the agitated depressive disorder, retarded depression begins in unrelieved anxiety and tension, and it neither includes nor leads to serious behavioral disorganization. For the retarded depressed patient, however, the initial anxiety and agitation give way to a general reduction in responsiveness. The patient seems preoccupied and dejected; he moves slowly and speaks with difficulty or not at all; he eats unwillingly, and he may refuse food altogether. Superficially, the retarded depressed patient seems dull and lifeless, without obvious signs of tension and anxiety. He resembles, on the surface, the widow who in grieving for her husband became quiet, distant and detached.[38] The clinician who succeeds in gaining contact with the patient, however, finds the patient taut, distressed, disturbed, and deeply concerned over delusional convictions of his own unworthiness and guilt. These reactions characterize the following case, which is typical of many retarded depressions.

[35] See page 65.

[36] Abraham, K., "Notes on the psychoanalytic investigation and treatment of manic-depressive insanity and allied conditions." In *Selected papers*. London: Hogarth Press, 1927, pp. 137–156; "The first pregenital stage of the libido." *Selected papers*. London: Hogarth Press, 1927, pp. 248–279; "A short history of the development of the libido." *Selected papers*. London: Hogarth Press, 1927, pp. 418–501. Freud concurred in these views; compare his paper, "Mourning and melancholia" (1919). In *Collected papers*, vol. 4. London: Hogarth Press, 1948, pp. 152–170.

[37] Korner, A. F., *Some aspects of hostility in young children.* New York: Grune and Stratton, 1949, pp. 131–132.

[38] See pages 315–316.

An unmarried man of forty came to the hospital with the complaint that he felt "numb." He explained further, "On account of some slowing down in the brain I have no direction. I try to get through my distressing thoughts but I can't. I didn't tell the truth and I should be put in the pen. The people I made suffer should all be released from jail and I should be punished." He spoke in a slow, delayed fashion, paused frequently in deep preoccupation, and repeatedly put his head down on the desk or covered his face with his hands. During his early interviews with his psychiatrist, and occasionally throughout his hospital stay, he implored those around him to tell him "the truth." On four occasions previous to his hospitalization, he had made sudden, impulsive attempts at suicide.

A few months prior to his illness, personal loss and a series of business reversals had increased this patient's chronic anxiety to an acute level. The background of his retarded depression, however, seemed to lie in a close but ambivalent relationship between the patient and his father. As a child, the patient had been extremely fond of his father; and in adulthood he seemed never to have emancipated himself from this close attachment. The father was a stern disciplinarian, who had administered frequent whippings to his young son, and who continued to rule him throughout his life. Although the patient chafed under this control, he supported and defended his father in public. On one occasion, he threatened in anger to shoot his father's associates who, by falsifying accounts, had ruined the father's business. That the son's attitude was not unmixed with hostility and guilt toward his father, however, became clear when the father developed carcinoma and died.

During his father's long and distressing illness, the patient insisted that he wished he could suffer in his father's place. At the same time, he could not help knowing that his father's death would bring him sizeable insurance benefits, and he found himself thinking of the money as often as of his father's pain. When finally the father died, the patient was greatly disturbed. He continued to mourn him long after the other members of the family had returned to their usual activities. He grew more and more despondent, began drinking heavily, went on long walks alone, had many crying spells and grew unable to eat. He began saying that he was sick of living and had no right to go on. At first the patient's family attributed his dejection to business failures, which had followed his father's death, but the patient soon made clear what was bothering him. With increasing frequency, he blamed himself for his father's death, saying that he had sinned and deserved punishment. "I wished my father's death — for money, I suppose — and it came true," he said.

In the hospital, the patient continued apathetic, listless and profoundly depressed. He was sleepless, and refused so persistently to eat that it became necessary to spoon-feed him. He believed he should be imprisoned for his sinful thoughts. He misidentified his psychiatrist at times as a policeman, and at other times as his father. He begged to be allowed to kill himself, and only constant vigilance prevented him from seriously harming himself. His self-punitive delusions spread to include events in his past life and persons in his present environment. He confessed and exaggerated early sexual indiscretions, and reproached himself endlessly for them. He believed that he had ruined his family, and that he had committed countless crimes for which innocent persons were now being punished. "Everything bad in the newspaper is about me," he said. When, however, these delusions were later discussed with him, he repudiated them angrily, and became sullen and resentful. Most of the time he remained dull and uncommunicative, preoccupied with his intropunitive thoughts.

This patient gained no release from his anxiety through his severely punishing self-reactions. He continued tensely fatigued and sleepless, he lost weight and became badly constipated. His continual background of anxiety was shown in occasional spells of perplexity, when he accused others of trying to confuse him, and in rare bouts of angry defiance at hospital regulations. "I've had fear in me for a long time," he said. Although he was still suicidal and deeply depressed, his family prematurely removed the patient from the hospital against advice. Eventually he was taken, even more retarded and depressed, to a hospital near his home where he remained without improvement until his death from intercurrent systemic illness.

It should be clear from this case that retarded depression *differs* from agitated depression mainly in the conspicuousness of the anxiety reactions involved in each. In agitated depression, acute anxiety reactions are prominent, while in retarded depression they are masked by a sustained tension which is shown in the patient's slowness and apparent apathy. Such a reaction to anxiety reminds us of the behavior of the grieving wife, who became listless and preoccupied after the death of her husband. It is similar also to the behavior of prisoners — whether in penitentiaries or concentration camps — who in the face of environmentally-induced anxieties become dull and unreactive.[39] Many soldiers develop the same hopeless unresponsiveness when, after the intolerable and unremitting strain of combat, they conclude that the next mission will be their last, that their "number is up."[40] Occasionally a retarded depressed patient formulates in words this reaction to anxiety. Thus a young woman told her physician, "I decided to kill my emotions so they wouldn't hurt any more. I didn't want to care what happened."

Our case also illustrates the ways in which retarded depression *resembles* the agitated depressive disorder. Both begin with heightened anxiety reactions in a chronically anxious person. For our patient, a series of business reverses and the painful illness and death of his father increased his customary anxiety to acute proportions. In both varieties of depression, the patient may show the ambivalent attitudes of love and hate toward the same person which Abraham emphasized.[41] Our patient turned his hostility toward his father against him-

---

[39] Allport, G. W., Bruner, J. S., and Jandorf, E. M., "Personality under social catastrophe: ninety life-histories of the Nazi revolution." *Char. and Pers.*, 1941, vol. 10, pp. 1–22; Friedman, P., "Some aspects of concentration camp psychology." *Amer. J. Psychiat.*, 1949, vol. 105, pp. 601–605.
[40] Grinker, R. R. and Spiegel, J. P., *Men under stress.* New York: Blakiston, 1945.
[41] See page 321.

self, and reproached and berated himself for wishing his father's death. In both retarded and agitated depression, initial anxiety reactions introduce the *crucial shift* to hostility toward oneself. Our patient's self-reproach, which arose first in relation to his father's death, spread to include trivial sexual incidents of his youth, and old sexual conflicts apparently settled years before. Eventually his self-punitive attitude over events which had occurred, generalized to events which had not; and the patient blamed himself for others' crimes, in which he could have had no part. His own cumulative and self-perpetuating reactions thus led him to develop delusional thinking.

Suicide is as great a hazard in retarded, as it is in agitated depressions. The retarded patient's apparent apathy masks a tenseness which may unexpectedly become overt in attempts at self-destruction. Our patient, it will be recalled, had made four suicidal tries — all of them sudden and impulsive — and was still begging for permission to kill himself when his family unwisely took him home. Suicide is not the only act which may bring tragic consequences to the depressed patient. In his silent brooding a depressed person may conclude that others are suffering as he is, and that death may be as welcome to them as it seems to him. Planned or impulsive homicide then becomes as great a danger as planned or impulsive suicide.[42]

Expert vigilance by nurses and attendants can usually protect the depressed patient from himself, and expert treatment can often bring him full recovery. Neither vigilance nor therapy, however, can protect the patient completely from the stresses of the environment to which he must one day return. Like other patients suffering from behavior disorder — and like any person who lives as part of a social group — the recovered depressed patient faces inevitable frustration and conflict. Like them also, he has acquired characteristic techniques for handling his problems. It is therefore not unusual to find such patients developing depressive reactions again when the strains of daily living become intolerable. Indeed, the tendency for recovered depressed patients to develop depressive reactions repeatedly is so apparent that many behavior pathologists view it as evidence that depression is a recurrent process.

Recurrent depressive disorders

Two investigations, typical of many in this field, provide us with information regarding the recurrence of depressive disorders. Rennie conducted follow-up studies on a carefully selected group of 208 patients, treated in an endowed psychiatric clinic.[43] Some of these suffered from manic disorders, some from depressive and some from both. Of his group, 93 per cent recovered completely from the first attack, which lasted on the average six and one-

---

[42] Batt, J. C., "Homicidal incidence in the depressive psychoses." *J. ment. Sci.*, 1948, vol. 94, pp. 782–792.

[43] Rennie, T., "Prognosis in manic-depressive psychoses." *Amer. J. Psychiat.*, 1942, vol. 98, pp. 801–814.

half months. However, over three-fourths of these patients had a second attack; 63.5 per cent had a third, and 45 per cent a fourth over the twenty-year period for which he had data. In general, the later attacks lasted longer than the earlier ones.

Rennie's figures, both for recovery and for recurrence, are somewhat higher than those usually reported. Huston and Locher, for example, found 79 per cent recovery in a group of eighty depressed patients treated in a publicly supported clinic; of those who recovered spontaneously from their admission attack, only about one-sixth had depressions later.[44] In these patients, as in Rennie's, depressions occurred more frequently with increasing age; and two-thirds of the patients with recurrent depressions had subsequent depressive disorders which were of longer duration than their first ones. Because of differences in diagnostic criteria and techniques of following up patients, reports on frequency of recurrence often disagree; but there is no doubt that there is a strong tendency for depressive disorders to recur.

This characteristic recurrence of depressive disorders is one of the sources of the popular hypothesis that depression is a "circular" or "cyclic" process. Indeed, the clinician who observes with care the behavior of a hospitalized depressed patient can often find in his patient's behavior from day to day, or even in the course of one day, evidence of a rhythmic change. Some depressed patients seem to suffer, in a fairly regular way, dips of increased depression and rises of higher spirits. A great many depressed patients report diurnal changes in their own behavior. Typically they feel more despondent in the morning, and by evening may feel quite well; but the following morning they are again depressed. As one patient put it, "The worst time of all is just before I get up, when I lie there in bed thinking." These changes, of course, have their counterparts in normal behavior. Both in depressed patients and in normal persons, the reasons for periods of optimism and hopelessness, of energy and lassitude, are still obscure. Contemporary behavior pathologists, however, are likely to single out for consideration, as possible conditions favoring these recurrent changes, *hereditary predisposition, metabolic change* and *environmental stress*.

Hereditary predisposition formerly occupied a prominent place among the postulated reasons for recurrent depressive disorders.[45] The family lines of depressed patients seemed to contain many more persons suffering from similar disorders than did unselected samples of the general population; and close relatives, more frequently than distant ones, appeared to develop depressive

---

[44] Huston, P. E. and Locher, L. M., "Manic-depressive psychosis: course when treated and untreated with electric shock." *Arch. Neurol. Psychiat.*, 1948, vol. 60, pp. 37–48.

[45] For typical studies, see Rosanoff, A. J., Handy, L. M., and Plesset, I. R., "The etiology of manic-depressive syndromes, with special reference to their occurrence in twins." *Amer. J. Psychiat.*, 1935, vol. 91, pp. 725–762; and Slater, E., "The inheritance of manic-depressive insanity." *Proc. Roy. Soc. Med.*, 1936, vol. 29, pp. 981–990.

disorders. We have seen elsewhere [46] how difficult is the twofold task, first of collecting reliable data, and then of ruling out alternative hypotheses, which confronts the student of human genetics. Poor records, family pride, and unfortunate fear of a "taint," conspire to prevent the investigator from obtaining necessary data on the incidence of depressive disorder in the total population. Moreover, greater-than-chance incidence of recurrent depression in particular families cannot alone verify the hypothesis of hereditary predisposition. We have seen [47] that both direct tuition and the prevailing pattern may encourage members of the same family to develop similar techniques for handling anxiety. At present, we can neither fully accept nor fully reject inheritance as a condition favoring depressive disorders.

Metabolic change as a predisposing condition to recurrent depression also has its contemporary adherents. A great many laboratory studies have accordingly been undertaken to investigate such a relationship — on basal metabolism, blood pressure, blood chemistry, gastrointestinal and genitourinary performance, and endocrine activity. For the most part, these studies also yield equivocal results.[48] Although certain biochemical changes seem to be consistently present, they are not pathognomonic of recurrent depression, and they do not seem alone sufficient to account for the complex changes in social interaction and self-reaction which characterize the depressed patient. The occasional onset of depressive disorders in a setting of pregnancy, childbirth or menopause, was at one time cited as evidence for the biochemical origin of depression; but greater emphasis is now laid upon the complex attitudes of the patient toward these biological events and their meaning to her as a biosocial person.

Environmental stress cannot be overlooked as an antecedent to recurrent depressive disorders. We have seen that depression commonly develops against a background of anxiety, as a reaction to personal stress which has become intolerable. Both our agitated and our retarded patients, it will be recalled, suffered severe personal and business losses just prior to their depressive illness. Long-range studies of depressed patients duplicate the picture which these two selected cases present. In almost 80 per cent of Rennie's patients, for example, disturbing personal events immediately preceded the onset of depressive disorder.[49] The close relationship between personally threatening events and depressive disorder is reflected in our recognition of "promotion

---

[46] See pages 28–31 and 179–180.

[47] See pages 55–63 and 293–296.

[48] For a critical review of these studies see Cameron, N., "The place of mania among the depressions from a biological standpoint." *J. Psychol.*, 1942, vol. 14, pp. 181–195; and Cameron, N., "The functional psychoses." In Hunt, J. McV. (Ed.), *Personality and the behavior disorders.* New York: Ronald, 1944, pp. 866–867.

[49] See pages 324–325.

depression" [50] and "retirement depression." [51]   In the former, increased job responsibilities which outstrip the individual's competence precede the onset of depression; in the latter, decreased responsibility and declining personal status provide a setting for depressive disorder. It is possible that the increase in frequency and duration of depressive disorders with age is in part a consequence of the increasing personal frustration which attends ageing in our culture.

To choose one among these three possibilities — hereditary predisposition, metabolic change and environmental stress — as forerunners of recurrent depression, and to reject the other two, is both impossible and unnecessary. The behavior pathologist who accepts his human subjects as biological organisms operating within a complex social field cannot afford to overlook inheritance, biochemistry, self-reactions, or cultural context in his attempts to understand his patients' behavior. Unfortunately for balanced research, however, we are prone, in studying depressive disorders, to neglect the social determinants in favor of genetic and biochemical ones. This is nowhere more apparent than in our interpretations of the depressive disorder which still appears, in many contemporary systems of classification, as *involutional melancholia*.[52]

Involutional melancholia

The descriptions of involutional melancholia do not differ from those of agitated depression, excepting for the age which, for involutional melancholia, is placed in middle and later maturity. The patient is restless, anxious, sleepless and self-condemnatory. When, however, this behavior occurs for the first known time in conjunction with the widespread bodily changes of the involutional period of life, it is frequently designated as involutional melancholia. Then, by the alchemy which labelling always sets in process, the hypothetical causes of the disorder become chemical, and research time and energy are funneled into the biochemical laboratory.

It is the social implication, as well as the biological fact of involutional change, that makes the human organism vulnerable to depressive disorder in middle life. For women, waning attractiveness and loss of fertility, and for men, declining vigor and decreased vocational status, herald the approach of senescence. Illness and death among close friends and relatives, and the

[50] Titley, W., "Prepsychotic personality of patients with agitated depression." *Arch. Neurol. Psychiat.*, 1938, vol. 39, pp. 333–342; Flanagan, N., "The promotion depression." *J. Amer. Med. Assn.*, 1942, vol. 120, p. 1383.

[51] Cameron, N., "Neuroses of later maturity." In Kaplan, O. (Ed.), *Mental disorders in later life.* Stanford University, Calif.: Stanford University Press, 1945, pp. 160–162; 176–177.

[52] Cheney, C., *Outlines of psychiatric examinations.* Utica, N.Y.: State Hospitals Press, 1934; Veterans Administration, "Nomenclature of psychiatric disorders and reactions." *V. A. Technical Bulletin*, TB 10A–78, 1947.

departure of grown children from the home, reinforce the conviction that one is ageing.[53] What is called involutional melancholia, like any other agitated depression, is the complex resultant of changes in social interbehavior and in socially-derived self-reactions.[54] This is as clear from attempts at chemical therapy in middle-life depressions as from the paucity of findings in bio-chemical research. Hormonal treatment of menopausal depressive disorders, for example, ordinarily alters the vasomotor symptoms, and therefore increases the patient's comfort, but seems not to affect the depressive reaction.[55] Neither in therapy nor in research can we single out, as the sole determinant of this depressive disorder, changes in body metabolism. Such changes can be isolated only in diagnosis, and then only because we attend to the patient's age at the expense of his total behavior.

"Manic-depressive psychosis"

We have considered recurrent depression, and involutional melancholia, as special problems, in part because of their historical importance. At a time when strict diagnostic classification was popular, it was believed that a circular process underlay recurring mood disorders, and that periods of depression alternated, more or less regularly, with periods of manic excitement. To this supposedly single disease was given the name *manic-depressive psychosis*.[56] Reference to such circular disorders can be found in medical writings as early as the first century A.D. and as recently as our contemporary systems of psychiatric classification. Kahlbaum, and later Kraepelin, at the close of the nineteenth century, maintained that most severe depressions and most manic excitements represented opposite poles of a unitary, phasic metabolic process. Their bipolar hypothesis ignored the factors of environmental stress and personal conflict which today we consider central. Even though there is little evidence to support such a view, depressive and manic reactions are still widely regarded as antithetical extremes of a unified circular process.

---

[53] For a discussion of this viewpoint, see Cameron, N., "Neuroses of later maturity." In Kaplan, O. (Ed.), *Mental disorders in later life*. Stanford University, Calif.: Stanford University Press, 1945, pp. 143–186.

[54] A careful study of the patient often indicates that the pathology which develops in middle life represents a resurgence or intensification of previous difficulties. See, for example, Greenhill, M. H., "A psychosomatic evaluation of the psychiatric and endocrinological factors in the menopause." *So. med. J., Bgham.*, 1946, vol. 39, pp. 786–794; Stern, K. and Prados, M., "Personality studies in menopausal women." *Amer. J. Psychiat.*, 1946, vol. 103, pp. 358–368.

[55] For an example of such investigations, see Ripley, H., Shorr, E., and Papanicolaou, G., "The effect of treatment of depression in the menopause with estrogenic hormone." *Amer. J. Psychiat.*, 1940, vol. 96, pp. 905–914. For a review of the literature, see Cameron, N., "The functional psychoses." In Hunt, J. McV. (Ed.), *Personality and the behavior disorders*. New York: Ronald, 1944, pp. 883–885.

[56] For a discussion of the history of this classification, see Cameron, N., "The functional psychoses." In Hunt, J. McV. (Ed.), *Personality and the behavior disorders*. New York: Ronald, 1944, pp. 873–875.

Evidence accumulating during the past three decades has called into serious question the bipolar hypothesis of depressive and manic disorders. The series of papers by Karl Abraham, to which we earlier referred,[57] made clear that ambivalent attitudes of love and hostility, directed toward one and the same person, could account for depressive reactions. Freud assented to this interpretation; and both Freud and Abraham considered the manic attack as a reaction against the anxiety of depression. A careful review of laboratory and clinical studies on biochemical change has brought out clearly the fact that no phasic metabolic changes have actually been demonstrated for mania and depression.[58] Moreover it has been found that the great majority of patients who suffer from depressive disorder never have a manic attack.[59] Thus the bipolar hypothesis of depression and mania, although logically attractive, lacks the support of both laboratory and clinical findings.

It is by no means uncommon to find a patient who reacts to anxiety and depression with elated behavior. Indeed, the agitated depressed patient described earlier [60] was occasionally excited, and apparently in high spirits, during his hospital stay. As any clinician knows, however, the manic patient's elation is neither an indication that the patient is happy, nor an automatic shift from prior depression. The elated patient often shows a forced and almost frantic hilarity which is far different from normal good spirits. Manic excitement, like depressive reactions, begins in personal stress, and like them also it develops as a reaction to heightened anxiety.

Manic Disorders

Bursts of enthusiasm, episodes of aggressive initiative, periods of mirth and even of excited hilarity are common events in normal behavior. Most people interpret such reactions as marks of freedom and relaxation in their own behavior, and stimulate and respond to them as welcome diversions in the behavior of their friends. A social evening is considered successful if there is a little noisy laughter, if the guests include a friendly humorist who keeps within reasonable limits, and if quips or puns appear occasionally in the general conversation. So thoroughly accepted are these signs of excitement that we rarely recognize them for what they may often be — reactions to tension and anxiety.

Excitement in normal behavior is also a common outcome of frustration, disappointment or minor irritation. The housewife who finds her home duties

[57] See page 321.
[58] Cameron, N., "The place of mania among the depressions from a biological standpoint." *J. Psychol.*, 1942, vol. 14, pp. 181–195.
[59] Less than one-fourth of Rennie's patients suffered a manic attack, for example, although 80% of them had recurrent depressive disorders.
[60] See pages 317–319.

boring, or her husband unusually exasperating, goes on a mild shopping spree, and returns with an unnecessary new hat and an air of excited triumph. The merchant whose customers have become unaccountably irascible may spend his free afternoon in vigorous gardening, working with a ruthless, unplanned initiative that may destroy his vegetables along with the weeds. The tireless raconteur is often covering up an uneasiness which neither he nor his friends identify or recognize. Some people find relief from tension in the excitement of alcoholic or sexual indulgence, and in the thrilling uncertainties of mountain-climbing and auto-racing. These reactions have their mass counterparts in boisterous conventions, as well as in the unrestrained festivities which, in some religious and national groups, climax a period of enforced restriction and self-sacrifice. Increased activity and tense hilarity may characterize the behavior even of mourners at the wake which follows a death.

One of the best illustrations of excited activity as a reaction to unremitting strain is to be found in the behavior of veteran combat airmen who are preparing for a mission.[61] Just prior to and during their briefing, the men are universally tense and apprehensive, but many of them exhibit their anxiety only in the disguised forms of bravado, horseplay and minor fighting. The same behavior occurs after the mission has been completed; on the return home and for some time afterward, the fliers are so noisy, overactive and distractible that they may be unable to give a coherent report of the military engagement in which they have participated. In a sizeable proportion of air personnel, this excitement carries with it a conviction of personal invulnerability.[62] The airman's close friends fail to return from missions, he sees planes from his own outfit crash in flames, but he persists in his belief that such tragedy cannot touch him. Thus, distraction, aggressive activity and overt denial of tension are all normal ways of handling anxiety; and they are all closely related to manic excitement.

Manic excitement

The manic excitement is an anxiety disorder which is characterized by energetic overactivity and by elation or aggressive self-assertion which may reach delusional proportions. Like the other anxiety disorders, manic excitement begins typically in chronic anxiety, raised to an acute level by intolerable stress. In some instances, a brief period of tense depression precedes the manic attack, but this initial depressive reaction is often concealed by the patient. Even if his friends or relatives are aware of the depressive episode, they usually forget it in the whirlwind of excitement that follows. In common with the other anxiety disorders, manic behavior typically neither involves, nor ends in, serious dis-

---

[61] Glavis, L. R., Jr., "Bombing mission number fifteen." *J. abn. soc. Psychol.*, 1946, vol. 41, pp. 189–198.

[62] Grinker, R. R. and Spiegel, J. P., *War neurosis.* New York: Blakiston, 1945, p. 120.

organization. The patient may appear elated, boastful, self-assertive, jolly, hyperactive and overconfident. But the alert clinician who can keep up with this manic behavior will quickly recognize the innumerable expressions of anxiety — sometimes desperate anxiety — which the patient is more or less successfully concealing from himself.

The particular directions which the manic patient's gaiety, excitement and self-assertion take are no different from the ones followed by a normal elated or aggressive person. The patient, however, overplays his part. If he is primarily elated, he may sing, shout, skip and prance. He may decorate himself with medals and odd bits of finery, or rip his clothes to shreds and exhibit himself stark naked. He is likely to tease and badger others, and to play pranks which often disguise only thinly an attitude of defiant hostility. He shifts abruptly from one activity to another, until his behavior seems to consist largely of interrupted segments of behavior. The manic patient's unrelieved tension may produce almost ceaseless motion, so that he sleeps only an hour or two in twenty-four, neglects his meals, cannot pause to care for his toilet needs, and, if untreated, may present eventually a picture of starvation and exhaustion. His self-assertiveness frequently develops into expansive and grandiose delusions of self-aggrandizement. To the inexpert observer, the patient in manic excitement then appears to have adopted the enviable role of the man who is completely happy and self-satisfied.

A few days spent in the company of a manic patient, however, will soon convince even the inexpert observer that manic excitement is the sign neither of happiness nor of self-satisfaction. Nowhere is this more evident than in the excited person's quipping, rhyming, punning speech, which shifts unexpectedly from one topic to another (*topical flight*). To be sure, he keeps talking, uses many words, and jumps rapidly from point to point, distracted by his own activity as much as by the reactions of others (*overinclusion*).[63] But a careful analysis of what he is saying indicates that while his talk is plenteous, it shows relatively little spread.

In other ways also, the patient in manic excitement resembles the patient who develops depressive reactions to anxiety. Both, for example, show upon X-ray investigation a decided slowing in gastrointestinal motility.[64] Both eat poorly and tend to become constipated. Furthermore, the manic patient, as well as the depressed one, occasionally recognizes that he is more concerned over cheerless and threatening events than his apparent levity would indicate. The manic patient plays the clown, but like the clown he is often tense and sad. Thus one patient, who developed manic excitement after the suicide of her beloved sister, repeatedly interrupted her own elated behavior to say perplex-

[63] For a discussion of overinclusion, see pages 74–75 and 456–458.
[64] Henry, G., "Gastrointestinal motor functions in manic-depressive psychoses." *Amer. J. Psychiat.*, 1931, vol. 88, pp. 19–28.

edly, "But it's all the time with grief." The following case illustrates many of the common characteristics of manic excitement.

A thirty-five-year-old biochemist was brought to the clinic by his frightened wife. To his psychiatrist the patient explained, "I discovered that I had been drifting, broke the bonds and suddenly found myself doing things and doing them by telegraph. I was dead tired, and decided to go on a vacation; but even there it wasn't long before I was sending more telegrams. I got into high gear and started to buzz. Then a gentle hint from a friend took effect and I decided to come here and see if the changes in my personality were real." He entered the ward in high spirits, went about greeting the patients, insisted that the place was "swell," and made quick puns on the names of doctors to whom he was introduced. Meanwhile his wife said she was "scared to death." "His friends used to call him 'Crazy Charley'," she said, "but I haven't seen this streak in him for years."

When his wife had left, the patient soon demonstrated what he meant by "high gear." He bounded down the hall, threw his medication on the floor, leaped up on a window ledge and dared any one to get him down. When he was put in a room alone where he could be free, he promptly dismantled the bed, pounded on the walls, yelled and sang. He made a sudden sally into the hall and did a kind of hula-hula dance before he could be returned to his room. His shouting continued throughout the night, and betrayed in its content the ambivalent attitudes which the patient maintained toward his hospitalization: "What the hell kind of a place is this? A swell place? I'm not staying here. I'm having a hell of a good time. Oh, I'm so happy. I have to get going. My gray suit please, my gray coat please, my gray socks, all gray on their way, going to be gay. I'm going out as fast as I came in, only faster. I'm happier than I have ever been in my life. I'm 100 per cent better than normal."

The following morning, after almost no sleep, the patient was more noisy and energetic than ever. He smashed the overhead light with his shoes and ripped off the window guard. He tore up several hospital gowns, draped himself in a loin cloth made of their fragments, said he was Tarzan, and gave wild jungle cries to prove it. "I've tasted tiger's blood!" he roared. "I'm a success and I'm the man for my boss's job. I've made a killing and this time I will keep on going." He made amorous remarks to the nurses, accused them of flirting with him, and announced loudly, "At the present time I am not married; but my body is not for sale, regardless of the price." From his talk it could be inferred that, far from being happily relaxed and irresponsible, the patient was in reality deeply disturbed over job competition, sexual conflicts and his own hospitalization. A study of his personal background confirmed this inference, and indicated that, as might be expected, affectional relationships and personal status had presented recurring problems throughout his life.

The patient was the elder son of a man whom he regarded as selfish, irresponsible and thoroughly despicable. The father was a medical missionary who had spent much of his life in the Belgian Congo, where he married and began to rear his family. Between the parents there was continuous friction, which the patient blamed entirely upon his father. According to the patient, his father nagged his mother ceaselessly, referred pointedly to sexual misbehavior in her relatives, and was unconcerned even when she was obliged to undergo a dangerous operation. During the patient's adolescence, his father became attracted to another woman, and in the course of subsequent events was dismissed from his medical post. The mother returned with her two sons to this country, but the father remained in Africa and was never again seen by his family.

As a child, the patient had been well aware of a lack of harmony between his parents; his own loyalties, however, had always been with his mother. He worked his way through preparatory school and university, supplementing his earnings with prizes and awards which he won for brilliant achievements in chemistry. He had never been a sociable person, and was always sensitive, reserved and shy, except with a few close friends. In small, intimate groups, however, he would occasionally perform erratic, impulsive and ridiculous antics which earned him the nickname of "Crazy Charley." Once while returning from a picnic, for example, he entertained his friends by driving at top speed through a small town, yelling and waving a blanket from the car.

By the time he entered graduate school to work for an advanced degree in biochemistry the patient was already recognized as one of the most promising young students in his field. For a year he continued his outstanding record; but then two events occurred which shook his confidence. He eloped impulsively with a socially prominent young woman and was unexpectedly berated and rejected by her family. Then, while he was trying to re-establish friendly relationships with his parents-in-law, he took the examinations for his graduate degree and failed them.

With the help of his wife, the patient ultimately managed to develop an acceptable relationship with her parents, although their economic security and obvious self-satisfaction continued to annoy him. He considered himself superior to his wife, whom he nicknamed "Stupid," and treated as if she were unintelligent. To his unprecedented academic failure, on the other hand, the patient reacted in an angry and accusatory way, calling his examiners prejudiced and unfair. He seemed discouraged and depressed for several months after his failure. During this period his wife gave birth to their first child, who died as a result of birth injuries. The patient seemed to recover from this shock more slowly than did his wife. However, the following year he resumed his academic work competently, passed his examinations with honor, and completed a chemical research project which was enthusiastically accepted and quoted by his colleagues.

The patient obtained a position with a pharmaceutical firm where he was promised an opportunity to continue with his research. His immediate superior was one of his former college teachers, a person for whom he had little respect. Relations with this man were unsatisfactory from the beginning, and they grew steadily worse during the six years the patient remained with the company. "Everything I did was shelved," said the patient. Although his own research progressed successfully, he was required to share the credit for his new developments with his superior. This seemed unjust to the patient. He brooded over his inferior status and resented the selfishness of his chief, much as he had resented the unfairness of his professors and the irresponsibility of his father years before. He thought often of resigning his position, but jobs were scarce and he could not bring himself to risk unemployment. Finally, over the head of his superior, he took the product of his most recent research to a rival firm in another city and sold it. At once, however, he recognized that this act was a serious breach of ethics, and he accordingly resigned from his own company in a 1200-word telegram.

Upon his return home after this overt act of rebellion, the patient announced to his wife that he had lost his inhibitions and found a new personality. He tipped a headwater $10, bought an expensive gold pencil, and sent three pheasants to the president of his former company — a man he scarcely knew — with a facetious cartoon, and a note which merely said, "I've gone the limit." He made plans to buy an expensive car which he could not afford, talked of buying his father-in-law's house, and wired congratulations to a classmate he had not seen for ten years whose wife was about to have a baby. He made long distance calls and sent lengthy telegrams all over the country concerning his new project. He decided suddenly to return to the city where he had sold his product, and from which he had just come. So he put his wife and some friends in his car, and drove all night at top speed over wet roads. His behavior was so wild and irresponsible that when morning came his friends persuaded him to drive on to the psychiatric clinic.

In the clinic, as we have seen, the patient was at first overactive and aggressive. As he became more calm, he proceeded to draft extensive plans for rebuilding the clinic and redesigning its medical laboratories. He insisted that he was the only biochemist in the world who could do a perfect job of laboratory organization, and he became irritable when his plans were not immediately acted upon. He confided to a nurse that he was to be made president of his former pharmaceutical company. These delusions of self-aggrandizement were mixed with feelings of self-reference; he believed the other patients were looking at him oddly, and that a radio sermon entitled "Fight the Good Fight" was aimed expressly at him. With the freedom provided by the simplified ward environment and, later on, through regular discussions of his problems with his psychiatrist, the patient gradually resumed his normal ways of behaving. He left the clinic after two months to take a new research position.

This case illustrates the background of tension and the setting of personal stress which are common to all anxiety disorders. For six years, this patient had worked under circumstances he considered humiliating, continually subordinated to a man he could not respect. His impulsive transgression of his company's rules, however, brought him no relief. Instead, he developed anxiety and further tension which even a 1200-word telegram of resignation could not dispel. His aggressive overactivity mounted to the distracted and irrepressible behavior of manic excitement. This kind of reaction to anxiety, it should be noted, was not unusual for this man; he typically handled his feelings of social inadequacy by developing a deceptive hilarity. We have seen that he rebelled against his wife's family by impulsively eloping, and became aggressive and accusatory toward the examiners when he failed in graduate school. Perhaps most significantly, he developed lifelong hatred toward a father he was expected to love.

This patient's resentment toward his father, and his reaction-sensitivity to the disgrace which his father's behavior had brought to his family, are strikingly like the ambivalent attitudes which often lead to depressive disorders.[65] In the development of manic excitement, however, anxiety over attitudes of forbidden hostility toward a loved person persists, and grows to a repudiation of guilt and self-blame which may then, in overcompensation, assume delusional proportions.[66] Thus our patient focussed his aggression upon others, interpreted his own minor and major failures as a result of injustice, depreciated his wife and his superior, and came at last to the unwarranted conclusion that he was the world's greatest biochemist, whose plans were completely flawless and whose genius would soon be recognized by everyone. The samples of his talk given earlier show in their topical flight the patient's characteristic inability, at the height of his illness, to entertain even momentarily the notion that he was frustrated or unhappy. At a later time, when he was recovering, the patient stated his attitude more succinctly: "I have pride, and I will fight like a fish on a line to prove that I am right."

Manic excitement develops from persistent anxiety and tension through a process of overgeneralization which is similar to that found in depressive disorders. As the patient's energetic overactivity increases, old conflicts and problems long settled recur, and are woven into his behavior. Our patient, for example, in his excitement repeated his former status-conflict with his wife's family when he decided impulsively to buy his father-in-law's house; and he demonstrated the revival of his guilt and shame over his own father's sexual irresponsibility by his noisy proclamations that *he*, at least, had not put his body up for sale. Thus for the manic patient, there is no crucial shift to exaggerated self-blame, such as we found in typical depressions. Instead there develops a wider and wider generalization of aggressive excitement to others — to the patient's relatives, his friends, and even to strangers. The overactive and expansive character of his reactions exposes the manic person to hazards beyond those the depressed person faces. To suicide and homicide, which are dangers for both manic and depressed patients, must be added the threat to the manic individual's status and reputation which his irresponsible public behavior constitutes. The patient's impulsive, irrepressible excitement may become a public spectacle which his community does not easily forget.

Our three varieties of pathological anxiety — anxiety disorder, depression and manic excitement — can now take their place as examples of behavior pathology which develops directly out of normal unconsummated excitement.

---

[65] See page 321.   [66] See pages 398–399.

All three arise out of a background of persistent tension, increased by personal frustration and stress.   In all three, conflicting or ambivalent affectional attitudes play an important part.   None of them, however, includes or leads to serious behavioral disorganization.

These disorders resemble one another in a final critical respect.   In all of them, the patient remains tense and taut; his disorder brings him little or no relief from the anxiety which induced it.   Whether he retains the tensions of chronic anxiety, suffers anxiety attacks, or acquires phobias, he cannot escape his unconsummated emotional excitement.   If he develops a retarded depressive disorder, he is little more relaxed and comfortable than if his reaction is one of direct, agitated depression.   In manic excitement he becomes exhausted and grows still more tense because of his strenuous and often frantic denial of his own frustrations.   Anxiety remains the most conspicuous feature of these three varieties of behavior pathology.   It is in this way that they differ most strikingly from the disorders in which repression is prominent.   In *hysterical inactivation* and *hysterical autonomy*, which we shall next discuss, anxiety has been minimized, through repression, until it may appear to be altogether absent from a patient's behavior.

12

Repression

The tensions of anxiety and unfulfilled need play a prominent role in the development of normal and pathological behavior. Human beings, we have said, have an almost irresistible tendency toward completion in their ongoing behavior.[1] If completion cannot be achieved in a direct manner, then the individual may learn such indirect techniques as rationalization, compensation or projection;[2] and in employing these he often sacrifices the social validity of his own behavior to the consummation of an unfinished act. The alternative to such compromise behavior may be a chronic inability to consummate emotional reactions, and an unusual susceptibility to acute anxiety attacks, panic, behavioral disorganization, or depressive and manic disorders.[3] In such pathological developments as these, the individual gains no relief from his tensions, but remains unsatisfied, apprehensive or disturbed.

A great many persons, however, achieve completion of their behavior sequences by controlling, excluding or denying certain of their own developing reactions. A guilt-laden person who has committed a secret misdeed, for example, may be safe from retaliation from others and rejection by them; but he is at the mercy of his own punishing self-reactions. And from punishing self-reactions there is no prompt or easy escape.[4] Indeed, the guilty person's only permanent relief from his anxious anticipation of punishment lies in his ability to modify or eliminate the developing reactions which bring him anxiety. He can alter the direction of his thinking and his fantasy through distraction, suppression or reactio_s of self-control. He can avoid places and topics which remind him of his transgression. And, if he is highly practiced in the tech-

---

[1] See pages 75–79. [2] See pages 376–387.
[3] Anxiety disorders are discussed on pages 304–314; disorganization is discussed in detail on pages 448–469.
[4] For a discussion of guilt and self-punishment, see pages 284–289.

niques of behavior exclusion, he can reach a point where he no longer responds with guilt to his recalled misdeed, and indeed no longer even recalls the episode. By means of controlling, excluding and denying his own developing reactions, the guilty person has then successfully eliminated his insupportable anxiety.

We give the name *repression* to this means of dealing with anxiety and tension. Repression is a special instance of the *exclusion* which we have discussed in relation to behavior organization; [5] like other examples of exclusion it may make for economy and efficiency in everyday living. Most people learn, sooner or later, the futility of rehearsing and preserving in their behavioral repertories recalled events and acquired reactions which make them anxious, angry or ashamed. They learn to ignore, deny and forget a great deal of their own behavior. The immediate consequence of this inhibition seems to be the disappearance of overt anxiety; the individual for the most part appears calm, controlled and even relaxed. By selectively excluding — or repressing — certain reactions, he presents to other persons and to his own self-reactions a more consistent and satisfying picture of himself.

Sometimes, however, the behavior thus excluded is so extensive, or so crucial to normal biosocial development, that the individual is left immature, ineffectual or eccentric. If we come to know such persons well, we find that they are unresponsive to particular patterns of stimulation, and unable to carry through, or even to initiate, certain important sequential acts. Often, too, these persons interrupt their ongoing behavior sequences to perform acts — either momentary or prolonged — which to the observer seem to bear no relationship to the behavioral context within which they occur. Extensive repression of reactions can in these ways bring relief from overt anxiety, but it also brings restriction, impoverishment and distortion of behavior. It is for this reason that, from Freud's time forward, widespread, inclusive repression has been considered a common predisposing factor to the development of behavior pathology.

Psychoanalytic view of repression

In two papers, both published in 1915,[6] Freud presented the first systematic outline of a theory of repression and sketched its relation to pathological behavior. The Freudian concept of repression, like most psychoanalytic concepts, grew out of Freud's keen observation of his neurotic patients' reactions, and reflects the dichotomy of conscious and unconscious ideas which we have already found characteristic of psychoanalytic theory. According to Freud, an instinctual impulse becomes inoperative, and goes into a state of *repression*,

[5] See pages 74–75.
[6] Freud, S., "Repression" (1915). In *Collected Papers*, vol. 4. London: Hogarth Press, 1948, pp. 84–97.

when the pain associated with its satisfaction is stronger than the pleasure of its gratification. If, for example, an instinctual impulse arouses reactions of anxiety, or anticipation of punishment, an individual will reject or repress the "ideational" components of the impulse, in order to avoid the anticipated pain. "The essence of repression," explains Freud, "lies simply in the function of rejecting and keeping something out of consciousness." [7]

From this generalized description, Freud differentiates two separate phases of repression: *primal repression* and *repression proper*. In the first phase — *primal repression* — the "ideational" aspect of an impulse is denied entrance to consciousness, much as an unwelcome guest might be barred from a home before he crosses the threshold. In the second phase — *repression proper* — attitudes, fantasies or thoughts which are related to the repressed material are themselves also denied entrance to consciousness; both the unwelcome guest and his near and distant acquaintances now stand excluded on the threshold, prevented by the host from entering his home. According to Freud, reactions so repressed neither die out nor remain static. They continue to exist in the unconscious, and even undergo further organization and ramification. The rejected guest may change in character, wear a disguise, gather a different troop around him, and one day knock again on the forbidden door.

A great many of the aspects of this theory of repression have far-reaching implications for the student of behavior pathology. For one thing, repression is represented as *mobile*. It is not an act which merely occurs once and disposes of the problem forever. Repression requires of the individual constant expenditure of effort; it may in itself be fatiguing, and even exhausting. For another thing, the "ideational" aspect of the impulse must be considered separately from its "charge of affect." [8] The former may be successfully repressed, while the emotional components of the reaction undergo change or distortion. Finally, repression is often not completely successful; and its very lack of success accounts, in Freud's view, for the development and persistence of certain symptoms of behavior pathology. Indeed, anxieties, phobias, hysterical disorders and compulsive rituals may all represent a *return of the repressed*. [9]

While many contemporary behavior pathologists would cast repression in a theoretical framework different from that of Freud's,[10] none of them would deny the central importance of exclusion and inhibition in the development of

[7] Freud, S., "Repression" (1915). In *Collected Papers*, vol. 4. London: Hogarth Press, 1948, p. 86.
[8] Freud, S., "Repression" (1915). In *Collected Papers*, vol. 4. London: Hogarth Press, 1948, p. 91.
[9] Freud, S., "Repression" (1915). In *Collected Papers*, vol. 4. London: Hogarth Press, 1948, p. 91ff.
[10] See, for example, Dollard, J. and Miller, N. E., *Personality and psychotherapy*. New York: McGraw-Hill, 1950, pp. 198–221; Shaw, F. J., "A stimulus-response analysis of repression and insight in psychotherapy." *Psychol. Rev.*, 1946, vol. 53, pp. 36–42.

behavior pathology. Furthermore, the issues raised by Freud's presentation of repression have provided students of normal behavior with new hypotheses regarding remembering and forgetting, hypotheses which can be tested in the experimental laboratory. Innumerable recent studies of early childhood recollections, and of the effects of pleasantness, unpleasantness, conflict, frustration and personal need upon learning, reflect the impact upon laboratory psychology of this concept of repression.[11] Many of these studies are, strictly speaking, irrelevant to psychoanalytic theory, and many others yield results which are disappointingly negative or ambiguous. Nevertheless, some of them represent important additions to our understanding of the manner in which behavior pathology develops out of the normal, everyday reactions that we all acquire.

Repression in Contemporary Behavior Pathology

Most of our activity is adjudged appropriate or inappropriate, in the eyes of our fellows, in terms of its suitability to the context within which it occurs. We all learn to anticipate, in one another's reactions, certain outcomes of certain ongoing sequences. We learn that this pattern of stimulation is ordinarily followed by that reaction, until we become relatively accurate predictors of our own and others' behavior.[12] In a sense, we develop our own concept of an adequate stimulus for many everyday acts, in terms of the thousands of daily situations in which we see ourselves and our friends following out characteristic behavior sequences. For us, the adequate pattern of stimulation, for our own or others' reactions, is simply that pattern which in the past has consistently preceded a particular reaction. When the usual stimulus-pattern is present, but the usual reaction does not occur, we are likely to become puzzled and uneasy, or to conclude that the behavior we see is inappropriate or inexplicable.

(a) If, for example, a friend who is an accomplished driver breaks his leg in an automobile accident, we expect him to be unable to drive a car until his leg has healed. If, on the other hand, our friend has been in no accident, suffered no organ or tissue pathology, but nevertheless becomes unable to make the movements necessary to drive his car, we are likely to find his behavior unintelligible. (b) When a combat soldier

[11] For reviews of this experimental literature, see Sears, R. R., "Survey of objective studies of psychoanalytic concepts." *Soc. Sci. Res. Council Bull. 51.* New York, 1943, pp. 105–120; Sears, R. R., "Experimental analysis of psychoanalytic phenomena." In Hunt, J. McV. (Ed.), *Personality and the behavior disorders.* New York: Ronald, 1944, pp. 306–332; Zeller, A. F., "An experimental analogue of repression. I. Historical summary." *Psychol. Bull.,* 1950, vol. 47, pp. 39–51.

[12] There are, of course, wide differences among persons in the accuracy and certainty with which they predict. For a discussion of this point, see page 15; for an experimental illustration, see Dymond, R. F., "Personality and empathy." *J. consult. Psychol.,* 1950, vol. 14, pp. 343–350.

has participated in a dangerous mission, acting with great heroism under fire, we expect him to be able later to describe and recall these vivid events. If he insists that he cannot remember the incidents at all, even with detailed promptings from others, we consider his reactions unaccountable. (c) A young woman may state verbally that she hates her father, but at the same time she fails to give the expected visceral reactions, or to attack or challenge him when she has a clear opportunity to do so. In all these instances, there is present a pattern of adequate stimulation, but the expected reaction does not follow. This discrepancy in the relationship between adequate stimulation and ensuing reaction, as contemporary behavior pathologists view it, is the distinguishing characteristic of repression.[13]

Let us now define *repression* as the *inhibition of one's own tension-provoking reactions with the result that they become inaccessible to one's self-reactions.* The behavioral consequence of repression is that the developing reaction does not occur, even though previously adequate stimulation is present. Thus our experienced auto-driver might say that he will drive, and seat himself behind the wheel; but he is actually incapable of carrying through the necessary coordinated movements which will start the car and keep it going. Similarly, our combat veteran might listen attentively to the story of his exploits in battle, but be unable to recognize them as part of his own past acts. And the young woman who verbalized her hostile attitudes toward her father, cannot initiate either covert or overt responses which these attitudes would support. All three individuals, in the presence of previously adequate stimulation, have inhibited or prevented the development of their own appropriate reactions.

From our definition it should be clear that repression is a positive reaction which the individual makes toward his own developing behavior. It is, as we have indicated, a special instance of *exclusion*,[14] and closely related to the techniques of *self-control* which we have earlier discussed; [15] and like them, it is behavior that has been acquired through social interaction. It should be clear, also, that the reactions which are inhibited in repression are by no means exclusively verbal ones. Any person, to be sure, may learn to prevent the occurrence of verbal recall of anxiety-provoking events — as in the case of the combat soldiers whom we have just described. But such widespread patterns of neuromuscular behavior as those involved in driving a car may also undergo repression, so that a driver may be rendered helpless at the wheel. Even the visceral components of a total reaction may be excluded or inhibited, as in the case of the young woman whose verbal aggression found no correspondence in her covert behavior. Finally, it should be noted that the prevention and inhibition which characterize repression are directed toward behavior that is

[13] Cameron, N., *The psychology of behavior disorders.* Boston: Houghton Mifflin, 1947, p. 175.

[14] See pages 74–75.   [15] See pages 95–98.

tension-provoking. It is in this respect that repression differs from the forgetting which follows interference, fatigue, or the simple passage of time.

Conditions favoring the development of repression

Like all the other constituents of one's behavior organization, the reaction we call repression is acquired and maintained because it is tension-reducing.[16] It is the reactions whose development brings increasing anxiety that we learn to deny to ourselves and others, and to exclude from our repertory of behavior. Consequently, any condition which favors the growth of anxiety reactions may encourage also the acquisition of repressive techniques.[17] From the many potential precursors of developing anxiety, however, we shall single out three which are particularly favorable to the occurrence and persistence of repression: (1) *unsolved personal conflict;* (2) *anticipation of unwelcome punishment;* and (3) *threat to positive self-attitudes.*

(1) *Unsolved personal conflict.* The immediate consequence of unsolved conflict — whether it be double-adient, double-avoidant or adient-avoidant in character — is the failure to complete either reaction, or the completion of one reaction at the expense of the other, which then goes unconsummated. The more remote and pervasive effect of unsolved personal conflict, as we have seen, is persistent, cumulative tension.[18] In such a situation, consummation, with its consequent tension-reduction, can occur only when the individual has excluded from his repertory those reactions which serve to initiate or to prolong his conflict. Thus a combat soldier, who cannot reconcile with his own needs for passive dependence the overt destruction and aggression which he sees around him, may become literally blind to external stimulation. In repressing his own reactions of seeing, he excludes from his behavior organization those constituents which might initiate or prolong the insupportable tensions of unsolved personal conflict. He achieves consummation, and tension-reduction, at the high price of visual inactivation.

The role of personal conflict in favoring repression, which is clear in much of our clinical material, has been also examined under experimental conditions. In one realistic study by Malamud and Linder,[19] for example, the experimenters presented a series of pictures to patients suffering from behavior pathology. For each patient, the areas of unsolved personal conflict which contributed markedly to his illness were known to the experimenters. Consequently, it was possible to include among the pictures many which represented situations close to the patients' private concern and preoccupations. Thus a picture showing an infant at the mother's breast was considered particularly

---

[16] See pages 75–79.   [17] See pages 280–293.
[18] See pages 272–275 and 298–303.
[19] Malamud, W. and Linder, R. E., "Dreams and their relationship to recent impressions." *Arch. Neurol. Psychiat.*, 1931, vol. 25, pp. 1081–1099.

significant for a patient whose difficulties stemmed from unresolved affectional conflicts with his mother.

The pictures were exhibited on one day, and the patients were asked to recall as many of them as possible on the following day. From our definition of repression, we would expect those pictures representing unsolved personal conflict to be recalled least well. The patient, according to this hypothesis, should inhibit his own reactions of recall if these tended to initiate the tensions of unresolved conflict. And so it turned out. The patients showed a distinct inability to remember the particular pictures which might remind them of their own areas of conflict, although they recalled with accuracy pictures which were personally neutral.

We shall find, in our clinical material, many examples of behavioral distortion and impoverishment which grow out of repressed conflict. Indeed, we have already seen that a great many conflicts, in normal and pathological behavior alike, are inaccessible to the individual's self-reactions.[20] And we have seen also that one of the most common reasons for this self-inaccessibility of conflict is repression. We shall find, when we turn to the development of other behavior pathology, and finally to its treatment, that it is the repressed and hence self-inaccessible conflicts which make a patient's behavior perplexing to himself and others. And it is these that become reorganized in relation to his total behavioral pattern in the course of successful therapy.[21]

(2) *Anticipation of unwelcome punishment.* Freud's view of repression, it will be recalled, emphasized the relative weights of pain and pleasure, accompanying the satisfaction of need, as determinants of primal repression.[22] This aspect of his view has stimulated a great many investigators to study the relationship between the "pleasant" or "unpleasant" character of behavior and its tendency to undergo repression. Early experimental psychologists, armed with the concept of hedonic tone, and with laboratory techniques for its investigation, undertook to find out whether unpleasant events were recalled by their subjects less readily than pleasant ones. Typically, these studies required the subjects to rate events as personally pleasant or unpleasant; or they utilized stimulus material which adult experimenters had prejudged as pleasant or unpleasant, regardless of changes in sign which the material might undergo with increasing age. Thus, such words as *love, kiss* or *romance* — rated pleasant by many adult subjects — might well have unpleasant or anxiety-provoking connotations in childhood, and consequently might be subject to repression. Although many of these early studies seemed to indicate that pleasant stimuli were learned and recalled more readily than unpleasant ones, it is doubtful whether they were actually relevant to Freud's concept of repression.[23]

---

[20] See page 274.   [21] See pages 561–563 and 617–620.   [22] See pages 338–340.
[23] For a detailed analysis of this point, see Sears, R. R., "Functional abnormalities of

Far more pertinent to the behavior pathologist's view of repression are investigations which single out guilt,[24] or the anticipation of punishment, as likely antecedents of repression. We have already seen that ongoing behavior sequences, which had previously culminated in unwelcome punishment, typically go unconsummated, and that the tensions of unconfirmed anticipation are fruitful sources of anxiety.[25] While recognizing this general principle as operative at any stage of maturation, Freud always emphasized infancy and early childhood as the period of earliest and most widespread repression — largely because infantile genital impulses bring parental punishment and rejection. Indeed, Freud believed that the repression of infantile sexuality was universal among persons in our Western culture, and that a partial amnesia developed in everyone which made it impossible for adults to recall their early genital behavior.[26] And through an associative amnesia, which Freud called *repression proper*, adults apparently obliterate most of the events of their preschool years.

This aspect of repression has encouraged investigators to attack the problem of *childhood recall*, in order to see whether or not adults were unable to recall the events of infancy and early childhood. Most of the published studies agree that recall of one's own life history is increasingly less efficient the earlier the period that is under consideration.[27] It is the rare adult who can, under laboratory or classroom conditions, recall with any clarity events from the first two or three years of his life.[28] A direct application of the Freudian theory of repression to these findings would assign the apparent amnesia to guilt, shame, or anticipation of parental disfavor, aroused by the sexual character of early childhood reactions.

There is some evidence that in a sizeable proportion of "earliest" recollections fear is indeed involved. But we cannot afford to overlook an equally plausible alternative explanation of these data. Only reactions which were originally well learned, and constituted a stable part of the individual's behav-

memory with special reference to amnesia." *Psychol. Bull.*, 1936, vol. 33, pp. 229–274; Sears, R. R., "Survey of objective studies of psychoanalytic concepts." *Soc. Sci. Res. Council Bull. 51.* New York, 1943, pp. 105–120.

[24] For a discussion of guilt, see pages 284–290.

[25] See pages 283–289.

[26] Freud, S., "Three contributions to the theory of sex." (4th ed., 1905). *Nerv. ment. Dis. Monogr. Series*, 1930, no. 7, pp. 36–38. There is some evidence that children comprehend inhibiting and prohibiting words when they are as young as 12 to 18 months of age. See, for example, Gesell, A., Thompson, H., and Amatruda, C. S., *The psychology of early growth.* New York: Macmillan, 1938.

[27] For a summary of these studies see Sears, R. R., "Survey of objective studies of psychoanalytic concepts." *Soc. Sci. Res. Council Bull. 51.* New York, 1943, p. 107 ff.

[28] For typical studies and representative results, see Dudycha, G. J. and Dudycha, M. M., "Childhood memories: a review of the literature." *Psychol. Bull.*, 1941, vol. 38, pp. 668–682; Thompson, G. G. and Witryol, S. L., "Adult recall of unpleasant experiences during three periods of childhood." *J. genet. Psychol.*, 1948, vol. 72, pp. 111–123; Waldfogel, S., "The frequency and character of childhood memories." *Psychol. Monogr.*, 1948, vol. 62, pp. 1–39.

ior organization, can properly be termed "forgotten" or repressed. We have ample experimental evidence that the original *learning* in infancy, and in the preschool years, is considerably less efficient than learning in later childhood and adulthood.[29] What appears as infantile amnesia resulting from primal repression and repression proper, therefore, may be only the consequence of incomplete and unstable learning by the prelanguage child.

More subject to experimental control than studies of childhood recall — but probably somewhat more artificial — are laboratory investigations which employ profane and sexual stimulus words along with neutral words. Here the assumption is made that, since most persons in contemporary Western culture have at some time been punished or reproved for profane or sexual talk, stimulus-words of this character should arouse anticipation of punishment. If this is so they consequently should also be learned and retained less efficiently than neutral words. In such experiments, for example, the experimenters utilized paired associates. Each member of a pair was meaningless in itself; but it suggested profane, sexual or neutral words when pronounced together with the other member of the pair. In most cases, the neutral lists were learned more readily, and later reproduced more accurately, than the other lists.[30]

In a somewhat differently designed experiment, anxiety-producing stimuli were recalled less well than neutral stimuli under ordinary laboratory conditions. But when hypnosis was induced, the anxiety-producing stimuli were recalled more efficiently than the neutral terms.[31] This finding, of course, fits well into the Freudian theory of repression. It suggests that the anxiety-producing reactions were repressed, and could consequently be recovered under hypnosis; whereas the reactions to neutral stimulation had not undergone repression, and were not similarly influenced by hypnosis.

(3) *Threat to positive self-attitudes.* The inhibition which we call repression is a learned reaction, and like all learned reactions it reflects the selectivity of personal need.[32] The particular sequences which one person excludes from his

[29] For a review of studies on this point, see Munn, N. L., "Learning in children." In Carmichael, L. (Ed.), *Manual of child psychology.* New York: Wiley, 1946, pp. 370–449.

[30] Reviews of these studies may be found in Sears, R. R., "Survey of objective studies of psychoanalytic concepts." *Soc. Sci. Res. Council Bull. 51.* New York, 1943, pp. 113–114. These findings are reminiscent of McGinnies' report that taboo words evoke GSR's below the perceptual threshold. See McGinnies, E., "Emotionality and perceptual defense." *Psychol. Rev.,* 1949, vol. 56, pp. 244–251. This study has been criticized by Howes, D. H. and Solomon, R. L., "A note on McGinnies' 'Emotionality and perceptual defense.'" *Psychol. Rev.,* 1950, vol. 57, pp. 229–234; and the criticisms discussed by McGinnies, E., "Discussion of Howes' and Solomon's note on 'Emotionality and perceptual defense.'" *Psychol. Rev.,* 1950, vol. 57, pp. 235–240. In a somewhat differently planned study, Miller found that a fear response conditioned to a spoken word generalized to thinking of the word. See Dollard, J. and Miller, N. E., *Personality and psychotherapy.* New York: McGraw-Hill, 1950, pp. 205–207.

[31] Rosenthal, B. G., "Hypnotic recall of material learned under anxiety and non-anxiety producing conditions." *J. exper. Psychol.,* 1944, vol. 34, pp. 369–389.

[32] See pages 59–75.

behavior differ from those which his neighbor may inhibit; but both are likely to repress developing reactions whose consummation does violence to their personal need. The selective inhibition of certain constituents of a patterned reaction, and the simultaneous sharpening of others, is to be found in human learning and remembering in a wide range of situations. Human beings learn in accordance with their needs, they structure ambiguous situations in their own private terms, and they distort their recall of events in the direction of their own supporting attitudes.[33] We have already seen the operation of such a tendency in the development of progressive reaction-sensitization, and in the constructions which anxious, depressed or excited persons place upon their environments.[34] We shall meet this tendency again when we come to consider compensation, rationalization, projection and the development of delusional thinking.[35]

A common personal frame of reference which determines selective learning and recall is that defined by a system of positive self-attitudes. We have said that, through social interaction from infancy onward, human beings develop reactions toward themselves as social objects (*self-reactions*).[36] Such self-reactions may be critical, rejecting or punitive; and if they are consistently so, they bring the individual tensions and anxiety from which he can find no easy or permanent escape. It is therefore not surprising that a great many of the reactions which individuals learn to repress are the self-punitive or self-critical reactions whose development threatens a system of positive self-attitudes. We are able to recount with relative ease the things we have done which we believe ought to be done, and to forget our sins of omission and commission.

This well-recognized characteristic of human behavior has been put to repeated experimental test. Subjects are made to fail in some laboratory tasks and to succeed in others, for example, and are then asked later to recall the tasks. Ordinarily they are more efficient at remembering their successes than their failures.[37] However, the extent to which the task is completed, as well as the degree of personal involvement in their performance which the subjects feel, also contribute to their selective remembering.[38]

---

[33] See, for example, the experiment briefly reported in Frenkel-Brunswik, E., "Intolerance of ambiguity as an emotional and perceptual personality variable." *J. Personality*, 1949, vol. 18, pp. 123–126; for a more general discussion of this viewpoint, see Bartlett, F. C., "Remembering: a study in experimental and social psychology." New York: Macmillan; Cambridge, Eng.: Cambridge University Press, 1932.

[34] See Chapter 11.

[35] See pages 372–405.

[36] For a discussion of self-reactions, see pages 95–105.

[37] For examples of such studies, see Alper, T. G., "Task-orientation and ego-orientation as factors in reminiscence." *J. exper. Psychol.*, 1948, vol. 38, pp. 224–238; Glixman, A. F., "Recall of completed and incompleted activities under varying degrees of stress." *J. exper. Psychol.*, 1949, vol. 39, pp. 281–295; Rosenzweig, S., "An experimental study of 'repression' with special reference to need-persistive and ego-defensive reactions to frustration." *J. exper. Psychol.*, 1943, vol. 32, pp. 64–74.

[38] Because the interruption of an ongoing reaction may affect the extent to which it is

In a somewhat different sort of experiment, students are asked to rate the degree of satisfaction they feel upon earning certain marks in weekly quizzes.[39] When later they recall their grades, they are likely to remember best the grades they rated most satisfying personally; and they recall next best either the next most satisfying grades, or the least satisfying of all, depending upon the threat which a low grade represents. In still another variety of this experimental approach, subjects are presented with falsified ratings of themselves, which are supposed to have been obtained from their close friends.[40] Here again, positive and flattering ratings are learned and remembered more efficiently than negative, critical judgments. All these studies single out, as an important determinant of repression, the threats to an individual's positive self-attitudes.

These three common conditions favoring repression — *unsolved personal conflict, anticipation of unwelcome punishment* and *threat to positive self-attitudes* — permit us now to make a further generalization regarding the inhibition of tension-provoking reactions. From our analysis, we would expect that certain aspects of one's behavior are more likely to undergo repression than others. In our culture, the conflicts between love and hostility directed toward the same person are most likely to go unresolved; parental punishment is most frequently aimed at sexual and aggressive reactions; and self-attitudes are typically threatened when the individual is unable to reward himself or when his performance exposes him to self-reproach. Consequently, we may legitimately expect — as Freud early suggested [41] — that persons who are accomplished in the techniques of repression will most often inhibit and exclude reactions of an affectional or a hostile character.

Individual differences in ease of repression

The ability to inhibit or deny one's own developing reactions seems to be learned more easily by some persons than by others. Most of us gain reasonable facility in interrupting and controlling the growth of certain tension-provoking reactions, but our areas of repressed behavior are not so extensive as to make us seriously impoverished or ineffectual. A relatively few persons practice so long, and learn so well, the procedures of self-inhibition, that wide-

recalled (the so-called "Zeigarnik effect"), many of the published researches on repression employing the interruption technique have been called into question. See, for example, Glixman, A., "An analysis of the use of the interruption-technique in experimental studies of 'repression.'" *Psychol. Bull.*, 1948, vol. 45, pp. 491–506.

[39] Koch, H. L., "The influence of some affective factors upon recall." *J. gen. Psychol.*, 1930, vol. 4, pp. 171–190.

[40] For examples of such studies, see Shaw, F. J., "Two determinants of selective forgetting." *J. abn. soc. Psychol.*, 1944, vol. 39, pp. 434–445; Shaw, F. J. and Spooner, A., "Selective forgetting when the subject is not ego involved." *J. exper. Psychol.*, 1945, vol. 35, pp. 242–247; Wallen, D., "Ego involvement as a determinant of selective forgetting." *J. abn. soc. Psychol.*, 1942, vol. 37, pp. 20–29.

[41] Freud, S., "Repression" (1915). In *Collected Papers*, vol. 4. London: Hogarth Press, 1948, pp. 84–97.

spread and highly significant constituents of their behavioral organization are functionally lost to them. We shall meet such persons among patients whose overcomplete repression has led them to the development of hysterical inactivation.[42]

The range of individual differences in ease of repression, which we find in our associates and our patients, is duplicated when we study repression under controlled experimental conditions. Our subjects, for example, differ widely from one another in the age at which they locate their earliest childhood recall. They differ also in their tendencies to inhibit the recall of failure and of unsatisfying personal ratings. In studies designed to produce repression artificially in the laboratory, we find a similar range. Instructing subjects to inhibit a particular class of response in a word association experiment, or shocking them severely for failing to inhibit, creates an artificial repression in some subjects, but is relatively ineffective for others.[43] Individual differences of this sort are of especial significance to the behavior pathologist because ease of repression may be in part responsible for personal susceptibility to the development of pathological behavior.

Like any other form of reaction and self-reaction, repressive behavior must have its beginnings in the early social interactions of infancy and childhood. The child of punitive and restrictive parents, for example, lives in the constant shadow of threatened punishment.[44] Not only his parents' overt reactions to him, but his derived self-reactions, are tinged with criticism and rebuke. This is a fertile social field for the acquisition and persistence of repressive behavior. The child of overly demanding, perfectionistic parents may also find relief from impossible requirements by denying those reactions which are at variance with his parents' ideals for him. If nothing short of perfection will win parental favor, then one's failings and misdeeds are better denied in public, and eventually excluded even from one's self-reactions.[45] We shall see that a great many of our patients who suffer from extensive, disabling repression have originally learned self-inhibition at the hands of punishing or perfectionistic parents.

Many children, whose parents are not otherwise rejecting or unduly demanding, learn repression because it is the prevailing pattern in their families. One

[42] For a discussion of hysterical inactivation, see pages 369–371.

[43] McGranahan, D. V., "A critical and experimental study of repression." *J. abn. soc. Psychol.*, 1940, vol. 35, pp. 212–225. For a critical analysis of this study see Sears, R. R., "Survey of objective studies of psychoanalytic concepts." *Soc. Sci. Res. Council Bull. 51.* New York, 1943, pp. 116–118. It will be recalled that in the Diven experiment, described earlier, subjects differed in the accuracy with which they reported the stimulus-word which led to shock. See pages 270 and 297–298.

[44] For an analysis of the conditions under which children may learn repression, see Dollard, J. and Miller, N. E., *Personality and psychotherapy.* New York: McGraw-Hill, 1950, pp. 204–208. A recent extensive study of prejudice affords additional evidence that parental discipline requiring submission leads to a tendency toward repression. See Adorno, T. W., Frenkel-Brunswik, E., Levinson, D. J., and Sanford, R. N., *The authoritarian personality.* New York: Harper, 1950, p. 423.

[45] Compare the discussion of muted speech on pages 107–109.

of the most common methods by which insecure parents handle painful or embarrassing topics and situations is that of studied indifference. Such parents ignore their children's bursts of hostility, remain unresponsive to their offspring's fears, and ignore sexual talk or allusion as completely as if they were blind or deaf. With overt unconcern, these parents act as if aggression, anxiety and forbidden interests simply did not exist. Nor is this studied indifference confined to the home environment. Many teachers, because of their own unresolved conflicts and preoccupations, ignore in the stories they read, the discussions they conduct, and the relationships they form with their pupils, the aggressive, anxiety-producing and affectional reactions which must be part of any complete person. In so doing, they may also establish, as the prevailing classroom pattern, an atmosphere of selective repression. The child whose parents or teachers seem to imply that certain reactions do not exist has as his objects of early identification models of self-inhibition which he may come to duplicate in his own behavior.

Still another condition which goes along with the development of self-inhibition is to be found in the coherence and stability of the individual's behavior organization. In the study of experimentally-induced frustration referred to earlier, where subjects learned through severe shock to inhibit certain responses, the subjects' tendencies to disorganize in a motor task were also measured.[46] Each subject performed on a pursuit-meter test under conditions of strong electric shock. Ability to "repress," on the association test, was positively correlated with ability to resist disruption, on the pursuit-meter test. The experimenter concluded that ability to repress was a function of the subject's behavior organization, the subjects with the least easily disrupted motor organization showing the most efficient repression.

Whether a stable and consistent organization of behavior is the cause or the consequence of successful repression cannot, of course, be decided on the basis of these results. A close relationship between repression and behavior organization, however, is clearly demonstrated in our clinical material. For it is apparent that when repressed reactions are suddenly reincluded in the individual's behavioral repertory — whether through free verbalization, fantasy or night-dreaming — one common consequence may be the disorganization of previously patterned behavior.[47]

Consequences of repression

By preventing himself from recalling, thinking about or fantasying on anxiety-provoking themes, as we have seen, an individual may protect himself from the development or spread of tension. He may also achieve gains in the

[46] McGranahan, D. V., "A critical and experimental study of repression." *J. abn. soc. Psychol.*, 1940, vol. 35, pp. 212–225.
[47] See pages 463–464.

precision and economy of his behavior organization. Indeed, extensive repression may result in a behavior organization of deceptive simplicity. A person who inhibits his own developing reactions may grow selectively insensitive to certain forms of stimulation. His repertory in certain areas of behavior becomes narrowed down to a few well-practiced acts, among which conflict and the necessity for choice seldom occur. Repression thus has its advantages as an instrument in behavior organization.

The apparent advantages of repression, however, are often outweighed by its disadvantages. The narrowing that contributes to behavioral precision, of course, may eventuate in behavioral *impoverishment*. Landis and Bolles have identified, among their cases of women suffering from permanent physical handicap, a sizeable proportion of persons who inhibited any overt recognition of their own limitations. These women had learned to obliterate those reactions which were related to their handicap, but many of them were still able to maintain a fairly adequate level of social adjustment.[48] Such extensive impoverishment as this is seldom accomplished without signs of maladaptation or even pathology. A great many reserved and distant persons show in their social detachment the price they have paid for sweeping repression.[49]

Repression commonly leads not only to impoverishment, but also to behavioral *distortion*.[50] There are two reasons for this. (*a*) For one thing, *repressed behavior is inaccessible to the individual's self-reactions*. This means that as long as they remain repressed, reactions cannot be formulated in words or shared with others. And behavior which is unshared, as we have seen, is insulated from the day-to-day social interchange which is necessary for social validation. Furthermore, repressed behavior is unaffected by a person's reactions of self-control. Lacking both social validation and the influence of self-control, repressed reactions are likely to deviate farther and farther from the cultural norm, until the individual's behavior organization becomes so distorted as to be pathological.[51]

(*b*) For another thing, *repression is a learned reaction, and like other learned reactions it may generalize to areas of behavior not originally implicated*. In common with all acquired reactions, repression as a rule spreads selectively, in accordance with individual need.[52] Thus a boy who grows tense and anxious

[48] Landis, C. and Bolles, M., *Personality and sexuality of the physically handicapped woman*. New York: Hoeber, 1942, pp. 85–88.
[49] In the study of prejudice referred to earlier (page 348), widespread repression seemed to underlie a personality pattern of rigidity and inflexibility. Adorno, T. W., Frenkel-Brunswik, E., Levinson, D. J., and Sanford, R. N., *The authoritarian personality*. New York: Harper, 1950, p. 463. See also Frenkel-Brunswik, E., "Intolerance of ambiguity as an emotional and perceptual personality variable." *J. Personality*, 1949, vol. 18, pp. 123–126.
[50] The study on prejudice also indicates the existence of a relationship between repression and "distortion of outer reality." Adorno, T. W., Frenkel-Brunswik, E., Levinson, D. J., and Sanford, R. N., *The authoritarian personality*. New York: Harper, 1950, p. 457.
[51] See pages 387–392.   [52] See pages 69–75.

over his own aggression may deny his aggressive reactions, and succeed eventually in inhibiting them so effectively that they seem to be absent from his behavioral repertory. Throughout the course of his life, he may generalize this inhibition to a wide range of stimulation which is potentially aggression-provoking. If his expanding repression is reinforced, so that it develops to an extreme degree, he may become eventually unable to maintain or even to state his convictions in an argument. He may show himself ineffectual in casual games, discussion or social repartee where initiative is required. As an adult, such an individual cannot perform adequately in the innumerable situations where aggressive advance is expected of a man. The product of pervasive selectively generalized repression is then a behavioral organization which represents a distortion of the common cultural pattern of masculinity.

Over-generalization of repressive reactions underlies many forms of behavior pathology. We shall meet patients who have inhibited not only the recall of painful events, but also all reactions which are even remotely related to the events. A patient who develops anxiety over a transgression, for example, may inhibit the recall of his transgression, and also the recall of any clues to his own identity. Another patient, who develops tension over authority-relationships in his job, may inhibit both his own attitudes of resentment and the particular reactions upon which his job-efficiency depends. He may become as helpless to type, to hammer or to weld as he would be if he were suffering from a neuromuscular paralysis. In instances such as these, repression is over-complete; self-inhibition has generalized to include so many reactions that the patient is powerless to carry on his work.[53]

Repression is not always so widespread and complete as this; often a person can inhibit his own reactions only temporarily. During times of relaxation, fatigue or special stress, formerly repressed reactions may be reincluded in an individual's behavior organization. We see this phenomenon in the behavior of normal persons whose cerebral functioning has been impaired by alcohol or other toxic agents.[54] Obscene and profane remarks, which the person ordinarily inhibits, creep into his conversation; and he may express attitudes which under other circumstances he would not formulate even to himself. Repression has momentarily failed. It is *incomplete*, and its incompleteness allows for the return of otherwise inhibited reactions. Such incomplete repression leads to the behavior pathology we find in compulsive disorders and in hysterical autonomy.

Incomplete Repression

By now it should be clear that repression is to a considerable degree the product of self-reaction, and particularly of restrictive reactions which inhibit

---

[53] For a discussion of overcomplete repression, see pages 367–371.
[54] See pages 469–477.

or prevent the development of one's own tension-producing behavior. Self-restrictive reactions, as we shall see, are at once the instrument and the product of socialization.[55] Every child learns, through the sequences of *permitted-act-approval* and *forbidden-act-disapproval*, to conform to the expectations of his culture, as these are interpreted by his parents, his siblings and his peers. His language, his gestures, his attitudes, and much of his covert fantasy come to follow the pattern outlined by a child's acquired reactions of self-restraint. For whenever speaking, thinking or fantasying leave prescribed channels, and pursue forbidden routes, the tension and anxieties of anticipated punishment are likely to arise.[56] And against such tensions and anxieties, as we have seen, the self-inhibition we call repression is often an effective defense.

Throughout their history, human beings have sought to control the uncertainties of their environment, as well as their own behavior. When direct attempts have failed to deal effectively with flood, famine, disease and disaster, human beings have typically imposed rigidity, ritual and magic upon their own reactions, as if by self-restriction they could deflect the threats of an unpredictable natural environment. Thus, to ensure productivity, a village may sponsor an intricate and highly stylized ritualistic fertility dance. In time of plague or pestilence, a medicine-man's stereotyped reactions — traditional incantations, gestures and maneuvers — take the place of the direct attack upon microorganisms with which Western civilization is familiar. In these other cultures, wars must be won and fields made fertile, not alone by more deadly weapons and more efficient implements, but also by ritualistic self-restriction. The tension and anxiety of unpredictable, uncertain natural events are thus reduced by predictable, orderly reactions of self-restraint.[57]

The procedure of mastering, through reactions of self-restraint, the anxieties which result from an unstructured situation is not restricted to preliterate groups. We have only to look at the play behavior of children in our own society to find illustrations of the same thing. Small boys playing follow-the-leader, for example, willingly subject themselves to the pattern of order and ritual which the leader provides. The *right* foot must be placed on the step first, the *left* hand must touch every third lamp-post, and no hands may be used in vaulting the fence. The boy who deviates in any respect, however minor, from the prescribed routine is in danger of temporary exclusion from the group.[58]

---

[55] See pages 372–376 and 478–481.   [56] See pages 283–289.

[57] For illustrations of such use of rituals, see Erikson, E. H., *Childhood and society*. New York: Norton, 1950, pp. 98–160.

[58] For a description of "magic" in childhood solutions see Lewin, K., "Behavior and development as a function of the total situation." In Carmichael, L. (Ed.), *Manual of child psychology*. New York: Wiley, 1946, p. 822. For a description of the development of "rules" in childhood play, see Piaget, J., *The moral judgment of the child*. New York: Harcourt, Brace, 1932. For examples of ritualistic childhood play in the Sioux and the Yurok, see Erikson, E. H., *Childhood and society*. New York: Norton, 1950, pp. 125–129; 150–154.

The ritualistic character of childhood play often has direct implications as protection against disaster. "Step on a crack, break your mother's back," chants the little girl, as she cautiously avoids cracks in the sidewalk. At night, she wishes on the new moon, but only if she sees it first over her left shoulder and keeps herself from looking at it again. At noon, she wishes on a load of hay, after three times repeating breathlessly, "Hay, hay, give me good luck."

Adults in our society also employ ritual, rigid order and magical practice to organize unstructured situations and to control anxiety.[59] Legal proceedings are invalid unless set phrases are spoken by bailiff and clerk, oaths taken with prescribed gestures, and evidence introduced at proper times and in proper language. Social, religious, industrial and patriotic clubs all have their unique passwords, mottoes and emblems, their individual lines of organization, and their own orders of procedure. Even death has associated rituals. Funereal attire and the conduct of mourners are carefully specified in our culture, and the careless motorist who unwittingly interrupts a funeral procession may find himself in difficulties with the police.

In all these illustrations, a rigidly prescribed pattern of behavior structures an otherwise unorganized or anxiety-provoking situation. The excitants to anxiety may be thus repressed, or the sequence of increasing anxiety is interrupted. Thus a child who talks and thinks only in terms of socially approved themes can escape the tensions of anticipated parental punishment. Tribal members who perform the ritualistic fertility dance seem to themselves protected from the helpless anticipation of drouth, unproductivity and consequent starvation. Children who make wishes on the new moon substitute pleasant anticipation for the uncertainties of an unknowable future. Mourners who follow funeral rituals meticulously protect themselves from anxious fantasying on themes of death and what may follow death. Repression of anxiety is achieved through highly-organized reactions of self-restriction.

The intermittence of these ritualistic acts of self-restraint is in itself a sign that repression is incomplete. For if anxiety reactions toward punishment, starvation or death were completely repressed, then sporadic attempts at their magical control would be unnecessary. It is when the threat of punishment, starvation or death becomes imminent, and anxiety consequently grows intense, that these restrictive reactions occur. Such a relationship between increasing anxiety and intermittent self-inhibition becomes obvious when the individual is for any reason prevented from carrying out his characteristic pattern of self-restraint. Thus, a person's fantasy may leave the channels prescribed by his self-restrictive reactions and wander along taboo paths. Re-

[59] For an analysis of the use of superstition to control anxiety, and for a discussion of the relationship between superstition and prejudiced and rigid behavior, see Adorno, T. W., Frenkel-Brunswik, E., Levinson, D. J., and Sanford, R. N., *The authoritarian personality.* New York: Harper, 1950, pp. 464–465.

pression has temporarily failed. If, under these circumstances, conversation is in progress the individual sometimes reveals, in slips of speech, inappropriate gesturing, blushing or mild incoordination, the presence of his transient anxiety.[60] Or a child who inadvertently steps on a sidewalk crack, when his restrictive rules have made this a serious error, may grow increasingly tense and anxious until he has retraced his steps without a breach. In both these instances, anxiety mounts when there is failure to maintain a pattern of self-inhibition.

The intermittent control of anxiety, when repression is incomplete, seems to be a dominant theme in certain forms of behavior pathology. For some persons, repression provides only a precarious defense against insupportable anxiety. Their self-restraint, their orderliness, their ritualistic behavior are frequently interrupted; and interruption brings anxiety which yields only to further and more rigid restraint. Eventually, such persons may find themselves so restricted and controlled in their own behavior that they are ineffectual in social interaction and can only with the greatest difficulty carry on their daily affairs. This is the situation in the compulsive disorders, to which we now turn.

Compulsive disorders

The distinguishing characteristics of compulsive behavior are exaggerated and distorted reactions of self-control, which provide a rigid but not altogether successful defense against intolerable anxiety. The compulsive patient is one who, like all of us, has acquired the techniques of repression, but who cannot maintain indefinitely the repressive reactions which inhibit his developing anxiety. When repression fails and tension mounts, the compulsive patient resorts to self-restrictive behavior which superficially bears little relation to his anxiety excitants. He performs serial acts, repeats sequences of words or numbers, arranges objects in careful order, utilizes self-coercion, or follows out ritualistic and magical routines in gesture, talk and thinking. His behavior often resembles closely that of normal children and adults who are following the rules of organized play. But repetition, orderliness, ritual and magic are far from play for the compulsive patient. For if he fails to complete his serial acts, or to perform his rituals, he suffers a return of incompletely repressed anxiety reactions which may sometimes lead to panic or to behavioral disorganization.[61]

We may now characterize compulsive disorders as *disorders in which intermittent anxiety reactions lead to irrepressible tendencies to do, say, or think something in a particular way.* Typically, the patient is unable to identify the origins or the excitants of his rising anxiety and of his consequent tendency to perform compulsive acts. He attempts initially to resist and control his own com-

[60] Freud, S., *Psychopathology of everyday life.* New York: Macmillan, 1914.
[61] See pages 458–460.

pulsive behavior, but this attempt commonly brings only more intense anxiety. Compulsive patients state that they *must* perform their acts: if they are restrained from consummating their rituals and sequences they develop intolerable anxiety; if they indulge in their compulsive acts they obtain relief and gratification.

The techniques of self-restraint which characterize compulsive behavior are many and varied. Often they seem to have been learned by chance, and to have persisted because they were initially effective in reducing tension.[62] Sometimes the compulsive acts seem to bear a symbolic relationship to the patient's anxiety excitants.[63] Like all learned behavior, compulsive acts may generalize to new excitants, until a patient employs his rituals or sequences to handle any unfamiliar situation, whether anxiety-provoking or not. The compulsive reactions themselves need not be pleasing or even acceptable to the patient; indeed, a great many patients are annoyed, frightened, disgusted or shamed by their compulsive acts. The following case illustrates some of the features common to compulsive disorders.

The patient was a fifty-year-old married man, the successful manager and owner of a grocery store in a small town. He came to the clinic complaining of "drawing sensations" in the back of his neck, "nervousness," "mental tension" and sleeplessness. As the patient described his behavior, however, these general complaints soon led to a galaxy of specific compulsive reactions. Whenever he stepped over a rug, for example, he had to kick it. At mealtime he had always to leave two bites on his plate; and he did a great many things, as he put it, "by two's and four's." Slight noises interrupted his conversation or thinking, and made him "tingle all over." He developed severe itching over many areas of his body; and he continually scratched himself, until his public conduct became embarrassing to him and exposed him to ridicule. His constant scratching resulted in patchy, painful excoriations.

Along with these overt compulsive reactions went covert behavior which was equally repetitive and routinized. The patient might realize that he felt poorly, for example, and he would proceed in his thinking at once to trace his malaise back to its source. A careful review of the events of the previous hours usually led the patient to some irritation or obstacle — a street noise or a quarrel — to which he assigned the reason for his tension. The review, however, commonly brought him further tension, sweating, itching, and profuse perspiration. Whenever he realized that he felt particularly well, the same covert tracing back to some precipitating event followed, with the same eventual tension, itching, scratching and perspiring again. "I strain to keep feeling well," he explained, "and that starts it all over again."

[62] For a discussion of learning through tension-reduction, see pages 75–79.   Compare the interpretation of compulsive acts as fear-reducing, in Dollard, J. and Miller, N. E., *Personality and psychotherapy.* New York: McGraw-Hill, 1950, pp. 163–165.

[63] Compare the situation in the development of phobic behavior, as described on pages 312–314.

The patient attributed his troubles largely to "toxins from the bowels." For the past thirty years he had been concerned over his eliminative functions, and had spent considerable time and money on various treatments for constipation.[64] He set the beginning of his compulsive reactions at the age of twenty-two, when he began resenting his father's dictatorial ways. His symptoms, he stated, became markedly worse when he was thirty-five, at which time street improvements around his store brought him noise, dirt and added expense. His complaints of gastrointestinal illness, however, found no support in medical examinations. A study of the patient as a person indicated that his compulsive behavior represented a lifelong pattern of sporadic, but unsuccessful, control of intermittent anxiety reactions.

As far back as he could remember, this man had been strongly dependent on others, and severely anxious if their support were withdrawn. He slept with his parents until he was fifteen years old; and he suffered from nail-biting, enuresis and terrifying nightmares throughout his childhood. He described his father as a stern, dictatorial, nagging man — a vigorous crusader against drinking and smoking, who had attacks in which he was "dazed" and "out of his head." Toward his father the patient had developed strongly ambivalent attitudes, seeking his support and affection, but at the same time resenting his restrictions, his outbursts of rage, and his severe punishments. For the most part, however, he had inhibited the signs of his resentment; he rarely showed in overt behavior the hostility which characterized his covert and often unformulated attitudes. The patient described his mother as warm, fun-loving, pretty and young-looking even at seventy-three. Toward her he had developed affectionate but passively dependent attitudes.

It was against this background of chronic anxiety, repressed hostility and dependent need that the patient acquired his compulsive reactions. At twenty-two, in a conflict over his vocational plans, he began openly stating his resentment of his father's despotic control. His own hostility, no longer completely inhibited, brought him tension, sleeplessness and eventually the successions of compulsive self-control which led him to seek expert help. His symptoms were intensified and crystallized by frustrations in his business, and by the noisy and expensive street construction near his store when he was thirty-five. From an anxious, dependent child he had grown into a touchy, fastidious adult who still needed the unswerving support of others in his social environment.

It is not surprising, in view of his history, that the patient arrived late at heterosexual maturity, and evoked in his marital relationships the same support and protection he had sought from his parents. At forty-one he married a widow somewhat older than he. The patient's continued need for dependency was clear from his behavior when his wife was away from home. Like a child separated from his parents, he developed severe anxiety whenever he was left alone. He found himself looking repeatedly in closets, behind doors and under beds in the

[64] It should be noted that some behavior pathologists have explained the development of many compulsive disorders in terms of early conflicts over toilet training. See, for example, Freud, S., "Character and anal erotism" (1908). In *Collected Papers*, vol. 2. London: Hogarth Press, 1924, pp. 45–50.

empty house. Sometimes he was able to control his rising anxiety by his routines of kicking rugs and doing things by twos and fours. If these techniques failed, however, he became depressed; and he often reached the point of suicidal ruminations by the time his wife returned.

In the clinic, the patient at first reacted favorably to the somewhat routinized life provided for him. He could not be induced, however, to enter into a genuine therapeutic relationship with either of the two staff psychiatrists made available to him. He quickly became hypercritical of the clinic personnel, accusing them of indifference, inefficiency and indecision. During therapeutic sessions, he could not get beyond a repetitious vacillation over the self-imposed problem of whether to stay for treatment or whether to leave. Eventually, he left and returned to his grocery store without any fundamental change in his pathology.

A great many characteristics of compulsive disorders are to be found in this case. The patient, even as a child, suffered from chronic anxiety, which intermittently took the more acute form of enuresis or frightening nightmares.[65] His inability to live up to his father's impossibly high standards, and the consequent threat of paternal punishment which was always present, both supported and intensified his chronic anxiety. To his sharply increased anxiety he learned to react with compulsive techniques of self-restriction; but if he interrupted or omitted these techniques, his penalty was further anxiety and eventual depression.

This patient, we have seen, harbored reactions toward his stern and rigid father which were at once affectionate and hostile, dependent and resentful.[66] His father rebuffed his attempts to remain dependent; but at the same time he threatened and often administered severe punishment whenever his son's rebellion became overt. In this setting the patient, like any other frightened, anxious person, learned to repress the signs of his own hostility, until these became unrecognizable to him and ultimately inaccessible to his own self-reactions. His unacknowledged attitude of hostility still remained part of his total behavior organization, however, and still characterized some aspects of his overt behavior. For example, his recurring bouts of intense anxiety, and particularly his fear of being abandoned by his parents, were indirect statements of the guilt aroused by the hostility he dared not state directly.[67]

When, at twenty-two, the patient openly challenged his father's dictatorial and punitive control, his own hostility brought him an upsurge of the guilt and anxiety which he had previously handled in indirect ways. To this sharply increased anxiety the patient reacted with techniques of self-restriction which were strongly reminiscent of his father's means of controlling him. In doing things by twos and fours, he con-

[65] See page 288.

[66] A similar ambivalence was thought by Abraham to underlie the development of depressive disorders. See page 321. Some writers today emphasize a close relationship between compulsive and depressive disorders. See, for example, Stengel, E., "Some clinical observations on the psychodynamic relationship between depression and obsessive-compulsive symptoms." *J. ment. Sci.*, 1948, vol. 94, pp. 650–652.

[67] For a discussion of the relationship between separation anxiety and hostility, see pages 290–293.

structed a rigid numerical framework for his behavior, just as his father's exacting, inflexible rules had brought his son's life into an unwelcome regularity. The patient felt impelled to trace back his behavior step by step to some ultimate source, as if he were scrutinizing his past for sins which he could then confess and repent. In controlling his own anxieties, this compulsive patient adopted toward himself the role of his own father, in whose stern and punitive reactions he had an unforgettable model for self-restriction.

The adoption of a punitive, restrictive parental role toward their own behavior is not uncommon among compulsive patients. Some of them direct punishing statements toward themselves, either in thinking or talking. When, for example, anxiety-provoking themes appear in their fantasy, they say out loud — or think — "Stop it," "Forget it," or "Go away." By so doing, they are often able to check their growing tension. Other patients employ compulsive gestures which seem to derive from parental punishment; they slap their own wrists, restrain their own hands or hit their own heads when anxiety grows acute.

Many compulsive patients seem also to develop symptoms which closely resemble rituals of purification and absolution from guilt. The well-known hand-washing ritual is usually interpreted as a symbolic act of penance and absolution. Some patients control recurring anxiety by dieting or fasting, and others by persistent sex denial, as if by fasting and asceticism they could make amends for an unidentified transgression. Others feel impelled to relate certain events of their past lives to any casual listener, as if they were confessing sin.[68] In all these instances, the character and the conditions of the compulsive reaction indicate strongly that the recurring anxieties are related to guilt and anticipated punishment.

Although compulsive reactions typically bring the patient transient gratification and relief from immediate anxiety, most patients eventually find their symptoms annoying, humiliating and even painful. Our compulsive grocer, for example, considered his need to scratch himself in public embarrassing and ridiculous. At the same time he continued with the practice until he had developed an unsightly and painful dermatitis. Patients who acquire hand-washing rituals sometimes scrub their skin with stiff brushes and harsh soaps, until their hands are cracked and bleeding.[69] Those who employ compulsive utterances or ritualistic postures and gestures are always at the mercy of unsympathetic onlookers, who may see in such symptoms only the marks of grotesque comedy.

Compulsive reactions, we have said, develop as techniques of controlling intermittent anxiety reactions. They are the product of incomplete repres-

[68] For a discussion of "need to confess," see pages 288–289.
[69] For a discussion of the persistence of acts which appear to be unrewarding — the so-called "neurotic paradox" — see pages 75–79.

sion, and they provide only a temporary control of intolerable anxiety. The compulsive patient is typically an anxious patient, made tense both by recurring, unpredictable episodes of increased anxiety, and by the insistent and often embarrassing character of his own symptoms. His anxiety remains accessible to him, even if its excitants do not. In this regard, compulsive disorders differ from the reactions of *hysterical autonomy*, to which we next turn. For in hysterical autonomy, the intermittent anxiety reactions which evoke added techniques of repression are themselves effectively disguised by the hysterical symptom.

Hysterical autonomy

Like compulsive disorders, hysterical autonomy is a product of incomplete repression. It develops in chronically anxious persons, whose anxiety intermittently increases and escapes the bounds imposed by their inhibitory reactions. For the hysterical patient, however, such failures of repression bring consequences different from those found in compulsive patients. When repression fails and anxiety mounts, the hysterical patient does not react with further efforts at self-inhibition. On the contrary, he surrenders to the anxiety and to its hitherto repressed excitants. Consequently, his ongoing sequence of behavior is interrupted, not by attempts at self-restriction, but by episodic acts, which seem to represent indirectly a resurgence of his anxieties and their original excitants. It is characteristic of the episodic acts in hysterical autonomy that they often closely resemble the symptoms produced by well-known forms of organ or tissue pathology.

It is largely because of the often striking resemblance between hysterical and neurological symptoms that hysterical disorders occupy a prominent place in the history of behavior pathology. The ancients were familiar with hysterical symptomatology and made serious attempts to understand it. They concluded that hysterical disorders were the consequence of a wandering uterus, which produced disturbances in any part of the body it visited. Indeed, the term *hysteria* is derived from the Greek word *hystera*, which means uterus. This theory, of course, made hysteria an exclusively female disorder, and this suggested a rational therapy. Because the wandering uterus was feminine, it was believed to be particularly responsive to foul or fragrant odors. Consequently, the ancient physicians applied foul-smelling substances to the patient's nose, and fragrant oils to her genitals, so that the uterus might be lured back to the pelvis and the disorder thus cured.[70]

In modern times, a strong interest in hysterical phenomena developed toward the latter part of the nineteenth century. It culminated in a highly important controversy in France regarding the relationship between hypnosis and hysteria. On one side was the Parisian school, represented by Charcot,

[70] Whitwell, J., *Historical notes on psychiatry*. London: Lewis, 1936, pp. 76–77.

who argued that only potentially hysterical patients could be hypnotized. On the other side of the controversy was the Nancy school, represented by Bernheim and Liébault; these men, who had long experience with hypnosis as a therapeutic procedure, insisted that anyone could be hypnotized, whether potentially hysterical or not. The Paris-Nancy feud solved neither the problem of hysteria nor the problem of hypnosis. It did, however, focus the attention of European physicians upon the problem of the origins and characteristics of hysterical disorders; and among these it aroused the continuing interest of Janet and Freud.

It remained for Pierre Janet, who succeeded Charcot at Paris, to inject a new viewpoint into the problem of hysteria. Janet turned his attention from the bodily symptoms of hysteria to the "mental state" of hysterical patients, and recorded the first of his important observations in two books: *L'automatisme psychologique* (1889), and *L'état mentale des hystériques* (1893–94).[71] From his investigations, Janet concluded that the discontinuity or split in the ongoing behavior of hysterical patients was the consequence of *dissociation*. At about the same time, Sigmund Freud was studying both with Charcot (1885) and with Bernheim (1889). Freud's first papers, which give a foretaste of his later highly original contributions to behavior pathology, were devoted to the question of the origins, characteristics and treatment of hysteria.[72]

Our legacy from this nineteenth-century controversy, and from its many ramifications, is clear in our contemporary view of hysterical disorders. We recognize today the importance of suggestion in specifying and defining hysterical symptoms,[73] although we accept the Nancy dictum that almost anyone can be hypnotized. We follow the lead of Janet and Freud in considering hysteria a disorder of the total personality, rather than the product of localized neurological disease. And we seek the roots of hysterical reactions, not in organ or tissue pathology, but in unsatisfied need, and in unrelieved tension and anxiety.

Let us now define *hysterical autonomy* as *the occurrence, in response to need and anxiety, of a behavior fragment which is out of keeping with the person's ongoing sequence of behavior, and which superficially resembles the autonomy produced by neurological damage or disease.* The autonomous act which interrupts the hysterical patient's ongoing behavior may be a simple localized movement, as in the case of *tremor, cramp* or *tic.* The act may be longer and more widespread, so that serious discontinuity is introduced into the patient's behavior, as in the case of hysterical *seizure, somnambulism* or *fugue.* In rare instances,

[71] Janet, P., *L'automatisme psychologique, essai de psychologie mentale sur les formes inférieures de l'activité mentale.* Paris: Alcan, 1889; Janet, P., *L'état mentale des hystériques.* Paris: Reuff, 1893–94.

[72] For a further discussion of these contributions, see pages 568–574.

[73] There is some experimental evidence favoring a positive relationship between repression and suggestibility. See Petrie, A., "Repression and suggestibility as related to temperament." *J. Personality*, 1948, vol. 16, pp. 445–458.

the autonomous fragment may involve so much of the personality organization that the patient lives for a time a role quite different from the one which ordinarily characterizes him. This is the situation in *multiple personality*. Whether it is a localized tic or a complex personality pattern, however, the hysterical symptom is an autonomously functioning part of an otherwise repressed anxiety-provoking episode.

Like any other form of behavior pathology, hysterical autonomy can be derived from normal, everyday reactions. Some degree of autonomy, in fact, characterizes any well-practiced act from which irrelevant or unnecessary parts have been excluded.[74] An expert stenographer can transcribe her shorthand notes accurately in type, while at the same time she fantasies, hums a tune, listens for her employer's step, smiles at the office boy and kicks her shoes off under the desk. Some of the autonomous acts she can report; others she performs so automatically that they are inaccessible to her own recall. In the same way, a skilled carpenter can lay shingles expertly, while he maintains his balance on a steep roof, whistles a tune, nods to a passer-by and thinks about last night's poker game. Later he can tell how far he progressed with his job, and what his poker winnings were; but he is unlikely to recall the techniques through which he kept his balance, to be able to say whether or not anyone passed by, or to recall the tune that he was whistling. Both stenographer and carpenter perform fragmentary acts which are out of keeping with their dominant ongoing behavior; and both exclude from recall the context of certain of these acts, and even some of the acts themselves.

Were we to come to know our stenographer and our carpenter well, we might discover some connection between their fragmentary acts and their needs, frustrations or anxieties. The snatch of fantasy may have been set off by an unrecognized tension; the whistled tune may belong to a half-remembered dancing party; kicking off the shoes may represent kicking off restrictions more widespread and more inhibiting than those imposed by patent-leather; and listening for an employer's footstep may be part of a generalized reaction-sensitivity to signs of authority. For our present purpose, however, the significance of these acts lies in the fact that they are autonomous. They lie outside the contexts of typewriting and laying shingles; the attitudinal background which supports them [75] is kept excluded from the dominant ongoing sequence of behavior — the typewriting and the laying of the shingles.

It is this occurrence of apparently irrelevant acts, and the exclusion of their supporting background or context, which seem also to characterize hysterical autonomy. And as in the case of the stenographer or the carpenter, so in hysterical autonomy, the act itself may be a clue to the wider anxiety-provoking reaction of which it was once a part. Hysterical *tremor* and *cramp*, for

---

[74] For an account of exclusion in learning, see pages 74–75.
[75] For a discussion of attitude and response, see pages 64–65.

example, so often involve muscles which are essential to the patient's daily work that they are sometimes called "occupational tremor" and "occupational cramp." Thus a skilled mechanic may develop a hand tremor which prevents him from doing his job, or a writer may develop a contracture of the fingers of his hand which makes it impossible for him to write. In all such cases, investigation directed not toward the tremor or cramp, but toward the patient's total needs and aspirations, usually unearths general frustrations in vocational and personal areas which account for the development of the autonomous acts.[76]

The same connection between individual tension and the occurrence of an autonomous act is to be found in hysterical *tic* — an organized repetitive movement or sequence of movements developed in relation to need or anxiety. The varieties of hysterical tic are almost endless. They include sniffing, throat-clearing, smacking the lips, blinking, shrugging the shoulders, twisting the neck, jerking the torso, and countless other acts. Ordinarily, the hysterical tic is the remnant of a former adjustment to tension. One young man, for example, who was concerned over his own hostile reactions to others, succeeded in repressing his hostility, but developed a tic in which he periodically shrugged his shoulders, as if to shrug off his unwelcome aggressive impulses. A would-be artist, who was forced to become a house-painter in order to earn his living, developed a tic in which he repeatedly flexed his fingers and inspected his fingernails, as if to assure himself that his hands were ready for more fastidious work than skilled labor.[77]

In hysterical *tremor*, *cramp*, and *tic*, the patient maintains an effective relationship with his environment while he is performing his autonomous act. The symptom briefly interrupts the pattern of ongoing behavior; but the patient can communicate with others while the symptom occurs, and he can recall his behavior when the symptom has subsided. In this respect, hysterical tremor, cramp and tic differ from hysterical seizures, somnambulism, and fugue, and from certain forms of multiple personality. For in the latter group of hysterical disorders, the autonomous act produces a decided break in the continuity of behavior. The patient loses contact with his environment while the symptom is occurring; and he typically shows amnesia for his autonomous episode afterward. The following case illustrates hysterical autonomy which disrupts the patient's previous relationship to the environment.

    The patient was a quiet, placid, smiling young woman of twenty-one, who came to the clinic accompanied by her twenty-five-year-old husband.

[76] See, for example, Smith, M., Culpin, M., and Farmer, E., "A study of telegraphists' cramp." *Indust. Fatigue Res. Board*, 1927, no. 43.

[77] Krout, M., "Autistic gestures: an experimental study in symbolic movement." *Psychol. Monogr.*, 1935, vol. 46, no. 208; Krout, M., "The social and psychological significance of gestures (a differential analysis)." *J. genet. Psychol.*, 1935, vol. 47, pp. 385–412; Krout, M., "Further studies on the relation of personality and gesture: a nosological analysis of autistic gestures." *J. exper. Psychol.*, 1937, vol. 20, pp. 279–287.

She explained that she had "crazy spells." "I get stiff and draw up," she said. "I don't know what happens in the spell except what they tell me. I remember what happens before it, and when I come out." The admitting physician noted that the patient seemed little concerned over her symptoms, and smiled contentedly as she described them. To her description, the patient's husband added the facts that the "spells" began with rapid breathing, after which the patient's body seemed stiff, and the wrists, fingers and ankles were flexed. She was unresponsive during the convulsions and for as long as three or four hours afterward. The attacks had begun one year before, and had increased in frequency until at the time of admission they occurred almost daily. A number of physicians had suspected a convulsive neurological disorder, but after repeated neurological examinations revealed no tissue pathology, the patient was referred to the psychiatric service and admitted at once to the clinic for study.

It soon became apparent that the patient's convulsive attacks occurred typically in a setting of emotional stress. Her first seizure, for example, followed a quarrel with her mother-in-law; and her second climaxed a week of argument with her brother-in-law. As domestic discord persisted, the convulsions appeared more and more frequently until they occurred daily. The patient attributed her attacks to "nerves" and to physical exertion. When she exercised and became breathless, she said, she was likely to have a seizure. In the clinic, however, forced hyperventilation failed to produce a convulsion; but a hostile letter which the patient received from her mother-in-law was followed at once by a typical attack. The patient made no response to pinches or pin-pricks during the seizure, but within three minutes after it had ceased she was alert and ready for dinner.

The patient was the eldest of three children, the daughter of an excitable, hypochondriacal mother and a driving, ambitious father. Largely because of her father's protection and indulgence, she had had a pleasant childhood; and in her early years she developed no unusual traits. She did suffer from recurrent attacks of pyelitis and appendicitis; during one of these, according to her story, her left leg became contracted and for some months seemed shorter than the right. This symptom disappeared suddenly one day when she rubbed her left ear and felt a "tingling sensation" throughout her entire body. In early adolescence, however, two events occurred which presented serious problems. She was forced to drop out of school because of repeated failure in her course work. At the same time, she received her first sex information from a nurse, who lectured to her and showed pictures to her from an obstetrical textbook.

To her school failure the patient reacted with shame, embarrassment and depression. She attempted to complete a secretarial course, but she failed that also. She then held two jobs, one as receptionist in a doctor's office, and the other as clerk in a novelty store; but she gave up each after a few weeks, and at length returned home and occupied herself with household chores. To her sex information the patient reacted with partial disbelief. She was disgusted and repelled at the thought of intercourse, and considered it sinful "even for married folks." She reached her early adulthood a simple, timid young woman, undemonstrative and excessively prudish in her attitude toward the opposite sex. Her principal interest lay in church activities, but even here she selected from the church doctrines those which she could interpret as supporting her conviction that sex was sinful, and dwelt upon them.

At twenty the patient married — because, she said, "it was the thing to do." Her husband was a passionate, demonstrative man whose demands upon his wife frightened and repelled her. His job as travelling salesman took him away from home for long periods of time, during which the patient lived with her husband's mother. The mother-in-law, according to the patient, was a careless, unsociable woman who complained continually about the patient's "running around" when her husband was away. The patient, for her part, complained about the mother-in-law, stating that the mother-in-law was jealous of her, and that she treated the patient's husband as if he were still a child. For eighteen months prior to her clinic admission, the patient had lived in an atmosphere of quarrelling and bickering. Her husband's occasional visits gave her some support and protection, but at the same time they entailed sexual demands which brought in her a resurgence of disgust and anxiety. It was in this setting that the patient developed her hysterical seizures.

In the clinic the patient made little progress. To be sure, her seizures declined in frequency and eventually disappeared, but the rigidity and immaturity which characterized her personality organization remained. She entered into a few social activities with the other patients, but in general she remained aloof and diffident. She gradually reformulated her own illness as no longer due to "nerves" but rather to the treatment she received at the hands of her mother-in-law. At length the financial strain of clinic care became too great, and the patient's husband removed her from treatment. She left with little insight beyond that indicated by the couple's decision to live with the patient's own parents rather than with her mother-in-law.

Some of the characteristics of this patient's symptoms are typical also of hysterical fugue, somnambulism and multiple personality. Her seizures introduced a sharp break in the continuity of her reactions. The convulsions seriously disrupted not only her ongoing sequence of behavior, but also her contact with her environment; for she was unresponsive to environmental stimulation during a convulsive attack, and she could not remember the attack when it was over. It is of importance to note that the seizure resembled so closely the convulsions of neurological disease or damage that the patient had been repeatedly diagnosed as epileptic. Only their occurrence in response to frustration, her failure to develop motor phenomena under conditions of hyperventilation, and the ineffectuality of medication, gave to her attacks the status of adjustive reactions in the total biosocial organism.

This patient's personality organization also is typical of that of a great many persons who develop hysterical autonomy. She was a simple, impressionable young woman who could accept easily events which a more complexly organized person would question. Thus she "cured" her contracture by rubbing her ear; and she uncritically identified her

mother-in-law's behavior as the "reason" for her attacks. Her childhood she had spent in a close, dependent relationship with a complaining,
hypochondriacal mother, and under the protection of an overindulgent
father. She herself gave a history of repeated, severe illnesses. Such
events as these are to be found over and over in the background of
persons who develop hysterical autonomy. Even this patient's attitude
of placid unconcern toward her symptoms is typical. Indeed, this
last-named characteristic of hysterical patients so impressed Janet that
he called it *la belle indifference.*

The evidence for incomplete repression is clear in this case. The
patient responded initially to the sex information she received in early
adolescence by denying it with repugnance. This denial she reinforced
by selectively reacting to her church doctrines in such a way that they
supported her fears and aversions.[78] Her well-practiced repression
remained successful until her marriage — an event which from her own
description meant to her only the routine acceptance of convention.
In her mother-in-law's home, however, she was continually and re-
proachfully reminded of her wifely obligations; and her husband's
demands upon her were insistent reminders of the anxieties she had repressed. When domestic discord or marital demands increased, her
repression failed. The consequence of this failure was the break in
behavioral continuity represented by her hysterical autonomous seizure,
in which a parallel may be detected between her convulsive episodes
and her sexual fantasies. The temporary failure of repression brought
the return of a complete episode of behavior which, for this patient,
was intensely anxiety-provoking.

Less stereotyped and in many ways more complex than hysterical seizure is
hysterical somnambulism. Like a normal sleep-walker, an hysterically somnambulistic patient performs coordinated biosocial acts in sleep or in sleep-
like states. His behavior may begin with a vivid night-dream, in which he
turns and tosses, gestures, and utters words appropriate to the dream rather
than to the shared social environment. From this beginning, the patient may
go on to act out in greater detail the content of his dream, including real objects and real persons in his reactions. Or the somnambulistic episode may
begin with a vivid daytime fantasy, which comes to dominate the patient's
overt behavior as well as his covert thinking. When somnambulism is diurnal,
it represents a definite break in the continuity of a patient's ongoing reaction
pattern, and typically there is amnesia for the episode after it is over.

If during a somnambulistic episode the patient actually flees from his
accustomed environment, we call his symptom *hysterical fugue.* Like somnambulism, fugue involves a complex organization of reactions in which the
continuity of a patient's ongoing behavior is interrupted. Amnesia is also
characteristic of fugue. During the fugue episode the patient is amnesic for
a large part of his everyday behavior; and after the fugue ends he can usually

[78] For a discussion of selectivity in learning, see pages 69–75.

recall little or nothing that went on while it lasted. What distinguishes fugue from other forms of hysterical autonomy is the fact that fugue represents a translation into overt behavior of hitherto repressed tendencies toward flight. The patient acts out literally the common urge to "get away from it all."

> Some of the characteristics of both hysterical somnambulism and hysterical fugue are to be found in the behavior of a successful young business-man, whose promotion to a managerial position only intensified his insistent need for money and power. He began using money from the till in his store for gambling purposes in an attempt to increase his earnings. During a period when his losses were high, the firm's books were audited, the discrepancy was discovered, and the young man was ordered to stand trial. On the following day, he disappeared from his home town, and was picked up a few days later by the police in a large city 500 miles away. He was unable to identify himself, and he could not recall his legal predicament or any of the events leading up to it. In a hospital in his home town, to which he was returned, he gradually recovered his former self-reactions; but he then immediately developed seizures of such severity that a diagnosis of neurological disease was made. The seizures proved to be episodes of hysterical autonomy. His autonomous behavior disappeared only when his employer, recognizing that the man was ill, withdrew his complaints, and arranged to accept gradual repayment of the embezzled funds from the patient.

In this example the patient, in a hospital setting, recalled the crucial self-reactions which helped him to identify himself and eventually to recover from his illness. Occasionally, an hysterical patient who has fled to a new environment develops a new system of self-reactions, assumes a new name and develops a new vocation and new leisure-time pursuits, without recalling his old system. He thus organizes a new pattern of role-taking behavior alongside his customary one; and he may even alternate between these two personality organizations. To this form of hysterical autonomy we give the name *multiple personality*. The popular and literary appeal of this form of hysteria has served to exaggerate its commonness. Actually, multiple personality is a rather rare disorder; there are probably not more than 150 acceptable cases which have been reported in the history of behavior pathology.[79]

There are two major types of multiple personality: *alternating personality* and *double personality*. In *alternating personality*, two or more organized systems become dominant, one at a time, in the patient's behavior. When one system is dominant, the patient is amnesic for activities and occurrences in his other personality systems. In *double personality*, there is one dominant personality organization, and one or more subordinate systems. Here the dominant organization is amnesic for the subordinate systems; but when the patient is involved in a subordinate system he can recall activities and occur-

[79] Taylor, W., and Martin, M., "Multiple personality." *J. abn. soc. Psychol.*, 1944, vol. **39**, pp. 281–300.

rences characteristic of his dominant personality organization. It is significant that, in double personality, the reactions which make up the subordinate system include criticisms, comments, advice and support directed toward the dominant system, as if this were a separate individual. The situation is thus similar to that found in the punitive, controlling self-reactions of compulsive patients; [80] and it has similar roots in repression which is incomplete. In double personality, however, as in all hysterical disorders, there is a relative lack of the severe anxiety which typifies compulsive disorders.

By now it should be clear that hysterical autonomy is a development in response to anxiety which is incompletely repressed. Like the intermittent anxiety which evokes it, hysterical autonomy is episodic in character. It may be a brief behavioral episode, as in tremor, cramp and tic; or it may be a protracted episode, as in seizure, somnambulism, fugue or multiple personality. What distinguishes hysterical autonomy, however, is the temporal discontinuity in ongoing behavior which it produces. In this characteristic, hysterical autonomy differs markedly from hysterical inactivation, to which we next turn.

Overcomplete Repression

Repression, we have said, is an important instrument of behavior organization in normal persons.[81] To render a tension-provoking act inaccessible to one's own self-reactions is to guard oneself from the consequences of severe and protracted anxiety. But repression is a learned adjustive technique, and in common with all learned behavior it acquires new excitants and generalizes to new situations. In some cases, this generalization of repression reaches an extreme, so that certain activities essential to biosocial effectiveness are absent from the person's repertory of behavior. Individuals who thus overgeneralize their repressive reactions are in danger of becoming one-sided, distorted persons who are insensitive to certain forms of stimulation and gravely inept in relation to certain varieties of response. This is the situation in *overcomplete repression*.

The beginnings of overcomplete repression are to be found in many everyday instances of generalized inhibition, of which the following incident is only one example.

A young man who had recently become engaged was walking along the street with his fiancée. Another man greeted him and began to chat in a friendly fashion. The young man realized that he must know this apparent stranger, and that both courtesy and pride required that he introduce the visitor to his fiancée. The name of the other man, however, eluded him completely; indeed, he had not even a fleeting recognition of his identity. When in his confusion he attempted at least to present his fiancée, he found that he had also forgotten her name.

[80] See pages 354–359.　　　　　[81] See pages 337–351.

Only a brief behavior analysis was necessary to make this incident comprehensible as an example of normal generalized repression. The apparent stranger was in fact a former friend of the young man; but the friendship had eventually brought frustration and disappointment in a situation identical with the one described. Some years before, our subject had become engaged to another young woman, and in his pride and happiness he had at once sought out this friend and introduced the two. Unfortunately the girl had become strongly attached to the friend and he to her; at length she broke her engagement and married the friend. The two men had not seen each other until this meeting, which repeated exactly the earlier frustrating situation. It is hardly surprising that the newly engaged man repressed all recognition of his former friend, all hints as to his identity, and even the name of the fiancée.

This incident, of course, involved only a temporary repression of familiar attitudes and responses. A single reminder of the friend's identity was sufficient to evoke recall of the original frustrating event, and of the fiancée's name as well. At the same time, even so transient an incident illustrates a great many characteristics of overcomplete repression. It is at once obvious that the young man's failure to recall familiar events and names is an example of *overexclusion* in behavior organization.[82] The newly engaged man excludes from his reactions those which might precipitate a repetition of the earlier traumatic episode. But this is exclusion carried to such extremes that the man is for the moment socially inept, unable to carry out the acts of greeting and introducing which the situation demands. Overexclusion thus involves a *selective reaction-insensitivity;*[83] the young man is unreactive to stimulation which under different circumstances would call out the socially appropriate responses. As in all learned behavior, this man's repressive behavior generalizes in accordance with his own individual need.[84] We call his repression *overgeneralized* and *overcomplete*, however, because it impoverishes and distorts his biosocial behavior in relation to culturally accepted and appropriate patterns.

In some cases, the consequences of overcomplete repression are more widespread and more protracted than this. Instead of a few brief responses, an entire function may be repressed, and the patient may become unable to walk, to see,[85] to hear or to use his hands. Instead of a circumscribed event, an entire pattern of personality organization may be repressed, so that the patient is helpless even to take the attitudes which might lead him to play a certain role. The patient is then literally disabled, the victim of his own extensive repression. When repression reaches this extreme, so that the patient is gravely incompetent in his biosocial behavior, we speak of *hysterical inactivation*.

---

[82] See pages 74–75.   [83] See pages 70–74.   [84] See pages 69–75.
[85] A case of hysterical inactivation involving seeing is described on page 67.

Hysterical inactivation

We define *hysterical inactivation* as a *persistent selective reaction-insensitivity, developed in relation to need or anxiety, which involves a loss of activity superficially resembling the loss which results from organ or tissue pathology.* Like hysterical autonomy, hysterical inactivation always involves the diagnostic problem of differentiating between the product of neurological disease or injury and the product of learned adjustment to need and anxiety. Indeed, a great many symptoms of hysterical inactivation are initially mistaken for signs of tissue or organ pathology. Because hysterical inactivation, like hysterical autonomy, is a disorder of a total biosocial organism, its symptoms follow the patterns outlined by personal need and tension, rather than those dictated by neuromuscular pathology.[86] And for the same reason, the symptoms of hysterical inactivation are resistant to treatment aimed at nerve or muscle function, but susceptible to therapy directed toward the patient's conflicts.

In hysterical inactivation there is an almost endless variety of specific symptoms. We may mention, by way of illustration, *hysterical aphonia*, in which the patient is unable to speak; *hysterical anorexia*, the inability to eat or to retain food; *hysterical paralyses and anaesthesias*, in which the patient is unable to move or to respond to tactile and vibratory stimulation; *hysterical amblyopia and amaurosis*, the partial or total inability to respond to visual stimulation; and *hysterical amnesia*, the selective inability to recall. In hysterical inactivation, these symptoms are always the product of repressive techniques which have generalized beyond the original excitants to such widespread functions that the patient is disabled. The consequences of overcomplete repression are clearly represented in the following case of hysterical inactivation.

A twenty-four-year-old woman came to the clinic accompanied by her husband. The patient calmly assured the admitting physician that she "felt fine," [87] except for the fact that she had lost the use of her right hand and arm. Her husband, in contrast, was greatly concerned over his wife's incapacity. He explained that the disability had resulted in his wife's first giving up her job, and then in her finding it impossible to keep up with the housework at home. This clinic was the fifth which the couple had visited in order to find a "cure" for the wife's symptoms. Each visit brought assurances that no organ or tissue pathology was present to account for the paralysis; but every suggestion of extended psychiatric therapy was at once rejected by the wife.

Although the patient again insisted that it was useless for her to undergo therapy, she was persuaded to remain in the clinic long enough

[86] For a discussion of the development of hysterical symptoms through fear-reduction, see Dollard, J., and Miller, N. E., *Personality and psychotherapy.* New York: McGraw-Hill, 1950, pp. 165–170. For a discussion of hysterical symptoms in terms of Pavlovian conditioning, see McGill, V. J., and Welch, L., "Hysteria as a conditioning process." *Amer. J. Psychother.*, 1947, vol. 1, pp. 253–278.

[87] Compare Janet's *la belle indifference.*

to give a fairly complete history. From her story it was clear that the paralysis was a symptom of hysterical inactivation, developed in relation to the patient's need for support and dependence which could not be satisfied in her marriage. As in many cases of hysterical inactivation, this patient's particular symptom, as we shall see, seemed to have been dictated by a severe and painful injury which for some months had prevented her from working. The spread and persistence of the symptom after the actual injury had healed, however, was the consequence of overgeneralized repression in response to personal need.

The patient was the youngest of four children and the only girl. She was considered to be so sickly as an infant that she had to be fed on barley water because, as she put it, she was "too weak to take milk." She contracted a great many childhood diseases, and in each case her convalescence was protracted. Her susceptibility to disease was a source of great concern to her parents. Her father was a kindly, affectionate but overprotective parent who hoped to guard his only daughter from every possible harm. Partly because of her lengthy periods of convalescence, the patient progressed slowly through school. At fourteen she stopped school altogether and remained at home with her parents. This decision was made largely because of the patient's reaction to a severe sore throat from which she was suffering at this time. She gradually lost her voice until, she said, "I had to holler to whisper." For some weeks thereafter she was aphonic, and then the voice came back — "more suddenly than it went away," she explained.

At twenty-one, the patient married a young factory worker, against her family's wishes. The husband's modest earnings, and the birth of a child, led the patient to decide to go to work in order to supplement the family income. This necessity only reinforced the parents' conviction that the husband was not a suitable mate for their daughter. Again in opposition to her parents' wishes, and in the face of their continual criticism, the patient obtained her first job — working in a cannery. Here she met with a series of accidents. First a fellow-worker accidentally dropped a heavy box on the patient's right hand, breaking one of her fingers. When the break had healed, but while she was still trying to spare the finger, the patient slipped in handling a cutting tool and gashed the little finger of her right hand so badly that it required amputation. This accident was both painful and frightening. The patient fainted repeatedly during the treatment of the finger, and during her convalescence at home she remained weak and sick. On several occasions she became so weak while walking from bedroom to bathroom that she fell; and each time she was unable to use her legs for some minutes.

Although the recovery from the hand injuries was surgically uneventful, the patient continued to be listless and apathetic. To her husband's suggestion that she get another job she answered that her arm was too weak to use. Gradually she lost interest even in her household duties, and at length became helpless to perform them. The weakness in her right arm and hand became more and more severe, until finally the arm dangled at her side. Occasionally the progressive nature of her symptom seemed to worry the patient; and she sometimes said that she might die because of it. However, she seemed neither frightened nor depressed by this possibility.

At the insistent urging of her husband, the patient followed the recommendation of the admitting physician that she be hospitalized for further study. On the ward she was cheerful and unconcerned; she described the hospital environment as "heaven." Attempts to encourage her to discuss her attitudes toward her parents, her husband or her child failed, however, and after a few days she became restless and irritable. When her parents added their hostile pressure to the patient's pleas that she be taken home, her husband finally acceded. The patient returned home unimproved, against the advice of the hospital staff.

The relationship between personal need, overcomplete repression and hysterical inactivation is not difficult to see in this case. The patient was an immature, dependent woman, unprepared either to oppose effectively her overprotective parents, or to take on the rather heavy responsibilities which her marriage brought her. By the time she was seen in the clinic, she had rejected completely the demanding role of economic helpmate to her husband; and her rejection included sweeping repression of the neuromuscular responses upon which this marital role depended. She could not even discuss, with her husband or her physician, the possibility of some time returning to work. She was as helpless to assume the attitudes preparatory to using her right arm in working as if the entire arm, and not just the finger, had been amputated.

This patient's special susceptibility to the development of hysterical inactivation grew partly out of her own repeated illness and prolonged convalescence. Illness early in her life had brought her special affection and protection at home. At fourteen, she reacted to slow school progress with hysterical inactivation, developing hysterical aphonia following a sore throat. Her weakness and transitory inability to use her legs, after the cannery accident, were additional evidence of her ease in developing hysterical inactivation. When her recovery from the amputation seemed to threaten a return to the unwelcome role of economic provider, she came to exclude completely from her behavior the reactions which defined that role. A great many symptoms of hysterical inactivation seem to begin with a particular illness or injury; but the spread and persistence of the symptoms are determined, as in this case, by the patient's personal need.

The overcomplete repression which characterizes hysterical inactivation handles an intolerable conflict by disabling the person. The patient solves his problem by rendering some essential part of his reactive system inoperative so that he no longer responds in such a way as to arouse anxiety. There are other techniques of denial and distortion in common use which lead likewise to the pathological solution of intolerable conflict and the mastery of anxiety. These are the techniques of compensation, rationalization and projection by means of which normal persons in everyday life so modify their behavior and its interpretation that they protect themselves from fruitless conflict and needless anxiety. But the exaggerated utilization of these behavioral instruments leads to the distortion and impoverishment characteristic of delusional conviction, the pseudocommunity and paranoid disorders. To a consideration of these important manifestations of behavior pathology we shall now turn.

$\mathbb{P}$ *seudocommunity and Delusion*

When we speak of a *community*, we ordinarily mean a group of individuals who share a system of activities in common. What they share is indicated by the kind of community we say it is. Thus, a village is an organization of persons who participate in the essential activities of a semirural population which typically occupies a closely grouped aggregate of buildings. But it is the human population with its relational activities, and not the buildings, that makes it a village. For, obviously, if the inhabitants were dispossessed and moved out to live *en masse* in the open, they could still remain a community, whereas the buildings and goods they left behind them would not.

The individuals constituting a community may or may not live in close contact; the important characteristic is that they share a system of activities. There are religious groups in the United States, for example, which are tightly organized along communal lines and occupy a restricted geographical area. But there are other communities of the faithful which, like Augustine's *civitas Dei*, are composed of individuals who may be widely separated from one another in space. Likewise, we have communities of scholars and scientists — whose common behavioral possession is a systematized body of instrumental and conceptual techniques — which does not necessarily coincide with political units or religious universals.

The individual's behavioral communities

Every human being gains membership in a community through acquiring role behavior that is characteristic of the community. The acquisition of social role-taking, as we have already described it,[1] begins with the direct, primary group relationships within the family. Here the infant's first roles are organized and differentiated in response to the culturally determined behavior

[1] See pages 114–122 and 134–143.

of his parents, and of the other persons in his immediate surroundings. His overt behavior is thus a function of a dynamic field of social interrelationships, in which the child is immersed from the moment of his birth. He learns not only to do certain things, and not to do others of which he is equally capable, but also to anticipate and allow for the interbehavior of the individuals who share his field of social operations.[2]

Looked at from the standpoint of the individual prelanguage child, the social community is constituted by the behavior of all the individuals, animals and objects with which he comes into functional contact. As the child develops self-reactions, and can behave toward himself as to a social object, his own behavior also becomes a component of his social community. And, with the development of communicative speech, he learns to take social roles verbally, and so to anticipate and allow for the interbehavior of others and himself symbolically, as well as directly. Eventually, as we have seen, the child is able to talk about what he does and what others do, about behavior he anticipates and behavior that is past, about the characteristics of other people and of himself.

When communicative speech is muted, this verbal representation of his own and others' social operations and social interrelationships is silenced with it — but, of course, not destroyed.[3] Indeed, a child is apt to find greater freedom in his silent, imagined accounts than in his spoken ones. The unspoken word and the unshared thought need not respect the wishes and opinions of one's companions. Self-communication and private fantasy are not subject to review and criticism by others; they need not agree with the consensus. Therefore, in private symbolization one can without fear of correction become highly individualistic. They need not even correspond to anything occurring in the shared field of social operations; therefore, in private symbolization one can structure fantasy so uniquely as to render unshared thinking highly deviant.[4]

In the present chapter, and in the succeeding one, we shall turn our attention to behavior pathology that arises primarily as an outgrowth of individualistic, unique and deviant symbolization. For convenience of exposition, we shall begin by distinguishing three kinds of behavioral community, each regarded from the standpoint of the organization of the individual. The first of these is the one we have already introduced, the *social community*. This corresponds to the interbehavior of others and oneself in the shared field of social operations. It includes also those of one's private, unshared reactions which are capable of validation in terms of the consensus. The second behavioral organization we shall call the *pseudocommunity*.[5] This organization contra-

---

[2] Compare the discussion on pages 1–3, 340-341 and 343–345.

[3] Compare the discussion of repression on pages 337–351.

[4] For a discussion of fantasy, see pages 414–426.

[5] Cameron, N., "The development of paranoic thinking." *Psychol. Rev.*, 1943, vol. 50, pp. 219–233; Cameron, N., "The paranoid pseudocommunity." *Amer. J. Sociol.*, 1943,

dicts the consensus; but it utilizes, at least in part, interbehavior which other social persons can share. The third form we call the *autistic community*.[6] This is a behavioral organization which is structured wholly in terms of the imagined activities of imagined persons in a fantasied context.

Incompleteness of the social community

Action must necessarily outdistance information. For when information about any action is complete, the action has already been finished. Thus the normal person in his everyday life continually supplements fact with inference,[7] the present with the anticipated and the past, the visible or audible part of something with its invisible or inaudible remainder. We see a crowd around two automobiles and infer a crash. We hear the doorbell ring and rush to greet guests whom we have earlier invited. We recognize a woman, whose back is turned, by her clothes and her stance; or we catch part of a sentence, and react as though we had heard all of it.

Such supplementation of the fragmentary and unfinished is made possible, of course, by the fact that each of us has already operated in many thousand similar situations. Over the years, we have acquired reasonably valid techniques of inference, of tying up the present with anticipation and with the past, of seeing and hearing parts repeatedly in relation to familiar wholes. We have, in short, learned to become adept at reacting adequately on the basis of minimal data.

Adeptness is not perfection. The mere fact that we learn to react adequately in dynamic, developing fields of stimulation is no insurance against possible error. A crowd gathering around two automobiles may be witnessing the arrest of the occupants of one, by police from the other. There may be a postman at the door instead of the expected guests; the woman may turn around and we discover that she is an utter stranger; and the balance of a half-heard sentence may be quite different from that which we supplied in our own thinking. Under these circumstances, the measure of behavioral adequacy then becomes one of the ease and speed with which we are able to correct our supplementation, so that it agrees with the situation as we now find it. And the ultimate test of adequacy is that of conformity of our behavioral interpretation with that of the consensus.

We have said that the social community corresponds to the interbehavior of others and oneself in the shared field of social operations, and that it includes also one's own private, unshared reactions which are potentially capable of validation in terms of the consensus. This behavioral community each of

---

vol. 49, pp. 32–38; Cameron, N., "Role concepts in behavior pathology." *Amer. J. Sociol.*, 1950, vol. 55, pp. 450–463.

[6] The autistic community is discussed in the following chapter, pages 414–426.

[7] See the discussion of *closure*, pages 75–79.

us constructs in his own activities, in the interbehavior with other persons and the products of such interbehavior in his private reactions, his symbolization in self-reaction, in recall of fantasy. It is obvious that such a dynamic system will likewise always be incomplete. For we must be continually responding to what others do before they have finished doing it.[8] Cooperative and competitive behavior shows the same characteristic. Football teams, for example, must be composed of individuals who can act rapidly and effectively upon the basis of minimal, incomplete data. Each must be able to shift from defense to offense, and back to defense again, from taking the role and having the perspectives of his teammates, to taking the role and having the perspectives of his opponents. Indeed, even spectator behavior, to be adequate, must include alert reaction, role-taking and shifting perspective, on the basis of incomplete patterns of stimulation.

In the more complex interpersonal relations of everyday life we meet the same fundamental problem in other forms. We are constantly responding to ongoing behavior, to behavior whose outcome we can predict, as we respond, only in terms of the direction it seems to be taking. A man moves his hand toward us. The movement may be the beginning of a handshake, a clutch or a blow; it may be preliminary to his giving us some object or to his defending himself; it may have reference to something beside or beyond us and only approach us incidentally. If the context is relatively unstructured or ambiguous, we will tend to respond within the framework of these possibilities in terms of our own needs, expectations or fears. Thus the ongoing act, the fragmentary, incomplete beginning of a movement, can perform the function of a projective stimulation.[9]

In social role-taking it is the same. We must be able to live any one of our own social roles, and at the same time play the roles of other persons in anticipating their next moves, in reciprocating with their ongoing behavior, and in understanding it after it has been completed. These are the actual conditions of everyday interpersonal relationships. They make it clear that *absolute certainty remains a fiction*, that one must always act without being completely sure.

Many of the gaps in the dynamic patterns of social stimulation are filled in by imaginal supplementation, at the time or retrospectively. Many gaps are not filled in, because there is no time or no need, or because our imaginal resources are inadequate. And, as we shall see later,[10] the supplementations —

---

[8] For a discussion of anticipant attitudes, see pages 65–66.

[9] For a discussion of projective stimulation as employed in a test situation, see Bell, J. E., *Projective techniques: a dynamic approach to the study of personality*. New York: Longmans, 1948; Sargent, H., "Projective methods," in Pennington, L. A. and Berg, I. A. (Eds.), *An introduction to clinical psychology*. New York: Ronald, 1948, pp. 416–439; Sargent, H., "Projective methods: their origins, theory and application in personality research." *Psychol. Bull.*, 1945, vol. 42, pp. 257–293.

[10] See pages 376–392.

by means of which we make our fragmentary situations seem to us more complete and unified — are as a rule themselves not validated.

All human beings show almost irresistible tendencies to complete incomplete patterns, to finish a series that has been started, to round out objects and statements, to balance masses and arguments, to weave an intricate story around the husk of a meaningless incident.[11] If time, need and the imaginal resources are sufficient, people try to account for the unexplained to others, but above all to themselves. They put the cloak of their imagination over the bare body of a fact. They embrace isolated elements, from recall, anticipation, or the immediately stimulating present, within coherent wholes that are held together by their own thinking, and by the need which their thinking satisfies.[12]

In following such tendencies toward completion and elaboration, human beings develop certain well recognized behavioral techniques. From among these we may single out, for special consideration at this point, three techniques which play a highly significant part in the genesis of delusion and hallucination, of pseudocommunities and of autistic communities. These three techniques are known as *compensation, rationalization* and *projection.*

Compensation

By *compensation* we mean *the substitution of some other need-satisfaction sequence for a frustrated or an anxiety-inducing one.* The substitution may be direct and simple.[13] A child who is not permitted to strike a rival sibling may complete his hostile pattern of behavior by pounding nails into a wooden block. His sister, who cannot for many years achieve maternity, plays the devoted mother in a substitute situation with a doll, which she makes in every way as much like a real baby as possible. The mother of these children, when she finds herself irritable and quarrelsome, throws herself into vigorous housecleaning where she can be aggressive, punitive and combative without fear of retaliation for the injury and annihilation she inflicts. Her husband exercises in the evenings an exaggerated freedom of action and word, because in his place of work he must appear silent and submissive. The frustrated need is freedom at work; the substitution is the marked self-assertion at home.

The substitutions in compensation are as often *indirect* as direct; and their relationship to frustrated or anxiety-inducing behavior may reach any degree of intricate complexity.[14] Indeed, it is not infrequently the case that such a

---

[11] Compare the discussion of *temporal sequences, closure* and *insight,* on pages 63–69 and 83–87.

[12] See, for example, Thorndike, E. L., "The psychology of invention in a very simple case." *Psychol. Rev.,* 1949, vol. 56, pp. 192–197. Compare the discussion of animism in thinking, pages 164–165, and of ritual and superstition on pages 354–359.

[13] Substitution has been emphasized in many of the so-called "field" theories of behavior. See, for example, Lewin, K., "Behavior and development as a function of the total situation." In Carmichael, L. (Ed.), *Manual of child psychology.* New York: Wiley, 1944, pp. 820–824.

[14] For examples of substitutions in experimental frustration, see pages 48–49.

relationship becomes completely obscured and can be reestablished only after prolonged investigation. Thus, for example, a young woman's devotion to violin playing, for which she showed little aptitude, grew out of her unsuccessful attempts to win her father's affection away from her sister, who was his favorite. This devotion became suddenly intensified, however — to the exclusion of all other interests — when her father died. Soon after his death, she made a number of attempts to date with men her own age, but found them uniformly unsatisfying. Her compensatory activity, which ultimately led to behavioral disorganization in this instance, was complexly rooted in compound affectional disappointments.

The variety of compensatory patterns is endless. Compensatory substitution is a product of social learning which is rarely planned or even foreseen. It is usually no more than the immediate reaction of a tense or needful person to his anxiety or frustration. Therefore, almost anything which alleviates the tension or satisfies the need — anything which permits closure, in the form of defense or escape — becomes fixed as a preferred kind of behavior in similar situations. Such an established preference may subsequently generalize to equivalent situations, and undergo progressive modification as its interrelation with other behavioral patterns ramifies. Moreover, the equivalence need not be of a verbal character nor even be subjected at any time to verbal formulation. It may belong wholly to the logic of non-verbal operations, the logic of object-arrangements and of the apparent sequence and concomitance of events.[15]

There are two important varieties of compensation that, in the past, have been given special names which are still widely used. One of these, known as *reaction-formation*, is the substitution of an opposite reaction for one which is frustrating or anxiety-inducing.[16] A mother, for example, may initially dislike and reject her baby; but because of the guilt which this taboo attitude arouses in her, she reacts instead with a chronically overprotective affection in which her hostility is almost buried.[17] A son, whose aged father's death will bring riches and freedom, compensates for his half-recognized or unrecognized death-wishes by the exaggerated solicitude with which he watches over his father's health and guards him from mishap.[18]

The other special variety of compensation is called *sublimation*.[19] By this we mean the substitution of socially approved reactions, particularly if they have

[15] Compare Chapter 3, for a general discussion of learning.

[16] This was described in Freud, S., "Three contributions to the theory of sex." *Nerv. ment. Dis. Monogr. Series*, New York, 1910.

[17] See, for example, Levy, D., *Maternal overprotection*. New York: Columbia University Press, 1943.

[18] For a case illustration of this behavior, see pages 322–323.

[19] This term is used in a somewhat different way in psychoanalytic theory. For a summary see Fenichel, O., *The psychoanalytic theory of neurosis*. New York: Norton, 1945, pp. 141–143.

an altruistic flavor, for socially discredited or taboo behavior. A great many competitive sports, in adulthood as well as in childhood, represent the substitution of culturally permitted aggression for forbidden violence. Much of the drama on the stage and the screen, on radio and television, represents a culturally approved opportunity for the spectator to participate in otherwise prohibited affectional relationships, through the medium of taking the role of the actors. Similarly persistent loves, hatreds and fears that cannot be acted out in their aboriginal form by a person with unique needs, or a person whose common needs cannot be directly satisfied, ordinarily lead to compensatory sublimation. The sublimated behavior is usually related to established social institutions, such as religion, the schools, the law, medicine, military establishments, one of the transportation industries, museums, slaughter houses, astronomy, the building trades, art, or any one of a thousand other activities.

But whatever the character of compensatory activity may be, it is obvious that it leads to the completion or realization of a vast number of otherwise inhibited trends in the social community. Thus, in addition to their function in reducing tension, the techniques of compensation also enrich overt behavior by fostering the elaboration of endless complex patterns, which take the place of activities that cannot escape social restriction. Indeed, industrial civilization and the machine age place in the hands of almost everyone a rich variety of means for the indirect satisfaction of needs, whose satisfaction is completely denied to many of the preliterate agricultural societies, which we often mistakenly envy. The possession of an automobile, a ticket to a show, membership in an urban community, the daily newspaper, the variety of food, dress and opinion tolerated, protection from disease and alleviation of inescapable pain — these go a long way in the direction of indemnifying us for the personal costliness of industrialization, by supplying us with behavioral riches that we can indirectly expend.

In all societies, one of the most inexhaustible sources of compensatory substitution is that of covert fantasy — the fleeting thought, the dream, the daydream.[20] What one cannot have to eat one can talk of eating, silently imagine oneself enjoying, or realize almost to the point of fulfillment in a dream at night. This, of course, is the mere substitution of thought for thing, of fantasy for overt action. But in thinking, dream and daydream, one can enjoy all manner of forbidden fruit, achieve every imaginable satisfaction, witness pageants of triumph and parades of disaster, turn light into darkness and night into day, bring contradictions together side by side, violate the arrangements of time and space, and make an unlikely beginning lead irresistibly to an impossible end.

On the dangers and disadvantages of compensatory fantasy we shall dwell

[20] These will be discussed further in the next chapter on hallucination and the autistic community. See also pages 112–113.

when we discuss delusion and hallucination, in this chapter and the next. Its benefits, however, deserve to be pointed out here. All group living necessarily imposes never-ceasing compromise and inhibition upon the participants. This restriction of individual freedom would unquestionably result in far greater impoverishment and distortion of habitual behavior were it not for the latitude we grant to fantasy. Most persons take no responsibility for what they dream at all, even when a dream remembered is clearly erotic, grandiose or murderous. Many persons consider daydreams in a somewhat similar light — for example, honestly denying activities, trends and intentions, merely because these occur only in their fantasy. All persons tend to disown a passing thought if it seems not to belong to their conception of themselves. And, of course, there is a vast amount of evidence to indicate that fleeting thoughts, dreams and daydreams are for the most part forgotten or repressed by everyone.[21]

Rationalization

Rationalization is a technique which, unlike compensation, always depends upon symbolic skills. It is essentially a process of assigning motives to behavior — often of selecting one from several possible motives — and such an operation cannot be carried through without the use of language or thinking.[22] Rationalization is similar to compensation in that it represents a tendency toward completion of the incomplete, an elaboration of small certainties and great uncertainties into something that seems reasonable, consistent and sure.

Traditional definitions have tended to emphasize social acceptability as the hallmark of rationalization.[23] That is to say, one rationalizes in order to ascribe socially approved motives to oneself. Social acceptability is undoubtedly the commonest determinant of rationalization; but it is important for us to recognize that this is by no means an essential characteristic. Indeed, as we shall soon see, persons frequently insist upon motivational interpretations of their own behavior which place them in an irredeemably bad light, simply because such interpretations will support a vitally important explanation, or cement fragments of fact and assumption together into a coherent story or a consistent picture. In short, it is not social conformity, but internal consistency or coherence, that characterizes rationalization.

Let us define *rationalization* as *the technique of inventing and accepting interpretations of behavior which an impartial analysis would not substantiate*. Thus, if a child loses in a foot race, or a man in billiards, he may blame his failure on the unfairness of a competitor, on an alleged unevenness of surface with which he alone had to contend, or on some distraction, a pain, malaise or ill luck. The

---

[21] For a discussion of repression, see pages 337–351.
[22] This point is further discussed on pages 33–34.
[23] See, for example, Dollard, J. and Miller, N. E., *Personality and psychotherapy*. New York: McGraw-Hill, 1950, p. 177.

mother who has a delinquent child may similarly blame paternal heredity, an incident in her pregnancy, a blow the child has received on his head, the badness of his playmates or the blindness of the law.[24]

In all of these examples the common factor is the invention and acceptance of an unsound interpretation in the interest of preserving consistency, of making something appear consonant with the fundamental thesis. The racing child and the man at billiards are "winners"; therefore, they cannot lose on the basis of inferiority in skill. The mother can have only a *good* child since it is she who bore him and reared him.

Rationalization, like deliberate lying,[25] may paradoxically lead to inconsistency, self-contradiction and, in extreme instances, even to incoherence. This happens because, in both rationalization and lying, an attempt is being made to preserve the integrity of a personal fiction against the attack of socially organized facts. Assertions and beliefs that oppose the consensus of one's peers cannot possibly withstand the assault of factual contradiction unless they, too, become well-organized and well-practised. We are witnessing today, in many areas, the large scale attempts of systematized social institutions — some new and some old — to oppose well-practised interlocking rationalization to the growth and spread of organized fact. When, however, an *individual* holds to a personal, unshared rationalization in the face of contradictory evidence, he is usually manifesting delusional behavior.[26]

Rationalization is an everyday occurrence in the lives of normal individuals. One reason for this is that human beings exhibit an irresistible need to account for what goes on around them.[27] The unwritten law seems to be that a nonvalid explanation is better than no explanation at all. Indeed, in normal as well as in delusional behavior, we find irrefutable evidence that a frightening or catastrophic explanation is more acceptable than none.[28] This is especially striking in the phenomenon of *sudden clarification* which characterizes certain delusional developments.

The need for explanation which rationalization satisfies is sufficient justification for the practice of rationalizing. Difficulties arise only when the rationalization is challenged, for this rearouses the need and thus demands either reassertion or the production of a new explanation. If the challenged explanation is one which, for personal reasons, the individual cannot abandon, he must either defend it by means of further assertions, or else retire from the threat of

---

[24] For a discussion of explanations employed by mothers of retarded children, see pages 167–170.

[25] For a discussion of deliberate lying, see pages 206–208.

[26] See pages 392–405.

[27] This is demonstrated in the sort of study performed by Piaget with young children. See, for example, Piaget, J., *The language and thought of the child* (Trans. by M. Warden). New York: Harcourt, Brace, 1926; Piaget, J., *Judgment and reasoning in the child* (Trans. by M. Gabain). NewYork: Harcourt, Brace, 1928.

[28] See pages 76–77.

contradiction and preserve what he values. Both of these strategies we shall see in delusion, the former commonly leading toward aggressive paranoid disorders, and the latter toward insulation and desocialization.

Projection

By *projecting* we mean *ascribing our own attributes to other persons, groups, objects and symbols.* This common, everyday technique of completion and elaboration is in a sense the converse of *identification,* which we have defined as a reaction to the attributes of other persons, groups, objects and symbols as if these attributes were also one's own.[29] Projection is a later development than identification in the genesis of an individual's social behavior. For, as we have pointed out, identification arises inevitably as a consequence of the conditions of early family living. The infant begins life as part of a family group; and his initiation into human interbehavior is basically a process of learning conformity with the patterns of persons around him. He lives among family possessions, with none that are uniquely his own. He is carried or wheeled wherever someone else pleases to go. His security or insecurity is part of the security or insecurity of others. It is only secondarily that his behavior increasingly differentiates him into an individual who will one day become distinct from the family group.

Projection, we have said, is the converse of this. In the course of time, every child begins to ascribe his own attributes to other persons and groups, to symbols, animals and plant life, to inanimate objects — indeed, even to whole situations, which inevitably include his own fantasy. Few direct studies of the origins of projection in early life have as yet been systematically carried out;[30] so that we are still obliged to fill in important gaps with intelligent conjecture. None the less, we have at our disposal a considerable body of common knowledge concerning the conditions of early childhood in our culture; and upon this basis we can reconstruct the evolution of projective procedures with a reasonable degree of certainty.

It will make our task of understanding delusion and hallucination much easier if we distinguish from the outset two varieties of projection. One of these we shall call *assimilative* and the other *disowning.* (1) The assimilative variety is genetically earlier in development than the disowning, and it is more closely related to identification. In its clearest forms, it is no more than *the assumption by a person, without adequate supporting evidence, that others are as he is, that they are behaviorally the same or closely similar.* (2) The disowning variety stems from the same implicit assumption; but *it is complicated by a stated or*

---

[29] For a description of identification, see pages 60–63.
[30] An example of an experimental approach to this problem may be found in Wright, B. A., "Altruism in children and the perceived conduct of others." *J. abn. soc. Psychol.,* 1942, vol. 37, pp. 218–233.

*implied denial by the projecting person that he shares the attributes which he
ascribes to others.* We shall have more to say about this curious contradiction
in a later section.[31]

(1) *Assimilative projection.* The origins of assimilative projection — the
assumption that others are as we are — lie in the conditions of the earliest
interpersonal relationships of infancy. The behavioral reciprocity which
infants learn in their interactions with older individuals [32] implies behavioral
similarity. The breast is made accessible to the hungry nursling, the spoon
and the cup approach the infant as he approaches them, the family table at
which he satisfies his hunger is peopled by hungry individuals, who eat in ways
similar to his, and give similar indications of satisfaction. The same general
interrelation can be found in the areas of body care, toilet training, affectional
behavior, cooperative play and the acquisition of language.

The infant, of course, does not learn in these earliest situations that others
share his attributes. This comes later with the growth of self-reactions. What
he learns at first is not symbolically formulated and therefore more or less
undefined. He simply acquires in endlessly repeated interactions with others
the behavioral anticipation of activity that parallels or reciprocates with his
own.[33] The game of *pat-a-cake,* although it comes later than infancy, gives a
clear illustration of such learned anticipation. In this game, both parallel and
reciprocal action depend upon similarities in dynamic attitude and response
organization between the adult and child participants. Even the verbalizations, the laughter and the errors support the assumption by each participant
that the other is sharing everything in the situation with him. A child's inability to engage a dog or a cat in such a game limits to that extent his success
in projecting assimilatively in relation to the dog or cat.

A child nevertheless does ascribe a great many of his own attributes to animals, plants and inanimate objects.[34] As a child masters language behavior,
he learns to make assertions about the way animals, trees and flowers feel and
what they think. He ascribes his own attributes to his toys and other playthings, to a door that will not stay shut and a gate that refuses to open, to the
tricycle that throws him off and the stove that welcomes him and warms him.
The automobile waiting in the rain outside the garage wants to come in and
get dry; the steam radiator is crying and the kettle is singing; the small animal
in the picture-book wants to be with the larger animal there, its "mother."
The flowers are all sad because their heads are hanging down; the sun is happy
and cheerful because it is shining brightly.

The anthropomorphic ascription of a child's own attitudes and responses to

[31] See pages 385–387.

[32] For a description of behavioral reciprocity, see pages 11 and 114–116.

[33] For a description of anticipant attitudes, see pages 65–66.

[34] Ames, L. B. and Learned, J., "Imaginary companions and related phenomena."
J. genet. Psychol., 1946, vol. 69, pp. 147–167.

animals and the inanimate world is obviously a product of social learning.[35] To a large degree it is inculcated by adult formulation and by the stories, pictures, plays and verses that adults manufacture for children. The commonest technique for teaching children to be considerate of animals and things is one of encouraging assimilative projection. The kitten or puppy that is being squeezed, mauled or beaten by the small child is described to him in terms of his own pains and pleasures — often with the direct suggestion that he would not like to be treated so. Occasionally, a parent illustrates the meaning by hurting the child in some way analogous to the hurt the child has just given the animal, and then says, "That's how the kitty feels when you do that." Comparable procedures are followed in story-telling and picture-interpretation by adults.

Assimilative projection with respect to other human beings, of course, is not difficult to understand. For one thing, all human beings look and behave more like oneself than like any other living thing. For another, the whole process of socialization, from the moment of birth on, is training in conformity. The child learns to behave and to appear like other children, then like other adolescents and eventually like other adults. In so doing, the child also learns to anticipate corresponding parallel and reciprocal behavior in others. He tends to take it for granted that others are like him, think as he does, have similar attitudes and tastes, speak the same language. He is so accustomed, in his home and neighborhood, to being understood by others like him that he becomes incredulous and even shocked when he meets with someone whose behavior or appearance differs radically from his own.[36]

The value of assimilative projection as a technique of completion and elaboration is obvious. It enormously simplifies daily behavior, since it eliminates the necessity for completely checking and validating every attitude and response of other persons. We can assume that others are like us, we can behave as if we knew it, and seldom go wrong. We can ascribe our own attitudes and responses to all of the animate and inanimate world, and lend it a familiar and a friendly tone. Thus, as long as an individual is reasonably secure himself, his gift of kinship to the world around him is repaid manifold by the security that his surroundings give him. They seem to him to share his attitudes and to meet his anticipations.

If, however, an insecure person becomes predominantly hostile toward his environment, he is likely to ascribe to his surroundings a similar hostility. If

---

[35] Piaget, J., *The language and thought of the child* (Trans. by M. Warden). New York: Harcourt, Brace, 1926.

[36] See, for example, Horowitz, R. E., "Racial aspects of self-identification in nursery school children." *J. Psychol.*, 1939, vol. 7, pp. 91–99; Horowitz, R. E., "A pictorial method for study of self-identification in preschool children." *J. genet. Psychol.*, 1943, vol. 62, pp. 135–148.

he is skilled in the techniques of social validation, and responsive to the consensus of his peers, he will proceed to test his assumptions, and to determine objectively the degree and character of the hostility his behavior may be arousing.[37] If, on the other hand, he lacks the necessary social skills for checking the validity of his assumptions, he will have no choice but to react with flight, defense or aggression to the consequences of his assimilative projection. This is the situation, as we shall see, in the development of *persecutory delusions*.[38]

Something comparable occurs in the growth of *grandiose delusions*. The expansive, self-assertive or amatory individual finds the world in tune with his prevailing moods and ready to participate in the greatness, the boastfulness or the love which he expresses. His reaction-sensitivity to signs that he is right in his delusional interpretations assures him of confirmatory evidence. For there is always material in the behavioral environment to confirm a fixed belief.[39] The grandiose person takes from this material what he needs to elaborate and complete the behavioral configuration which he has already begun in his fantasies. He finds his own self-attitudes reflected in the attitudes of others, and justified by this appearance of unanimity.

(2) *Disowning projection.* In disowning projection the acknowledged attributes of the person projecting are different from those he ascribes to others. He finds others hostile while he is only fearful or passive or aggressively innocent. Others are in love with him or make amorous advances, but he neither shares this love nor responds positively to the advances. He says that he has been brought under the influence of some individual, a group, a force or a god; but he makes it clear that this is not his wish or his will, but the power of something or someone else. The patient may or may not resist the influence, the persecution or the amatory assault; but the important point is that he does not find it in harmony with his own trends, or his own trends in agreement with it.

It is clear that in disowning projection a major role is played by repression.[40] For there can be no doubt that what a person ascribes unjustifiably to others is at the time an integral part of his own behavior.[41] If what is ascribed is not true of others, then its source can only be in the person who is projecting, even though he cannot acknowledge this. This is what is meant by the popular verdict, "It's all in his imagination." The crucial point, of course, is that a person usually cannot recognize his ownership, even with the help of others. If his tension-provoking need or anxiety diminishes, the repression may become unnecessary and the projection may disappear.

---

[37] It goes without saying that the environment may *be* exceedingly hostile to a person, and that neither his validation nor his failure to validate need influence the attitudes of his surroundings.

[38] See pages 394–396.

[39] Compare the discussion of selective learning, pages 69–75.

[40] See pages 337–351.

[41] For a further development of this, as the principle of *opposition*, see pages 386–387.

However important disowning projection may be in the development of delusion and paranoid disorder, it must not be supposed that it is necessarily pathological behavior. On the contrary, disowning projection is a common, everyday matter with normal persons. The man who breaks the law and endangers the lives of others in the way he drives his car will characteristically denounce the driver of the car he hits as a reckless, stupid lawbreaker. The woman who, her arms full of packages, elbows her way through a commuting crowd is quick to complain that others push her aside or deliberately block her way. Tax-dodgers are often the loudest in accusing the government of defrauding them and in asserting their own integrity — or in describing their loss of civic honesty as an inescapable consequence of governmental seduction. Gossips characteristically slander those from whom they gather information, openly disclaim their own intentions, and insinuate to their listeners that they fully expect this confidence to be in turn betrayed.

There are two common pathways along which disowning projection may develop. One is by way of *assimilative projection* and the other, a more direct route, is by way of *behavioral reciprocity*.

(a) In many instances of *assimilative projection*, a need for repression comes after the ascription of one's attributes to others has been well established. A characteristic or an attitude which has been extended to others may then appear in these others to be evil or dangerous. The effect upon oneself of this magnified reflection of one's own traits may arouse sufficient guilt and anxiety to induce repression secondarily, in the usual way.[42] If this repression extends to everything, we do not have disowning projection. But if — as is frequently the case in normal as well as in pathological behavior — the repression is reserved to protect oneself from a share in the general calumniation, then we have disowning projection. The others have our evil and we have lost it.[43]

(b) Disowning projection may also spring directly from *behavioral reciprocity*, without an intervening assimilative phase. We have already pointed out [44] that everyone acquires anticipant attitudes by means of which he is able to prepare his own behavior to meet the behavior of others in advance. In its developed form, this becomes skill in taking the role of a cooperative or competitive person, of an intended aggressor or a victim, of the donor of love or of its recipient. Unless a person can take realistic anticipant attitudes, in fantasy as well as overtly, he cannot rehearse probable, feared, or hoped-for activity in such a way as to be thoroughly ready for it when it comes.

[42] Compare pages 343–345.

[43] It has been claimed that disowning projection underlies many cases of prejudice and scapegoating. See, for example, Veltfort, H. R., and Lee, G. E., "The Cocoanut Grove fire: a study in scapegoating." *J. abn. soc. Psychol.* (CS), 1943, vol. 38, pp. 138–154; Zawadzki, B., "Limitations of the scapegoat theory of prejudice." *J. abn. soc. Psychol.*, 1948, vol. 43, pp. 127–141; Lindzey, G., "An experimental examination of the scapegoat theory of prejudice." *J. abn. soc. Psychol.*, 1950, vol. 45, pp. 296–309.

[44] See pages 65–66.

What this means is that when any of us fantasies himself as a hostile aggressor, he is likely at the same time to fantasy the injury and fear of his victim. And, of course, the person who imagines himself victimized must at the same time have the perspective — and imaginatively play the role — of an attacker. Likewise, if one thinks himself dominated by some power or influence, he cannot escape having the role of this power or influence in his own behavioral repertory. There is no other place where it can be. And the same holds true for grandiose fantasies. Kings have their subjects and generals their armies; God has his saints and supplicants; the great inventor and the social reformer have their worshippers, those whom they help and those over whose antagonism they prevail.

In disowning projection, one member of a behaviorally reciprocal pair is ascribed to others, and its origin in one's own fantasy is repressed. The determination of which member is acknowledged as one's own, and which repressed and ascribed to others, rests with the question of which provokes the more intolerable tension, or which becomes inevitable in terms of the past and of one's general behavior organization. Thus, the dominance of a sadistic component, which can be accepted as one's own, will favor hostility as one's role. It will favor assault upon someone who fulfills the aggressor's need for a victim. The inability to acknowledge such hostility, on the other hand, will favor the masochistic role of victim; and the repressed sadistic component is then ascribed to others.[45] The same principle — the repression of one member of behavioral reciprocity — is fundamental to delusions of influence and of grandeur.

Although assimilative projection, as we have indicated, can serve to precipitate delusional behavior also, it is disowning projection that is the commoner source of delusion. For the trend that is not only ascribed to others, but disowned as well, becomes by virtue of the disowning act foreign to oneself. The more strongly and insistently a person must deny and repress the trend, as anything belonging to him, the more strongly and insistently it must be ascribed to others. Thus a denial and repression can lead to an intense and even violent opposition which, of course, is lacking in assimilative projection. This, in turn, increases the person's need for defense and further intensifies the delusional opposition. In a similar manner, by disowning praise and sanctification, a person can allow himself to develop opposition in his own self-reactions, in the guise of others' behavior, to an infinite degree. Since he conceives of these self-reactions as coming from without, he is no longer answerable for their excesses.

The advantages of disowning projection are sometimes multiple. For example, it permits one to engage in taboo activities, such as vengeance, while

---

[45] Where repression is incomplete, and both members present, we have one of the conditions underlying compulsive disorders. See pages 354–359.

at the same time it provides further satisfactions from the consequences of these activities. Thus, an individual can persecute himself — through the agency of imagined persecutors — and gain the rewards of the martyrdom he inflicts upon himself. And he can then engage in counteraggressions against persons whom he needs to injure, by attributing to them his own repressed hostility. In this last phase he may gain profound, though usually temporary, relief by an act of destructive violence that serves him as consummation.

The completion and elaboration of the behavioral field in disowning projection are thus achieved by setting up an *opposition* — a person, group, force or purpose — which may be hostile or may be merely antiphonal. As a result of the repression involved, this opposition seems to the individual to belong to an autonomous agency which operates upon him from without. Such ascription of one's own repressed attitudes to outside agencies we shall see most clearly developed — along with compensation, rationalization and assimilative projection — in the behavioral organization we call the *pseudocommunity*.

The pseudocommunity

We have pointed out that our interbehavior with other persons in our social environment is almost always an incomplete, ongoing, developing structure.[46] This structure is present in anticipation before it is realized in shared operations. It shifts and reshapes at the very moment when we are reacting in terms of its design. What is objectively present we must constantly supplement by means of overt and covert symbolic activities. Through the use of such fallible techniques as compensation, rationalization and projection, we succeed in consummating and elaborating our developing behavioral organizations in ways that turn out, in action, to be for the most part reasonably dependable.

The circumstances of ordinary, everyday living seldom leave us free to check rigorously and validate the results of such consummation and elaboration. The constantly shifting patterns of personal need and environmental configuration do not as a rule encourage reflection and critical self-analysis. In consequence, we inevitably make frequent errors of interpretation, inference and conclusion. Much of the time these errors go uncorrected and unnoticed. Usually this makes no essential difference and does not threaten to develop along pathological lines. Occasionally, however, the unchecked observation and the unvalidated interpretation contribute to a behavioral organization, the pseudocommunity, which is basic to delusion. We may define the pseudocommunity as *a behavioral organization, structured in terms of the observed or inferred activities of actual and imagined persons, which makes an individual mistakenly seem to himself a focus, or a significant part, of some concerted action.*

Although the concept of the pseudocommunity was developed originally in

[46] See pages 374–376.

connection with behavior pathology,[47] it is now obvious that normal persons not infrequently complete and elaborate their behavioral structures by means of pseudocommunity organization. Let us take as one hypothetical example the following.

An important politician has been invited to speak in a city away from home. He arrives by train to find a large and enthusiastic crowd waiting in the station. His experienced eye quickly identifies reporters and news photographers in the front ranks. The fantasies which he has been entertaining on his trip now call forth anticipant attitudes which lead him into misinterpretation. These anticipant attitudes render him reaction-sensitive to components of the situation which allow him to conclude that the crowd has been organized — or has spontaneously gathered — to do him honor. He singles out this person and that, from the crowd, and assigns to them in his thinking the roles of individuals with whom he has communicated, or about whom he has been written.

Our politician now prepares to meet the newscameras with appropriate dignity and warmth, rehearsing in imagination the facial expression and the gestures with which he will greet them. As he reaches the car platform there is a cheer, and he responds with a wave of the hand and a warm smile. In a moment, however, the crowd's behavior shows clearly that its focus is not he but a man just ahead of him — who, it later appears, is a movie actor. The immediate effect upon the politician is that of momentary disorganization, followed quickly by the sudden behavioral reorganization which we have earlier described in relation to insight.[48]

We shall take, as our second hypothetical example, a situation involving fear. An adolescent girl, who has been alarmed by a too vivid account of the dangers of walking at night through the streets, is likely to develop a pseudocommunity organization when next she goes out after dark. A group of young men approaches with talk and laughter. To her, they seem to be converging upon her or about to surround and imperil her. As couples pass, the men seem to be showing unwelcome interest, and the women unjustified disdain. Her behavioral organization is structured in terms of the reaction-sensitivities engendered by her fears. These fears, in turn, arise out of the misinterpretations of her presence unescorted in the street which she has been told that passersby will make. Her need and her anxiety lead her to project the anticipated attitudes of others into their reactions, and to see in their responses the reflection of the attitudes she ascribes to them.

Our third example deals primarily with hostility. Let us suppose that an office-worker, who has suffered severe frustration at home, comes to work in the morning irritable and angry. As he carries on his routine work, his manner, the way he speaks and what he says annoy or offend

[47] Cameron, N., "The development of paranoic thinking." Psychol. Rev., 1943, vol. 50, pp. 219–233; Cameron, N., "The paranoid pseudocommunity." Amer. J. Sociol., 1943, vol. 49, pp. 32–38.
[48] See pages 83–87.

his fellow-workers. At the same time, his own dominant attitudes make him reaction-sensitive to hostility in others, so that he quickly picks up and magnifies the signs that his human environment is unfriendly. A file-clerk, to whom he has just been rude, goes to another file-clerk and they speak together. Our office-worker feels sure they are talking about him. He finds the clerk at the next desk staring at him; and this seems also to express hostility directly related to the immediate situation.[49]

Actually the staring clerk is staring only because he is preoccupied with his own problem — how he can get his pay increased. After awhile, he goes over and speaks earnestly with the office-manager who then disappears into the general manager's office. The clerk returns to his desk and smiles grimly at our hostile office-worker, saying, "Well, if they don't do something, I will!" The latter glances around and notices that everyone seems to be looking at him with unpleasant satisfaction. The irresistible conclusion he draws is that the whole office force has ganged up in a complaint against him which is now being presented to the general manager. At this point, he begins expostulating angrily to his neighbor whom he has cast in the role of chief complainer. But his expostulation is met by surprise, incredulity and a prompt disclaimer by the other clerk, who proceeds to explain his own behavior.

In each of these examples — the politician, the girl and the office-worker — we have the organization of a pseudocommunity under conditions of emotional stress. To the politician we have already conceded behavioral reorganization and insight. If the frightened girl gets home without mishap, finds a worthy confidant, and succeeds in communicating her fears and sharing her confidant's more realistic perspectives, she too will achieve a realistic reorganization. Likewise, the hostile clerk may be able to accept the explanations of his fellow-worker with relief, and share to some extent the other's amusement over the misinterpretation. Indeed, such reorganizations represent by far the commonest outcome in incipient pseudocommunity development; the situation gets restructured and the pseudocommunity is dissolved. If this were not so, all of us would lead a delusional existence.

A great many persons actually do lead a delusional existence. In most instances, the delusional episode is relatively brief and terminates in recovery. But for the more unfortunate, a pseudocommunity, once started, tends to persist indefinitely and may come in time to dominate social interbehavior. Should our politician have been unable to effect a realistic reorganization, for example, he might have progressed to a manic excitement in which he continued to seek and find acclaim all around him.[50] The girl's pseudocommunity might not have yielded to the persuasion of a confidant, or the girl might have been unable to confide and to share another's perspectives. The outcome might then be a paranoid disorder such as we shall describe later in the chap-

[49] See the discussion of emotional displacement and cumulative sequences, pages 125–127.
[50] See pages 330–336.

ter. The office-worker might have found his fellow-clerk's explanation unconvincing, in the face of all that had preceded it, and with the background of his own anxiety. He might have gone on to build a chronic persecutory pseudocommunity, and perhaps eventually to desocialize and disorganize.[51]

Conditions favoring the development of pseudocommunities

It is clear that incipient pseudocommunity organizations develop at one time or another in the behavior of everyone, and that there is no sharp line dividing mere misinterpretation from delusion. Neither is there one kind of person whose pseudocommunity can develop into a lasting delusional disorder, and another kind who is immune to such development. From what we know, it seems probable that under one or another variety of stress or strain everyone has his limits of tolerance.[52] When these limits are exceeded, the individual may show delusional behavior; and even after the stress or strain has been eliminated, the delusion may persist.

There are also certain *immediate* conditions which favor the organization of persistent pseudocommunities and the development of pathological delusion. (*a*) One of these is *a reduction in the relative biological efficiency* of the individual, particularly the efficiency of cerebral mechanisms. In delirium and in other forms of cerebral incompetence, as we shall see,[53] a person faces his usual environment without his accustomed integrative capacity. He attempts to do the things he has always been able to do, and he gets into situations that are too complex now for him to handle. Moreover, he may be no longer able to restrict his behavior judiciously, so that he actually undertakes more than he has ever been able to achieve. Under these circumstances, many persons tend to blame their environment for their failure; and unless their relative incompetence soon clears up, this projection may become fixed in a chronic delusional reaction.

(*b*) Something similar occurs — with or without a change in cerebral competence — when *environmental complexity increases* beyond an individual's ability to cope with it. This we see occur in normal and superior persons who are faced with increased complexity in wholly unfamiliar situations, or who are obliged to respond discriminatively when the bases for discrimination are inadequate.[54] The misinterpretations, unwarranted inferences or unjustified conclusions, which then arise, frequently lead to pseudocommunity organization. If anxiety, frustration or emotional excitement does not reach a high pitch, such delusional organizations do not usually persist.

(*c*) *Emotional excitement, acute anxiety* and *urgent need* may also be significant

[51] See pages 494–515.
[52] For a discussion of tolerance, see pages 49–52.
[53] See pages 469–477 and 531–555.
[54] See, for example, Marquart, D. I., "The pattern of punishment and its relation to abnormal fixation in adult human subjects." *J. gen. Psychol.*, 1948, vol. 39, pp. 107–144.

factors in instigating, supporting, and perpetuating delusional developments. One witnesses striking examples of this in such group phenomena as the political rally and the religious revival, when disaster threatens or strikes a community, and particularly if the anticipated visitation seems magical and unfamiliar.[55] But whether we deal with individuals or groups, it is the atmosphere of tense, excited expectation that favors a pseudocommunity organization of behavior. The marked disequilibrium impels anyone, whose limits of tolerance have been exceeded, to find closure. The pseudocommunity is a behavioral instrument which can eliminate contradiction, terminate suspense, and replace doubt with certainty. It characteristically involves distortion, and often behavioral impoverishment; but it permits closure to occur in situations which might otherwise not provide closure.

The more remote, *predisposing* conditions which favor the growth and persistence of pseudocommunities (a) include *whatever factors are responsible for chronic anxiety and severe frustration.*[56] (b) They include also *whatever contributes to increased cerebral incompetence.*[57] (c) In addition, as we have elsewhere indicated, *anything that interferes with the acquisition and the continued practice of adequate role-taking skills* may render a person susceptible to pseudocommunity development.[58] Training in childhood anxiety and guilt, for example, not only increases both the need for security and the obstacles that make it unattainable. It also prevents effective parent identification; and it is through parent identification that many social skills are best acquired and most readily practiced, including the highly important techniques of social interaction outside the family.

Families and communities in which outsiders are habitually looked upon with suspicion and hostility will foster corresponding attitudes in the children they rear.[59] To be habitually suspicious of others, and hostile toward them, means to be sharply limited in the opportunities for acquiring and practicing social skills — not the least of which is skill in affectional interbehavior. A child reared in such an atmosphere will leave the family or the community under a handicap which he may never successfully overcome. He lacks adequate techniques for making inferences regarding the behavior of outsiders; and when he must live among them the likelihood is great that he will assign to them attitudes, intentions and even interrelationships which do not agree with fact.

Similar difficulties face the child who has been reared in comparative isola-

[55] See, for example, Cantril, H., *The invasion from Mars.* Princeton, N.J.: Princeton University Press, 1940; Douglass, J. H., "The funeral of 'Sister President.'" *J. abn. soc. Psychol.*, 1944, vol. 39 (CS), pp. 217–223; Johnson, D. M., "The 'Phantom Anesthetist' of Mattoon: a field study of mass hysteria." *J. abn. soc. Psychol.*, 1945, vol. 40, pp. 175–186.

[56] See pages 49–52 and 293–298.

[57] See pages 531–555.

[58] See pages 114–122, 231–242 and 484–491.

[59] Compare the learning of anxiety, discussed on pages 294–296.

tion, or who is moved so often from place to place that he has no chance to enter into stable friendships with his peers.[60] For role-taking is socially delineated; it can be learned effectively only through prolonged social interbehavior with a variety of other individuals. Identification with parents is highly important in establishing a child in some of his basic role-taking, but it cannot prepare him for the behavior of the great majority of social situations in which he must operate. Interaction with siblings is also distinctly advantageous, but they cannot provide practice in approaching, contacting and dealing with strangers outside the family circle.

To put the matter simply, a person cannot deal effectively with the parade of strangers he must encounter in adult life until he has practiced, with strangers, the necessary behavioral techniques.[61] He cannot learn to cooperate and compete — or even to mingle easily — with a variety of other individuals, until he has tried it a great many times with a great many persons. He cannot confide in others profitably, under conditions of stress, unless he has been free to exchange confidences with others before sudden stress demands it. He cannot take the role of someone else effectively, even in private fantasy, unless he has already practiced similar and reciprocal roles. Such a person will not be able to anticipate the behavior of others because he cannot share their perspectives, and therefore cannot predict the responses which their dominant attitudes may be expected to support.

The person who is relatively incompetent in role-taking skills, whatever the reason, will operate successfully only as long as the environmental structuring makes no unusual demands upon him. And even under favorable environmental circumstances, he will perform adequately only provided his own anxiety or excitement is not greatly heightened, and his frustration tolerance not exceeded. Whenever these conditions are absent, the socially incompetent individual may develop delusional behavior, and this may become crystallized into paranoid disorder.

Delusion

By *delusion* we mean *a conviction based upon misinterpretations, unwarranted inferences, or unjustified conclusions.* This definition clearly includes a great deal of normal as well as abnormal behavior. We consider delusion to be *pathological* only if it introduces behavioral distortion or impoverishment, if it makes a person ineffectual in his social relationships or interferes with his attainment of important satisfactions. The relative character of behavior pathology is nowhere more evident than in delusion, for there are many flourishing

[60] Compare the situation for Levy's overprotected children. Levy, D., *Maternal overprotection.* New York: Columbia University Press, 1943.
[61] For a further discussion of this point, see pages 485–491.

systems of belief, the foundations of which seem delusional to the consensus. And yet the biosocial behavior of the believers is neither distorted nor impoverished, it does not lead to ineffectual social relationships, and it may facilitate rather than hinder the attainment of important satisfactions.

Characteristics of delusion

The dimensions of delusional behavior that deserve special mention are (a) the temporal variations, (b) the degrees of systematization, and (c) the varieties of delusional pattern.

(a) *Temporal variations.* Delusion may be *transient, progressive* or *chronic.* The single transient delusion is unlikely to induce behavior pathology. If, however, a transient delusion recurs, it may become established as an habitual mode of behavior, and the individual will then become reaction-sensitive to stimulation that tends to arouse his unwarranted inferences. Moreover, if the recurrent delusion generalizes and acquires new excitants, it is likely to undergo a change into a progressive or a chronic form. The transient delusion is characteristic of normal emotional excitement,[62] including anxiety,[63] of normal sleep, and of the relative cerebral incompetence[64] common in exhaustion, mild intoxication, and systemic illness.

In *progressive* ("expanding") *delusion* both the variety of excitants and the inclusiveness of the reactions are steadily increasing. Such expansion may be directly related to intense or mounting tension, as in anxiety disorders,[65] to progressive disorganization,[66] or to disorientation such as one finds in cerebral incompetence.[67] Delusions may also expand, however, simply because an individual lacks the social skills necessary to validate his interpretations, inferences and conclusions, once they have brought him emotional satisfaction.[68] The *chronic delusion* is, as a rule, the relatively constant and predictable end-stage of a progressive or expanding delusion. It is encountered most frequently in schizophrenic and paranoid disorders of long standing. Sometimes it is the sole remnant of an otherwise recovered illness, and as such its effects upon general behavior may range from disabling severity to insignificance in the person's life.

(b) *Degrees of systematization.* The extremes of systematization in delusional behavior are to be found in paranoia,[69] where an internally consistent organization may dominate a patient's whole life, and in deliria and normal dreams, where the delusions are momentary, unstable fragments. Most pathological delusions are poorly systematized. Where such behavior is the direct result of emotional excitement, temporary incompetence or momentary behavioral disorganization, this is not difficult to understand. The conditions giving rise

---

[62] See pages 122–129. [63] See pages 279–280. [64] See pages 469–477.
[65] See pages 306–314. [66] See pages 452–469. [67] See pages 531–539.
[68] Compare the discussion on pages 116–122 and 485–491.
[69] See pages 405–406.

to the pathological reactions are not those which ordinarily promote learning, or favor the production of stable patterns of behavior.[70]

The relatively poor systematization of chronic and progressive delusions has another basis. The patient characteristically develops his pathological thinking in isolation, that is, he relies habitually upon solitary fantasy, unchecked observation and unshared interpretation. But socially valid behavioral organization, we know, can be achieved and maintained only through continual social interchange.[71] Solitary, unvalidated and unshared thinking is not subject to the same conditions as those prevailing in social operations. It inevitably includes ambiguities, ambivalences, contradictions and obscurities, such as are to be found in any fantasy. Thus, the delusional organization of asocial persons, in spite of infinite practice, is likely to elude the kind and degree of systematization which socially shared and valid behavior achieves. If there is also general disorganization [72] in a patient's behavior, the delusional structure, of course, will not escape the common fate.

(c) *Varieties of delusional pattern.* The possibilities of variation in delusional pattern are practically infinite. In behavior pathology there are certain varieties which are common and important. These we shall discuss under the following heads: (1) *persecutory delusions;* (2) *delusions of influence;* (3) *grandiose delusions;* (4) *self-depreciatory delusions;* (5) *delusions of body-change;* (6) *delusions of unreality.* The kind of misinterpretation, unwarranted inference and unjustified conclusion that a given patient develops will always be a reflection of his own dominant behavior trends at the time. He will react to apparent threat and opportunity with the kind of adjustive techniques which have been his preferred and practiced modes in the past — whether the preference and the practice have been recognized by him or not, and whether the techniques have been utilized overtly or covertly. Thus, it has repeatedly been shown that a patient tends to exhibit closely similar delusional organization in widely separated episodes of stress, regardless of the particular character of the stress involved.[73] This is especially evident where cerebral incompetence complicates the situation in one such episode but not in the other.[74]

(1) *Persecutory delusions.* Delusions of persecution represent the commonest of all clinical forms.[75] In them, the patient considers himself threatened, discriminated against, deliberately interfered with, defamed or assaulted. In spite of the variety in detail, from person to person, there is a striking similar-

[70] Compare the conditions favoring learning of behavior pathology, discussed in Chapter 3.
[71] See pages 478–484.   [72] See pages 448–469.
[73] Wolff, H., and Curran, D., "Nature of delirium and allied states." *Arch. Neurol. Psychiat.*, 1935, vol. 33, pp. 1175–1215.
[74] See pages 540–541.
[75] According to one study, persecutory delusions are favored by patients of older chronological age. See Albee, G. W., "Delusions in schizophrenia as a function of chronological age." *J. consult. Psychol.*, 1950, vol. 14, pp. 340–342.

ity in persecutory delusions. The threats, unfair treatment, frustration, slander or attack, that patients complain about, follow in general the themes to be found in stories, plays, newspaper accounts and common folklore. The enemy, likewise, is conceived in familiar social terms or in the language of religion and mythology. Thus, the aggressor may be an envious neighbor, a competitor, a fellow-worker or an employer.[76] The patient seldom confines his pseudocommunity to one person. His behavioral organization soon expands to include a suspected individual in a larger hostile group — gangsters and racketeers, spy rings and dope rings, political, civic and religious organizations, the police or the military. From the individuals making up his pseudocommunity the persecuted person expects disgrace, violence, torture, enslavement, imprisonment and death.

Where does the patient find evidence in support of his delusional convictions? He finds it all around him. The fear, hostility and guilt that he has developed, on the basis of his own personal trends, render him reaction-sensitive to retaliation. He is now alert for signs and signals — clues to guide and protect him from the situation he has built out of his imagining. He is like the terrified cat or dog that responds to a proffered friendly hand by biting viciously in defense.

To a frightened man, for example, who is driving in panic from a supposed danger, every automobile, bus and truck seems to be chasing him, and every horn, whistle or siren is tracking his course and heralding his capture. If, now, he pulls abruptly to a stop, and jumps out ready to attack the men who seem to have him cornered, he will find plenty of further evidence that his offensive move is justified. For the other automobiles are likely to screech as they swerve or come to a sudden stop, and the drivers will sound their horns in chorus, and perhaps add shouts and cursing to the general commotion. If everyone but he drives on, the patient will conclude that his defiance has for the time being saved him from assault. And if, instead, angry men get out of their cars and come toward him, or the police arrive and take a hand, he will be convinced that the attack is on, and conduct himself accordingly, by counterattack, flight or a protesting surrender.

By no means all persecutory delusions come to so clear and dramatic a climax. But whether or not they do, there is nearly always a prolonged phase during which the patient gathers and mulls over his spurious evidence. He develops progressive reaction-sensitization in terms of his growing convictions.[77] Everything around him seems to refer in some way to him (*self-reference*), even though he may for a long time be unable to comprehend what is apparently brewing. Scraps of conversation, the looks others give him, their

---

[76] For an illustration of the development and structure of persecutory delusion, see the cases on pages 394–396, 497–500 and 504–506.

[77] See pages 71–74.

gestures, smiles, frowns and laughter find their place in his pseudocommunity, whether or not they can at the time be interpreted with certainty. People seem to be watching him, following him, discussing him and reporting what he says and does. His personal effects are intentionally disarranged to test him or show up his incompetence. Objects are left about so as to instruct him in something unpleasant, warn and threaten him, try his patience, impugn his integrity and call his intelligence into question. Even the newspapers, magazines, radio, movies and sermons contain humiliating, reproachful or accusatory references to his most intimate personal life. To this growing calamity most patients react with fear, anger and indignation. Some, however, view it with passive resignation; they may fear it but they do not resist it. Some seem, indeed, to welcome and invite persecution, as punishment they deserve or as martyrdom they accept.

The pseudocommunity, we have said, is one product of our common need for behavioral completion and elaboration. When something that interests us lacks an acceptable explanation, almost anyone — child or adult, man or woman — will supply an explanation, and thus terminate the need. He may do this in the company of others, using shared observation and conjecture, or by himself, with the aid of solitary watchings and unshared pondering. The persecuted patient, if he begins by communicating his suspicions and apprehensions with another, soon finds that all he gains is opposition, incredulity and derision, which force him to conclude that no one sympathizes with or understands him. With this conclusion his usually inept social skills conspire to exclude him from the company of others who might help him. So he is thrown back upon the lonely techniques which originally gave rise to his uneasiness, and left to work out satisfactions for his needs for closure by himself. It is in this general framework that *sudden clarification* makes its appearance. The purpose of the patient's pseudocommunity becomes abruptly "clear" to him — as in all closure — and he objectifies this purpose as he has objectified the pseudocommunity.[78] Like the "pursued" motorist, he is now ready for the next step, be it attack or defense, to build a bulwark or negotiate surrender.

(2) *Delusions of influence.* If we remember that anxiety is prevalent throughout behavior pathology, it will not surprise us to find that delusions of influence usually deal with threatening or malicious agents. They are, in other words, more often persecutory in character than comforting or grandiose. But there is about them an atmosphere of passivity, of magic and mysticism that earns for them a consideration separate from the ordinary persecutory delusion. Moreover, it is not uncommon for delusions of influence to arise in which the patient believes himself benefitted, sanctified or exalted, at the same time that he regards his fate already sealed in martyrdom, transfiguration or extinction.

[78] See pages 83–87.

The distinguishing characteristic of the delusion of influence is that its interpretations are in terms of the loss of personal control. The patient arrives at an explanation of his predicament — whether this be antisocial aggression, self-punishment or helpless ineffectuality — by postulating some agency which has robbed him of his will and therefore of his responsibility. Or if it is improvement, holiness or elevation that seems to be in store for him, he pictures this change as occurring by virtue of a submission to destiny. Thus, in either case, the patient achieves closure through ascribing irresistible power to something acting upon him from a distance. What he cannot acknowledge as his own act, accept as the consequence of his own distorted or impoverished behavior, or recognize as his own compensatory and rationalizing wish, he disposes of by making it the effect of some dynamic force that constitutes the field in which he is caught.

The delusion of influence suffers from a vagueness that makes it difficult to formulate in words. The *agents* most commonly accused by patient are gods and devils, parent surrogates — authoritative or protective persons who can usually not be identified — and individuals or groups having erotic, overpowering intent. Often the agent is frankly unknown to the patient, who refers uncertainly to the source of influence as "he," "she," "they," "something," or "a voice." The *means* used to control or direct the patient are usually designated in terms of folklore and popular science. Thus today one finds patients complaining of atomic energy, television, radio and X-rays as the instruments by which they are dominated, while the older accusations still persist against hypnotism, electricity, magnetism and telepathy, against poisons, drugs and anesthetics. The influence machine has been a favorite focus of invention by deluded patients, and its design and mode of operation, as might be expected, follow the trends of scientific and pseudoscientific advance.

As in all of behavior pathology, the patient's complaints appear to be based upon fact. Unfortunately, there has been so little scientific investigation of delusional behavior that we must admit our ignorance of the specific facts upon which most of the specific complaints are based. Reaction-sensitivity to local paresthesias, particularly when these are genital in origin, seems to underlie the claim that currents and energies are being passed through one's body. Complaints of passive ineffectuality, of fatigue and lassitude, and of powerless submission, are commonly ascribed by patients to drugs and toxins, or to telepathy and hypnotism.[79]

Because speech and thinking are of such enormous importance in human life, we find great galaxies of complaints referring to symbolic functions.[80] To the general statement, that one's mind is being controlled and manipulated, a

[79] For examples of delusions of influence, see pages 497–500.
[80] Further discussion of these phenomena will be found on pages 88–113, pages 453–454, and pages 506–515.

variety of detail may be added. Patients maintain that the words they speak
and the thoughts they think are not their own; their minds and their tongues
are used as passive or unwilling instruments by someone else whom they may
or may not identify. And some patients extend this influence to include the
source of acts they perform but disown. These self-reactions, pathological as
they may be, are not wholly unfamiliar to the normal person who has been surprised by something he has done, or said, or thought. The same is true of the
pathological complaint that one's words and thoughts have been stolen,
changed, blocked, slowed or put under unusual pressure. These are, in fact,
ordinary symptoms of anxiety which receive from confused patients, under
severe emotional stress, an unusual interpretation.[81]

(3) *Grandiose delusions.* Delusions of grandeur are for the most part exaggerations of ordinary optimism, self-confidence, conceit, arrogance and self-
assertion; their source is frequently to be found in exaggerated need for hope,
pride and domination. Thus, for example, one finds manic grandiosity developing in persons who are habitually inhibited, reserved, self-deprecatory and
sometimes depressed. One finds it also in persons whose self-reactions of inadequacy have prompted them to seek release in alcohol and narcotics. The delusions of grandeur that appear in paranoid disorders and in schizophrenia
represent either the end-result of progressive compensatory daydreaming, or a
reaction against overwhelming anxiety which self-destructive fantasies have
induced. Grandiose convictions, in other words, may arise in direct response
to frustrated need, or as a counterreaction to real or fancied threat.[82]

The pseudocommunities that grandiose individuals organize in their behavior are usually peopled with followers instead of pursuers, admirers and lovers
instead of enemies and revilers, servants rather than masters, the envious
rather than avengers. The patient identifies himself with great personages
belonging to history, fiction or contemporary life; he is a religious, political or
military leader, a famous athlete, scientist, artist or inventor, an architect, a
man of letters, a great actor, a singer or a surgeon. Grandiose men and women
boast of their abilities, their attractiveness and their fruitfulness; they suit
their behavior to their claims and play the part of masterful, superior, irresistible and amorous persons.

> A schizophrenic young man believed that he was destined to become
> Emperor of the United States. "I could do a lot for the world," he said.
> "The United States has presidents. Will it ever have an emperor? I'll
> bet you think I'm nuts to ask about that. I must have the morning
> paper to keep track of world affairs. . . . If the people of the United States
> want me to rule them, I'm willing to do so; but no one has been in to
> see me and tell me. I'll be glad to lead them." Later he spoke of hear-
> ing public announcements that he was to be crowned emperor. "It's
> been heard all over the country," he said. "The world is in chaos.

[81] Compare pages 279–280 and 311–312.   [82] See pages 330–335.

Thousands will be killed. I'm not a god or a devil, but I'm a supernatural being." All nations would come under his rule but Egypt; and Egypt would eventually fall to him through marriage. Along with these delusional convictions, the patient believed that attempts to kill him were repeatedly being made so that he lived, like Damocles, in constant greatness and in constant danger.

A manic young man was certain that he could solve a critical international situation single-handed. He demanded thirty radios so that he could be connected with the principal capitals of the world. He called himself superman, said that he was next to God, and exacted strict obedience from his father. An unmarried manic young woman went on an extravagant shopping trip, buying herself luggage and a trousseau on the grounds of the marriage she expected to effect with a movie actor whom she knew only slightly. She carried newspaper clippings which she interpreted as supporting her contention that the actor loved her. A manic farm-hand boasted of unlimited strength, saying that he could lift up a heifer with one hand, and lick any prize-fighter living. He claimed to be a close friend of a famous general, whom he had actually never seen, and said that the President and he were going to open a new bridge for traffic in a joint ceremony.

A not uncommon delusion is closely related to the fantasy of adoption which children and adolescents take refuge in when they feel ill-treated or rejected by their parents, and when they are for any reason ashamed of their parents. In the fantasy of adoption the child or adolescent imagines himself as the kidnaped or abandoned offspring of kinder and more nobly born parents. The delusion of adoption, in effect, continues this fantasy, elaborates upon it, and extends it to include shared activities no longer confined to the private daydream.

Delusions of grandeur tend to lead the individual into conflict with others. The claims and demands that he makes encroach upon others' rights, either restricting their activities or requiring them to relinquish privileges to the grandiose patient. The assumption by anyone of a style of behavior belonging to a social status that he does not actually possess exposes him to ridicule, retaliation or restraint. If, as is usually the case, a grandiose patient adopts a role which he has not previously lived, he is sure to reveal his inadequacies, to overplay his part awkwardly as braggart, clown or fanatic, and so defeat his own purpose.

In delusions of grandeur there is apt to be a greater dependence upon behavioral reciprocity from the pseudocommunity than in delusions of persecution or of influence. The persecuted may flee and the influenced may wait; but the grandiose needs to be waited upon, worshipped, obeyed, acknowledged. He is thus in a more precarious position than the others; to achieve completion through delusion he must have a degree of cooperation from other persons — real and imagined — that is difficult to obtain.

(4) *Self-depreciatory delusions.*[83] The person with self-depreciatory delusion is a hostile person. His hostility is an attitude of aggression, spite and vengeance turned against himself.[84] His projection is assimilative projection. He sees in the behavior of others the attitudes of hatred, contempt and contumely which he also acknowledges as his own. He publicizes his worthlessness and sinfulness; he puts his words of self-condemnation in others' mouths. He invites punishment, and if it is not forthcoming he may indignantly demand it. Indeed, one of the puzzling characteristics of the person with self-depreciatory delusions is his lack of even ordinary humility, of anything approaching submissiveness or resignation. He judges, condemns and sentences himself; but he often demands that the sentence he passes be executed exactly as he prescribes. There is a degree of self-assertion in the whole performance that seems to contradict the patient's insistence upon his little worth.

Unlike persons with persecutory delusions, the self-depreciatory patient asserts and reasserts his own guilt, uselessness, stupidity or fraudulence. His dominant public attitude is masochistic; he insists that he obviously deserves to be reproached, contemned, ostracized and castigated — or killed. He expects retaliation on the basis of what he considers to be justice, and not misunderstanding or malice. Sometimes he takes matters into his own hands and punishes himself by acts of self-denial or self-injury, by deliberately making a public spectacle of himself, by courting dangerous accident, or carrying out a clearly self-punitive suicide.

Self-depreciatory patients vary greatly in the definiteness with which they formulate what it is that they have done, and what retribution they expect. In many depressions,[85] for example, something concrete and definite from the recent or remote past is cited in detail and reiterated over and over in exactly the same way. The incident is often trivial and banal, in marked contrast to the punishment which the patient demands and to his vehement denunciations of himself. In schizophrenic disorders,[86] on the other hand, it is common to find the patient vague and uncertain as to the exact character of his offense, and as to the retributive justice he anticipates. Sometimes the schizophrenic person is content with an insistence that everyone knows what he has done and what will happen to him; but he may give evidence later that he is as unclear about it all as his listeners are. Some of these characteristics appear in the examples which follow.

A middle-aged woman, in a postoperative delirium, asserted over and over that she was "eternally damned" because she had "committed

---

[83] Self-depreciatory delusions seem to characterize patients of younger chronological age. See Albee, G. W., "Delusions in schizophrenia as a function of chronological age." *J. consult. Psychol.*, 1950, vol. 14, pp. 340–342.

[84] This point is discussed in further detail on page 321. For examples of the relationship between hostility and intropunitive behavior, see Korner, A. F., *Some aspects of hostility in young children.* New York: Grune and Stratton, 1949, pp. 131–132; Levy, D. M., "Studies in sibling rivalry." *Res. Monogr. Amer. Orthopsychiat. Assn.*, 1937, no. 2.

[85] See pages 314–329.   [86] See pages 494–515.

every sin there is." She said, "They fed me slops today like they feed pigs. I have a swine's body. Let them cut anything they want out of me. I don't deserve anything that's good. Give me a match so I can burn up quickly." A depressed clergyman insisted that he had been cheating and lying all his life, and asked to be wrapped in a sheet soaked in acid. A schizophrenic man believed himself guilty of "the sins of the world," and deplored the suffering that he was causing everyone. He called himself wicked, low, vile and degenerate; yet, at the same time, he expressed resentment over the way his "condition" was broadcast by the clinic to the world. He was certain that he had heard staff physicians discussing a plan to put out his eyes. He was frightened, but he considered that he deserved punishment for his misdeeds, although he never seemed able to specify what they were.

As one might expect, delusions of self-depreciation are commonest of all in depressive disorders, and next most common in schizophrenia. They also occur in the emotional upheaval which sometimes characterizes delirium; and they are not uncommon in compulsions. Indeed, the rituals practiced in compulsive disorders often represent an attempt to atone for overwhelming guilt which has been only partially and unsuccessfully repressed.[87] In protracted intense or acute anxiety, one's guilt reactions may rise to delusional levels and the fear of and need for deserved punishment grow proportionately severe. In some religious sects, such anxiety and apprehension over divine retaliation are handled by public statements of the penitent's worthlessness, accompanied or followed by ritualistic demonstrations of abasement.

(5) *Delusions of body change.* Delusions of body change can be understood only if their normal background is understood. During his first twenty years of life, every person is exposed to almost daily discussion of changes in his height and weight, in his facial form and body conformation, in the size of his hands and feet, and in the status of his secondary sex characteristics.[88] Comments are freely made concerning one's similarity or dissimilarity to other persons at corresponding ages in these characteristics, and in hair, skin and eye color, in growth of facial hair or clearness of complexion. During another twenty years there are fewer changes to observe in men, but the experience of pregnancy introduces women of this period of life to changes which commonly involve the face and the extremities as well as the torso. The third and fourth twenty years — if a person lives to see them — bring the inevitable involutionary alterations, which are endlessly discussed and universally deplored.[89]

To all these normal body changes must be added the effects of disease,

---

[87] See pages 357–358.

[88] See, for example, Stolz, H., and Stolz, L., "Adolescent problems related to somatic variations." *Yearb. Nat. Soc. Stud. Educ.*, 1944, vol. 43, pp. 80–99.

[89] See, for example, Shock, N. W., "Physiological aspects of mental disorders in later life." In Kaplan, O. (Ed.), *Mental disorders in later life.* Stanford University, Calif.: Stanford University Press, 1945, pp. 23–68.

injury and surgery,[90] of malnutrition and of overeating, in men the growth or removal of moustache and beard, and in women the artistic alterations in appearance which fashion and individual taste suggest. On the fictional level there are other important sources of body change delusion. Mythology, folk-lore, plays, poetry and prose abound in tales of human beings made into monsters and animals into men, of persons made large or small by magical means, or rendered immortal, given indescribable beauty or unspeakable ugli-ness. Similarly entrenched in our culture, and much more generally accepted, are the superstitions which equate good looks with social virtue and ugliness with sin; clear eyes with truth and shifty eyes with craft and falsehood; an upright carriage with honesty; size and strength with courage and dependabil-ity; a receding chin with weakness and a lofty brow with high intelligence.

Individuals differ in their reaction-sensitivity to body changes in themselves.[91] Some of those who are unusually responsive to such alterations have heard body appearance or performance overemphasized in childhood; they have taken over in their self-attitudes the attitudes shown them by parents and parent surro-gates. Often this trend is given special impetus by repeated comparisons, favorable or unfavorable, with siblings and other children. Parents who believe they can detect truth or falsehood by simple inspection of a child's face sometimes unwittingly train the child to inspect his own face for signs of the guilt or unworthiness that he may later feel. Children, adolescents and adults whose social status as loved or respected persons seems to depend heavily upon appearance and bodily integrity will also become reaction-sensitive to change; so will anxious and hypochondriacal individuals who mistrust their adequacy.

A person thus rendered reaction-sensitive will have no difficulty in finding genuine changes in his body's appearance and performance. In the first place, no one looks exactly the same even during one twenty-four hour span. And when he is worried his anxiety will have tangible and visible effects which can be interpreted to mean almost anything. The same is true of physiological functions; anxiety and concern may affect them profoundly. Preoccupation with body change makes one progressively reaction-sensitive; and continued observation sharpens one's ability to detect and to exaggerate insignificant variations.

It is upon such foundations as these that anxious, neglected or frustrated persons build their acquired self-reactions into delusions of body change. The commonest foci are the face, the body conformation and the viscera. An anxious, puzzled, preoccupied individual may spend as much as an hour staring at his face in the mirror. His anxiety, his puzzlement and his preoccupation will be reflected in what he sees before him; but the interpretation of what he sees will in large part be determined by his personal preconceptions. He may

---

[90] Compare the discussion on pages 235–237.   [91] See pages 311–312.

find his eyes malevolent, vacuous or ecstatic; he may conclude that his features have grown distorted and grotesque; he may see a beauty that is hidden from others.

> Thus a schizophrenic young adult insisted that his face was changing into a boy's face and that his man's flesh was coming off it. A delirious woman complained that her eyes were running out through her body. A schizophrenic girl with brown eyes was certain that the physicians had given her blue eyes which did not belong to her. "They've got to be brown," she said. "Yes, they must give me back my eyes." A depressed man said that his eyes had turned green, his face had become lined and depraved-looking and his head was now full of granite, "hard inside," with his forehead hanging down. A grandiose paranoid patient maintained that his face had acquired "the royal look," and that people averted their eyes from him because of his power.

Delusions of change in general body conformation are most commonly associated with sexual concern. Persons are sometimes convinced that they are losing the proportions characteristic of their own sex and acquiring those of the opposite sex. With this there may also be the belief that a corresponding transformation in the external genitals is taking place. As might be expected, the hands come in for special attention. They are the principal instruments by means of which good and evil are performed; and patients ascribe to them structural characteristics which seem appropriate in terms of the cultural background. Thus, patients complain that their hands appear swollen or shrunken, that they are strange-looking and misshapen, and sometimes that they seem to have become devil's claws.

The viscera undergo so much change during normal activity, as well as in disease, that their involvement in delusion can hardly be surprising. The gastrointestinal system leads the list, just as it does in hypochondriacal overconcern. Patients complain that they have no stomach or no bowels, that the stomach has shrivelled up and the intestines turned to stone, or — especially among schizophrenic persons — that stomach and intestines have disappeared, rotted away, or been devoured. Most patients who make such complaints, whether schizophrenic or not, still continue to eat and drink, and to eliminate without much more than ordinary urging. The genitourinary and the cardiovascular systems are only less common sources of delusional complaint than the gastrointestinal; and the brain, with the increased attention given it in magazines and newspapers, is becoming a favorite delusional focus. The character of the delusion depends, of course, upon what the patient knows and what he thinks he knows about the biology of the viscera involved.

(6) *Delusions of unreality.* Among anxious patients, one commonly hears the complaint that familiar objects, people and events seem to have become unfamiliar, unnatural and unreal. To some individuals everything appears suddenly to stand still; animals look like stuffed animals, flowers look artificial,

and people look like waxworks. To others, animals move as if they were
mechanical toys, while human beings act as though they were robots driven by
internal machinery. To some patients, animals and inanimate objects stand
out with exaggerated sharpness and clarity; to others, everything is vague
and confused, or far off and unapproachable. When these complaints express
a persistent conviction, we are dealing with delusions of unreality. Two examples follow, one that of a depressed and one that of a schizophrenic person.

> An agitated depressed woman, in her middle forties, called a nurse
> to the window and said, "Look at that tree! If this is a seven story
> building, how can that be a natural tree?" She complained that her
> teeth were not her own. When dental X-rays were one day taken,
> she remonstrated, "You know perfectly well these aren't X-rays. You've
> doubled up bits of paper and put them in my mouth." She said that
> conversation was artificial; people say the right words, but they don't
> sound right. "I'm not my real self. I must be somebody else. Do
> I look like someone else now? I'm different from everybody else. Who
> are you (nurse)? In some ways you seem myself; but that couldn't
> be, could it? I feel when I'm somewhere, I'm somewhere else. I feel
> like I'm a different person. I'm not the same any more. I'm lost."
> A schizophrenic woman, thirty-two years of age, after returning to
> the clinic from a walk, asked earnestly if she had actually been out.
> The pavement, she said, looked peculiar, there were trees she had never
> seen there before and the buildings were "somehow all wrong." Con-
> cerning a woman with whom she had been conversing, she asked, "Is
> she a real person? She might represent you (nurse) or a doctor; and
> even you seem like somebody else or not a person." On one occasion,
> a nurse found her squeezing feces through her fingers. "It doesn't seem
> real," she explained, "and I have to find out." The patient could not
> believe that her menstruation was real. She spoke of the sun's not
> being in the right place because it could not be so warm in April. An-
> other time she said, "That's not the real sun; I know it's night."

As these two examples indicate, delusions of unreality are often exceedingly
distressing to the patient. Their strange and sometimes weird character is in
itself frightening; but still more disconcerting is the difficulty in communication which quickly becomes apparent. For when the frightened patient reaches
out for sympathy and reassurance, he finds that he cannot formulate his
predicament adequately in words. His listeners, who either have not suffered
unreality at all, or else have formulated it differently to themselves, cannot
understand the patient. Consequently, they tend to make light of his complaints, which makes them seem heartless; or they ease their own discomfort
by declaring the complaint meaningless and unintelligible, which increases the
patient's sense of hopelessness and isolation.[92]

Delusions of unreality are common wherever there is severe anxiety, as in
panic reactions, agitated depressions, deliria, and some compulsive disorders.

[92] Compare the discussion on pages 420–424.

They are also of frequent occurrence in schizophrenic disorders and in deliria, both of which illnesses are characterized by disorganization with exaggerated overinclusion. In the syndromes to which we next turn, the paranoid disorders, the incidence of delusions of unreality is relatively low, considering the prevalence of anxiety among paranoid persons. This is probably related to the fact that, unless a paranoid panic reaction develops, the patient typically maintains a comparatively high level of behavior organization.

Paranoid Disorders

Delusion, as we have indicated, may be found in any of the behavior disorders. Delusional reactions are especially prominent in schizophrenic disorganization and in delirious disorientation. They are always unmistakably present in depressions and manic disorders where, however, they are more or less incidental to the dominant sadness or elation. But there are also syndromes characterized by more or less systematized delusional behavior, without disorientation and with little or no disorganization, which show neither marked sadness nor marked elation. These syndromes we call *paranoid disorders*.

Let us define *paranoid disorder* as *behavior dominated by more or less systematized delusional reactions, in which disorganization, disorientation, sadness and elation, if present, are incidental.* The word *paranoid* means literally *paranoia-like.* The term *paranoia* is itself taken directly from antiquity. It was current in the medical literature of Greece and Rome up to about the second century A.D., and seems to have been used in a sense roughly equivalent to our term *insanity.* In the latter part of the nineteenth century, Kraepelin gave *paranoia* a more precise formulation, reserving it for cases of highly systematized chronic delusion, in which neither disorganization nor deterioration was present.[93]

Thus narrowly defined, paranoia has turned out to be a clinical rarity and a virtually incurable end-product. But paranoia-like illnesses, in which delusion is not highly systematized and rigid, are relatively common and by no means incurable. Their relatively greater clinical importance has led to the reduction of Kraepelin's *paranoia* to the status of a rare variant under the paranoid disorders to which it gave its name.

In *paranoid disorders*, only delusions of persecution and of grandeur play a prominent role. This restriction is probably an artifact, the consequence of our current mode of classification of the behavior disorders. For delusions of influence, of body change, and of unreality tend toward behavioral disorgani-

---

[93] For a discussion of this historical development, see Cameron, N., "The functional psychoses." In Hunt, J. McV. (Ed.), *Personality and the behavior disorders.* New York: Ronald, 1944, pp. 904–907.

zation, which our definition of paranoid disorder specifically rules out. Of the two, delusions of persecution are far commoner among paranoid patients than delusions of grandeur; and this, of course, agrees with their relative incidence in the total picture of behavior pathology.[94] Persecutory delusions appear to be direct reactions to anxiety, which is prevalent in the everyday life of our culture. Grandiose delusions seem usually indirect attempts to escape anxiety through developing rigid attitudes of self-aggrandizement, which are difficult to maintain in any continued interpersonal relationships.

Development of paranoid disorder

The development of paranoid disorder is essentially the growth of perse-cutory and grandiose delusional convictions into a fairly stable and well-organized pseudocommunity. Hence, the factors which favor the amplification and persistence of delusion can be looked for in the background of the paranoid patient. These factors we have already touched upon in relation to delusion formation and the evolution of pseudocommunities; [95] it remains only to sum-marize them at this point. In the interest of clarity and simplicity of exposi-tion, we shall confine our discussion chiefly to the common persecutory type, bringing in grandiose delusions only incidentally.

The paranoid person, as we have pointed out, is one who is seriously de-fective in role-taking skills. In consequence of this, a conclusion at which he arrives in some critical and personally important situation becomes for him im-mediately the only possible conclusion. His chief inadequacy lies in his being unable to put himself in the place of other persons, to gain their perspectives and thus to be able to share — at least momentarily — their attitudes. He remains on one side of the chasm and they on the other; and he has no tech-niques with which to cross from one side to the other. Moreover, such an individual typically has not learned facility in social interchange; he does not know how to confide and receive confidences. His habitual procedure, when in difficulty, is to think things over in solitude, to observe silently and ruminate over what he observes, to keep his conclusions to himself and test them out in secret.

Solitary, unshared procedures have limited usefulness in operations that involve the attitudes and intentions of other persons. If anyone becomes un-easy, puzzled, suspicious or frightened, because of what those around him say or do, he must have recourse to certain techniques by means of which his conclusions can be tested and validated. One of these techniques is that of taking realistically in imagination the roles of other individuals, shifting through a succession of plausible roles, and thus having in succession a variety of probable perspectives. Each perspective holds out the possibility of an interpretation different from the person's own and therefore makes alternative

---

[94] See pages 394–396.   [95] See pages 387–393.

choice immediately possible. Another technique is that of free communication, with persons who make one anxious, or with a neutral person whom one can trust. This also requires, however, that one be able to share the other's perspective in order to see it as a possible alternative to one's own, or as an important modification of one's own.

For the person who is seriously deficient in role-taking skills, trouble can be staved off as long as no serious threats arise, no imperative need is frustrated, and there are no insistent demands for cooperative behavior that exceed an individual's capacity. Patients become paranoid because threat, need or demand comes upon them under conditions that make avoidance impossible. The paranoid patient is usually a chronically anxious person who, partly as a result of his defective communication, tends to build up tensions, and is characteristically intolerant of suspense. The development of a distinct paranoid disorder, therefore, begins with some situation which suddenly increases a person's habitual insecurity and throws into sharp relief his social incompetence under stress. The following case will illustrate a characteristic onset.

An unmarried stenographer, twenty-eight years of age, was brought to the clinic for admission by her parents, who reported that she believed herself the victim of an organized plot. Her own statement was, "I'm nervous and I can't sleep; and there are some things I'd like to see cleared up." The parents were agreed that her illness began when the patient returned from a two-week vacation in the Rocky Mountains about three months previously. There she had entered with wholly unexpected enthusiasm into the gaiety of summer resort life. She had hitherto been a reserved, shy, prudish person, who had always been ill at ease with men. But now she began going off on hikes with them, and on evening strolls and moonlight canoe trips with a particular man who showed her ardent attention. Her younger sister, who was sharing the vacation, but not the gaiety, became increasingly critical of the patient's conduct. One night, shortly before their departure for home, the patient returned from a date at two o'clock in the morning. Her sister made this the occasion for letting loose a stream of accusation and reproach, in the course of which she asserted that the patient's behavior had set tongues wagging and brought down disgrace upon them both.

Back home, the patient seemed gloomy and sullen, and she was obviously preoccupied. She sat at the family dinner table silently and with downcast eyes, and spent nearly all of her time, when not at work, alone in her little bedroom. To her parents, she was courteous and moderately affectionate, but more than usually uncommunicative. Toward her sister, she maintained an attitude of studied, formal politeness, behind which her hostility was plainly discernible. The only overt interest the patient displayed was in the mail; but after two or three weeks, when it became obvious to everyone at home that an expected letter would never come, she ceased looking for it on her return from work. She avoided the few close friends she had, excusing her neglect on the basis of malaise and previous engagements; and she frequently absented herself from home to go off on walks and bus trips alone which, however, she declined to discuss.

On several occasions the patient spoke briefly with her father and mother of having been "seriously misjudged," of having been dropped by her friends "for due cause," and of being treated unkindly and derisively by fellow-workers. When her parents attempted to reassure her, and to point out inconsistencies in what she said — for example, her actual avoidance of friends who sought her company — she would break off the discussion with vague allusions to people talking out of turn, her reputation being at stake, people trying to get her fired, "rumors flying," and "intrigues all around." Three or four times she brought the open newspaper to her parents, and said abruptly, "Look at that, will you!" When they expressed puzzlement and asked questions about this, she would say in an irritated manner, "Well, if you don't get it, I certainly can't explain it to you!" She complained that she was being jostled on the elevated trains, on her way to and from work; but she declared she could not understand what was happening or why "they" were doing it. She said she thought she recognized some of the individuals involved.

It was after a Sunday evening bus trip, three weeks before her admission to the clinic, that the patient called her mother into her bedroom shortly before midnight. As soon as her mother came in, she closed the door and locked it, pulled the shade down to the window-sill, and then seated her mother and herself on the bed in a corner of the room. There she spoke in earnest whispers, after cautioning her mother not to speak aloud. She said that early in the evening she had attended an evangelistic service at a church across town where the topic of the sermon was, "Youth at the Crossroads." It dealt with the temptations of modern life and the ease with which young women nowadays yielded to them. The preacher launched forth into a vehement denunciation of current immorality, and followed it up with vivid descriptions of the disgrace and ruin that daughters brought upon their parents, and the certain punishment that would visit offenders in this world and the next.

During the service, the patient began to suspect that the whole revival meeting might have been inspired by public knowledge of her vacation sinning. The preacher, she told her mother, had stared directly at her in the midst of some of his most fervid accusations. She could not believe that this was wholly accidental. She agreed readily with her mother's statement that she was not a "fallen woman" — which the preacher seemed to have called her. But she pointed out that, if her own sister could misjudge her and impute wickedness to her on such slim evidence, there was no telling what others might believe. She begged her mother tearfully to be careful of what she said and of whom she allowed to enter the house. She conceded readily that her suspicions might be exaggerated, but she ended the whispered conversation with the disquieting statement that she knew they were being watched and spied upon, and that she intended to find out who was behind it all.

Following this episode, the patient spent less time in her bedroom.

She went out a great deal more than she ever had before, but always alone. Often she left the house suddenly, without warning, and as abruptly returned. These sorties were sometimes of brief duration — a few minutes to perhaps half an hour; sometimes they lasted several hours. Once the patient took an overnight bag with her to work on Saturday, and did not come home until Sunday evening. She declined so emphatically to explain her comings and goings, and behaved so threateningly when she was challenged, that her parents and her sister learned quickly to pass them over in silence. It was evident, from her occasional comments, and from the cross-questioning to which she subjected her parents when alone with them, that she was engrossed in some kind of a solitary investigation; but exactly what she was doing, no one could discover. In relation to her sister, she never relaxed in her dominant attitude of cool, wary aloofness and formal courtesy.

Two days before admission, the patient came home from work in the middle of the afternoon and announced that she had resigned from her position. It turned out that actually she had been peremptorily discharged because of the following incident. Soon after arriving at work that morning, she had walked straight past the private secretary and into the president's office. There she told the president that she was completely fed up with the whole business of gossip and slander, and proceeded to accuse certain individuals of being in league against her. He asked her to sit down, rang for his secretary, and called in the office manager and the head stenographer.

In the conference that followed, with the secretary taking notes, the patient asserted defiantly that these two persons, the manager and the chief stenographer, were ringleaders in a conspiracy against her. Their aim, she said, was to get her fired and to discredit her, by spreading defamatory rumors, so that she could not be re-employed. This she accused them of doing on the basis of information originally given them by her sister, and since then by others who, tipped off by her sister, watched and followed the patient wherever she went. When the president asked why these two should be doing all this to her, she replied that she had so much on them that they had to get her out of the way and silence her. At this, the manager laughed and the head stenographer broke out in angry rebuttal. The patient instantly pointed to this as absolute proof of their complicity. The president then told her that she had better go home and see a doctor, to which she retorted that he had better watch his step, too, because she could say a thing or two about him. It was at this point that he lost his temper and immediately discharged her.

At home, the patient told her mother that she had been gathering evidence for several weeks, and was now certain she could clear her own name and incriminate those who were persecuting her. Neighbors, as well as fellow-workers and other company employees, were in on the plot. The persons who kept jostling her on the elevated trains lived in a nearby street. She had seen them watching her home in the evening; and she had trailed one of them across town to within a few blocks of the office manager's house, when he had eluded her. The jostling, she said, was deliberately provocative — intended to trick her into making a public scene. She thought that some of the business slogans carried by delivery wagons in the neighborhood might be references to her — for example, "Say it with flowers." There was a lurid serial story being advertised in large letters, on newspaper wagons, which she felt must be a distorted dramatization of her life.

Her sister, the patient explained to her mother, acted as principal go-between because of envy and resentment over the patient's success with men, on the vacation, and the sister's failure. The watchers, spotters and jostlers were company employees, some of them unquestionably trained detectives. The patient was convinced that her sister planned now to disgrace the parents also, as punishment for their having failed to take punitive action on their own initiative. She knew the sister was an active agent, she said, because she had heard stones being thrown into the open window downstairs, and she had watched her sister on numerous occasions sneak out of the house to mail a letter on the corner. The stones undoubtedly had notes attached to them, bringing messages from the detective; and the letters were reports and replies.

The patient had her dinner alone with her mother, in her bedroom, and afterwards she repeated her story there to her father. It was deemed advisable to send her sister off to stay with relatives. The patient asked her mother to remain with her through the night; but in spite of this company she was too frightened and apprehensive to sleep. She kept repeating that it had been "a fatal mistake" to send her sister away, thus not only offending her but also leaving her freer than ever to scheme things with her confederates. In the morning, the family physician was called in. He persuaded the patient to go to the psychiatric clinic on the grounds that she was nervous and sleepless; and he implanted in her the hope that there she might clear up the whole situation.

The history taken at the clinic yielded some significant material regarding the background of this paranoid disorder. When the patient was three years old, her real mother died, and she was boarded with cousins in another city until she was seven. Meanwhile, her father remarried; but he did not bring his orphaned daughter into his new home until two years after her half-sister was born. In her cousins' house, the patient had felt herself an intruder, a child without a home and without parental love. She reacted to the other children's teasing by retreating into lonely play and fantasy. In her stepmother's house, she always felt at least in part a stranger and, in spite of her stepmother's attempts at acceptance, she considered herself less loved than her half-sister. These parents were unusually undemonstrative and puritanical. They discouraged heterosexual friendships during their girls' adolescence but talked marriage to each of them after she had reached her majority. The daughters had responded to this confusing orientation by exhibiting no overt interest in men's company until the vacation incidents which precipitated the patient's illness.

The patient at first reacted to her hospitalization by feeling more secure; but before long she expressed strong suspicions that some of the student nurses, and patients who were newly admitted, might actually be detectives planted to spy upon her. At one time she spoke of the whole clinic set-up as "a racket," and seemed to be including staff physicians in her hostile pseudocommunity. Eventually, however, these suspicions waned and the patient sought out and benefitted by interviews with the resident in charge of her case. She ultimately gained considerable insight into her affectional problems and, through this, she achieved some understanding of her paranoid illness. It was agreed on all sides, however, that she ought not return to her half-sister's home. And since she could not go back to her job, she decided to move to another city and find work, which she did with at least initial success.

In this case we have a person who, from her third year of life, had never managed to feel wanted or even accepted. Because of her reactions to her unhappy living conditions, she failed to develop intimate ties in her two homes. She made few close friendships with other girls and none with men. She was thus denied adequate opportunity, throughout childhood and adolescence, to acquire and practice realistic social role-taking, especially in affectional relationships. The source of her sudden interest in gaiety and the company of men she never revealed, and may not herself have understood. But the patient's childhood training in guilt, and that of her sister, conspired to defeat this unplanned attempt to break through her own reserve. She felt cheated and humiliated at receiving no further word from the man to whom she had been particularly attracted on the vacation. Finally, her lifelong habits of preoccupation and solitary brooding, and her incompetence in the techniques of sharing perspectives, of checking objectively on her suspicions, and of socially testing her conclusions, left her unable to avoid formation of a pseudocommunity or to escape its persecution.

Intolerance of ambiguity and paranoid disorders

In the beginning, as our case has shown us, a pseudocommunity is nearly always relatively diffuse, unstructured, unstable and unclear. Its development into a paranoid disorder is essentially a development in the direction of precision, organization, stability and clarity. The early stages are characterized by a generalized vigilance which sometimes leads to a certain degree of overinclusion and consequent initial disorganization. The patient has not yet, at this point, formed a preliminary conviction which can serve him as a nucleus for his delusional elaboration. He may do a great deal of solitary observing without drawing definite conclusions. His heightened reaction-sensitivity is like that of a sentry who is certain that danger is approaching but cannot name it. He is alert to an unquestionable menace which he cannot identify. Sometimes, during this phase, everything seems to be somehow related to the unformulated threat.

Vigilance without interpretation can lead an anxious person only in the direction of greater and greater anxiety, since something is always going on in any environment. Under these circumstances, the paranoid patient does what everyone else does; he forms a tentative hypothesis, a formulation that to some extent unifies what he observes. However, because of his incompetence in social testing and validation, a great many inevitably ambiguous situations cannot be resolved as the socially competent person might resolve them. The patient who becomes intolerant of ambiguity must somehow overcome the contradictions that he faces.[96] In terms of his personal insecurity, and in the direction of his dominant needs, he will accept one element and distort, neglect or repress its opposite. Likewise he will distort and reinterpret more or less irrelevant material to bring it into apparent relationship to his ongoing, dominant delusional trends.

The formulation of tentative hypotheses is often a reaction to the initial overinclusion with its threat of disorganization. The immediate result of hypothesis formulation, of course, is to restrict the range of the patient's vigilance by more closely defining his reaction-sensitivities. We have just seen, also, that the paranoid person tends to resolve the ambiguities that face him by distortion, neglect and repression. Some organization of behavior is thus preserved, and the danger of panic reaction or schizophrenic disorder is averted — at least for the time being. But this result is achieved through serious sacrifices in behavioral integrity. Accordingly, we may speak of this second phase in paranoid development as a restrictive-distortive one.[97]

The intolerance of ambiguity and suspense increases as the pseudocommunity crystallizes into a more and more stable organization. Choices that fall within its scope are made on the basis of agreement with the ongoing delusional development; and they are prematurely fixed as unalterable facts. The result is that the dynamic structure moves forward so inflexibly and irresistibly that new contradictory evidence no longer introduces doubt. The evidence itself undergoes a transformation, so that it seems to further the paranoid hypotheses, or else it is rejected. The function of the pseudocommunity thus comes eventually to be one of changing reality to fit a fantasy organization, and of neglecting, denying or repressing the remainder.

There is some experimental evidence which tends to support the clinical observation that spectator behavior is more conducive to error, when personal bias is involved, than is participative behavior.[98] Throughout most of his pseudocommunity development the paranoid patient remains almost entirely a spectator. He watches vigilantly and notices much that others miss. But in the construction he places upon what he sees and hears, he is likely to disagree widely with the consensus. And because of his deficiencies in social skills, the paranoid patient cannot test his interpretations by participating genuinely

[96] Compare Frenkel-Brunswik, E., "Intolerance of ambiguity as an emotional and perceptual personality variable." *J. Personality*, 1949, vol. 18, pp. 123–126.

[97] Compare the findings of Frenkel-Brunswik, *et al.*, of a relationship among intolerance of ambiguity, repression, and "distortion of outer reality." Adorno, T. W., Frenkel-Brunswik, E., Levinson, D. J., and Sanford, R. N., *The authoritarian personality.* New York: Harper, 1950, p. 457.

[98] Bruner, J. S., and Postman, L., "Tension and tension release as organizing factors in perception." *J. Personality*, 1947, vol. 15, pp. 300–308.

in a variety of social contexts, and thus being able to see things from the different perspectives that differing contexts permit.

Suspense ends and ambiguity is destroyed if a developing pseudocommunity reaches dramatic closure. Characteristically patients say something like, "Suddenly it all became clear to me!" and this has given rise to the term *sudden clarification*.[99] It seems to the patient that the whole pattern of the persecutory plot or grandiose plan stands revealed at last. Sudden clarification usually precipitates action because no further evidence is needed to confirm the dominant hypothesis. The paranoid person can now proceed with absolute certainty, since he has achieved complete conviction. The pseudocommunity at this point has reached the status of a closed system, the basis no longer for vigilant observation, but for final execution.

The shift from a spectator to a participator role, which frequently follows sudden clarification leads as a rule to unfortunate — and sometimes to disastrous — consequences. For what the patient takes for objective reality has validity only in his private unshared fantasy, where the ultimate bases for his pseudocommunity rest. The individuals in his delusional organization may all be actual persons; but the intentions he imputes to them, and the interrelationships he assigns, are always wholly or in part spurious and fantastic. The patient operates in a social field as a solitary individual, with unshared attitudes, taking action with which no one else can agree or fully sympathize.

Sudden clarification is not confined to paranoid disorders, and by no means all paranoid patients go through it. Indeed, the commonest outcome in these disorders is that of a fairly uneventful recovery. If recovery is complete, the person returns to his premorbid condition relatively unharmed; if it is incomplete, he may still lead a fairly normal life, with perhaps some residual eccentricity, suspicion and aloofness in his manner. In cases with more severe chronic residuals, the individual may succeed in finding conditions outside of a hospital where he manages to get along in a restricted environment of his own choosing. Otherwise, indefinite hospitalization may be necessary because the areas of behavior implicated in the pseudocommunity leave no possibility of even minimal cooperation with others, or of self-sufficiency in solitude.

Some paranoid patients, with or without an episode of sudden clarification, develop an acute panic reaction,[100] with hallucination and violent offensive-defensive behavior; and such panic may be in turn succeeded by a chronic schizophrenic disorder.[101] Others pass directly over into a schizophrenic disorganization, the remnants of their disintegrating pseudocommunity becoming transformed into an *autistic community*. In this form, as we shall see in the next chapter, behavior can be sustained which has so little relevance to the background present at the time that autistic community and social community need have almost no important points of correspondence.

[99] For a discussion of closure, see pages 75–79, and pages 302–303.
[100] See page 306.   [101] See pages 494–515.

14

Autistic Community and Hallucination

We have found it useful to distinguish three kinds of behavioral community, each considered from the standpoint of the organization of the individual. The *social community* corresponds realistically with the interactions of other individuals and oneself, in the shared field of social operations. The *pseudo-community* on the other hand, contradicts in part the actual structure of social interrelationships; but it always utilizes at least some interbehavior which can be shared by other social persons.[1] The *autistic community*, to which we now turn, differs from both these others in that it is wholly structured in terms of the imagined activities of imagined persons and things, operating within a fantasied context.

The Autistic Community

In behavior pathology, the significance of autistic communities is no less than that of pseudocommunities. We have already encountered autistic behavior in somnambulism, fugue and episodic hysterical seizure.[2] It has appeared more or less incidentally in our discussion of regression and with-drawal into invalidism,[3] and in connection also with hallucinatory activities of depressed and manic persons.[4] We shall meet its most dramatic and most ominous manifestations in the disorganized behavior of deliria and panic reactions,[5] and in the desocialization characteristic of schizophrenic disorders.[6] Indeed, so impressive are autistic manifestations in pathological behavior, that we are apt to forget their central role in normal everyday life — in the dreaming and daydreaming which together constitute a considerable proportion of every twenty-four hour cycle.

[1] For a discussion of social community and pseudocommunity, see pages 372–392.
[2] See pages 362–366.   [3] See Chapter 8.   [4] See pages 314–336.
[5] See pages 469–477.   [6] See pages 495–515.

414

We shall now define the *autistic community* as a *behavioral organization, structured in terms of the imagined activities of imagined persons and things in a fantasied context*. This, of course, is nothing more than the organization of fantasy, the structuring of dreams and daydreams. The autistic community, far from being exceptional and occasional — the weird product of rare and deviant thinking — is one of the commonest activities in everyone's behavior. It passes by for the most part unnoticed; but this does not mean that it passes by unused. On the contrary, autistic behavior performs functions that cannot be successfully carried out by either pseudocommunity or social community behavior.

The evolution of autistic community organization is the evolution of organized fantasy; if we understand one, the other must also be clear. Every child who learns to speak with others in public, we have said,[7] learns also to speak privately with himself. For the indisputable advantages of a muted system of private self-communication ensure its persistence as instrumental behavior, including such functions as entertainment, compensation and escape. Thus, in spite of the considerable difficulty involved, all of us ultimately acquire techniques of transforming audible communicative speech into inaudible, and for the most part invisible, symbolic behavior. Each of us in this way achieves communicative privacy; and from that time onward he can engage in effective silent discourse which need be shared with no one.[8]

The techniques of silent discourse are learned, just as other behavioral techniques are, and their acquisition is in part the outcome of direct social pressure. Under the conditions of group living, there are for everyone innumerable situations which demand silence when speech would otherwise be possible. When a child's overt talking is hushed because it disturbs the peace of others, or interferes with conversation, it can still continue as whispering and muttering; and if whispering and muttering are frowned upon, one learns to speak inaudibly and even without moving the lips. The rules of etiquette that govern polite conversation are to some extent observed by everyone throughout life; and if there are several persons present, or someone dominates the situation through a disregard of etiquette, silent discourse may come to pursue its own ends along solitary paths.

Covert speech is also encouraged by the regulations that apply to public meetings. The child encounters these first in situations which afford him little

[7] See pages 105–109.

[8] For discussions of the development of fantasy behavior, see Ames, L. B., and Learned, J., "Imaginary companions and related phenomena." *J. genet. Psychol.*, 1946, vol. 69, pp. 147–167; Despert, J. L., "Dreams in children of preschool age." In Freud, A. (Ed.), *The psychoanalytic study of the child*, vols. 3/4. New York: International Universities Press, 1949, pp. 141–180; Despert, J. L., "Delusional and hallucinatory experiences in children." *Amer. J. Psychiat.*, 1948, vol. 104, pp. 528–537; Murphy, L. B., "Childhood experience in relation to personality development." In Hunt, J. McV. (Ed.), *Personality and the behavior disorders*. New York: Ronald, 1944, pp. 652–690.

chance for participation, and little in the way of entertainment. He is introduced to church and school, for instance, long before these hold sustained interest for him. He must not talk, he must not sleep, and he is not allowed free movement. The habits of covert fantasy which he acquires under such circumstances, and the autistic communities which he learns to organize and practice, will come to his rescue when, somewhat later in life, he must attend boring lectures, mediocre shows, and routine business or professional conferences, and spend evenings with dull company. He falls back upon them also when he is thrown with strangers, in adulthood, and finds no real community of interest, and when he is walking or travelling long distances alone. Clearly, if silence meant the cessation of all symbolic activity, each of us would spend a large share of his life in symbolic inaction, if not in virtual stupor.

The silent self-communication that saves us from symbolic inaction gains reinforcement from a need which we also acquire early in life — the need for privacy. This need, as we have already pointed out,[9] arises originally from the untoward effects of our childhood verbal publicity. The child who talks while he is playing, we said, gives notice of his intentions, indicates what he is doing or has just done, and advertises his motives, his judgments and his personal opinions. He quickly discovers that his talking leads to adult interference and punishment. He finds that, once a verbal statement has been emitted, it can only with the greatest of difficulty be disclaimed or modified to make it acceptable to his elders. Gradually the child learns to signify his intentions, state what he is doing or has done, and formulate his motives, judgments and opinions, in such a manner that only he himself is kept informed. Thus, he acquires habits of restricting what he says aloud to that which is socially acceptable, and of granting freedom chiefly to behavior that cannot be shared with others.

Behavioral duplicity [10]

The private world of self-communication, as we all know, enables a child to profit from imagined victories and their unreal rewards, to achieve the impossible, and to continue in fantasy what someone else has stopped him from concluding in fact.[11] Covert symbolization also affords the child the most varied opportunities for engaging in taboo activities without danger of direct social retribution. He can daydream vengeance against a punishing or denying parent, and at the same time imagine himself comforted with affection by the other parent. He can commit imagined violence upon a sibling rival, and

[9] See pages 107–109.
[10] Behavioral duplicity is briefly discussed on pages 109–112.
[11] This is particularly clear in the "fantasy of adoption," discussed on page 399, and in the development of imaginary companions. See Ames, L. B., and Learned, J., "Imaginary companions and related phenomena." *J. genet. Psychol.*, 1946, vol. 69, pp. 147–167.

gloat over the injury, humiliation and distress which he has just invoked.[12] In fantasy, he can enjoy erotic stimulation without receiving punishment, disgrace or ostracism.

The secret character of covert symbolization, of course, is the source of that *behavioral duplicity* to which self-communication always leads.[13] For, as a child learns to restrict to silent soliloquy much of what he has previously said in public, he learns also the technique of maintaining simultaneously a publicly expressed and a privately held attitude. These two attitudes, and the responses they favor and support, need not correspond one with the other. Thus, the small and practically defenseless child finds that he can agree publicly with those in power, while secretly he persists in an unspoken disagreement. He can defy his elders and his stronger siblings silently, provided only that he appears to acquiesce; he can accept defeat verbally and reject it imaginally; he can mislead others by claiming intentions which at the same time he may recognize are not actually his.

Behavioral duplicity plays an important part throughout life in making it possible for a person to preserve behavioral consistency in the face of the never-ceasing social pressure to which he is exposed.[14] Many of these pressures compel the individual to do, say, and accept, and to cooperate in things which are contrary to his own interests and trends. It is one thing to agree successively with three or four mutually contradictory formulations — or at least to hear them without overt dissent — and quite another to accept them fully, and try to act upon them. In the former instance, one can continue acting and thinking with single determination, while deviating verbally this way and that; in the latter, single determination is impossible, consistency almost absent, and self-prediction useless.

But whatever the advantages or disadvantages, the desirability or undesirability of the outcome, each of us learns in many areas of behavior to act in accordance with one set of standards — self-interest, for example — and to formulate or describe his action in accordance with a different set — that of community approval, let us say. All of us in childhood, receive a great deal of instruction in formulating, describing and explaining what we do in ways that fall within the narrow limits of what is socially permitted and encouraged. Such instruction may be in the form of direct verbal statements. A shocked adult tells the child that he "must not *say* that!" or that he "*couldn't* have done such a thing!" and proceeds to pronounce what the only decent actions,

---

[12] There is some evidence that young children learn to handle both anxiety and aggression through fantasy developments. See, for example, Murphy, L. B., "Childhood experience in relation to personality development." In Hunt, J. McV. (Ed.), *Personality and the behavior disorders*. New York: Ronald, 1944, pp. 675–677.

[13] Behavioral duplicity is briefly discussed on pages 109–112.

[14] Behavioral duplicity should not be equated to deliberate hypocrisy. The two are obviously related, even closely related in the same general sense that hysteria and malingering also are — but they are still not identical.

opinions and intentions must be. The child soon adopts the substance of the adult's pronouncements as statements applying to his future acts, opinions and intent.[15] The same end can also be achieved indirectly, of course, through punishment, rejection and disgrace for socially inacceptable verbalizations, and through reward, acceptance and admiration for statements that conform to the group mores.

On the other hand, children are not punished for non-correspondence between what they say and what they originally intended, unless it becomes evident that the original intent still prevails in spite of what they say. Thus, for example, if a child is hostile, fearful or erotic, and says as much, he may be severely punished; but when he has learned to deny his hostility, fear or sexual arousal, he can escape adult reprisal completely. It is plain that his verbal disclaimer can earn him the same exemption, and often the same reward, that friendliness, courage or sexual indifference would have earned. No one doubts that training in verbal conformity does have some effect in modifying also the rest of behavior in accordance with the group mores.[16] But this modification varies greatly in completeness — from person to person, from time to time, and in the same person, at the same time, for different areas of behavior. Behavioral duplicity, and the complications it introduces into self-reactions, play a highly significant part in the organization of autistic communities and, as we shall soon see, in the emergence of hallucination.

Self-reactions and the autistic community

One of the most important modifications brought about by training in verbal conformity is the moulding of self-reactions in accordance with prevailing mores. Self-regulation, we know, is derived from regulation imposed by others upon oneself.[17] Each of us eventually wins a measure of independence from the direct control and surveillance of others by becoming capable himself of exercising self-guidance and self-scrutiny which corresponds to that earlier imposed upon him. Something similar occurs in the development of self-evaluation. We all go through long periods of training in passing judgmental comments upon our own behavior, while it is going on, and afterwards in retrospect. We learn to give approval, praise and pardon to our own actions, our words and our thoughts; we learn to visit them with disapproval, threat, warning and condemnation. We grow able to tell ourselves that we have done well

---

[15] There is some evidence, however, that, although the overt reaction may be inhibited, a covert reaction may remain. See the discussion of this point on pages 98–105. See also McGinnies, E., "Emotionality and perceptual defense." *Psychol. Rev.*, 1949, vol. 56, pp. 244–251.

[16] This principle has been employed to explain the process of therapy in behavior pathology. See, for example, Shaffer, L. F., "The problem of psychotherapy." *Amer. Psychologist*, 1947, vol. 2, pp. 459–467.

[17] For a discussion of self-regulation, see pages 95–98.

or done badly, that we are clever or stupid, shrewd or gullible, brave or cowardly, righteous or evil, strong or weak.

When we were little children, we all learned first-hand the value of parental approval and acceptance. We found out what followed threats and warnings, what condemnation meant in fact, and how welcome forgiveness could be.[18] Now as each child takes over these functions into his own behavior organization, he continues to respond to the evaluation as though it were still coming from his parents. Thus he may glow with pride when he tells himself in words or thought that he is good, courageous or intelligent; and he may shiver with anxiety and apprehension when he says or thinks that he is wicked or craven. He has now acquired, in his own private world of self-communication, the behavioral materials for a further modification by which his evaluation of himself is made to conform to social sanction.

For if a person's self-evaluation can punish or reward him, he must find ways of avoiding the one and inviting the other. We have already seen that children learn to give statements about their conduct that please others. In a similar fashion, they also acquire techniques for meeting the demands of social self-regulation. They learn, in short, to inhibit a great deal of activity that cannot readily be formulated in socially acceptable terms. A great deal more they distort and disguise, so that their behavior seems to their self-reactions to be in conformity with social standards. The rest may be dealt with in any one of several ways — by compensatory "reaction-formation,"[19] by denial which to be sustained demands repression,[20] or by disowning projection which involves both repression and denial.[21]

Thus we see that, as a person's self-regulatory behavior organizes in terms of the prevailing mores, he learns to meet the challenge of self-evaluation as he had previously learned to meet his critics. His analysis of his own behavior, as he presents it even to himself alone, may eventually resemble the formulations he has learned to prepare for the approval of others around him. This does not mean that his behavior is now all in conformity with what is considered proper for one of his status. It means only that his self-evaluative reactions have evolved forms which protect him from much of the anxiety that self-criticism might otherwise induce.[22] Motives, intentions and the recall of previous activity may in this process of transformation become self-inaccessible because they are overlaid by such socially acceptable self-evaluations or because we habitually distort and repress important components in preserving our equanimity.[23]

The development of organized self-reactions greatly enriches fantasy, and

---

[18] This point is discussed in greater detail on pages 284–289.
[19] See pages 376–379.   [20] See pages 337–351.   [21] See page 387.
[22] See pages 98–105, and pages 376–387.
[23] One sees the effects of failure of such protection in depression. See especially pages 320–321.

complicates enormously the structure of autistic communities. By means of the self-reaction, a person can think of doing or saying something; and afterwards, or at the same time, he can also think about the deed or word as though it were not his at all. He can imagine doing something, as himself, while he also imagines praise or criticism of it as coming from someone outside the act. Or he can think of doing or saying something as though it were the behavior of another person, while he recognizes as his own the evaluation of that which he has imagined being done or said. Sometimes, on the other hand, both roles seem completely his, and sometimes both appear foreign to him. But no matter how they may at the moment be conceived of by the thinker, both the acting and the evaluating roles, of course, are merely aspects of the same daydream. Both of them are located entirely within one person's behavioral organization.

Autistic communities in dream and daydream

The identifying characteristic of dream and daydream is this: that they are symbolic activities lying wholly within one person's behavior and having no necessary relationship to the immediate environment. Of the two, the daydream is the easier to describe and understand.

Realistic daydreaming. The structure of the daydream, much more often than that of the dream, corresponds closely to the organization of discourse, and to the temporal and spatial arrangements of objects and persons. Indeed, many daydreams amount to little more than the recall of events and places belonging to one's past, involving minimal distortion, and containing nothing impossible or even unlikely. Many daydreams are fantasies of something which may at the moment be going on somewhere else, for example, at the play one could not attend, or something a friend may be doing in another town. And many daydreams about the future are made into more or less authentic prophesies by the structure of subsequent events; one plans a dinner, a vacation, a coup or a career, and the plan is later realized with no sweeping changes.

Autistic communities such as these are peopled by the thinker with real persons, who play ordinary social roles in a realistic setting. In them, fantasy runs roughly parallel to fact; it reproduces the past or foreshadows future fact with reasonable accuracy. Although it is seldom purely verbal, the realistic daydream often resembles a soliloquy. There is a dominant sequential train of thought, which may at times retrace its steps — as a soliloquy may, but the march of events cannot — and sometimes it moves swiftly from one thought sequence into another, and back again. But there is little more fragmentation and dislocation of events than one would expect in a protracted tale that is told in leisurely fashion for entertainment. The main theme is never altogether lost until the daydream closes or some other main theme takes its place. There are no sudden kaleidoscopic shifts, no weird condensations, and no inexplicable appearances or disappearances.

The materials we use to construct such daydreams are all derived from behavior that we have carried out or witnessed in the field of social operations. They are, as we have earlier indicated,[24] public before they become secret. The daydreams that we keep realistic are never allowed to lose completely their effective contact with social interbehavior and the structure of the shared environment. They remain realistic as long as we envisage them against a context that resembles closely the context of social interbehavior. Their social usefulness will depend, therefore, upon the degree of correspondence between the context we provide and the configuration of the social field.

Unrealistic daydreaming. The realistic, well-organized sequential daydream, while it has many uses, has also many limitations. Because it does not go beyond or run counter to fact and likelihood, it cannot possibly offer the variety of entertainment or provide the fullness of escape that the unrealistic, meandering daydream can. The idle, easy-going, unproductive kind of fantasy is one of the most useful and important forms of human recreation. The child shut-in at home, or kept in school, can still run and jump in his imagination, build things, play jacks, marbles or baseball, spin tops, enter a contest of boasting — and excel in everything. Moreover, whether he is restricted or at liberty, a child can make himself large, grown-up and strong in fantasy, play the part of his favorite hero, or enjoy honor and possessions without work or waiting that might, in reality, take decades of unremitting labor and unheard of luck.[25] If he believes or knows he is not loved, he can create in imagination children and adults who love him dearly and without reserve.[26] If his peers treat him with contempt, or pity him, he can fantasy himself their master or their envied hero.

The child, grown to adulthood, does not find everything there that his fantasies have promised him; and he meets a great deal that he has never imagined. Success comes to few who seek it; and affection passes many persons by who cannot live without it. Prizes often recede as fast as one travels toward them; or they are finally overtaken and found not to be what, at a distance, they had seemed. But the techniques of fantasy remain. The range and complexity of favorite daydreams usually increase as one matures, and their topics and populations undergo a corresponding maturation. The frustrated, deprived, disillusioned or neglected adult, like the rejected, unloved or restricted child, turns from the dissatisfying life around him to the satisfactions and protection of his daydreams. Here he can give himself what others deny

---

[24] See pages 105–113.

[25] Murphy, L. B., "Childhood experience in relation to personality development." In Hunt, J. McV. (Ed.), *Personality and the behavior disorders.* New York: Ronald, 1944, pp. 675–677.

[26] For a thoroughgoing study of the development of imaginary companions in young children, see Ames, L. B., and Learned, J., "Imaginary companions and related phenomena." *J. genet. Psychol.*, 1946, vol. 69, pp. 147–167.

him and withhold from him; here he creates an imagined context as the background for his imaginary triumphs, his pleasures and his solace.

For a great deal of ordinary daydreaming, and for most of dreaming, there is no good reason to expect a close correspondence between the imagined context and the structure of the social field. Indeed, realism can seriously *hamper* the free exercise of fantasy, just as too great fidelity to fact may severely limit the value of a story or a play. Autistic communities are commonly the elaborations and condensations of fictions whose origins, of course, go back ultimately to social fact. The dream or daydream that provides tension-reduction, relaxation and entertainment need not be concerned with accurate recall, the duplication of an absent reality, or the faithful rendering of a future probability. It performs its function best when it evades reality — escapes from an unhappy past, an unfruitful present, or the unwelcome probabilities of a barren, burdensome future.

Present fantasy can improve upon *past recall* by deviating from its factual course — beginning with what actually has happened at some point, and reshaping what next followed so that failure, misery, monotony and guilt are eliminated. Sometimes, instead of doing this, one utilizes fragments of fact and weaves them into an imagined past that violates the spatial and temporal organization to which the fragments originally belonged. One finds this particularly in normal night dreams and in the daydreams of detached schizophrenics.[27] In structuring his autistic community, a person may also proceed by preserving the remembered context, the main themes and even the sequence of events, much as they were, but exchange in his fantasy his own status for that of a more satisfying role. And finally, one may deny and disown one's past outright, replacing it with a purely fictional past which is claimed and defended as one's own. This is the situation in the *fantasy of adoption*, so common among imaginative unhappy children, and in its pathological counterpart, the *foster-child delusion*.[28]

Fantasy improves upon the *present*, also by beginning with things as they actually are, and restructuring the contemporary situation to make an autistic community from which current frustrations disappear, and in which absent or imaginary persons replace the unwanted persons of the social community. Sometimes present circumstances are in the main retained in structuring an autistic community; but the thinker alters his own status and plays the situation through from the perspective of an assumed role. This technique is obviously derived from realistic role-taking and shifting perspective.[29] Here, however, it is being utilized as evasion or escape, and not as a basis for the explanation of social fact, or as preparation for it. In normal dreaming, in hysterical trances, in some depressions and manias, and in a great many schizo-

---

[27] See pages 503–506.   [28] Compare the discussion on page 399.
[29] See pages 114–122, and pages 374–376.

phrenic disorders, the socially shared present is openly rejected and denied as unreal, while an autistic community is accepted and proclaimed as the real world. Two illustrations of such usurpation follow, in each of which an autistic community supplants the shared social community.

> A depressed middle-aged woman insisted over a period of several months that she was actually in another world where no one in this one could reach her. "I am in another sphere, a million miles from anybody. No matter what you do there it can't help me where I am. I'm not in this world; I'm not celestial or terrestrial. There isn't any time where I am; but things are going on continually." A schizophrenic woman in her thirties stated consistently that she had "crossed over" into another world, the "right world" where she was to be married. The world she had left was the "wrong world, your world." In her new world her name was Jude. "O, it is terrible," she said, "I am being told things all the time to do, and I don't know how to do them. These voices! They talk to me all the time. My mother and father talk to me. I can't do all the things they're asking me to. They come from the wrong world, and I can't get back to it."

Fantasy frequently avoids taking paths in the direction of what would seem objectively to lie ahead, and unrealistically promises or threatens an unlikely or an impossible future. Thus, by ignoring the inevitable obstacles, denying the clash of contradiction, and neglecting troublesome but highly pertinent details, one can start from the present and project an imagined on-going future that fulfills every desire or realizes every fear. A person can, by means of identification,[30] act through in his own autistic community a future that is possible for someone else but not for the fantasier himself. This is what parents often do with the imagined future of a child, what moralizers do in relation to those of whom they disapprove, and what schizophrenics do in identifying with persons of wealth and power, or with honored martyrs. In schizophrenic disorders, and sometimes also in depressions, the probable future may be insistently repudiated, while a fictitious and impossible one is prophesied and prepared for as in the following case.

> An unmarried stenographer, in her middle twenties, heard a voice one night which called her "consecrated." She decided the next day that she was to bring salvation to those who loved her, and she predicted that she would go about the country performing miracles. She told her parents that she was greatly frightened by her missionary future, but she could not be brought to doubt its inevitability. For six months she managed to keep her position and perform her office duties satisfactorily. Then her imagined future began encroaching upon the present that she was living, and she soon required hospitalization.
> The depressed middle-aged woman previously mentioned believed that she would never die. "All the doctors will die and all the nurses will

[30] For a discussion of identification, see pages 60–63.

die," she said, "and I will live on forever. Ten hundred million years from now I will be the same. I am a body fastened to the earth by a demon monster. . . . I will wander over the face of the earth and nobody will be left alive. Even if I did this (passes finger across throat) I would live on and on."

The organization of dreams and daydreams

We have said that some daydreams are well-structured, sequential, and peopled with actual persons who are imagined playing ordinary social roles in an appropriate social context. These are the realistic fantasies which do little more than reproduce the past, parallel the present, and project a probable future. It would be a mistake, however, to suppose that the realistic daydreams represent the most closely organized autistic community. For, as we have already pointed out,[31] in the field of social operations everyone is continually responding in terms of incomplete, developing, ongoing activity. Everyone must constantly supplement what is objectively present with symbolic representations. Realistic fantasy, if it corresponds closely to social fact, must also retain some of the incompleteness, the onmoving, unconsummated character of the indefinitely bounded environment.

There are dreams and daydreams much more tightly organized and homogeneous than realistic fantasy. They possess some of the properties of a self-contained story or a play, from which the irregularities and inconsistencies of socially shared existence have been excluded, and the parts made subservient to a dominant, intelligible whole. The close-knit dream or daydream may be less rich, less variegated and less colorful than realistic imagining; but, like the finite, bounded play or story, it can be far more absorbing and intense, and often it is unforgettable. We shall find its counterpart in the single, hallucinated voice, proclaiming a brief message which leaves an ineradicable impress upon the hallucinating person, and in the visual appearance of a clearly defined person, or of an object without context. No ordinary conversation and no realistic hallucinatory discourse can rival in effect the singleness, the concentrated organized intensity, of the terse communication or the simple apparition.

There is an infinite series of gradations, from the close-knit, self-contained dream or daydream — at one end of the organization continuum — to the weird, disjointed, fragmentary fantasies which we find toward the opposite end, as behavioral disorganization is approached. But, as we shall soon see,[32] disorganized behavior need not mean pathological behavior. An excited, anxious or disoriented person, for example, is certain to exhibit fragmentary, haphazard or chaotic behavior, regardless of the background for his excitement, his anxiety or his disorientation. Thus, a frightened or an extremely

---

[31] See pages 374–376.   [32] See pages 452–469.

happy person may become temporarily disorganized; and so may any normal individual, who is neither particularly happy nor frightened, when a sudden environmental change renders his anticipant attitudes incapable of supporting appropriate sequential responses.[33]

Normal dreams and daydreams seem often to be fragmentary or haphazard in character, and sometimes they impress the dreamer or daydreamer as having been chaotic. This relatively disorganized structure may occur as a result of excitement or anxiety, but it also appears when the fantasier seems neither particularly excited nor anxious. This should not surprise us, inasmuch as we have already pointed out the conglomerate and often disjointed character of self-conversation, even when it is overtly carried on.[34] Moreover, in covert self-communication, we have said,[35] verbal and non-verbal components are so intricately interwoven that an attempt to tease out one from the other would raise — with our present day techniques — insuperable obstacles. To all of this we may add the fact that many of the connecting links in self-conversation and the intermediary, transitional symbols in self-communication are forgotten or repressed. It can no longer surprise us to find that dreams and daydreams often, if not usually, lack the orderly spatial and temporal composition which we ascribe to socially shared behavior.[36]

All dreaming and daydreaming are made possible by the highly important organizational property of behavioral exclusion.[37] To perform any one complex act well means to exclude all responses to intrusive stimulation which would otherwise break up a behavioral configuration. A person can carry on two organized activities at once provided one of them does not interfere with the other, use the same response systems differently, or lead toward opposite concurrent action. Thus, for example, one can type from copy and fantasy about something else, simultaneously, if these precautions are observed. The coordinated overt typewriting behavior has its context in the observable social field, and it is kept organized in those terms; the fantasy, on the other hand, provides its own context, and it proceeds as covert responses within an unshared covert field.

The fact that dream and daydream provide their own private, unshared context has some interesting corollaries which we shall find useful in the study of hallucination. One of these is that success in dreaming and daydreaming depends primarily upon success in keeping fantasy out of contact with the surroundings. Daydreams — normal as well as hysterical, depressive and schizophrenic — frequently rival night dreaming in their exclusion of the shared environment and in their autistic self-contained ongoing organization. Often they rival night dreaming also in the degree of disorganization they can

---

[33] See pages 64–66.   [34] Compare pages 109–110.   [35] See pages 111–112.
[36] This characteristic of dreaming was early pointed out and elaborated by Freud. See, for example, Freud, S., *The interpretation of dreams.* London: Allen and Unwin, 1927.
[37] See pages 74–75.

develop without leading to cessation of fantasying altogether. Presumably, the reason that the night dream is more likely than the daydream to show fragmentation and condensation is that the sleeping person, because of lower level of general reactivity, normally excludes exteroceptive stimulation more surely and for longer continuous periods than one who is awake.[38]

One other corollary of the self-contained context deserves special attention here. Fantasy that provides its own imagined context shuts out all the usual bases for disbelief. There is no environment outside the organism to be dealt with, no object arrangement and interpersonal field to which one must conform. Consequently whatever seems to happen seems also to be appropriate, since it has its context structured for it in the fantasy organization that made it possible. There is no more need for checking imagined responses in an appropriate imagined context than there is for checking the reality of trees against a background of the countryside. The clash of interpretation, inference and conclusion with a stable, objective configuration does not occur, unless one fantasies such a conflict. In other words, dreams and daydreams are normally delusional in character and, to the extent to which responses in them are attributed to sources outside the fantasier, they also involve hallucination.

Hallucination in Behavior Pathology

By *hallucination* we mean *a response whose stimulus is within a person's fantasy behavior, but is mistakenly attributed by the responding individual to sources outside of it*. It is obvious that hallucination, so unhesitatingly dismissed in popular thinking as relatively rare and absolutely pathological, is actually common and usually normal — as common and normal as dreaming and daydreaming are. Nevertheless, popular opinion is entirely correct in ascribing by implication a considerable importance to hallucination in deviant thinking. For the projection of fantasy stimulation against a background of social operation plays a significant part in the development and persistence of many forms of behavior pathology.

We have anticipated the present discussion of hallucination in the chapter on symbolization and emotional reactions, and in the earlier part of the present chapter.[39] In hallucinating, we said, a person misidentifies his remembered past and his own past imaginings, making both into a present occurrence and giving to both an existence which seems to him independent of himself. The structure of hallucination clearly illustrates the biosocial origins of fantasy, its unmistakable relevance to the individual's social *milieu*, to his own particular past, and to the workings of his own body. The mountain Swiss hallucinate a mountain background; the Netherlanders near the Zuider Zee dream of wind-

---

[38] Compare the discussion of hysterical somnambulism on pages 362–366.

[39] See pages 88–129, and pages 414–426.

mills and canals.[40] Men dream predominantly masculine dreams, and women fantasy specifically feminine hopes and expectations.

The distinction between normal hallucination and pathological is difficult to make. This is in large part due to the popular prejudice already mentioned, that hallucination is the hallmark of grossly abnormal conduct — a prejudice that pervades the literature of our culture and the textbooks in our field. And yet everyone recognizes that he hallucinates in dreams, and a great many persons realize that daydreaming also involves frank hallucinatory behavior. But there persists, at the same time, an almost universal tendency to regard vivid fantasies, even in normal dreams and daydreams, as queer and unnatural, as something to laugh off and to consider unworthy of serious consideration. Still more pronounced is the tendency to disparage the visions and voices reported by persons in trances, or when wide awake, which others do not share — unless, of course, a voice or a vision coincides with some strong cultural or subcultural belief.[41]

If we apply to dreams, daydreams, trances and wide awake fantasies in which hallucination occurs, the same criteria that we applied to delusion, it becomes at once apparent that everything mentioned in the preceding paragraph may be either normal or abnormal. In the interest of clarity and consistency, let us repeat and adhere to these criteria. We consider hallucination to be *pathological* only if it makes a person ineffectual in his social relationships or interferes with his attainment of important satisfactions. With these criteria clearly before us, we may now turn to a consideration of the characteristics and varieties of hallucination, and of the conditions favoring hallucinatory activity.

Characteristics af hallucination

(a) *Cultural influences.* Hallucination, like fantasy that is neither projected nor disowned, always bears the marks of its cultural origins. The Irish report seeing leprechauns which, if captured, are said to reveal the whereabouts of hidden treasure; while those Arabs who thirst for wealth or power see genii take form out of the great whirls of sand and dust they continually witness. The Taos Indians, who do not look for subterranean gold, see their gods appear over the rim of the Sandia Mountains, where an Arab or an Irishman would find only the sky. Likewise, the voices one hears nearly always speak in one's own native tongue or in a religious or magical tongue such as the vulgate or the accepted formulas of sorcery. The identity of the apparent speaker also

---

[40] See, for example, Taylor, W. S., "Fantasy preference and Indian education." *Indian J. Psychol.*, 1946, vol. 21, pp. 62–68.

[41] This is in line with the observation that hallucinations seem to occur more frequently in societies where social training favors the reporting of hallucinatory reactions. See, for example, Dollard, J. and Miller, N. E., *Personality and psychotherapy.* New York: McGraw-Hill, 1950, pp. 178–181.

reflects one's culture. Catholics hear the Virgin Mary speak comfort, Moslems hear the voice of Mohammed Ali, while Buddha or Confucius speaks to the hallucinating Chinese.

In dreams and daydreams, wherever an appropriate context is fantasied in support of imagined activities, or of an imagined static figure, both the context and what appears against it are biosocially derived. In most instances, pathological as well as normal, it is possible with skill and patience to trace the cultural and biological sources, or to infer them from ancillary information. Even if an alien culture or an extramundane setting is hallucinated, it is usually traceable to beliefs, current or traditional, to which the fantasier has been exposed. Hallucination in the wide awake has similar properties. In aerially oriented America, with its current military perils and weird "comic strips," the frightened common man sees "flying saucers" in an innocent sky, and imagines Martian men reconnoitering before they launch a celestial assault.[42] His utter dependence upon the cultural context appears in the anatomy and costume of the Martian that he fantasies; for these depart insignificantly from the pictures of gnomes and elves out of the common man's childhood fairy tale books.

(b) *Role-taking.* The role-taking that one hallucinates, whether in dream and daydream or against the background of shared social behavior, is never created out of nothing. It occurs always in terms of socially derived behavior organization, even though considerable distortion, fragmentation and condensation may be introduced. The roles are usually drawn from familiar everyday activities. They are defined and delineated by the behavior of others — either shared or fantasied behavior — and they correspond to what is permitted or forbidden in the culture to which dreamer or daydreamer belongs. The same general limitation applies to hallucinated role-behavior that we recognized in relation to shared role-behavior: it is always to some extent determined by the degree of conformity, reciprocity and resistance that the individual at the time can manage.[43]

The role fantasied in hallucination, like that lived out in everyday existence, may be one's own as it actually is; or it may be in some modified form which still is directly derivable from one's own. But it is much more commonly the case that the hallucinated role bears a reciprocal relationship to one's social role, or represents neither one's own nor a reciprocal role, but the role of someone only indirectly related to the hallucinator. In the fantasied reciprocal role, the hallucinating person obtains the support he needs for his own imagined behavior; or he achieves rewards and other gains through the fantasied efforts of others on his behalf. By assuming the roles of other persons, unrelated to

---

[42] See, for example, Cantril, H., *The invasion from Mars.* Princeton, N.J.: Princeton University Press, 1940.

[43] Pages 114–122.

everyday activity, the hallucinator can imagine himself engaged in all kinds of activities foreign to his ordinary, prescribed life. To these assumed alien roles he may also react, of course, by fantasying appropriately reciprocal roles which he can likewise disown and reify.

The transition from the everyday fantasying of reciprocal roles to hallucination is a transition by way of disowning projection.[44] The hallucinating person fantasies a voice or a scene, just as the non-hallucinating person does, but he disowns it as his own product. This he manages, as a rule, through repression of the source in his own behavior [45] and ascription of the voice or scene to something outside himself. As we shall see especially well illustrated in auditory verbal hallucination, an *antiphonal opposition* is in this way established. The imagined voice can be argued with, objected to, blamed and execrated. One can plead with the disowned projected words as though they came from another person; one can disclaim responsibility for obscene and blasphemous comments, as the devil's products, and accept as God's words the benedictions that come from one's own fantasied speech. It is this opposition of reciprocal roles, with repression of the source of one of the two, that characterizes hallucinatory conflict and discourse — the same opposition which we found basic to delusion and the pseudocommunity.[46]

(c) *Social conformity.* Hallucination is learned, practised, and by some persons carried to the level of a highly skilled and sometimes semi-autonomous act.[47] Human learning, we have pointed out, is social learning which is structured in terms of a highly organized human environment.[48] Learning to fantasy in terms of reciprocal role-taking obviously involves the acquisition of social conformity; and it is this social conformity that we see reflected in the otherwise extraordinary sameness of hallucinatory structure from person to person. This accounts for the fact that the dreams and daydreams of one individual can be compared usefully with those of another. It explains the fact that a person can more readily understand dreaming and daydreaming by individuals in his own than in an alien culture, and that a study of the hallucinatory products of patients in any culture helps one to comprehend those of other patients subsequently studied in the same culture.

Two factors conspire to diminish social conformity in hallucination. One of these is that the success of continued hallucinatory behavior depends to a

[44] For a discussion of disowning projection, see pages 384–387.
[45] See pages 337–351.   [46] See pages 387–405.
[47] Attempts to produce hallucinatory behavior through the application of laboratory learning techniques have yielded equivocal results, however. See, for example, Corn-Becker, F., Welch, L., Fisichelli, V., and Toback, E., "Factors productive of conditioned images or sensations." *J. genet. Psychol.*, 1949, vol. 75, pp. 149–164; Ellson, D. G., "Hallucinations produced by sensory conditioning." *J. exper. Psychol.*, 1941, vol. 28, pp. 1–20; Leuba, C., "Images as conditioned sensations." *J. exper. Psychol.*, 1940, vol. 26, pp. 345–351.
[48] See pages 55–63.

considerable extent upon one's keeping it out of contact with social interaction. It is the rare person who can hallucinate, without long practice, against a background of public, shared behavior which must inevitably include so much that contradicts private fantasy. Habitual fantasy that develops a favorite theme can develop it in directions which deviate further and further from conformity with shared operations. Thus, the structure of an autistic community may undergo progressive desocialization and its hallucination may grow more and more aberrant, unfamiliar and bizarre. This is sometimes the situation in long-standing schizophrenic disorder.[49]

The other factor diminishing social conformity in hallucination is that of behavioral disorganization. Through participation in shared social operations the individual is able to acquire and maintain a considerable degree of continuity and homogeneity in his behavior patterns. These patterns will conform to those of other persons because they have been organized and practised in relation to the other persons. The fantasying which is derived from such overt social interaction will tend to share some of this acquired continuity and homogeneity. However, as we shall later see, there are numerous conditions under which individual behavior grows disorganized. The distinctions between fantasy and social fact then break down, the origin and the location of things imagined may become as uncertain as they often are in dreaming, and disowning projection leads to frank hallucination. This we encounter clinically in delirium, panic, schizophrenic disorders and sometimes in mania.

The semiautomatic character of well-practised hallucination may have beneficial or harmful consequences. If autonomous fantasy is dominant, it must interfere with shared, overt behavior, and make a person's social operations seem queer, unreasonable and disjunctive. The outcome, under these circumstances, is likely to be a gradual withdrawal from social participation and therefore an intensification of the already dominant covert fantasy. On the other hand, hallucination which cannot be disposed of may nevertheless interfere relatively little with a person's shared behavior if it becomes sufficiently autonomous. One can then virtually ignore it and go about one's business with the general attitude that a voice heard is a nuisance — and at times a resented annoyance — but not something to be heeded, argued with or obeyed.

(d) *Systematization*. The composition of hallucinatory behavior, and its varied systematization, might have been inferred from our discussions of thinking as self-communication and as fantasy.[50] There we alluded to the fact that, even though the acquisition of language behavior helps organize imagination along linguistic lines, it does not transmute all fantasy into words. The imagery of recall is also the imagery of hallucination; and the intricate commingling of remembered words, phrases, sounds, scenes, objects, persons, tastes and smells, which characterizes rumination, can be matched in halluci-

[49] See pages 494–515.   [50] See pages 109–113.

natory projection. If to this we add the systems of private, abbreviated and condensed symbolization that all of us use in active self-communication, we begin to approach a statement of the conglomerate structure which hallucination may exhibit.

At one extreme of systematization, the hallucinatory episode consists of a mere fragment which seems to come from nowhere and leads apparently to nothing. This we encounter in the common hypnagogic voice or vision which appears just as one is falling asleep.[51] A face seems suddenly to loom up and quickly vanish or a phrase is enunciated that sounds meaningless or lacks a context. Sometimes there is a sentence or two, instead of an isolated phrase; or perhaps a somewhat less fragmentary visual apparition comes. In sleep, there is often a well-structured visual hallucination which, however, may be without discoverable antecedent or consequent; it stands alone, motionless, and disappears without fading. The same holds true of auditory hallucination in sleep: a complex sound structure — organized music or a clear verbal statement — may come and go without apparent context.

Fragmentary, disconnected and somewhat haphazard hallucination is common in schizophrenia. For example, a schizophrenic girl seventeen years of age made the following statement: "I see all sorts of hallucinations whenever I relax. I want to relax and somebody holds out a paper with 'Relax! Relax! Relax!' on it. It's maddening. I hear a voice saying words to me. I see all kinds of figures — a stairway and a bannister, it was straight and now it's curving, an oval mirror. Then I open my eyes and see dots and circles everywhere. I can feel myself floating in the air. I'm so horribly frightened. I don't have a moment's peace. I close my eyes and see large rooms and many colors. I always think someone is going to jump at me."

Hallucination in delirium and panic, as well as in schizophrenia, is often as fragmentary and discontinuous as this. But it may also show some relationship to an immediately antecedent event, in the field of social operations or in the delusional structure of a pseudocommunity. Thus, following rounds in a hospital, the delirious patient hallucinates preparations for surgery to be performed upon him. The patient in panic hears voices warning him of the evil intentions of someone who is actually approaching him at the moment. A schizophrenic patient sees a heavenly figure before him as he looks up from a concluded prayer. On the other hand, an hallucinated voice or vision, without an apparent antecedent, may precipitate immediate action. To this group belong the sudden command that makes a patient supplicate or strike, and the flash of a scene that leads him to rush to the rescue or to flee in terror.

Diffuse, loosely organized hallucinatory behavior belongs both to early and

---

[51] See, for example, Froeschels, E., "A peculiar intermediary state between waking and sleeping." *Amer. J. Psychother.*, 1949, vol. 3, pp. 19–25; Mintz, A., "Schizophrenic speech and sleepy speech." *J. abn. soc. Psychol.*, 1948, vol. 43, pp. 548–549.

to late pseudocommunity development. Early in delusion formation, the increased vigilance of the patient makes him reaction-sensitive to anything within a wide range of threat or promise. This is a phase during which over-inclusion, with initial disorganization, is nearly always present. Now this and now that fantasy response is mistaken for stimulation outside of fantasy with little organized selectivity. However, as the patient formulates tentative hypotheses, his range of vigilance is narrowed and his selectivity tends to fall into some kind of pattern.[52] This secondary organization in a great many chronic patients gives way to disorganization in which there is confusion of contexts and a return to fragmented hallucinatory activity. We see such reversions in the course of schizophrenic disorders which neither end in recovery nor lead to the structuring of a well-knit autistic community.

We find well-organized hallucination under a variety of conditions. Normal daydreaming sometimes includes transitory disowning projection and a sequence of visual and auditory hallucination almost as realistic as a play. Night dreams are also sometimes fairly accurate hallucinatory reproductions of well-structured remembrance, and even fantastic, unrealistic dreaming may be highly organized and internally consistent. The hallucinatory episodes that sometimes mark a religious revival meeting may be clear, easily described and evidently realistic; so may also be those occurring in times of threatened disaster, and those responsive to extreme need for comfort and relief.[53]

Hallucination in religious ecstasies, and when great danger or great deliverance seems imminent, often resembles that of hysterical autonomy. The hysterical trance, of course, is made possible by overcomplete repression. All response to the social context, during the autonomous phase, is inhibited and behavior is restricted to that which the dominant fantasy context will support. Thus, for example, the sequences appearing in hysterical seizure include well-organized and often vivid hallucination. Here the overexclusion of the field of social operations permits fantasy activities to go on without contradiction or distraction; and the result is a dramatic, internally consistent action-dream.[54]

Sometimes in schizophrenic disorders a patient is successful in shutting out the social context, while he fantasies, without developing serious behavioral disorganization. The autistic community which he structures may under these circumstances show a high degree of systematization and include coherent and congruent hallucination. Thus, a young engineer built for himself an organized

---

[52] Compare the development of delusional behavior. See pages 387–392.
[53] Compare the hallucination of rescue ships by exhausted fighters in open boats. Critchley, M., "Exhaustion in relation to fighting efficiency; reactions of men to long periods in open boats." *Inter-Allied Conf. War Med.*, (1942–45), 1947, vol. 1, pp. 289–293; Anderson, E., "Abnormal mental states in survivors, with special reference to collective hallucinations." *J. Res. Naval Med. Serv.*, 1942, vol. 28, pp. 361–377.
[54] Compare pages 359–367.

fantasy life in which he imagined himself married to an imaginary companion, and the hallucinated structure of this autistic community seemed to him more real and reasonable than anything in the social context. In such retreats from overt shared interpersonal relationships, a continued resistance to the disorganizing effects of desocialization can rarely be maintained. For, as we have indicated, the goals as well as the methods of autism and of social participation are in direct conflict.

Varieties of hallucination

When one recalls in fantasy something that has happened in the past, or imagines something projected into the future, it is usually not a voice alone that is heard, or only a face seen, or the smell of fresh grass and nothing else. To remember, for example, last summer's ride in a motor launch is to imagine the motor noise, the splash of the waves and the cold spray on one's face, the hot sun, the smell of the paint on the launch and of human sweat, the buoyant pitching of the craft, the sound of talking and laughter, the green water, one's companions moving about, the curving in to the pier, the thud of landing, and the hunger before eating.[55] To imagine the ride on mule-back down into the Grand Canyon, even for one who has not taken it, is likewise to fantasy movement, sound, sight, heat, the smell of beasts of burden, and the discomfort of looking over the edge of a precipice.

In normal hallucinating we often do the same. We dream about the dead and they speak as we see them, there is the pressure of a hand, and perhaps a cold gust of wind. Hallucination in behavior disorder is likely also to be multiple. A schizophrenic patient, with fantasies of dying and going to heaven, saw and heard angels, felt the blood run out of her body, seemed to herself to rise from the bed and float upward, and smelled a dry, lethal gas. An acutely delirious patient heard voices reviling him, saw a dog apparently about to attack him, felt snakes in his bed, tasted poison in his food, and complained that his mattress kept moving in waves as if it had a machine under it.

The vision or the voice alone, the strange smell or taste that seems to come without antecedent warning or adequate background, the peculiar feeling suddenly of being touched or of having something alien and unnatural inside one's body — these also are not uncommon in behavior pathology, just as they are not unfamiliar in the dream. It is probable that such seemingly isolated hallucination belongs to a larger context of imagination, but, for the fantasier, whatever context there may have been is lost. He hears without recognizable precursors a voice that gives him a command, rebukes him or tells him of future greatness. He sees materialize abruptly before him, in a corner of the room, a smiling vision of the Virgin Mary; there is neither sound nor fragrance, but only the vision. Or he smells gas which is being pumped into the room; he sees and hears nothing unusual.

[55] Compare the explanation of learning through redintegration discussed on pages 66–69.

In the discussion that follows, we shall use illustrations in which one or another variety of hallucination is clearly dominant or appears alone. By thus restricting the scope of our examples, we can reduce the complexity of the clinical picture, and bring exposition within easily intelligible bounds.

(a) *Auditory hallucination.* In behavior pathology, the auditory hallucination is second to none in potential significance; and of all varieties it is the commonest. By far the greater proportion of auditory hallucination consists of verbalization. The *non-verbal*, however, is by no means rare, and it covers a wide range of apparent sound. Thus, patients complain of hearing cries and groans, of hearing screaming and sobbing; they tell of laughter, shouting and clamoring, of a confused din and of the indistinct murmur of crowds. They report that there is knocking and thumping going on, the noise of machinery, the rush of automobiles and trucks and trains, the roaring of aircraft, the sound of splashing water or the rhythmic beating of waves. Some patients say they hear whistling — of human beings, animals, machines, the wind — or they hear bells, auto horns, music playing, shots being fired and explosions.

> An agitated depressed woman said, "Whistles go all the time. Do you hear them? Is there water near? And so many bells ring; there must be a lot of churches near. It's all such noise. All the time people are whistling, and drums beating, and street cars." A woman in a post-operative delirium, of undetermined etiology, complained of hearing "horns and other sounds — why are they doing it? Screaming voices and things that frighten me. Funny sounds and shooting, far away." All this, she said, was terrible and tortured her. A schizophrenic man insisted that he heard the pattering of rain, although there was no sound like rain that was audible to others, and the patient himself was mystified by the fact that the sun was shining. At another time he spoke of "bells, and trains in tunnels" and of fish jumping out of the bathtub water and falling back into it — when actually no water was near and no bath filled or filling.

It is hardly surprising that *verbal* hallucination, the sound of voices saying something, is both common and important in behavior pathology. Man is, above all else, the talking mammal. In no other form of life does organized, consecutive sound reach comparable complexity; and in no other animal has sound been systematized into a comparable instrument of communication. Human society without language behavior is inconceivable; and whether or not language *could* have been developed by mankind without vocalization — without audible, heard speech — the fact is that communication among human beings has been actually built from the spoken word.[56]

In the everyday life of ordinary men and women, the spoken word is the link that connects one person with another, the thread out of which the web

[56] See Chapter 4.

of communication is constructed in action. Not alone is it the thing somebody says at the moment, but the echoes also of past words that are recalled in fantasy, recast and improvised in one's own private imagining. There are also the words each of us speaks to himself — conventional words, slang, abbreviations, intimate verbal notations that no one but the thinker can understand, exclamations, fragments. There is the verbal preparation or rehearsal of something later to be spoken, or later to be discarded and forgotten; and there is the highly significant use made of word fantasy as self-entertainment, denial and escape.

As we have already pointed out, taboo subjects can be explored and taboo attitudes can be maintained in private, without fear of social retaliation, excepting for the retaliation that one visits upon oneself, with the voice of conscience.[57] A person can also give himself words of praise or criticism, of support or rejection and contumely — and do this with his own voice, or with the imagined voice of parent, sibling or friend, of a lover, a marital partner, a son or a daughter, of God, the devil, a saint or an angel, of someone unknown, of an acclaiming multitude or an avenging mob. The voice of conscience, or the superego,[58] may warn or frighten a person in his sleep, speak to him in the deep preoccupation of a daydream or pursue him in his self-accessible waking thoughts.

This is the essential background for all verbal hallucination. Indeed, much of what we have just been discussing is itself hallucinating. The words a person seems to hear or to speak, in a dream, he characteristically attributes to sources outside his own fantasy; it is this or that person saying something, or he himself is saying it. Only in exceptional instances does the dreamer doubt the verity of what he imagines. In deep preoccupation, also, the fantasier at the moment seems to be hearing or speaking in fact, even though a fraction of a second later he may realize the true situation. In that transitional borderland between waking and sleeping — the hypnagogic state — some persons seem to hear their own thoughts spoken aloud, by themselves or by others, or perhaps by a chorus of many voices. Occasionally, this apparently occurs in moments of wakeful preoccupation, startles the hearer, and sometimes makes him afraid.

Many persons who develop persistent auditory verbal hallucination begin by asserting that, even when they are fully awake, they seem to hear their own thoughts expressed aloud. We have here, of course, an intermediate phase between normal thinking, in which a person is able to recognize the products of his fantasy as his own, and frank hallucination, in which a part of fantasy is projected and disowned. In this intermediate phase the words are more or less successfully projected, but they are still identified by the patient as belong-

[57] Compare the discussion of hostility and guilt on pages 287–289.
[58] For a description of conscience, see pages 284–286.

ing to his own imagining. Thus, a schizophrenic young woman said of her thoughts, "I sort of imagine I hear them. They seem real, that's the trouble. Sometimes I hear a voice speaking at the same time I do; but it says something else. It's awful. I think something, and I hear it."

Patients describe other intermediate phases between ordinary thinking and hallucination. A schizophrenic woman, for example, expresses her vagueness and uncertainty when she says, "It seems like spiritualism; and I don't know what it is. It seems like other people are talking to me, but I don't know." And at another time, "Sometimes it seems like something would say to kind of end things. (Is it a thought or a voice?) Sometimes it would seem like a voice. When I'm talking here, is it just you? Or is there somebody else too?" The voice, she said, was "off in the distance," and might not be a voice. Patients often say that they hear a voice in their minds, their brains, or their bodies. The fantasy product in these instances may be disowned, but it is still acknowledged as coming from within.

Among the patients who take the next step, and locate an hallucinated voice outside themselves, some describe its location as merely around them, outside, in the air — they do not quite know where. They express their perplexity over the strange experience by saying that something queer is going on, and ask, "*What are they (or you) doing to me?*" The voices themselves sound mumbled, whispered, or muttered to many patients. One schizophrenic patient complained that "they don't say anything but they're always making some noise." Another, who later hallucinated clear talk, began by hearing only grunts of approval and disapproval.

Complete disowning projection is achieved in verbal auditory hallucination when a fantasied voice is mistakenly attributed to sources outside one's fantasy, and heard clearly and distinctly. This occurs in the dreams of a great many persons in ordinary life, as well as in many patients with behavior pathology. It occurs seldom in normal daydreaming, and rarely in the normal person who is not deeply preoccupied, acutely anxious, or in intolerable need. In certain forms of behavior pathology — particularly in deliria, panic and schizophrenic disorders — hallucinated voices in the patient's thinking nearly always appear; and for many of these persons the voices they imagine can be compared to the voices occurring in the field of shared social operations. This relative clarity of hallucination, in persons who have become unable to distinguish clearly between social fact and fantasy (*overinclusion*), tends further to hasten the trend toward behavioral disorganization.[59]

> Thus, a college graduate, who was still able to carry on his work as a salesman while actively hallucinating, asserted with assurance that the voices he heard were as loud and clear as that of his questioner. Another man spoke with certainty of voices telling him he was in England. He

[59] See also the discussion of overinclusion in visual hallucination on pages 439–441.

told persons around him that he did not "trust you English," and kept informing them that "in America we do" thus and so. A schizophrenic woman was sure that she was being followed because certain voices continued talking to her wherever she went; she never doubted their reality. A delirious woman reported, "I hear voices. Somebody is calling me. I must get up and go to them. Someone is calling me and I can't even get up." A schizophrenic woman said of the voices, "I happen to know it's *not* imagination. I want to eliminate them; it's been so long now." She insisted that she would engage a lawyer to stop the voices, and that she would "search every house in the neighborhood until we find where they're coming from."

The voices hallucinated may be ascribed to some specific known person or spirit. A schizophrenic young woman wrote in a letter, "Dad's voice I've heard all the time, and someone else's too. Those are what have encouraged me on. . . . I hear Ralph Connor's voice all the time; that's hope in the greatest." She told a nurse that she had been carrying on conversations with a certain hallucinated young man; she spoke to him and he responded, and she derived great pleasure from this. Another patient, recovering from a severe schizophrenic illness, could still hear at times the voice of a young man making love to her. Although she called the sound her own imagination, she admitted that she replied to this voice, "just to see what he would say." It is common for schizophrenic patients to hear the voice of God directing them to do things, encouraging, warning or threatening them. Occasionally, one hallucinates the devil's voice, that of dead relatives or of the historically great. One of our patients heard the President of the United States talking to her constantly.

Often the hallucinated voice is not identified. The patient makes a vague reference to "someone," "that man," "the woman," "people," "they" — and the investigator cannot penetrate beyond the reference to something more exact. One patient is crying in fright. "What's the matter with me! I keep hearing voices and people calling." They seem to want her to do many things quickly, she does not know what. But later, "The spirit voices tell me to sleep." Another complains, "If only those voices would stop yelling at me all the time! I'd be willing to give up trying to rule the world." And, "The voices in the wall tell me my folks are dead. I hope it isn't true." A delirious patient said, "I hear them paging Mamie. I hear them calling Chuck (brother). They're calling me out of hell." A schizophrenic girl could hear people telling her to go to visit certain relatives; and they informed her that there was an underground passage under the clinic which led directly to her home. She could not guess who it was that spoke to her.

As we have indicated, some of the hallucinated voices seem to emit statements, prophesies, aphorisms, warnings, and sometimes unintelligible neologisms; while others appear to speak directly to the patient, instead of merely making pronouncements. In addition to these, there are also hallucinated conversations in which two or more persons discuss the patient, often passing judgment on him. A delirious patient hears "men and women talking things over and over; sometimes they say nice things about you." A schizophrenic woman says that a man and a woman discuss everything she does. "When they disapprove, I grope for what they want me to do, and do it if I know. . . . When they disapprove it upsets me. I sit up late when I hear the voices. I want very badly to please them, so I stop and listen." A schizophrenic man repeatedly complained of crowds hailing him as their great leader or threatening him with a horrible death. He was frightened of either prospect and sought for some means of escaping what he believed was his destiny.

It can be seen that in all of the auditory verbal hallucination described, there is disowning projection with more or less complete repression of the source which is, of course, within a person's own fantasy. This is the situation that we earlier characterized as a reversal of the process by which public opinion originally grew into private self-evaluation.[60] Communicative speech which early in the patient's life had been transmuted into thinking, once again takes up its abandoned function of communication.

The soliloquies, dialogues, debates and conversations which the patient hallucinates are set up apart from or in opposition to the rest of his behavior.[61] This achieved, he may engage in discussion with his own projected accuser or comforter. He may react to the part of his fantasy that seeks to compel him as though it were in fact an irresistible outside force. He may play the role of a passive listener to a pair of hallucinated persons who keep constant vigil over his every act; and he can then adopt a submissive or a resistive attitude toward advice, opinion and command.

A great deal of auditory verbal hallucination is obviously derived from the evaluations which others have made of a person's conduct, and which have been taken over ultimately as the person's self-evaluative reaction in his own behavior.[62] The patient who was eager to please the couple she hallucinated seems to be repeating in disowning projection the situation in her childhood home, where there were father and mother to please, and their approving or disapproving voices to be heard. Likewise the voices urging another patient to do things quickly sound like parental chiding; and the "spirit voices" that tell her to sleep must be those of her parents also. The woman who was uncertain as to whether it was a voice or not that told her "to sort of end things" was evidently more successful in repressing the antecedent self-condemnation than in projecting the suicidal end-product of it.

A recent study indicates increased activity in the speech muscles of persons engaged in auditory hallucination. Gould [63] compared groups of state hospital

---

[60] See pages 98–105.   [61] See pages 386–387.   [62] See pages 98–105.

[63] Gould, L. N., "Auditory hallucinations and subvocal speech; objective study in a case of schizophrenia." *J. nerv. ment. Dis.*, 1949, vol. 109, pp. 418–427; Gould, L. N., "Verbal hallucinations and activity of vocal musculature; an electromyographic study." *Amer. J. Psychiat.*, 1948, vol. 105, pp. 367–372; Gould, L. N., "Verbal hallucinations as automatic speech. The reactivation of dormant speech habit." *Amer. J. Psychiat.*, 1950, vol. 107, pp. 110–119.

patients with (N = 64) and without (N = 36) auditory hallucination. From each he obtained electromyograms of the vocal musculature, the leads being on chin and lower lip. He was able to demonstrate a significant relationship between increased muscle potential and hallucination. Eighty-three per cent of patients with auditory hallucination showed increased muscle potential, whereas only 10 per cent of non-hallucinating patients did. A heterogeneous group of 100 normal persons showed increased vocal musculature potential in 28 per cent. Evidently speech is usually associated with auditory hallucination. It may stimulate auditory hallucination, be stimulated by hallucinated sounds, or intimately participate in the hallucinatory phenomena.

The reasons for the predominance of auditory hallucination in behavior pathology are not altogether clear. What evidence we have at present seems to indicate that patients reporting auditory hallucination are relatively deficient in auditory imagery,[64] whereas the reverse might be expected on a priori grounds. That is, one might predict that persons with vivid auditory imagery might more easily misrefer it than persons deficient in it. On the other hand, it might also be supposed that the individual with defective role-taking would be less practiced in speaking with the voice of others in his fantasy. Thus, his deficiency in auditory imagery might be an incidental by-product of his failure to practice in imagined speech the role of others; while his hallucinating arises from the needs to which his insulation and his social ineptness expose him. This problem obviously needs further empirical clarification.

Auditory hallucination has definite advantages over visual which go a long way toward accounting for its much higher incidence in behavior pathology. It provides the patient with an inexhaustible source of communication to which nothing visual can compare. Even the written or printed word is not remembered by most of us in visual terms, but usually as heard or spoken; and the recall of conversation, admonition and command is nearly always in auditory terms. It would be a mistake, however, to underrate the importance of visual hallucination. In the dreams of a great many persons, visual imagery plays a dominant role; it is for many an effective vehicle of recall; and in the behavior disorders the visual hallucination may be almost continually present or appear suddenly as a dramatic and decisive event.

(b) *Visual hallucination.* Although much less frequently reported by patients than the auditory varieties, visual hallucination is by no means uncommon in behavior pathology. We meet it most often in deliria, panic reactions and schizophrenic disorders. Here, as in ordinary dreaming, we deal with disowning projection [65] in which the origin of the hallucination in one's own fantasy is completely repressed, but the imagined person, object or scene is not.

[64] Seitz, P. F. D., and Molholm, H. B., "Relation of mental imagery to hallucinations." *Arch. Neurol. Psychiat.*, 1947, vol. 57, pp. 469–480.
[65] For a discussion of disowning projection, see pages 384–387.

Thus, as also in auditory verbal hallucination, an apparent *opposition* is established, between the behavior which the patient recognizes as his own, and the behavior which he cannot acknowledge.

In ordinary dreams and in deep preoccupation, the visual hallucination is characteristically provided with an appropriate fantasy context.[66] This tends to give continuity and coherence to an individual's responses and to a considerable degree protects him from behavioral disorganization.[67] In deliria, panic reactions and many schizophrenic disorders, on the other hand, a clean separation of fantasy and social fact is not achieved. *Overinclusion* is the typical development.[68] The hallucinated person, object or scene is either commingled with components of the field of social operations — so that confusion, bewilderment, and chaotic responses often result — or it appears as an addition to the social context, an hallucinated figure projected against the objectively shared background.

What is visually hallucinated may belong to the remembered past, even though the patient often does not recognize this origin. It may, instead, picture things belonging to a feared or hoped for future, in which case the components of hallucination are probably derived likewise from the past. One of our patients expressed it thus: "They're always things we've done, or things that are going on or new things — pictures of what we may be mixed up in at that minute. They aren't memories because some of them are entirely new. They're different from dreams. I can't describe them so anybody can understand. I go into this and come out again, and think I ought to be in my own room, but I find myself here" — in the hallucinated place. The patient actually was in her own room.

In discussing auditory hallucination, we pointed to the wide variations to be found in the clarity and distinctness of what patients seem to hear, in the degree of their certainty as to whether the voices are real or imaginary, and in the completeness of the projection.[69] There are comparable variations in visual hallucination.

> Thus, a schizophrenic college student, recalling some of the development of her hallucinating, said, "I'd see something like people but they weren't clear; they were blended with objects and in groups. From people it went to scenes and places. There was more action. . . . Then all kinds of people came into my room at night. They are some of the people I see during the day. They get close to me, during the day, too. I get different thoughts. It isn't just me alone, it brings in other people, too. I see people — handicapped, detestable, monstrous — during the day and at night. They come all around me, on my arms, on my bed, on the ceilings and walls. They look as clear as anything real."
>
> Patients reporting visual hallucination usually describe what is seen

---

[66] See pages 112–113.   [67] See pages 452–458.
[68] Overinclusion is discussed on pages 456–458.   [69] See pages 381–387.

as located outside themselves. Thus a delirious patient, greatly frightened, said, "I can't stay here any longer! I don't want to be eaten by snakes." To the nurse, "How can you sit there with snakes all around! . . . All right, then. You say you don't see any snakes. I do. They are crawling all around. They're trying to eat me." A schizophrenic woman was hallucinating a man behind a floor lamp. "He's looking at me. I can't stand seeing him like that! Stop that peeping! I can see you up there. You thought you could get away with it five years ago, but you can't." Screaming, "There he is at the window! Do you think you're God?" Another schizophrenic patient, in giving his history, said that for a year — "possibly two" — he had been seeing people and animals. "I'd see things and I'd quick light a cigarette or take a drink. I've seen dogs and cats and horses, men and women, when I shouldn't."

Some patients do not project as successfully as this in visually hallucinating. Thus, a schizophrenic man said, "I see things behind my eyes. . . . I thought I'd swallowed a splinter of diamond — or in my eye — and those things came out of my eye." An agitated depressed woman, who was constantly troubled by visual hallucination, spoke of being "turned inside out. . . . My eyes look ahead but they're turned in. Everything's in my head at once — dogs and pipes and machinery and people and everything." While hallucinating, she loses all realization of where she is; it seems to her that she is actually in the scenes she imagines, and not in the clinic. "They come themselves — always of people doing things, very muddled, sometimes of places I've been to, or of the family or of strangers; and sometimes they have no faces on them. . . . All of these things are actually in my head — bed lamps, tables, food, people."

The degree of systematization described by patients varies from a fragment or a succession of discrete visions, to well put together scenes like those dreamed by normal persons. A schizophrenic patient looked into a cold cream jar and started back horrified, saying, "There's a symbol of a fish in there." She declined to elaborate. Another complained that everything she looked at made her see a face. "I can't explain it," she said. A delirious man saw someone being chopped up with a butcher knife, then pigs with the heads of bulldogs, and two eagles as big as the room, each carrying a horse. There were mice that went right through the wall. When he was placed in a continuous-flow tub, he saw waves and believed he had been thrown overboard. Another patient described well-organized scenes in which he had a part. Noises disturbed his hallucination. "I want quiet!" he insisted. "I want nothing but quiet, and to be God of it all."

(c) *Olfactory, gustatory and other hallucination.*[70] Of the remaining varieties of hallucination, the most important in behavior pathology are the olfactory and the gustatory. In *olfactory hallucination* patients sometimes hallucinate

---

[70] An unusually complete series of patients suffering from olfactory and gustatory hallucinations is described in Alliez, J., and Noseda, M., "Considérations statistiques et cliniques sur les hallucinations olfactives et gustatives." *Année méd. psychol.*, 1945, vol. 103, pp. 134–141.

fragrance, the smell of fresh air or the odor of cooking; but by far the commonest olfactory hallucinations are those of harmful or annoying smells and of death. A lethal gas or suffocating smoke is being pumped into the room to kill one or a disgusting odor is loosed to drive one out. There seems to be a human corpse nearby or a rotting animal carcass. Not uncommon is the complaint that one's own body is giving off an offensive smell, which other people seem to indicate by fingering their noses, or by moving away as one approaches.[71]

Persons with *gustatory hallucination* occasionally imagine that they taste good food and good drink; but, as in the case of olfaction, the most usual hallucination seems to mean harm, annoyance or corruption. Thus, the patient tastes poison or some dangerous medicine in his food, opium is in his coffee, and he can detect the flavor of contamination in the water or the milk.

> A schizophrenic patient insisted that everything tasted queer to her — a combination of sweet and bitter, she said — so that she was sure she was "crazy." Another patient, a profoundly hypochondriacal physician with many strange interpretations of his other symptoms, complained that he always tasted carbolic acid at the end of his meals. He attempted to account for this in terms of a somewhat unique system of body chemistry, according to which phenol was a persistent by-product of his own metabolism. Body delusion and gustatory hallucination reinforced each other and made a stable pattern which therapy could not alter.

In *cutaneous hallucination*,[72] patients complain of things crawling on or under the skin, of electric currents passed through the skin, of burning sensations and of coldness and wetness.

> The woman who spoke of seeing people come in to her room and get on her bed,[73] said that she could feel them on her arms as well as see them; and the woman who saw snakes all around her spoke of feeling them in her bed and crawling over her body.[74] A schizophrenic young woman complained that her body was burning — she could feel the heat of her skin. Actually, her skin temperature and her oral temperature were normal; the cutaneous hallucination had as its background a delusional conviction of sin and damnation. A delirious patient said, "Last night they poured ether all over my face, and then asked me questions about sex practices." A schizophrenic patient, while eating dinner, jumped up suddenly with a look of horror and cried, "I just felt a toenail pressed against my finger!" A delirious man could feel vermin all over him, especially when the lights were out, but to some extent in bright light also.

[71] Concern over body odor characterizes a great many normal adolescents. See, for example, Stolz, H., and Stolz, L., "Adolescent problems related to somatic variations." *Yearb. Nat. Soc. Stud. Educ.*, 1944, vol. 43, pp. 80–99.

[72] A description of such reactions in fifty-one patients is to be found in Wilson, J. W., and Miller, H. E., "Delusion of parasitosis (acarophobia)." *Arch. Derm. Syph.*, Chicago, 1946, vol. 54, pp. 39–56.

[73] See page 440.   [74] See page 441.

We have already considered *visceral hallucination*, more or less incidentally, in discussing delusions of body change.[75] The viscera, as we pointed out in describing the background of emotional reactions,[76] are constantly changing in size, form or location, in tension and in physicochemical activity. The shifting patterns of visceral performance undoubtedly contribute to the fantasy material from which hallucination comes. But of still greater significance is the vast body of knowledge, belief and superstition which is current concerning the functions and the pathology of the internal organs. What a patient hallucinates in relation to his brain, his lungs, his heart, his liver, kidneys, stomach or intestines — will reflect his anxieties and his needs in terms of what he considers possible for them. Hence we find that hallucination with respect to one or another system of internal organs may change as knowledge or belief about it changes, and that increased public attention to certain viscera will increase the incidence of hallucination reported for these viscera.[77]

Hallucination of movement, of changes in equilibrium and steadiness we may group together as *kinetic hallucination*. Delirious and schizophrenic patients not infrequently say that they are rushing through space, that the room or the bed they are in is being rocked or turned, or that they seem to be flying, floating, or swimming. Occasionally a depressed person makes similar complaints. Thus, the patient who reported that she was constantly seeing "pictures" in her head [78] said that she often soared or floated off into them herself, as if she "had taken ether." At times she seemed to be falling interminably through space, she said, and at other times her body appeared to her to be swaying so much that she could do next to nothing. The significance of kinetic hallucination, as in the case of the other varieties we have been discussing, can usually be understood best in terms of the delusional context supporting it and the conditions favoring its occurrence.

Conditions favoring hallucination

The conditions favoring hallucination are those which make it possible for fantasy material to dominate an individual's behavior, or render a differentiation between fantasy and social fact exceptionally difficult. We encounter hallucination, in normal everyday life as well as in behavior pathology, when one's anticipant attitudes are so tightly organized that specific reaction-sensitivity to a narrow range of stimulation becomes high (*overexclusion*).[79] This we have already seen in dreaming, in deep preoccupation and in delusion. Hallucination is also common under conditions of emotional arousal, whether or not specific reaction-sensitization has developed. It is likewise of frequent occurrence in situations which are in some respects the opposite of these — in

[75] See pages 401–403.   [76] See pages 122–125.
[77] Compare the development of delusion, discussed on pages 387–392.
[78] See page 441.
[79] For a discussion of *overexclusion*, see page 74, and pages 367–368.

behavioral disorganization, when a person cannot distinguish between his private imaginal behavior and the social context which he shares with others (*overinclusion*).[80]

(1) *Anticipant attitudes.* The anticipant attitude, as we have seen,[81] operates in such a way as to favor the occurrence of certain responses and to inhibit the occurrence of others. It selectively sensitizes a person to a relatively narrow range of stimulation, within which range the response threshold is lowered. Thus, while a great deal that might otherwise elicit a reaction is excluded, whatever fits the attitudinal context is reacted to with ease and alacrity. However, when one is responding with great ease and alacrity, there is always the possibility that his behavior will be uncritical; and the more highly developed a specific reaction-sensitivity, and the narrower the range of stimulation it includes, the more uncritically may an individual respond. It is under circumstances such as these that fantasied material is accepted as social fact, if it is congruent with a well-structured attitudinal context — and particularly if it tends to bring completion, or *closure*, to a previously unstable behavior organization.[82]

Common illustrations of this can be found among the professional magician's tricks. By his talk and his preliminary manipulations, the good showman structures anticipant attitudes in the members of his audience. These attitudes are intended to restrict the responses of the watchers to some one aspect of a developing situation, and to bring about the neglect of other aspects. If this work is skilfully done, the audience will hallucinate the occurrence, which they have been led to expect, when the climax of the trick is reached. In other words, they respond to stimulation within their own fantasy — which completes what they see and brings them closure — as if that stimulation had originated on the stage. The tightly organized attitudinal structure gives the right-of-way to stimulation which, under other conditions, would have been recognized by each member of the audience as his own imaginal activity. In short, magic that requires persons to hallucinate depends heavily upon the exclusion from their behavior of whatever would contradict it or make it unnecessary.

The familiar hallucination of dreaming and daydreaming depends upon comparable conditions. The *overexclusion* common to preoccupation and the dream eliminates most of the surrounding stimulation, and the hallucinatory responses can thus develop more or less unimpeded in terms of the dominant fantasy context. Since this overexclusion does not allow contradiction from

---

[80] *Overinclusion* is discussed on page 75, and on pages 456–458.

[81] See pages 65–66.

[82] For a discussion of *closure*, see pages 75–79. It should be noted that the completion of an incomplete figure in terms of "set" has long been observed in experiments on perceptual response. A great many relevant experiments on this point have been summarized in Woodworth, R. S., *Experimental psychology.* New York: Holt, 1938, pp. 69–91.

the surroundings to operate in the dream or daydream situation, there is nothing in the behavior of the moment on the basis of which the person can identify fantasy and distinguish it from social fact. As in the magician's tricks, the attitudinal structure so narrows the range of effective stimulation that hallucinatory responses occur with an ease and vividness foreign to ordinary shared social operations.

From what has just been said, it is not difficult to see why it is that delusional organization so often favors hallucinatory behavior. In the restrictive-distortive phases of pseudocommunity and autistic community development, we have seen,[83] there is characteristically a sharp restriction of the range of effective stimulation. With the progressive reaction-sensitization goes a progressively marked lowering of the threshold of response within the restricted delusional range. The hallucinatory responses which thus occur are by no means random fantasy; they are limited to phenomena that are relevant in some way to the dominant convictions. Here, then, we again encounter the highly structured anticipant attitude — this time delusional — that facilitates the occurrence of fantasy which is mistakenly attributed to sources outside of one's imaginal behavior.

(2) *Emotional arousal.* Like delusion, pathological hallucination is most likely to occur under conditions of strong emotional arousal, when there is great anxiety or irresistible need. Often it comes as the climax in a developing behavior organization, as closure, and sometimes it is in the form of sudden clarification. This is a well-recognized dramatic incident in many delusional pseudocommunities. A person's strong need may be abruptly satisfied by a vision that fulfills his expectation; or his intense anxiety seems to him justified when he hears a voice confirming his worst apprehension. Tense, emotional expectation renders an individual generally vigilant. If, at this point, the appropriate stimulation necessary to achieve closure appears within his fantasy behavior, it may readily be accepted, and as readily misreferred to the environment from which such stimulation was expected.

We know that under conditions of intense anxiety or need a person's tolerance of suspense is low. His dominant behavior organization is in a state of unstable equilibrium. Under these circumstances, ambiguous stimulation — whether from the surroundings or from his own fantasy — is likely to be incorporated into the dynamic structure, if it contributes toward consummation.[84] It then becomes difficult or impossible to maintain a judicious attitude of suspended decision, to remain critical and skeptical, for one's behavioral organization is now pointed in the direction of imminent closure. This is a hair-trigger

---

[83] See pages 411–413, and pages 427–433.

[84] See, for example, Frenkel-Brunswik, E., "Intolerance of ambiguity as an emotional and perceptual personality variable." *J. Personality,* 1949, vol. 18, pp. 108–143. This point is also discussed on pages 69–70 and 75–79.

situation. Almost any stimulation, and therefore almost any hallucinatory stimulation, may be sufficient to bring closure.

It hardly needs saying that emotional arousal tends to intensify the effects of anticipant attitudes in facilitating hallucination. An excited audience will more readily hallucinate for a magician than a calmly attentive one. Vivid imagery is more likely to appear and to be accepted in a strongly emotional dream than in an emotionally neutral one; and the same is true of daydreams. In relatively well-organized delusion, strong persecutory or ecstatic trends favor the appearance of hallucinated voices and persons. In all of these, the acquired specific reaction-sensitivity of the individual is reinforced by the more general vigilance of emotional arousal.

The importance of both anticipant attitude and emotional arousal becomes evident in group hallucination. If several persons, having closely similar cultural backgrounds, are confronted by the same emergency together, they may all hallucinate in agreement. Thus, men adrift in small boats at sea sometimes agree in clearly sighting rescue vessels by day, when actually none are visible, and in hearing voices comforting them by night, when no one has spoken comfort.[85] Or, in desperate thirst two shipmates may hallucinate a hatchway just beyond the boat's edge, and step off together to their death in the sea.[86] In instances such as these, the effects of thirst, starvation and exposure upon cerebral competence must of course be added to those of protracted, unrelieved anxiety, in setting the stage for hallucinatory misidentification.[87]

(3) *Disorganization*. In behavioral disorganization, as we shall see in the next chapter, there is frequently a disintegration of the attitudinal background. The organism's behavior becomes overinclusive.[88] Responses appear as fragments, in a haphazard or chaotic manner. Under these circumstances, the distinction cannot be maintained — and often cannot be made at all — between one's private unshared fantasy and the shared activities of social operations. This occurs commonly in emotional upheavals, in acute anxiety, in extreme rage and in panic reactions.[89] We see it also in cerebral incompetence when the environmental complexity becomes relatively too great. The attitudes then no longer reflect adequately the structure of the surroundings. In deliria, hallucination is fleeting, it comes and goes as cerebral competence fluctuates.[90] In senile deterioration, hallucination is likely to show greater

[85] Anderson, E., "Abnormal mental states in survivors, with special reference to collective hallucinations." *J. Res. Naval Med. Serv.*, 1942, vol. 28, pp. 361–377; Good, H., "Fifteen days adrift on a raft: a clinical evaluation of five survivors." *Naval Med. Bull.*, 1943, vol. 41, pp. 367–373.

[86] Critchley, M., "Exhaustion in relation to fighting efficiency: reactions of men to long periods in open boats." *Inter-Allied Conf. War Med.*, (1942–45), 1947, vol. 1, pp. 289–293.

[87] Compare the discussion of deliria on pages 469–477.

[88] See pages 74–75.   [85] See pages 304–310.   [90] See pages 470–472.

stability; persons and things from a remembered past are brought into a present situation and responded to as if they actually were there.[91]

The most persistent hallucination to be found in behavior pathology occurs in persons whose behavioral disorganization has either led to or been reinforced by, a process of progressive desocialization. These are the patients whom we usually designate as schizophrenic. Many of them succeed in restructuring, from the remnants of their earlier social behavior and their fantasy material, a fictitious behavioral world by means of which they live. Each patient's universe is uniquely designed, in ways that appear to some extent to meet his individual needs. But he can survive, as a rule, only because society provides him with food, lodging, a certain degree of protection and a simplified environment. In the next two chapters we shall consider in detail the characteristics of disorganization and desocialization, and the consequences to the individual of their behavioral interaction.

[91] See pages 546–555.

Disorganization

15

There is perhaps no other common incident of everyday life that has received as little systematic study as behavioral disorganization. We see examples of the disruption of organized behavior all around us — in the motorist who stalls at a busy intersection and fumbles with the starting mechanisms, in the bus passenger who is completely flustered when the exit door closes before he reaches it, and in the pedestrian who prances in front of an oncoming stream of cars when the semaphore lights change. Boys spinning tops in the street, and girls skipping rope or playing jacks, abruptly lose their skilled coordination when they are made angry or afraid. The man in a group, who is caught contradicting himself in a heated argument, is likely to disorganize momentarily, so that the ready flow of language is replaced by word fragments and haphazard sounds. And something comparable happens to the overt reactions of the housewife who finds a thin stream of water descending from the ceiling on to her best living-room furniture.

Clearly there is no need for us to look beyond the routines of normal living for illustrations of behavioral disruption and disunity. If, however, we do turn to a study of such pathological developments as *deliria* and *schizophrenic disorders*, we shall find degrees and patterns of disorganization that are unsurpassed in complexity, intensity and persistence. But before going on to a discussion of these syndromes, we must first define and delineate behavioral disorganization, differentiate it from the regression we have discussed in an earlier chapter,[1] and distinguish it from the deterioration that we shall consider later on.[2] Then we shall be ready to describe the conditions favoring disruption and disunity, and to understand their remarkable consequences in behavior pathology.

[1] See pages 217–230.   [2] See pages 518–531.

448

Definition

By *disorganization* we mean *the disruption of a unified reaction, or system of reactions, and its replacement by behavior that is fragmentary, haphazard or chaotic.* Let us illustrate this definition with three examples taken from everyday life.

The first concerns a man, going to work in the morning, who the evening before has heard disquieting rumors that, because of business conditions, unemployment is widespread and increasing. He gets to his factory only to find it closed against him. At this point his ongoing, unified behavior terminates abruptly. Odds and ends of habitual movements perseverate or follow one another in hit-or-miss fashion. He pulls and jerks the door handle, kicks the door and beats on it, calls the name of his foreman or the timekeeper, thrusts his hands into his pockets, swears, runs his fingers distractedly through his hair, calls out again, and falls to kicking, jerking, pulling and beating the door once more. As other workers arrive, and add their disorganized reactions to his own, his responses may lose their sequential character completely, so that for a time his behavior disintegrates into a confused jumble of ineffectual, abortive movements and exclamatory phrases.

In our second illustration, a housewife is preparing an elaborate dinner on the occasion of entertaining for the first time her husband's boss who, she has good reason to know, is exceedingly proper and an exacting tyrant. With just enough time left to set meticulously an attractive table, she discovers that all her silverware, which she had polished only the day before, has vanished. Her immediate behavior, before she arrives at a point where she can work out her predicament, will consist of a succession of startled and incredulous ejaculations, of hurried and usually abortive searching movements, of useless perseverative returns to the places where the silverware should be, and perhaps finally motor incoordination, inappropriate laughter and despairing tears. However normal and understandable such reactions may seem, under conditions of severe and unanticipated stress, they nevertheless exhibit clearly the distinguishing characteristics of behavioral disorganization. For the highly skilled, unified patterns of the competent housewife's conduct have been disrupted, and replaced by behavior that is fragmentary, haphazard and chaotic.

Young children not infrequently develop behavioral disorganization when there is a radical change in the dynamics of the human environment that has been supporting the routines of their lives. Suppose that a three-year-old child, who is accustomed to the exclusive care of a tirelessly attentive mother, awakens in the presence of complete strangers to find his mother gone.[3] His behavior under these circumstances is almost sure to show disorganization. At first he looks in a bewildered and uncertain fashion, staring and soundless, from one stranger to the next. Then he begins to whimper, speaks his mother's name, and finally bursts into loud crying and screaming.

[3] For a discussion of separation anxiety, see pages 290–293.

Even after the child has quieted down, the disruption in his previously unified behavior is unmistakable. In his play — whether he is apathetic or excited — he remains distractible, shifting restlessly from one plaything to another, or from one fragmentary activity to another.[4] He does not maintain his usual level of constructiveness in play, and cannot seem to finish what he starts. His previously established routines show the same disunity. That which the strangers stigmatize as naughty, bad or willful, may be an actual inability to cooperate and carry through the business of eating and body-cleansing, of dressing and undressing, of going to bed and getting up. The child's disorganization is usually less dramatic and long-lived than an adult's, under comparable circumstances, because his behavioral organization is simpler; but the disruption that he shows is quite as important as any that we have depicted for adults.

Behavioral disorganization in groups, as well as in individuals, is a widely recognized phenomenon. Disruptive developments within a sales organization, a production line, or a whole industry, can lead to fragmentary, haphazard and chaotic interbehavior that is strictly comparable with the individual examples we have been discussing. Indeed, studies of group disorganization have already far outstripped those of individuals. Military outfits have given us some striking illustrations of the quick disintegration of highly structured groups when they are leaderless and surrounded, or thrown into a retreat for which they are neither prepared nor adequately trained.[5] Communities, likewise, under a variety of circumstances, show marked and often progressive disorganization. And this disorganization is sometimes unmistakably present long before the routines of its constituent members are seriously disturbed.[6]

Disorganization and regression

We have already observed [7] that, in behavioral disorganization, reactions commonly appear which belong to a less mature phase of personal development. Thus, the three-year-old child among strangers may wet himself, or resort to the comfort of thumb-sucking, even though neither of these has been a part of his repertory for many months. The woman in a domestic crisis may fly into a temper tantrum which is not at all according to her custom. And the man who finds a locked door interposed between him and his means of livelihood may finally sit down on the curb and cry like a little boy.

[4] This phenomenon has been termed *play disruption* by Erikson, and employed by him in therapy with young children. See Erikson, E. H., "Studies in the interpretation of play: I. Clinical observations of play disruption in young children." *Genet. Psychol. Monogr.*, 1940, vol. 22, pp. 557–671.

[5] Some reports of this sort of disintegration are to be found in Sherif, M. and Cantril, H., *The psychology of ego-involvements.* New York: Wiley, 1947, pp. 396–417. See also Grinker, R. R. and Spiegel, J. P., *Men under stress.* Philadelphia: Blakiston, 1945.

[6] For a discussion of community disorganization, see Faris, R., *Social disorganization.* New York: Ronald, 1948; Mowrer, E. R., *Disorganization, personal and social.* Philadelphia: Lippincott, 1942.

[7] See pages 220–226.

But, notwithstanding their frequently intimate relationship, regression and disorganization are not identical. Restrictive situations, such as illness and imprisonment, call for regressive dependence but, partly because they impose a simplified routine, do not necessarily involve disorganization at all.[8] Moreover, under certain circumstances regressive behavior protects the individual from disorganizing. For if environmental stress or personal conflict threatens to exceed the limits of a man's endurance, regression becomes in effect a kind of retirement from the field. It then provides one with respite from the disintegrating influence of intolerable stimulation. If such retirement is successful in providing a breathing spell, a person returns from it refreshed, and sometimes with a reorganization of attitude which renders the same kind and degree of stimulation no longer intolerable or disorganizing.

Disorganization and deterioration

We have just seen that disorganization may include regression, but is still not identical with it. Similarly, disorganization may lead to deterioration, or deterioration to disorganization, and yet the two are not the same. Disorganization, as our definition indicates, refers primarily to a disruption of unified activity; and this disruption may be momentary or enduring, mild or severe, trivial and inconsequential or of grave and far-reaching significance for personal integrity. Deterioration, as we shall later see, always implies an important reduction in the level of behavioral effectiveness over a period of time. We do not, for example, speak of the day-to-day fluctuations in adequacy, which most persons exhibit, as episodes of deterioration and recovery; neither do we refer to longer term variations as deteriorative unless they involve a considerable reduction in effectiveness.[9]

In normal persons, disorganization typically occurs without deterioration when an individual enters a strange, unstructured situation, or when he is frightened, embarrassed or in sharp conflict. As soon as the crisis is well past, and its after-effects have waned, he again operates in the ways that are characteristic of him. Disorganization without deterioration is also the rule in anxiety disorders [10] and acute deliria,[11] provided only that they be not too severe and too prolonged. Disorganization without deterioration is less common in schizophrenia than in anxiety disorders and deliria; but it is far more common than was supposed when its earlier phases and milder manifestations were not studied and, indeed, frequently not recognized.

Deterioration without disorganization is most frequently encountered in senility. The ageing man or woman undergoes a gradual, progressive reduction in behavioral effectiveness extending over a period of years, or even

[8] See, for example, pages 229–231 and 243–245.
[9] Compare the discussion of *duration* on pages 526–527, and of *severity* on page 527.
[10] See pages 304–314.   [11] See pages 469–477.

decades. But unless there is a sudden physiological change, or some drastic alteration in the accustomed environmental pattern, no recognizable disorganization is likely to occur. Deterioration without disorganization is also quite characteristic of chronic invalidism and protracted depression; and it is common in prisons and concentration camps, as well as among those forlorn hospital patients who must sit all day in empty idleness.[12] Later in the present chapter,[13] we shall see that disorganization, if sufficiently acute, may also induce deterioration; and in the succeeding chapter we shall find that deterioration is an all too frequent outcome of the desocialization which goes hand in hand with schizophrenic disorganization.[14]

Characteristics of disorganization

Having now defined and partially delineated behavioral disorganization, we are prepared to consider next certain of its general characteristics. This we propose to do under the headings of (1) *incoordination*, (2) *interpenetration*, (3) *fragmentation* and (4) *overinclusion*. These four do not constitute a graded series of increasing or decreasing severity or complexity. Neither are they to be treated as mutually exclusive categories. On the contrary, as we shall see, they are merely convenient groupings of the most commonly encountered features in behavioral disorganization.

(1) *Incoordination.* By *incoordination* we mean *the occurrence in behavior of disturbing tensions and movements in otherwise synchronous and synergic activity.* The disturbance may thus be in both timing (synchrony) and in functional harmony (synergy) of behavior. This often appears simply as unsteadiness, or as a tremor, which interferes with one's precision. It may also be in the form of awkward floundering — one overreaches, underreaches, or shows gross defects in the timing of component, synergic movements.[15] The so-called "associated movements" may fail to occur in their accustomed relationships.[16] These are the usual, but often not essential, accompaniments of an integrated act — for example, swinging the arms while walking, or moving the empty hand rhythmically while brushing one's shoes. If the disorganization grows sufficiently severe, a person's stance, his locomotion and his manipulation may all show incoordination. He sways, missteps, staggers, fumbles, and even shows defects in speech and thinking.

---

[12] See pages 529–530. See also Cutts, R. A. and Lane, M. O'K., "The effect of hospitalization on Wechsler-Bellevue subtest scores by mental defectives." *Amer. J. ment. Def.*, 1947, vol. 51, pp. 391–393.

[13] See page 477.

[14] See pages 521–522.

[15] See, for example, Brown, J. S., Knauft, E. B., and Rosenbaum, G., "The accuracy of positioning reactions as a function of their direction and extent." *Amer. J. Psychol.*, 1948, vol. 61, pp. 167–182.

[16] See, for example, Vujic, V. and Kurtes, K., "Influence of restraint on automatic movements." *Lancet*, 1948, vol. 255, pp. 527–528.

Incoordination of speech and thinking are often especially important. The disorganized person sometimes grows dysarthric — he slurs his words and mispronounces parts of them — he may lose whatever fluency he ordinarily possesses, and he is likely to show the same unsteadiness in talking that he does in manipulating.[17] Likewise the unspoken thought and the unshared rumination seem to a disorganized individual to suffer in precision and integrity. Thinking may speed up, slow down, lose its direction, and manifest a lack of dependability and predictability for the thinker that is at least analogous to his manipulative, locomotory and speech disturbances.

Because we all hold the word in reverence and the thought in awe, these incoordinations of symbolic behavior usually give rise to startled self-reactions that may disorganize a person further. We misspeak, stammer, block, or slur our speech, and react to the defect with still greater stumbling. The moment we find we cannot think as clearly or consecutively as we should, we become frightened, and are then less able than ever to think in an organized, sequential manner. Disturbances in speech and thinking have similar effects in delirium, panic and schizophrenia. For the patient, they may become sources of bizarre and terrifying interpretations; and the self-reactions thus aroused may in turn hasten and aggravate an already developing disorganization.

The most extensive and systematic study of incoordination in disorganized normal persons is that of Luria.[18] He required his subjects to do three separately recorded things at once: to give a speech response upon demand, to press a bulb with the right hand, and to keep the left hand inactive, resting lightly upon another bulb. Under a variety of conditions — such as speeding up, slowing down and breaking rhythm, inhibiting one or the other active response, introducing or capitalizing upon emotional disturbances, making sudden shifts in the task — Luria was able to obtain records of incoordination in any of the three reaction systems. He particularly noted the seriously disorganizing effect upon the rest of behavior which a comparatively slight disturbance in *speech* function had, a finding that we shall need to remember when we turn to schizophrenic disorganization and desocialization.

(2) *Interpenetration.* By *interpenetration* we mean that *an intrusive movement, word or thought appears, in an ongoing sequence, which belongs to some other coordinated activity sequence.* For example, a preoccupied carpenter, having marked a board for sawing, picks up his hammer as if to drive a nail. Likewise, a worried harrassed store clerk begins wrapping an article which the customer has rejected, instead of replacing it upon the shelf. At home, he picks up his

---

[17] Compare pages 279–280.

[18] Luria, A., *The nature of human conflicts: an objective study of disorganization and control of human behaviour* (Trans. by W. H. Gantt). New York: Liveright, 1932. For a brief account of Luria's technique, see pages 261–262. For a recent application of his method, see Albino, R. C., "The stable and labile personality types of Luria in clinically normal individuals." *Brit. J. Psychol.*, 1948, vol. 39, pp. 54–60.

fork to stir his coffee, and later puts on his pajamas when he is changing his clothes for an evening out. His wife, if she also is troubled and distraught, hangs the baby's diapers indoors on the towel rack instead of outdoors on the line, lights the oven for dinner when she had gone to the kitchen only to prepare the baby's bottle, and picks up her shopping bag as she leaves the house dressed for a formal afternoon call.

The concept of interpenetration was originally formulated in relation to symbolic operations; [19] and it is in talking and thinking that we find our richest and most significant examples. These range all the way from a single intrusive word or phrase to entire statements, reminiscences and plans of action that belong to some other sequence in some other context. Frequently the intrusive material, in entering a dominant ongoing sequence, becomes distorted in such a way as to indicate clearly that it has a double origin in two competing themes. Thus, a woman, out of a sense of obligation tries to compliment her visitor on a new hat which actually strikes her as unattractive. She hears herself say, "My dear, your hat is *a duty!*" whereas she had intended to say, "*a beauty.*" [20] A raconteur recalls an episode from his childhood, which is rendered with fair accuracy, excepting for one incident identified by his hearers as coming from a well-known published biography. A business man, at home in the evening, reviews the appointments he will keep on the morrow, but discovers suddenly that he is including one person who belongs wholly to a vacation period, which has recently ended.

Freud has given us the earliest extensive, systematized account of the relationship of word- and phrase-substitution to preoccupation and to conflict, both accessible ("conscious" or "preconscious") and inaccessible ("unconscious"), in sleep and out of it.[21] Slips of the tongue, pen or typewriter, may be meaningful and significant, or meaningless and incidental — regardless of whether they occur in a normal or in a pathological setting. Thus we find interpenetration in the talking and thinking of persons whose reactions are merely divided between two competing or unrelated activities; and we find it in acute anxiety, excitement, fatigue, delirium and schizophrenia. The resultant distortion of speech or thought may be isolated, and quickly corrected by the speaker or thinker. It may, on the other hand, have important ramifications and significant consequences for the individual's further behavior, even though it may go unnoticed at the time and uncorrected.[22]

(3) *Fragmentation.* By *fragmentation* we mean *the occurrence of a miscellany of discontinuous and abortive responses, or of sudden inaction that is not followed by resumption of the original theme.* The former is what we described in the

[19] Cameron, N., "Reasoning, regression and communication in schizophrenics." *Psychol. Monogr.*, 1938, vol. 50, no. 1.
[20] For a more detailed discussion of slips of speech, see pages 271–272.
[21] Freud, S., *The psychopathology of everyday life.* London: Fisher and Unwin, 1914.
[22] See pages 262 and 267.

behavior of the man who found his place of work closed in his face, and in the housewife who faced the prospect of serving her vitally important guest without benefit of silverware. Sometimes fragmentary behavior exhibits great variety. In marked disorganization, whether normal or pathological, no two successive acts may be alike or show relatedness. The opposite of this, however, is also characteristic of fragmentation: the discontinuous responses are perseverative, repetitive and stereotyped; and occasionally one finds this state of affairs persisting for a considerable period of time.[23]

Fragmentation, we have said, also includes the interruption of ongoing behavior by sudden inaction which is not followed by a resumption of the theme preceding the pause. The duration of such a pause varies from a few seconds up to several minutes, or even hours. The man shut out from his work, and the woman in her domestic crisis, might have responded with sudden inaction instead of a medley of inadequate responses. We see comical examples of such interrupted behavior in everyday surprise, when a person meets the unexpected with wide-eyed, speechless, fixed amazement. We see it also in the mute, unreactive individual stunned by personal tragedy who, when he finally begins to move about again, seems aimless, out of contact, mechanical, and behaviorally unrelated to the man he had been earlier.[24]

When pauses of this character occur in speech and thinking, when the word- or thought-flow seems suddenly checked and cannot be resumed, it is customary in behavior pathology to call the interruption *blocking*. Although blocking may be found in many pathological syndromes, it is generally considered to be most characteristic of schizophrenic disorders. And, indeed, whether or not it actually is most characteristic of schizophrenia, blocking is certainly seen there most impressively and with the most dramatic consequences.

Fragmentation of speech and thinking is clearly a common and well-recognized component of both normal and pathological disorganization. Individuals forget what they were about to say, complain that their thoughts are jumbled and mixed up, or seem to go around and around on one unchanging theme. Some complain that words or thoughts seem suddenly broken into, cut off, snatched away or substituted, as though it were the work of an outside agency. The consequence is often that talk grows unintelligible to others and sometimes unintelligible also to the person speaking.[25] Fragmentation of speech has received a great deal of special attention in certain areas of study — for example, stammering and stuttering in speech pathology; the aphasias in

---

[23] Perseverative, repetitive responses characterize some subjects in experiments on emotional excitement. See, for example, Patrick, J. K., "Studies in rational behavior and emotional excitement: II. The effect of emotional excitement on rational behavior of human subjects." *J. comp. Psychol.*, 1934, vol. 18, pp. 153–195.

[24] Compare the description of grief and mourning given on pages 314–316.

[25] See pages 506–515.

clinical neurology;[26] thought deprivation, topical flight and verbal scatter in psychiatry.[27] But the fact deserves re-emphasis at this point that all of these manifestations of disorganization are characteristic of normal behavior as well as pathological.

Cameron and Magaret have recently reported the experimental production of verbal scatter — characterized by fragmentation, with considerable blocking and some interpenetration — in normal college students.[28] The task was one of listening to a recorded case history while attempting to finish incomplete sentences, which were read to each subject by an experimenter. A great many of the responses thus obtained resemble closely those reported earlier for schizophrenic patients faced with the same task of completion, but without having to listen to a case history.[29] Wide individual differences in scatter-susceptibility were found among the normal subjects.[30] However, as we shall see, it is in schizophrenic disorganization that one encounters the most striking illustrations of fragmentation and interpenetration — in manipulation, gesture, speech and thinking.

(4) *Overinclusion.*[31] Effective behavior, we have already said, depends as much upon the *exclusion* of the unrelated and inconsequential from an act, as it does upon the *inclusion* of what is requisite and relevant. In the more or less unstructured, developing situation, behavior organization is most effective when it is comparatively *unstable and inclusive;* for then it is sufficiently flexible to adapt to unanticipated changes in the stimulating field. On the other hand, behavior organization that is *stable and exclusive* is most effective in structured situations where precision in close-knit sequential operations is essential. We have also pointed out that learning is never the simple addition of a new response, and skill is always more than mere timing and fitting together.[32] For the acquisition and the practice of effective skilled behavior demand that a person be capable of organizing and maintaining a unified and smoothly integrated dynamic system. And this he must do even in the presence of stimulation that tends to evoke competing and contradictory responses.

It is the failure to exclude effects of such interfering stimulation that char-

[26] See, for example, Grinker, R. R., *Neurology* (3rd ed.). Springfield, Illinois: C. C. Thomas, 1943, pp. 504–510; Weisenberg, T. and McBride, K. E., *Aphasia.* London: Oxford, 1935.

[27] See, for example, Kasanin, J. (Ed.), *Language and thought in schizophrenia.* Berkeley, Calif.: University of California Press, 1946.

[28] Cameron, N. and Magaret, A., "Experimental studies in thinking: I. Scattered speech in the responses of normal subjects to incomplete sentences." *J. exper. Psychol.,* 1949, vol. 39, pp. 617–627.

[29] Cameron, N., "A study of thinking in senile deterioration and schizophrenic disorganization." *Amer. J. Psychol.,* 1938, vol. 51, pp. 650–665.

[30] Cameron, N. and Magaret, A., "Correlates of scattered speech in the responses of normal subjects to incomplete sentences." *J. gen. Psychol.,* 1950, vol. 43, pp. 77–84.

[31] For a discussion of exclusion-inclusion, and of the contrast between stable and exclusive, on the one hand, and unstable and inclusive, on the other, see pages 73–75.

[32] See Chapter 3.

acterizes *overinclusion*. The reacting individual no longer maintains the boundaries of the stimulating field. He responds to successive and simultaneous stimulation regardless of whether or not the components are part of the dominant organized pattern, or habitually call out responses that are adequately interrelated. We may now define *overinclusion* as *an exaggerated instability of behavior organization in which the number and kind of simultaneously effective excitants are not restricted to a relatively few coherent ones*. The consequence of this failure in limitation is that contradictory, competing and more or less irrelevant responses are not excluded from a developing or an ongoing act, and behavioral disorganization is inevitable.

The concept of overinclusion was first developed operationally, in connection with the sorting behavior of schizophrenic patients.[33] But its use since then has been expanded to cover a wide range of behavioral disorganization, both normal and abnormal.[34] In behavior pathology, overinclusion is most clearly illustrated in delirium, panic and schizophrenia.[35] However, as we have elsewhere noted, it is also prominent in compulsive disorders,[36] and it may enter significantly into the pathology of anxiety attacks, phobias, depressive agitation and manic excitement.[37]

Overinclusion can be found in a great variety of normal behavior, induced by many different situations, of which the complex, novel and exciting may serve us for illustrative purposes. In all problem-solving, whether undertaken in play or in earnest, and whether carried on overtly or in fantasy, one of the essential first steps is that of delimiting the field of operations.[38] A person must begin problem-solving by establishing behavioral boundaries within which to develop unified attitudes; the unified attitudes will then support specific, relevant responses. This beginning operation requires a balance of inclusion and exclusion, that permits the necessary behavior to develop, but at the same time protects the developing organization from irrelevant, disruptive stimulation.

By way of example, suppose a person to be confronted by a new kind of business or household equipment — an automatic card-sorter and filer, a motor-driven home milling machine, or a master mixer — the operation of which is wholly unfamiliar to him. Even with a set of detailed instructions before him,

---

[33] Cameron, N., "Schizophrenic thinking in a problem-solving situation." *J. ment. Sci.*, 1939, vol. 85, pp. 1012–1035.

[34] Cameron, N., *The psychology of behavior disorders.* Boston: Houghton Mifflin, 1947, pp. 58–60; Zipf, G. K., *Human behavior and the principle of least effort.* Cambridge, Mass.: Addison-Wesley, 1949; Shneidman, E. S., "Schizophrenia and the MAPS test: a study of certain formal psycho-social aspects of fantasy production in schizophrenia as revealed by performance on the make-a-picture-story (MAPS) test." *Genet. Psychol. Monogr.*, 1948, vol. 38, pp. 143–223.

[35] See pages 469–477 and 494–515.   [36] See pages 354–359.

[37] See Chapter 11.

[38] See, for example, Maier, N. R. F., "Reasoning in humans: I. On direction." *J. comp. Psychol.*, 1930, vol. 10, pp. 115–143; Maier, N. R. F., "Reasoning in humans: II. The solution of a problem and its appearance in consciousness." *J. comp. Psychol.*, 1931, vol. 12, pp. 181–194; Duncker, K., "On problem solving." *Psychol. Monogr.*, 1945, no. 270.

he is likely to include in his initial behavior many inappropriate responses to functionless parts and incidental properties of the stimulating field. He fingers a knurled knob that merely holds the frame together, twirls a shaft which has nothing whatever to do with starting the machine in motion, and peers intently under a hood that conceals nothing. His mastery of the equipment depends fully as much upon his eliminating these overinclusive responses as it does upon his acquiring and maintaining a unified organization of the essential ones. And if, for any reason, the new skill disintegrates — temporarily, or progressively and permanently — overinclusion will almost certainly become again a prominent part of the behavioral disorganization that ensues.

Excitement of any kind can lead quickly to overinclusive behavior. In the preceding example, the newly learned organization may be quickly dissipated during an episode of anger, disappointment, great good news or sudden fright.[39] An acutely excited person may respond indiscriminately to a large number of unrelated and often inconsequential parts of his environment. Sometimes the stimulating field arouses such variegated, incompatible responses that the individual can give no unified reaction, and stands in his confusion helplessly gazing about him. The treatment usually given, in either case, is remarkably similar to that employed professionally to reduce pathological excitement with overinclusion. The situation is simplified as much as possible, and the excited person is given reassurance and support; or he is removed to a more restricted environment — a quiet office or a bedroom — where he can recover his normal, structured behavior in relative isolation.[40]

It was inevitable that in our discussion of *incoordination, interpenetration, fragmentation* and *overinclusion*, we should have included more or less incidentally some descriptions of the circumstances giving rise to behavioral disorganization. Thus, we spoke in this vein of the disruptive effects of sudden environmental change, of excitement and unpredicted interruption, of extreme novelty and complexity, of deep preoccupation and — in Luria's experiments, for instance — of abrupt shifts in pace. We shall now take up, more or less systematically, the conditions which are most conducive to the development of disorganization.

Conditions favoring disorganization

Organized behavior is so commonplace and nearly universal in human beings that we all tend to accept it unquestioningly, like the alternation of day and night. We seldom think that for each person, individually, there is an optimal range of conditions within which behavioral organization may be efficiently

[39] Compare, for example, the inefficiency of anxious pilots in performing their newly-learned skills. Glavis, L. R., Jr., "Bombing mission number fifteen." *J. abn. soc. Psychol.*, 1946, vol. 41, pp. 189–198; Grinker, R. R. and Spiegel, J. P., *Men under stress.* Philadelphia: Blakiston, 1945.

[40] See pages 583–585 and 606.

maintained, a suboptimal range within which its maintenance is difficult and costly, and limits beyond which it cannot be maintained at all. And just as we found that disorganization has identifiable characteristics, so we shall see also that there are certain recognizable conditions under which, individual differences aside, it is most likely to occur. These conditions we may group, for convenience and simplicity of exposition, into the following categories: (1) *Interruption of ongoing activity,* (2) *Environmental change,* (3) *Preoccupation,* (4) *Emotional excitement,* (5) *Ineffectual role-taking,* (6) *Situational complexity,* and (7) *Cerebral incompetence.*

(1) *Interruption of ongoing activity.* The dynamic structure of ongoing activity is such that each temporally prior pattern in a sense prepares the responding organism for what comes next.[41] Thus, if a man is typing a letter, each unit of behavior in the sequence carries the action forward into the next unit — whether we conceive of this unit as a stroke, a sentence or a paragraph. In other words, the organization of a developing act depends to a considerable extent upon continuity in time. It is possible to analyze out of a preceding phase the anticipant attitudes which prepare the organism to respond adequately in the succeeding phase. If something suddenly interrupts the dynamic temporal sequence, there is almost certain to be a period, however brief, in which disorganization appears.

This effect is perfectly obvious, in the performance of a moderately skilled amateur typist, when somebody without the least warning suddenly interferes in the midst of a fast-moving sequence. The keys pile up, the carriage jams, the typist's body jumps forward and his neck jerks up, widespread disintegrating tensions instantly develop, exclamations are emitted, there is ugly grimacing, and there may be violence. Moreover, the ensuing activity, whether it be further typing or something else, will for a time suffer also in precision. The picture here presented is clearly neither one of simple cessation of a skilled activity, nor one of a shift from one organized sequence to another. It is that of unmistakable behavioral disorganization, in which a unified reaction has been disrupted, and replaced by behavior that is fragmented, haphazard, and to some extent chaotic.

Interruptions such as this clearly constitute *frustration,* as we have earlier defined it.[42] Indeed, any of the forms of frustration that we have distinguished — *simple delay, thwarting* or *conflict* — can be considered also as situations characterized by an interruption of ongoing activity. Thus an eagerly anticipant wife might disorganize momentarily when she discovers, at the railroad station, that she must wait three hours longer for the arrival of her husband, returning from the war. So might a weary camper who, having missed the trail, finds himself blocked toward sunset by a towering cliff. And the

---

[41] For a discussion of temporal sequences and learning, see pages 63–69.
[42] See pages 47–49.

person facing a nicely balanced choice is likely while in conflict to make fragmentary and haphazard little movements, give evidence of tremors and tensions, and otherwise exhibit disruption and disunity.

The disorganizing interruptions of ongoing activity that lead one into behavior pathology, however, are rarely as simple or as fleeting as this. The delay is not suffered at a railroad station, and it promises to reach forward into the years, or into eternity. The thwarting is more subtle and less accessible than a cliff, and the way around it harder to encompass or imagine. The conflict is not between two happy choices; neither does it hold the prospect of quick resolution. Moreover, we have always to reckon with the cumulative and self-perpetuating effects of secondary interruptions upon disorganization that is already in progress. As we shall find in schizophrenic illnesses, the many interferences with ongoing activity that disorganization itself induces, become themselves focal points around which delusions develop; and these then further disrupt and disunify behavior.[43]

(2) *Environmental change.* Behavioral disorganization is often the immediate result of a change in the dynamics of the effective surroundings, especially if the change is sudden, sweeping or dramatic. It will be recalled that the continuity and stability of behavior — even of routine behavior — depend upon the maintenance of adequate anticipant attitudes, and that these attitudes, in turn, obtain their support from a continuing and dependable environment.[44] An abrupt or drastic alteration in the previously supporting environment may thus, at least temporarily, destroy the patterned and sequential character of an individual's responses, leaving behavior fragmentary, haphazard or chaotic.

During World War II, the change both from civilian to military life, and from military back to civilian life, was responsible for precipitating a great many episodes of behavioral disorganization.[45] Most of these were transient and relatively mild, but some of them were severe and persistent enough to lead to prolonged hospitalization. Civilians imprisoned for the first time may likewise react with disorganization to the catastrophic alteration in living conditions imposed upon them. The plight of elderly men and women who are obliged to change their homes and their mode of life is often disorganizing in its effects. Ageing individuals are nearly always less able than younger ones to learn new ways to cope with their new surroundings. They miss the support of their long accustomed routines and familiar satisfactions; they lose both their cultural roots and their personal significance.

---

[43] See pages 494–515.

[44] For a discussion of *attitude* and *response*, see pages 64–66.

[45] See, for example, Curle, A., "Transitional communities and social reconnection: a follow-up study of the civil resettlement of British prisoners of war. Part I." *Hum. Relation.*, 1947, vol. 1, pp. 42–68; Curle, A. and Trist, E. L., "Transitional communities and social reconnection: a follow-up study of the civil resettlement of British prisoners of war. Part II." *Hum. Relation.*, 1947, vol. 1, pp. 240–288. This point is further considered on pages 484–491.

Something similar to this occurs in the case of prisoners of war. Indeed, it is often necessary for self-appointed leaders in groups of such individuals to take heroic measures, if the tendencies toward social disintegration and personal disorganization are to be counteracted. An effective procedure commonly adopted is one of establishing a miniature community that capitalizes upon the mores and conventions characteristic of the wider communities from which the prisoners, or the displaced persons, have been drawn. This essentially duplicates the original biosocial environment upon which the maintenance of adequate attitudes must depend; the disorganizing behavior can thus be reorganized in the restructured environment and the whole process of personal and social disintegration arrested.[46]

A special difficulty confronts the individual foreigner who is suddenly transplanted to a land he understands imperfectly, and for which he has no liking. In the following case, we can see disorganization developing under comparable circumstances in real life, with reorganization following return to the familiar supporting subculture.

A twenty-four-year-old Costa Rican came to this country to do graduate work in one of the agricultural sciences. His family belonged to a political group that had never forgiven the United States for signing a treaty with Nicaragua which they believed had deliberately disregarded Costa Rican rights. The selection of the United States as a place of study was made solely on the basis of its preëminence in a branch of agriculture directly related to the family's economic prosperity. Nevertheless, this choice was made by the elders with considerable reluctance; and it was received by the patient with open resentment. He landed in New York and stayed on Manhattan Island for a few weeks in a Spanish-speaking neighborhood where a fellow-countryman of his lived. Here he heard some talk of Yankee imperialism and discussions of prejudicial treatment of Latin Americans.

It was in this general setting that the patient began his series of cumulative misunderstandings, which resulted in his building up a threatening pseudocommunity, and led ultimately to serious disorganization. In Costa Rica, he had been accustomed to courtesy from strangers, and either deference or warmth from those who knew him. He was therefore unprepared for the brusque, uncouth and sometimes hostile conduct of the islanders whom he encountered in street, subway and restaurant. After a short period of perplexity and amazement, the patient began interpreting every blind collision as an intentional assault, and every oath or admonition as a personal insult. His uncertain grasp of conversational English made it easy for him to misconstrue what was said to him in such a way as to support his growing conviction of deliberate mistreatment.

The patient had already made a number of angry statements, some of them in public, criticizing the United States and its citizens, when an

---

[46] See, for example, Fensterheim, H. and Birch, H. G., "A case study of group ideology and individual adjustment." *J. abn. soc. Psychol.*, 1950, vol. 45, pp. 710–720.

acquaintance told him that he might be reported to the F.B.I. This frightened him at once, and led him to anticipate arrest and imprisonment by secret political police. He decided to leave New York, without informing anyone of his intentions, and proceed to the agricultural college of his family's choice by bus, so as to avoid appearing in a railroad station where the police might be watching for him. On the bus he found some of the passengers too friendly and inquisitive. There was one man in particular who asked many personal questions about his name, where he was from, where he was going and what he would do there and how long he would stay.

This man and his companion made disquieting comments about foreigners, particularly Latin Americans, and about agriculture, higher education, war and politics. They seemed at home in all of these fields, speaking with assurance and apparent authority. The patient was soon convinced that the two were *agents provocateurs* who were shadowing him, and trying to goad him into the expression of opinions which would incriminate him. At a bus stop, where the passengers got off to eat, he decided upon a showdown. He accused the inquisitive man of spying, struck him and challenged him to a fight; but the bus driver intervened and threatened to leave the patient behind unless he behaved himself. During the rest of the trip, the patient was shunned and no longer treated as a fellow-passenger by the two whom he suspected. He observed that everyone on the bus, including the driver, eyed him with aversion and apparent malice.

At the agricultural college the situation grew still more confusing. In registering as a student, he was forced to give in writing all kinds of information regarding his parentage, his religion, the details of his past schooling and his future plans. There was some difficulty over his obtaining a place to live, and in this he again detected prejudice. He suddenly found that registration clerks, and other persons whom he had never seen before, addressed him familiarly by name. Strangers smiled at him as he made his way down the corridors. When he finally met the professor under whom he had come to study, the latter seemed to him to behave in a manner wholly unbecoming a great scholar and scientist. Here, again, was the same overfriendly and overinquisitive approach.

For a few days the patient attended classes and made a beginning on some laboratory work. But by this time his behavior was dominated by attitudes belonging to the pseudocommunity which he had built up on the basis of cumulative misinterpretation. He had become intensely reaction-sensitive to signs of espionage, of hostility, aversion and ridicule. In terms of his pseudocommunity, his responses to such signs were appropriate enough; but in terms of the social community, which saw him with quite different eyes, they grew increasingly fragmentary, haphazard and chaotic. The patient was finally admitted to the college clinic, as the result of a telephone call from his landlady, who had become alarmed by his furtive manner and strange talk. In the clinic he was clearly frightened, in spite of his air of defiant bravado, and he showed in language reactions a rather profound disorganization. He was transferred to a state hospital, and later returned to his native country. Back home, in familiar surroundings and among persons he understood completely, the patient underwent rapid behavioral reorganization, and recovered without further hospitalization and without psychiatric treatment of any kind.

This case illustrates certain points of general significance for behavior pathology. The most obvious of these is the far-reaching disorganization that can follow environmental change, and the remarkable recovery that a mere return to the familiar subculture can induce — an outcome which is by no means rare. Another important point brought out by this patient's history is that words half-understood are frequently more dangerous to a person under stress than words not understood at all. The half-understood word is inevitably interpreted by a brooding patient in terms of his specific reaction-sensitivities.[47] The interpretation then seems to support unshared and socially invalid preoccupations, and so contributes further to disorganization. Thus we see the ways in which a person may, by his own behavior, increase the complexity of his situation to a point where he can no longer handle it unaided. In the next section we shall give detailed consideration to preoccupation as a disorganizing factor; in a later section we shall take up the influence of situational complexity.

(3) *Preoccupation.* We mean by preoccupation the protracted domination of behavior by a single theme — or by a restricted system of themes — to the exclusion of virtually everything else. Preoccupation so conceived is in itself obviously neither an evil nor a good. It may be a necessary forerunner of socially shared activity, or precede the decision to cease cooperating and competing. It may be confined to fantasy, include a fusion of fantasy and overt action, or be almost wholly overt. When preoccupation is retrospective — in fantasy or social conversation — it provides the occasion for reflection; and this may be gratifying to the individual, exciting, soothing or distressing. And when it deals with future expectation or intent, it may likewise raise premature doubt and apprehension, or bring the individual unearned delight.[48]

Preoccupation, we know, is a common development in serious conflict which sometimes intensifies or hastens the disorganization that conflict initiates.[49] But preoccupation often sets the stage for disorganization without antecedent serious conflict. Suppose a person to be completely absorbed in something he is doing, saying or thinking, and stimulation intrudes that is outside the absorbing activity. For example, a hand is placed on the preoccupied person's shoulder, a face unexpectedly peers into his, the telephone rings, or a peremptory question is asked. The outcome is familiar to everyone. The engrossed person responds characteristically with fragmentary, haphazard and

[47] See pages 70–74.
[48] Some of the potentialities of fantasy for delusion formation have been discussed on pages 390–392 and 421–424; others will be considered in relation to desocialization in the next chapter.   [49] See page 274.

even chaotic movements, words or thoughts. The intensely anticipant attitudes of his preoccupation leave him unprepared for any exigency lying outside
their narrow scope.

Preoccupation often begets further preoccupation — just as disorganization
may also perpetuate itself.[50] In general, the longer a restricted theme of preoccupation persists, and the more insistently it returns to exclude rival activities, the more likely it is to lead toward behavioral disorganization. For not
only do the excluded activities suffer impairment through disuse, but the
restricted theme itself tends to undergo distortion because of its isolation. The
matrix of social behavior, from which even the most individualistic fantasy
gets its materials, cannot effectively influence isolated, unshared activities.
Moreover, if a restricted theme begins to dominate and recur, it can readily be
overlearned; and if it is overlearned, it has greater potentialities then for
continued domination and recurrence.[51]

Shared preoccupation, as well as unshared, can be disorganizing. We see this
exemplified in two behavior disorders whose outstanding characteristic is disorganization: schizophrenia and panic. By no means every schizophrenic
patient is silent concerning his confusing pseudocommunity; and neither is the
person developing a panic reaction typically uncommunicative or overtly
inactive. Indeed, both the sources and the manifestations of behavioral disorganization are often overt and publicly shared.

Nonetheless, it is the private, unshared and predominantly covert preoccupation that is most conducive to progressive, cumulative behavioral disorganization. For one thing, it can proceed without interference or contradiction
along lines which would be impossible for shared preoccupation. It easily
escapes the modifying and regulating influence of shared acts, the restraints
imposed by the design of one's environment, and the critical evaluations of an
independent observer. Things private and kept hidden are the most readily
organized into pseudocommunities and autistic communities. Moreover, a
devotion to covert preoccupation tends further to isolate an individual, to
limit and ultimately to destroy his opportunities for checking and validating
his behavior and its consequences, in terms of the shared social community.
This isolation spells desocialization and, for a disorganizing person, to become
desocialized inevitably means a deepening and widening of his disorganization.

(4) *Emotional excitement.* In normal as well as in pathological behavior, emotional excitement is perhaps the most generally recognized precursor of behavioral disorganization — its only possible rival being cerebral incompetence.
This recognition is given elliptical expression in such phrases as, "deliriously
happy," "beside himself with fear," "going to pieces," "in a frenzied rage,"
"wildly in love," "striking out blindly." These are manifestly statements of

[50] This relationship receives further attention on pages 485–492.
[51] For discussions of *overlearning*, see pages 78–79 and 148–153.

disorganized emotional behavior, and the situations thus characterized are familiar to everyone. Indeed, so much emphasis is laid upon the disordered aspects of emotional excitement by all of us that we tend to forget an equally important fact: that angry, frightened, or erotic human beings often exhibit highly integrated, effective behavior.[52] Nevertheless, emotional excitement is one of the conditions which commonly favors disorganization, and it is this relationship that we must consider next.

Some of the fundamental characteristics of disorganization, as we shall see, can be directly derived from the known properties of emotional excitement — particularly from the *increased dimensions* of behavior which are typically involved.[53] (*a*) The excited person is likely to *move faster* than the unexcited, (*b*) his movements go through *greater excursions*, and (*c*) he develops *more marked tensions.* There are limits within which such increases can occur without disrupting integrated, ongoing behavior. In other words, the human organism as a system has optimal conditions for operating in an organized fashion; and these conditions may cease to exist because of the increased dimensions incident to emotional excitement.

(*a*) We witness innumerable examples of the disruptive effects of *extremely rapid* behavior in everyday life — even in the absence of emotional excitement.[54] The person who tries to finish quickly a task requiring deliberate precision is likely to demonstrate disruption; so also are two individuals pitted against each other in a competitive game, where fine coordination is essential and swiftness is rewarded. "More haste," says the adage, "less speed." If the competition engenders strong emotional reactions, there will usually be an upswing in haste that carries the individual far out of his optimal range of operation. This relationship comes out most dramatically and most tragically in fire panics, where it is often the case that more persons die in the wild rush for safety than perish in the fire.

(*b*) The *excessive excursion* of movement also may be disruptive in non-emotional as well as in emotional behavior. Adults whose trade has accustomed them to work in large movement-units become suddenly awkward when faced with an unfamiliar task, calling for small meticulous coordinations. The housebuilder makes a poor cabinet-maker, the stone mason a poor engraver, and the

---

[52] See, for example, the current controversy in Leeper, R. W., "A motivational theory of emotion to replace 'emotion as disorganized response.'" *Psychol. Rev.*, 1948, vol. 55, pp. 5–21; Young, P. T., "Emotion as disorganized response — a reply to Professor Leeper." *Psychol. Rev.*, 1949, vol. 56, pp. 184–191; Duffy, E., "Leeper's 'Motivational theory of emotion.'" *Psychol. Rev.*, 1948, vol. 55, pp. 324–328; Webb, W. B., "A motivational theory of emotions. . . ." *Psychol. Rev.*, 1948, vol. 55, pp. 329–335; Waters, R. H. and Blackwood, D. F., "The applicability of motivational criteria to emotions." *Psychol. Rev.*, 1949, vol. 56, pp. 351–356.

[53] For a description of emotional excitement, see pages 122–125. See also Darrow, C. W. and Henry, C. E., "Psychophysiology of stress." In *Human factors in undersea warfare.* National Research Council, 1949, pp. 417–439.

[54] See also the discussion of *tempo* in relation to stress, on page 45.

expert tennis player an awkward performer at ping-pong. It is a common observation that in emotional excitement people tend to push too hard, swing too far and jump too high.[55] Thus the enraged fighter characteristically misses his mark by slugging, and he is more easily thrown off balance than is his cooler opponent. The frightened man, also, makes greatly exaggerated movements of avoidance and withdrawal; and these may bring him the injury he fears, from a direction he does not anticipate.

(c) The disruptive influence of *exaggerated muscular tension* — and the rigidity which marked tension inevitably induces — are known to every wielder of a tool, to the baseball player, the dancer, the golfer and the public speaker, and to everyone who eats with knife, fork or spoon. The angry mother holds her child at arm's length, stiffly, and is speechless. The frightened motorist, who has just injured someone else but is himself unhurt, cannot write legibly, walk freely or speak clearly because of his excessive muscle tension. Half-grown kittens, with their slow-motion, steppage gait, give us a kind of caricature of rigid fear when they are in the presence of a strange dog. One sees the disorganizing effects of increased isometric tension in a wide range of behavior pathology, but particularly in schizophrenia, depression and anxiety disorders.

When emotional excitement cannot be consummated, and anxiety develops, the resulting tensions frequently take on a cumulative and self-perpetuating character, such as we have already described in the chapter on anxiety.[56] These reach a dramatic disorganizing climax in the *panic reaction*. They develop their most chaotic form among the *schizophrenic disorders*,[57] where patients sometimes reach a degree of ineffectuality which matches almost anything that one encounters in the consequences of cerebral degeneration. The conditions underlying schizophrenic chaos, however, are not those of cerebral incompetence.[58] They consist in the establishment of a vicious cycle between persistent disorganization and increasing desocialization, with which the anxious patient, unskilled as he is in social role-taking, cannot cope.

(5) *Ineffectual role-taking.* We have already discussed, in some detail,[59] the importance to the individual of acquiring an adequate repertory of culturally defined roles, of gaining through practice a certain degree of skill in concerted and reciprocal behavior, and of learning to shift perspective readily in overt act and in fantasy. And we have seen some of the consequences in behavior pathology of an inadequate repertory of social roles, of maladroit attempts at social cooperation and competition, and of difficulty in shifting perspectives.[60] It is not surprising, therefore, to find that ineffectual role-taking is an important source of behavioral disorganization.

---

[55] See, for example, Davis, D. R., "Increase in strength of a secondary drive as a cause of disorganization." *Quart. J. exp. Psychol.*, 1948, vol. 1, pp. 22–28.

[56] See pages 305–314.   [57] See pages 494–517.

[58] See pages 531–555.   [59] See pages 114–122.

[60] See especially pages 197–198 and 387–392.

This relationship is clear even in normal everyday life, particularly in situations calling for socially more mature or more sophisticated behavior than an individual is accustomed to exhibit. The small child, allowed to stay up with adult dinner guests, cannot long endure the strain of playing the little grown-up. He becomes restless, commits haphazard little playful aggressions, falls to giggling inappropriately, and is finally taken away in complete disorder to bed. The adolescent boy, out on his first date with a girl, develops incoordination, blocks and misspeaks, omits and forgets parts of ordinary acts of courtesy, and shows a degree of responsiveness to irrelevant stimulation that borders on overinclusion. The same boy, after further practice in taking girls out, will show none of these characteristics of disorganization, once his role of escort is socially organized and he has gained familiarity with feminine perspectives.

Adults give similar performances of ineffectual role-taking when a situation casts them in a new and unaccustomed role, in which they have not had adequate practice, directly or in talk and covert fantasy. A new father, for example, be he twenty years old or forty, can no more handle his baby without disruption of his unified behavior than can the adolescent maneuver smoothly in his new role of escort. A new mother, on the other hand, for all her awkwardness in details of infant handling, will never show the same degree of disorganization; for she has acted the part of mother for many years, realistically and wholeheartedly, in doll-play, talk and fantasy. The new salesman, facing his first customer unaided, drops things and cannot find them, is unable to make something work that he has just demonstrated smoothly for another employee, cannot make appropriate shifts in perspective when the customer raises objections and, if he makes the sale, cannot remember the date, must consult the price tag several times and may be vague about even his own exact whereabouts. A month later, both new father and new salesman have mastered their socially defined roles, gained skill in shifting perspectives, and lost all signs of behavioral disorganization.

As one might expect in behavior organization so complex and so long in developing, there are wide individual variations in the skill that different persons ultimately achieve in social role-taking. The same person may show adequate or superior skill in a few related roles, and inadequacy in other equally important ones, because of grossly unequal opportunities for practice in different social activities during childhood and adolescence. Some unfortunate individuals never succeed in acquiring a degree of role-taking skill that will enable them adequately to define their own part in certain essential human functions — cooperating in a group, competing reciprocally, accepting mature responsibility for their behavior, being a marital partner and a parent.[61] In consequence, they cannot thoroughly establish themselves as mature members

[61] See pages 387–392 and 406–411.

of the culture in which they must live. And it is in the behavior of these individuals that we find disorganization most readily appearing when the situation seems to demand the simultaneous performance of competing and contradictory roles.

(6) *Situational complexity.* If a person is to maintain his organized behavior at an adequate level, he must of course be able to react with stable and consistent attitudes to the demands of his compound environment and of his own intricate self-reactions. Moreover, as these demands continually shift and change, his attitudes must shift and change appropriately to meet them. When, in this context, we speak of situational complexity, it is obvious that both person and environment must be included in a single interacting field. For surroundings in which a superior adult can operate with ease may overwhelm the average man; and circumstances that the average man accepts, as everyday routine, may precipitate in the developmentally retarded a reaction of hopeless confusion.

We have already witnessed the behavioral disorganization that may occur when a relatively unrestricted environment, which the normal person can handle, proves too complicated for the developmentally retarded.[62] But, of course, retardation is by no means the only personal factor in situations of too great complexity. For we see similar disorganization in the shy, inexperienced normal adolescent who is thrown without social practice into the midst of an energetic social group. Likewise the business man, propelled suddenly into his superior's job, through his superior's accident or defection, finds sometimes that one step upward is a step into the unstructured infinite for him. Then the familiar "promotion panic"[63] follows, leading in the more fortunate cases to demotion, reorganization and recovery. In all of these we see examples, from ordinary daily life, of behavioral disorganization favored primarily by too great situational complexity, in terms of the individual's behavioral resources.

Even when it is conflict that culminates in behavioral disorganization, it is not alone the recurrence or persistence that may tip the balance;[64] the complexity of the conflict situation can also be a factor. This we see most clearly in the disorganizing schizophrenic. For the ramifications of his multiple conflict seem to spread out endlessly in all directions, leaving him helplessly indecisive — like Hamlet ruminating with sword poised over the praying king. Anxiety and stress-distortion may likewise so complicate the situation for a person, by indiscriminately heightening his readiness-to-react, that his behavior grows fragmentary, haphazard and chaotic.[65] And, finally, the confused reactions that other people often give to the man who shows the beginning effects of conflict, anxiety and stress, may add significantly and sometimes critically to the complexity of an effective stimulating pattern.

---

[62] See pages 176–178.   [63] See pages 326–327.   [64] See pages 272–275.
[65] Compare the discussion of stress on pages 44–46, and of anxiety on pages 279–280.

(7) *Cerebral incompetence.* A peculiarly difficult and important problem is posed by the person who, because of impaired cerebral function, suffers a significant reduction in behavioral adequacy — whether the reduction be gradual or sudden, temporary or permanent, stationary or progressive.[66] For such an individual becomes unable to maintain his previous level of organization, and is no longer able to meet situational demands as he formerly could. And the moment he grows incapable of carrying on his usual coordinative operations, one of two things will happen: the range of his reactions will undergo restriction — sometimes even to the point of sleep or of coma — or his behavior will disorganize.

We see behavioral disorganization develop on this basis in a great many familiar situations. The exhausted factory hand, returning home by subway after long hours of overtime, may mutter incoherently when addressed, and lurch out of the door as he leaves the standing train. The young saleslady, on too strict a reducing diet, shows fine tremors as she displays goods across the counter; she repeatedly misspeaks, makes strange mistakes in adding, and cannot recall what she has just been doing. The ageing man grows confused in his own home at night, he cannot find his bedroom after leaving it, and he answers even the most sympathetic questions disjointedly and irrelevantly. The factory hand exhibits the disorganizing effects of exhaustion upon complex coordination, the saleslady of a lack of necessary foodstuffs, and the ageing man of cortical degeneration.

Usually more dramatic, but still common enough, is the behavioral disorganization in cases of high fever, intoxication, brain injury and cerebral disease. We see examples of these among persons with a febrile illness,[67] victims of industrial poisoning, of alcoholism and of bromidism, motorists with recent brain damage, encephalitic patients and paretics. But whatever the source of the reduction in cerebral competence, if the change is sufficiently sudden and severe, we are likely to witness a rapidly fulminating and acute delirium. Indeed, as we shall see in the following material, the delirious syndrome presents some of the most striking and clear-cut pictures of behavioral disorganization.

Delirium

Delirium is characterized by gross disorientation, defective retentivity, delusion, hallucination, and signs of central nervous system dysfunction. As we have already indicated, reduced cerebral competence has many possible antecedents; and any of these may become factors in the production of delirium. In delirious intoxication, the commonest agents are alcohol, bromide, the barbiturates,

---

[66] For a general discussion of behavior pathology in cerebral incompetence, see pages 531–555.

[67] See pages 540–543.

opium derivatives, marihuana and cocaine. Other important but less common agents are such industrial poisons as lead, illuminating gas and benzene. Any acute infectious disease with high fever may be complicated by and occasionally followed by delirium, whether the brain is directly affected or not. Exhaustion, exposure, starvation, dehydration, and a wide variety of metabolic disturbances may precipitate delirium. So also may cardiovascular, respiratory and renal disorders, and surgical operations, particularly if there is infection or intoxication present. It goes without saying that delirium is a common episode in inflammatory and degenerative cortical disorders, in severe brain injury, in intracranial tumor and in intracranial hemorrhage.

The typical delirious attack is ushered in by a premonitory period of restlessness, irritability and disturbed sleep, often with terrifying dreams. The patient shows difficulty in concentrating on any activity for long; he seems vigilant and distractible or dull and inattentive. Before long, he begins to give definite indications of oncoming behavioral disorganization. He has difficulty in sustaining attitudes appropriate to his surroundings, and accordingly misidentifies his whereabouts, the people and objects around him, or the functions that he and other persons may be performing. At first, these misidentifications are made only at intervals and are quickly corrected with help; later they occur continually and are not corrected even with repeated prompting. If the patient is asked a brief, direct question he may answer it coherently; even so, he will then characteristically drift to something unrelated, and can recall neither what was asked him nor what he said in reply.

Along with these manifestations of behavioral fragmentation go signs of obvious incoordination. The patient's speech grows thick and slurred, he mispronounces and misspeaks, rambles confusedly, answers irrelevantly, and may ultimately become wholly incoherent and unintelligible. His other complex coordinations show parallel disintegration. Tremors appear in his fingers, hands, tongue, eyelids and facial muscles. His movements become grossly ataxic, so that he fumbles when he manipulates, and he sways or staggers if he tries to stand or walk. Delirious patients frequently engage in more or less haphazard attempts to carry on activities resembling their habitual occupation. Thus, a shoemaker pounds imaginary nails with slow and awkward movements; a seamstress goes through the motions of unsteady basting and ripping; a taxicab driver executes wobbly gear-shifting routines in bed while he talks to unseen fares.

Delusion and hallucination are characteristic of this — as, indeed, they are of other — pronounced behavioral disorganization. The delusional structure in delirium is typically dreamlike — fragmentary, overinclusive and interpenetrative, shifting from one thing to another. Hallucination, similarly, is for the most part dreamlike, fleeting and kaleidoscopic, difficult for the patient to formulate in words, and much of it impossible for him to remember. It may to a considerable extent be influenced by the incidental stimulation of the moment. Thus, the designs and defects in bedcovers, wallpaper and carpeting are favorite nuclei about which visual hallucination crystallizes; so are spots, stains, cracks, and plaster discolorations. Sounds, smells and tastes operate similarly to give substance and direction to hallucination and delusion, into whose unstable, moving pattern they are quickly woven.

In spite of the over-all picture of severe disorganization, some delusional and hallucinatory behavior may for brief periods show remarkable persistence and coherence.[68] Thus, a patient may insist upon getting up to do his work, or to help someone who needs him and who seems to be calling him. His behavior, although poorly coordinated, may nevertheless doggedly maintain its general direction in the face of continued frustration and restraint. When a patient hallucinates animals, particularly insects, he may busy himself for long periods of time with watching and catching them. Likewise, conversations held with imagined persons are occasionally carried on with sufficient organization present to enable a listener to follow the drift for a few sentences without difficulty; the patient sounds as though he were talking somewhat alertly in his sleep.

As is the case also in sleep and dreams, the delusion and hallucination of deliria may be sad or happy, threatening or comforting, tragic or comical. Sometimes one can observe a delirious patient smile, chuckle and laugh over what he seems to see and hear, as well as cower, tremble and cry in fear, or shout in defiance and try to attack an imaginary tormentor. But the dominant themes are usually frightening, horrible and repulsive — a fact which the anxiety-provoking disorientation, confusion, and sick helplessness render easily intelligible. Of course, exactly what the individual sees and hears, what he believes is happening around him, and what he tries to do about it, will depend primarily upon his own particular behavioral background — just as they do in normal dreaming and daydreaming.[69]

The total duration of delirium varies from a few hours up to several months and, in rare cases, even years. Recovery, excepting in cases of permanent brain damage, is as a rule complete. In the course of a delirious illness, the depth of behavioral disorganization commonly fluctuates — from moment to moment and hour to hour — in the same general way that the depth of normal sleep is believed to fluctuate. Thus, at one time in the morning, the delirious patient may be mildly disoriented, a little haphazard in his manipulations and rambling in his talk. Later in the same morning, he may become greatly confused, ataxic, and out of effective contact with his biosocial environment. In the afternoon, his activity may be reduced to muttering and restless fumbling; that evening he may grow noisy and excited, more responsive to people and

[68] Compare, for example, the repeated themes characterizing the delirium of a young man recovering from the severe exhaustion and shock of a near-drowning. Thurmond, C. J., "Last thoughts before drowning." *J. abn. soc. Psychol.*, 1943, vol. 38, pp. 165–184.

[69] Compare pages 112–113 and 420–426.

things around him, but also more actively delusional and hallucinatory than before. If he falls asleep, no one can with certainty predict the depth or severity of disorganization that he will show when he awakes. Such fluctuations are universally interpreted as reflections of physiological change, but no systematic study has yet been undertaken to work out this relationship.

In the following case, in which a delirium developed on the basis of an abuse of bromide medication, some of the salient features we have been discussing will appear.

A grocer, forty-six years of age and married, was brought to a general hospital by relatives, who complained that he was "cantankerous," excited and all mixed up, that he was seeing things and seemed to be out of his head. When asked what was the matter, the patient said, "A little bit of something." According to the relatives, he had been worrying for some months over the successful competition of a new chain store in the neighborhood, and had resorted to a patent medicine in order to "quiet his nerves" and give him sleep. During several weeks preceding his admission to the hospital, he had been growing more and more anxious and restless; and, accordingly, he had been stepping up progressively his doses of the medicine — which turned out to include in it generous quantities of bromide.

For about ten days prior to admission, the patient seemed to be increasingly irritable, restless, talkative and confused. He slept badly, complained of nausea, and could scarcely be persuaded to eat anything. His walk became unsteady and his fingers tremulous, he stumbled over things in the store, dropped articles and could not seem to find them. He could no longer make change accurately, or add, and his speech grew thick and indistinct — "like his mouth was full," his relatives said. The customers began to complain that the patient was intoxicated — as indeed he was, although not by alcohol. Because of this accusation, he was removed from the store, not without considerable resistance, and kept at home. Here he began seeing animals and absent people in his room, heard voices jeering at him and threatening him, and said once that he was being poisoned. The general practitioner, who was called in at this point, at once recognized the gravity of the situation, and had the now fully delirious man taken to the hospital by ambulance.

In the hospital, the patient was overactive, moving his arms and legs about constantly, at times reaching for an imaginary object, or pushing something invisible away. He frequently sat up in bed and rumpled the bed coverings clumsily together, as if making up a bundle, but soon dropped back heavily upon the pillow, mumbling to himself. Every now and then he would suddenly try to get out of bed, as though there were some task that he must immediately attend to. Like his manipulations, his talk was usually incoherent, fragmentary, and often unintelligible and chaotic. There was occasional stereotypy, both of manipulation and of talk. Certain movements of his hands were executed over and over without interruption for awhile, and he said certain words in rapid repetition. He complained of stereotyped hallucination — of voices "that say, 'Jing, jing, jing, jing' and then stop, 'Jing, jing, jing, jing,' and then stop; there they go, 'Jing, jing, jing, jing,' and then stop," and so on.

The discontinuity, interpenetration and overinclusion in his responses — his inability to maintain organized sequential attitudes — were most evident when the patient tried to answer questions. Asked how long he had been ill, he replied with fair clarity, "Two weeks ago I got all mixed up." But having said this, he immediately trailed off into irrelevant snatches of words and phrases, and could not be brought back again to the subject. Here are other illustrations. (*Do you see animals?*) "Sure, what kind would you like? Right here!" pointing to a crack in the wall. (*What is it?*) "Aw — just dirt. You go into the store now and pick out something." (*What day is it?*) "March eighth, tenth and twelfth" — followed by adding, and then by drifting to fragments of incoherent talk. (*What year is it?*) "1948," correctly given, but a moment later it was "1946," he was born "in 1945," and he has three grown daughters, "born in '46 '47 and '48. Get the boys in line," indicating some medical students present, "and I'll talk to you later." Then followed a confused remark about his wife in the kitchen, and suddenly, "The skin is all coming off my face!" The patient looked horrified, but in a moment this theme was fortunately lost, and further rambling talk followed. Asked who the president was, he said, "Roosevelt." (*How about Truman?*) "I thought he left the keys there," — the nurse had taken her keys from her belt. (*Who is president now?*) "So many Roosevelts — mix up and run together — so many come in and go out all the time — up to the little short hospital —" and the rest is inaudible.

In the night, the patient showed fear much more often than he did in the day. Sometimes, he seemed to be fighting off vicious animals, or removing animal pests from his bed. At other times, he covered his head with the bedclothes, because of "all those faces." Occasionally, he spoke of being dead. He conversed disconnectedly with hallucinated persons, becoming now and then argumentative, abusive and obscene, but rarely speaking a whole sentence. To the observer, the talk sounded like a one-sided battle of words in a tavern, heard indistinctly through a heavy door. Throughout his delirium, the patient looked the part of a gravely ill, tired and harrassed man who was overwhelmed by complex problems which he could neither formulate nor resolve. After three weeks of this, during which the bromides had been eliminated by appropriate measures, he began gradually to improve. The delusion and hallucination grew infrequent; he was less voluble and more connected in his talk; his manipulations gained slowly in continuity, appropriateness and general adequacy of coordination. Two weeks later he was discharged completely well, but with little more remembrance of his delirium than he might have had of a night's dreaming.

In this case we see illustrated all of the fundamental characteristics of delirious disorganization. The *incoordination* is obvious from the very start — the tremulous hands, the stumbling and dropping things, the slurring and thick talk. The *fragmentation* can be seen in almost everything the patient tries to do — dropped things cannot be followed and found, sequences of adding and of making change are lost, all movement ultimately becomes disunified, talk loses its continuity, the topics of delusion and hallucination shift unstably or harp repetitiously on a single isolated theme. *Interpenetration* appears clearly now and then in the talk as, for example, in the comment about the Roosevelts, which carries parts of at least two themes together in it, and in the date-giving which is also at the same time an adding operation. There are numerous instances of *overinclusion*, the simplest being the comment about Truman and the keys, and the most complex the shifting visual hallucination in bed at night.

The most striking defects in the behavior of the delirious person, of course, are the discontinuity of his responses, and their inappropriateness to the total pattern of stimulation. Both defects arise from disturbances in attitude organization, and both can be attributed in delirium to known cerebral incompetence.[70] Because of the cerebral impairment, the delirious patient is deprived of his ability to maintain habitual anticipant and supporting attitudes in the presence of competing and discordant stimulation. He no longer reacts with stable, consistent and predictable attitudes to the demands of his environment, or to the demands posed by his own antecedent or simultaneous behavior. Therefore, his responses are no longer organized sequentially, as they were; and they cease to form an integrated, interrelated simultaneous pattern that corresponds in any effective way with the dynamic structure of his environment.

We have said that the fact of disorganization in delirium can be ascribed to known cerebral incompetence. For even though one finds almost as striking fragmentation in schizophrenia, where typically no cerebral incompetence is involved, there is not in schizophrenia the same pattern of tremulous incoordination, gross disorientation, defective retentivity and patchy, dream-like recall, which is so characteristic of deliria. But the story is a very different one when we examine the specific fragments of a delirious individual's behavior — the nature of whatever haphazard manipulations he attempts, the words and phrases that he speaks, his conflicts, fears and worries, or his pleasure and surprise, and even the objects, animals and persons that he hallucinates. These will always come from his own subculture, from his habitual surroundings and what he does in them, from his own past history, and — however they may be distorted — from his own personal and particular life-pattern. So it is that observers can predict the delirious behavior of any patient far more accurately from a knowledge of his individual background, occupation, modes of entertainment, family life, conflicts, anxieties, hopes, plans and fears, than from the most precise and detailed knowledge of the etiological agent or of the typical physiological reactions to it.[71]

[70] A detailed discussion of *cerebral incompetence* appears on pages 531–539.

[71] In some instances, the behavior pathology occurring in toxic states may develop along the lines of a behavior disorder. See, for example, Levin, M., "Transitory schizophrenias produced by bromide intoxication." *Amer. J. Psychiat.*, 1946, vol. 103, pp. 229–237.

Similar considerations apply to the pathology of remembering in the delirious patient. The acute cerebral incompetence is directly responsible for behavioral disorganization; and the defective retentivity is intimately tied up with the disorganization of behavior. Thus, for example, we can safely predict relatively slight disturbances of recall in mild delirium, and serious disturbances in severe delirium, without knowing much about the individual who is delirious in either case. Recall of an organized sequence of events rests upon the person's having reacted continuously while the sequence was in progress. Recall of a complex pattern of interrelated happenings — such as human beings constantly meet — depends first of all upon one's having been able to react adequately to the pattern organization.

But the delirious person — even at the beginning of his oncoming cerebral incompetence — can neither follow a succession of events sequentially, nor maintain a degree of behavioral organization at any one moment that enables him to grasp a complex environmental pattern. We have already referred to the disruption of attitude organization in delirium. It is this disruption that makes behavioral continuity impossible; responses in a series lose their behavioral relationship and each becomes a discrete fragment. Similarly, the components of some configural stimulation arouse individual fragmentary responses which lack an attitudinal matrix. Even for the normal individual, a breakdown in attitudinal behavior reduces dramatically the efficiency of the acquisition which must precede recall.

We see almost daily some instance of defective recall that stems from attitudinal disorganization in the course of ordinary normal living. A frightened or excited child, for example, may be unable to remember what has frightened him or the details of what has taken place to excite him. Adults who have been present at an accident, or who have been overawed by some wondrous or fearsome situation, make notoriously bad witnesses.[72] They at first recall this and that detail, which may show obvious distortion from the start; and it is only later on that they improvise and modify to produce a more or less connected — but inaccurate — report. In other words, after they have recovered sufficient organization to be able again to supply an attitudinal matrix, they weave the fragmentary responses they can recall into a fiction which they then consider fact. Thus four witnesses may give four different stories of the same event.

The delirious person cannot manufacture a good sequential story to fit his fragments of recall. The attitudinal disorganization which prevented him from adequately responding to the original situations continues to prevent his giving them an attitudinal background. More than this, his behavioral inadequacy makes it difficult and sometimes impossible to recall events that ante-

[72] There is some evidence that the anticipation of threat may be an important determiner of amnesia. See Rudolf, G. DeM., "Brief retrograde amnesia." *J. ment. Sci.*, 1947, vol. 93, pp. 342–353; Rudolf, G. DeM., "Further aspects of brief retrograde amnesia." *J. ment. Sci.*, 1948, vol. 94, pp. 641–649.

date the delirium, when acquisition was unimpaired. To recall is not merely to regurgitate. It is to perform an organized act, to react to immediately present stimulation in terms of past behavior; and for this it is necessary that the reaction include an attitudinal background capable of sustaining response complexity and continuity.

After recovery from delirium — and if we except the deliria incident to terminal disease, the great majority of delirious patients do recover — the recall remains characteristically fragmentary or "patchy." It is usually compared to the recall of dreams. Little incidents here and there can be remembered, the patient's imaginal products inextricably mingled with happenings in the shared environment. Hallucinatory distortions and delusional misinterpretations — again as in the normal dream — are recalled by the recovered person with perhaps amusement, or with still some trace of the anxiety and bewilderment of the original experience. It is customary to postulate transient shifts in the level of cerebral competence, in both delirium and dream, to account for what is remembered afterwards and what forgotten.

There is no good reason to doubt the importance of momentary changes in cerebral physiology in determining acquisition, retention and recall. Nevertheless, to stop with the unquestionable fluctuation in brain competence would be to leave out entirely the personal equation. We have pointed out that what a delirious person says and does, what specifically frightens or entertains him, the conflicts and worries he expresses, are all related to him as a person and, through his individual organization, to the subculture in which he has been reared. The same can with equal cogency be urged concerning his recall. Indeed, what a patient hallucinates in delirium is itself in large part a product of recall, and so also is every one of his delusional misinterpretations. Delirious hallucination and delusion reflect what is significant in a person's past — his remote and his recent past — just as hallucination and delusion do in the normal dream.

What is recalled after recovery from delirium, like what is recalled after normal dreaming, will also depend upon the significance of the "patchy" incidents in terms of the patient's unique behavior organization. Although we lack any considerable body of confirmatory evidence, it seems extremely probable that distortions, omissions, reversals and condensations, appearing in the recall of persons who have passed through an episode of acute delirium, have the same meanings they have in the ordinary dream and daydream.[73] It is to be hoped that the organized behavioral study of delirious patients, intoxicated persons, and patients going into and coming out of general anesthesia, may throw some much-needed light upon the relation of transient cerebral incompetence to the problems of behavior pathology.

[73] Compare the report in Thurmond, C. J., "Last thoughts before drowning." *J. abn. soc. Psychol.*, 1943, vol. 38, pp. 165–184.

It is a fact of considerable importance in behavior pathology that in disorganization, desocialization and deterioration the patterns of behavior always reflect the individuality of the patient. Thus a delirious disorganization which is unquestionably precipitated by cerebral incompetence, may lead over into a more enduring behavior disorder that is characteristic for the individual. And this behavior disorder may then persist long after the delirious syndrome of confusion, gross disorientation, defective retentivity and other signs of cerebral incompetence has completely disappeared. Sometimes the behavior disorder that develops during delirium is a typical panic reaction[74] — a maximal anxiety attack — which may then clear up also, or terminate in a schizophrenic illness. Once in a while, the delirious disorganization gradually changes to the disorganization and desocialization characteristic of schizophrenia, from which the patient may or may not recover.

[74] For a discussion of panic reactions, see pages 306–307.

$\mathbb{D}$esocialization

16

Prolonged disorganization so frequently ends in desocialization, and protracted desocialization can so easily have disorganizing consequences, that the discussion of one leads inevitably to a consideration of the other. Indeed, some of the commonest and most dramatic syndromes in behavior pathology are essentially the outcome of a dynamic interaction between disorganizing and desocializing trends, which terminates in behavior dominated by socially invalid fantasy. These syndromes it is customary to group together as *schizophrenic disorders;* and to them we shall devote the latter part of our present chapter.

In spite of this close relationship, however, it would be grossly incorrect to assume that desocialization is inseparably bound up with disorganization. For we have already described desocialization without disorganization in connection with regression and withdrawal into invalidism; [1] and we shall have occasion to return to it when we study the effects of cerebral injury, degeneration and disease. [2] Let us begin, then, with a brief restatement of the essentials of socialization — its development and its maintenance — and then proceed to a discussion of the characteristics of desocialization and the conditions favoring its occurrence.

Development of socialization

The process of socialization begins at birth, and it continues as long as the individual remains capable of socially adaptive learning. Early in life this consists chiefly of the induction of infant and child into the prevailing culture, through membership in the primary family group. [3] This membership can never be had for nothing, and although the price differs widely in different families, payment is always in the form of achieving social conformity. At first, a

---

[1] See pages 220–226 and 230–242.   [2] See pages 540–555.
[3] For a detailed account of biosocial maturation, see pages 130–143.

child's effective human environment is limited to parents, or parent surrogates, whatever siblings there may be, and the family's close relatives and close friends. When the child grows able to enter into the neighborhood by himself, the community of human beings responsible for his socialization greatly increases. And eventually, the more formal secondary groups — school, church, clubs and the like — make their special contributions in his progressive biosocial maturation.

The social learning, by means of which conformity is acquired and effectively maintained, occurs always in a social context.[4] For it is in the setting of membership in the primary family and neighborhood groups, that a child takes his first lessons, and acquires his early skills, in the basic techniques of social living. It is there that he acquires feeding, toilet and dressing habits, schedules of sleeping and waking, of play and work, relationships of affection and reciprocal dependence, cooperative ways and competitive ways. There, also, he begins a long career of social role-taking, of learning to play the real-life parts which he chooses and which social custom assigns to him.[5] In play, he learns the delights and the gains in taking the roles of other individuals — father, mother, postman, fireman, dog or horse. He learns, in earnest, the indispensable techniques of shifting roles — from quarrelsome brother to reasonable son, when an annoyed parent appears, and from reasonable son to defiant rowdy when his critical playmates arrive.

The general outcome of early social learning — of the acquisition of conformity — is that of organizing the endless complexity and potential confusion of the biosocial environment into relative simplicity and actual clarity. The routinization of behavior, as we have seen,[6] reduces enormously the number of choices that a child may or must make. At the same time, he is gaining skill in arriving at socially valid decisions, where he is left free to decide, and in abiding by their self-denying as well as their satisfying consequences. The child is acquiring socially acceptable techniques for dealing with the conflict of alternatives, when choice is difficult or remote, and for meeting the perpetual frustrations of thwarting and delay.[7] He is gaining first-hand acquaintance with the rewards for social usefulness, and the penalties for social guilt.

Two achievements of the maturing human being stand out above everything else in making effective socialization possible. One is the acquisition of an enormously versatile system of interpersonal *communication*.[8] This system, when it has also resulted in the organization of socially valid thinking, frees the individual from the strict dual bondage of space and time, in which all lower animals are held. The other is an elaboration of self-reactions into behavioral

---

[4] Social learning is discussed on pages 55–63.

[5] See pages 114–122.   [6] See pages 138–141.

[7] For a detailed discussion of frustration, see pages 47–52; for an account of conflict, see Chapter 9.

[8] See pages 90–95.

systems which regulate personal conduct in accordance with social demands.[9] This elaboration releases the individual from perpetual servitude to the immediate evaluations of other persons, and places him in the custody of himself. Both of these human achievements are necessary for the development of adequate role-taking skills; and both are likely to suffer damage — sometimes irreparable damage — when desocialization occurs.

The child who becomes highly skilled in the techniques of socially derived language behavior, and of socially validated thinking, is thereby enabled to take an indefinite number of social roles in talk and fantasy, to practice them endlessly, vary them infinitely, and shift with ease from one into another.[10] He can test his symbolic roles, when necessary, and modify them in accordance with the logic of non-verbal operations — of object-arrangement and the apparent sequence and concomitance of events. Thus, as he grows from childhood, through adolescence and into adulthood, a person can carry on learning to a considerable extent in the absence of any equipment other than his own organized, and intermittently validated, symbolic behavior. And, as his self-reactions increase in socially evaluative skill, he can even supply sound critiques for the predictions, procedures and results of his own overt and covert role-taking behavior.

This necessarily heavy emphasis upon the uses of symbolic behavior must never blind us to the prime importance of all non-symbolic participation — of gaining and maintaining social skills by the direct use of hands, arms, feet, legs, head and trunk, in social contexts peopled by something more substantial than words and daydreams. That man, we all recognize, is only half a human being who has high manipulative skill but cannot communicate intelligibly, think consecutively, or elaborate self-reactions into self-regulation. But so also is the man, as we shall see, whose word and thought seem to encompass the infinite, but who has grown desocialized and incompetent to carry through the simple manipulative skills of daily living.

Maintenance of socialization

The biosocially mature human being enters adulthood an intricately organized, dynamic behavioral system. He is, as we have seen, trained in manipulative and locomotory skills. He is versed in the techniques of interpersonal action, schooled in the procedures of communal participation, and well-practiced in the symbolic arts of communication, role-taking, fantasy and self-reaction. He is neither tied down to the present in space and time, nor

[9] This development is described on pages 95–105. See also Cameron, N., "A biosocial approach to ethics" (in press).

[10] For a description of the development of fantasy reactions in children, see Ames, L. B., and Learned, J., "Imaginary companions and related phenomena." *J. genet. Psychol.,* 1946, vol. 69, pp. 147–167; Murphy, L. B., "Childhood experience." In Hunt, J. McV. (Ed.), *Personality and the behavior disorders.* New York: Ronald, 1944, pp. 675–676.

dependent for his self-regulation upon the moment-to-moment opinion of every passer-by. He has attained behavioral stability without becoming rigid and unchangeable; his reactions remain fluid without becoming formless.

Unless something makes us give the problem special thought, we all tend to see in the structured equilibrium of socially mature behavior a kind of petrification.[11] We take it for granted that, once behavioral organization has been established, it will endure without further attention — like a monument — until time erodes it or an accident destroys it. But organized human behavior is never inert. And although time can indeed erode it, and an accident destroy it, there are also potentialities in desocialization which can become as catastrophic for behavioral organization as erosion or destruction.

The attainment of adulthood subtracts nothing from the fundamental interdependence of individual person and social field. It means, of course, that the adult has reached a level of maximal growth and physiological maturity. This allows him to perform a variety of culturally determined roles from which his society has previously barred him — but which he has practiced frankly in talk and fantasy, and perhaps surreptitiously carried out in overt deed. To attain to adulthood does not mean, however, to achieve unalterable fixity in the dynamic social field.

The human being can never become a fixed point in the field of social operations. Throughout maturity he must continue to maintain an equilibrium between stability and fluidity of behavior, in a continually fluctuating situational pattern.[12] He must be able to shift the design of his reactions, like a good boxer, to meet shifts in the design of his environment. For the preservation of such highly complicated skills, the most necessary condition is that a person participate actively in the social behavior of everyday life. This participation includes, of course, reactions that are reciprocally related to the reactions of other social persons. There must also be genuine communication to ensure that one's individualistic interpretations are socially validated through a free interchange of perspective. When such interbehavior lapses, whatever the reason, we have the beginnings of desocialization.

Loss of socialization

By *desocialization* we mean *a reduction in the social articulation of behavior, resulting from the partial or complete detachment of an individual from participation in the activities of the social community.* Thus defined, desocialization is seen to be a product of social isolation. The detachment of a person from participation in the activities of the social community occurs under two general conditions. One of these involves complete separation of the individual from

---

[11] Compare the discussion of social codes and law, on pages 187–189 and 210–211.

[12] For a discussion of the contrast between *stable, exclusive organization* and *unstable, inclusive organization*, see pages 73–75.

contact with the rest of the social community, such as that imposed upon prisoners, and that which hermits impose upon themselves. This we may call *segregation*. The other involves a person's own insulating behavior, that is, his avoidant shyness, distrust or aversion, or his adient fascination with autistic daydreams. This we may call *insulation*. We shall have more to say about segregation and insulation when we consider the conditions favoring desocialization.

But whether it results from one's segregation or from one's insulating behavior, desocialization has as its most fundamental characteristic a decline in social communication. An imprisoned or a deeply preoccupied person, for example, cannot freely converse with others in his accustomed ways, by gesture and speech or by the written word. He can no longer adapt continuously to the fluid change of normal interpersonal relationships, since these are now relatively inaccessible to him. Thus, in losing free communication with others, he is deprived of the chief instrument by means of which his socialization has in the past been effectively maintained.

Other behavioral insufficiencies follow in the wake of a decline in interpersonal communication. For the detached individual, to lose this chief means of free social interchange is to lose access to the most dependable techniques of social validation. The man who cannot validate and modify or discard his interpretations of the behavior of other persons must inevitably arrive at conclusions that do not correspond with social fact.[13] Things that seem supporting or threatening to him may have actually no such implication. But without the test provided by an exchange of perspective, this actuality is unlikely to supplant a person's glad or frightened expectation. Moreover, communication and the ready sharing of perspectives depend for their adequacy upon their practice. Hence, the detached person usually exhibits a progressive loss in social skills through disuse.

The detached person shows also a decline in the social validity of his self-reactions. At the same time, his very detachment cuts him off from the sources of social control upon which he depended earlier in his life. Then, as we have pointed out, it was the immediate evaluation of other persons that provided the regulation of his conduct. Now he must rely upon self-reactions which are no longer under the correcting influence of community participation. The loss in social skills that marks desocialization is almost certain to include distortion of self-regulation, and a consequent deviation from cultural mores, as an individual's self-reactions lose functional contact with the social operations from which they were originally derived.

Many persons who have been obliged for a protracted period to live in isolation report that they lose the need to be with others. At first they may seek

---

[13] This point is elaborated in connection with the discussion of pseudocommunity and delusion. See pages 387–393.

the companionship of some other living thing as a substitute for the company of human beings. Some ranchmen who find themselves snowed in alone for the winter, for example, talk at considerable length to their pets and their livestock, casting these animals in the role of understanding persons. But for those whose solitude is not mitigated by the comfort of familiar things, or by the certainty of a not too far distant release, there may next develop an habituation and then an addiction to aloneness.

The preoccupied asocial person, denied participation in communal activities chiefly by his own insulating behavior, may arrive ultimately at the same endpoint without undergoing segregation. Thus, an adolescent boy who later developed a schizophrenic disorder, gradually gave up social participation while still operating largely in its terms. At first he continued in school to maintain his usual level of social interaction; in the evenings, at home, his behavior seemed to have remained much as it had been. However, he spent all of his spare time, after school and on weekends, in the swamp lands near his home where he sought to substitute the company of wild things for the unsatisfying companionship of human beings. He filled a notebook with detailed observations on animal and plant life, and he made a collection of butterflies and snakes. But eventually he abandoned this attempt, lost interest in all objects around him, and confined himself almost wholly to operations within his own private autistic community where no one could reach him.

The final step in the desocialization of segregated and insulating individuals is the most difficult for the naïve to understand. This is the development of an aversion with respect to human companionship. Some segregated persons dread the return to community life — whether from prison or from months in the jungle or desert.[14] Many of those whose insulating behavior has isolated them from the society of human beings, among whom they still move, give every sign of distaste for proffered social interchange. They seem, like the segregated ones, to be addicted to their habitual aloneness as well as to their fantasied activities. Of course, any asocial avoidant behavior arouses the suspicion that it is the product of anxiety, insecurity or fear of rejection and ridicule. But, even though these are probably the commonest origins of desocialization, we must not lose sight of this other fact: that solitude, however one arrives at it, will in time engender new needs for privacy and new satisfactions of these needs.[15]

[14] This reaction is common among returned prisoners of war, and is sometimes referred to as a "fear of freedom." See, for example, Curle, A., "Transitional communities and social re-connection: a follow-up study of the civil resettlement of British prisoners of war. Part I." *Hum. Relation.*, 1947, vol. 1, pp. 42–68; Curle, A., and Trist, E. L., "Transitional communities and social re-connection: a follow-up study of the civil resettlement of British prisoners of war. Part II." *Hum. Relation.*, 1947, vol. 1, pp. 240–288. A similar phenomenon is found among patients discharged after long hospitalization; see pages 231–240, House, J. W., and Marquit, S., "Reactions of mental patients to attendance at a businessmen's luncheon club meeting." *J. abn. soc. Psychol.*, 1950, vol. 45, pp. 738–742.

[15] For a discussion of the development of need, see pages 38–42.

There are two possible attitudes that a desocialized individual may maintain with respect to the opinions of others. He may preserve some degree of consideration for them, or he may more or less completely disregard them. Both attitudes can be found among segregated and among insulating persons. Everyone has seen or heard about the meticulously attired social isolate, punctilious but unfriendly, who lives his life out aimlessly as a neighborhood eccentric or a state hospital patient. The opposite extreme is no less familiar. The beachcomber and the hobo, the schizophrenic man who cares only about his fantasies, and the depressed man who sees horror and hopelessness on every side — these grow indifferent or contemptuous toward the judgments of their fellows.

In all desocialization there is some impairment in social skills. Many desocializing persons suffer damage so great that what once had been communication falls below an intelligible minimum. Language behavior loses its accustomed structure and develops an individualistic idiom that is useless as an instrument of communication. In some patients speech ceases altogether and the patient is mute. The ordinary routines of daily life may also disintegrate and disappear, so that unless the environment cares for the now disorganized individual, he cannot survive. Thus we see that in extreme desocialization a human being may come at last to lose most of his behavioral organization and sink to a level of utter helplessness.

Conditions favoring desocialization

Segregation. Among the conditions favoring desocialization must be reckoned, of course, those leading to segregation of an individual from his social community. We have already discussed the importance of prolonged illness, including chronic invalidism, which cuts a person off from effective contact with others.[16] And we shall later [17] have occasion to consider the effects of desocialization upon the vast numbers of prisoners, who are caged or fenced in like wild animals, and those others who are confined — often for life — in the bleak desolation of our understaffed hospitals and county homes. Any of these individuals may grow into chronic social isolates under such circumstances and, if returned finally to the normal social community, are likely to find life there strange and unpredictable.

Common to all these segregated individuals is a behavioral reorganization that may adapt them to the restricted and distorted environment in which they must live — sick room, prison, hospital or county home — but is not adequately responsive to the larger community of normal men.[18] With these

---

[16] See pages 231–240.   [17] See pages 529–531.

[18] See, for example, the descriptions of behavior of prisoners of war given by Arntzen, F. I., "Psychological observations of prisoners of war." *Amer. J. Psychiat.*, 1948, vol. 104, pp. 446–447; and by Fensterheim, H., and Birch, H. G., "A case study of group ideology and individual adjustment." *J. abn. soc. Psychol.*, 1950, vol. 45, pp. 710–720.

products of segregation belong also hermits, whatever their reasons for retreating into solitude, and whether they live in an apartment or a farmhouse, in a shack or on an estate. Among these are individuals who continue to work alone on socially oriented problems in socially valid ways — novelists, for example, and writers on historical, economic and political issues — but whose personal behavior becomes otherwise asocially reorganized. Explorers, especially those on arctic and antarctic expeditions, who are separated for months from normal social contact and normal everyday activities, sometimes undergo striking behavioral changes which make them seem strange even to themselves.

Insulation.[19] Of much greater concern to contemporary behavior pathologists than persons who have been set apart from the social community are those whose desocialization is initiated and maintained almost exclusively by their own insulating behavior. Let us take as our relatively normal examples of this group the immigrant from a foreign country who successfully resists acculturation, and the domestic immigrant — from New England to Kansas, or from Alabama to New York — who does likewise. Perhaps because they have lost their accustomed status and been thrown on the defensive in an unsympathetic environment, they feel out of place, ill at ease, unhappy and misunderstood. Sometimes they manage to preserve a little island of their native subculture in the ocean of unfamiliar customs and mores, preferring cultural impoverishment to cultural change.[20] Often they take refuge in compensatory talk and fantasy which centers nostalgically around the absent and the past — what they used to do at home, and what they would be doing now if they were there. In all of this, they resemble ageing and retired persons, whose present situation fails to support their old, familiar ways of living and permits them to become behaviorally detached and desocialized.[21] For these individuals also react defensively with attempts to surround themselves with outmoded relics, and with talk and fantasy about the absent and the past.

A numerous, but uncounted, population of unsegregated isolates is made up of anxious, uneasy, suspicious, and often apparently haughty individuals, who move about in the social community but are seldom a genuinely interacting part of it. They characteristically share the life-space of other persons, but

[19] For a more detailed discussion of *insulation*, see Cameron, N., *The psychology of behavior disorders*. Boston: Houghton Mifflin, 1947, pp. 170–172.

[20] This procedure is also employed by prisoners of war during their imprisonment; it has also been used therapeutically to assist prisoners in the transition from prison to their own family and social groups. See, for example, Curle, A., "Transitional communities and social re-connection: a follow-up study of the civil resettlement of British prisoners of war. Part I." *Hum. Relation.*, 1947, vol. 1, pp. 42–68; Curle, A., and Trist, E. L., "Transitional communities and social re-connection: a follow-up study of the civil resettlement of British prisoners of war. Part II." *Hum. Relation.*, 1947, vol. 1, pp. 240–288.

[21] Compare the discussion of *retirement deterioration*, pages 528–529; and Cameron, N., "Neuroses of later maturity." In Kaplan, O. J. (Ed.), *Mental disorders in later life*. Stanford University, Calif.: Stanford University Press, 1945, pp. 143–186.

share no more of their own behavior or its consequences than they absolutely must. This population includes men and women who have found their adolescent peer culture or the demands of adult competitive and cooperative reciprocity threatening, unsavory or humiliating. The great majority get along reasonably well by building up a defensive bulwark of insulating behavior that detaches them socially, but still does not obviously disorganize them. They are looked upon by those who know them as reserved, aloof or enigmatic individuals; while those meeting them casually are apt to dismiss them as snobs who are unpleasantly self-assured and self-sufficient. We have already discussed, under paranoid disorders, members of these groups who develop serious defensive and compensatory delusions without disorganizing.[22]

Some anxious, uneasy, suspicious adolescents and adults suffer a further handicap from their practice of habitually relying on fantasy — not merely as occasional entertainment or escape, but as their chief resource in all situations of monotony, difficulty, loneliness, failure and frustration. Their existence may likewise be one of behavioral detachment without segregation from the community. Judging from the frequency with which we casually encounter vague, dreamy, reticent and aloof persons in our everyday environment, there must be large numbers of chronically fantasying, withdrawn individuals who have grown desocialized but apparently not disorganized. Nonetheless, it is largely from this group that persons with schizophrenic disorders are recruited, and it is they who will later illustrate for us the typical syndromes of disorganization and desocialization.

(a) *Childhood learning and desocialization.* We may begin with the observed fact that individuals differ widely, even as children, in the adequacy and completeness of their socialization.[23] If, for example, the social situation in which a child is reared includes a home atmosphere of parental overprotection, the child will learn selectively to behave as the dominated or indulged role assigned to him demands. He will be unable, of course, to analyze and identify the character of the excitants which organize his behavior along one or another of these lines; he will simply react in ways that bring him tension-reduction and therefore satisfy a prevailing need. But the cost of such inescapable conformity may be serious incompetence in reciprocal role-taking skills, and consequently ultimate failure to become securely established in one's society and culture.[24]

What has just been said of the dominated and indulged child holds true for a great many rejected children, whether or not they live also under compensatory parental overprotection. The rejection may go unrecognized by either parent or child; but the consequence will still be that the child's early affec-

[22] See pages 405–413.
[23] For a more detailed discussion of these individual differences, see pages 22–24.
[24] For an account of the social incompetence of overprotected children, see Levy, D., *Maternal overprotection.* New York: Columbia University Press, 1943.

tional deprivation prevents his gaining skill in achieving close relationships with anyone. Suppose, for example, that a child is continually contrasted with his parents and siblings, or constantly corrected for behavior that stems from identification with one or the other parent. The result, in either case, is likely to be that the child is blocked in his attempts to react to the family attributes as though they were his own, and thus he loses essential early practice in the particular role-taking which identification initiates and supports.[25] Such a child, if he carries inadequate socialization into adolescence and adulthood, can be expected to show greater susceptibility to desocialization than the child of accepting parents.

A child is sometimes encouraged or permitted to overemphasize one aspect of social skill to such a degree that he is prevented from gaining minimal practice in other social skills.[26] This lop-sided selective learning may lie in mechanical, symbolic or ethical fields; and it may result from direct parental tuition or simply from parental indifference or indulgence. Perhaps the least dangerous is overtraining in mechanical skills. Nevertheless, it does happen that a child develops so marked a fascination for mechanical toys and gadgets, and in adolescence shows so marked a preoccupation with machines and mechanisms, that he fails to see the importance of social interaction. As a result, the role-taking skills upon which interpersonal relationships depend remain relatively unpracticed and therefore immature. The child grown to adolescence and adulthood with such one-sided development will tend to hold these interpersonal skills in contempt, to go on selectively neglecting them for his preferred asocial techniques, and perhaps eventually give them up entirely. This is one origin of the highly skilled mechanic who is socially inadequate or inept,[27] who is too attached to his ship, his airplane or his invention to love another person, or who misinterprets the social behavior of others because he cannot understand a human being in human terms.[28]

Such one-sided products of selective learning are far commoner, however, in relation to overemphasis upon symbolization and moral principles. We live in a culture that rewards with special status the individual who excels in a symbolic skill. Accordingly, if a child shows early fascination with words, or likes to speak and think abstractly, he is almost sure to be treated as different from other children and usually as superior to them. But verbal dexterity and a sense of superiority will not gain status for such a child among children; [29] he is likely to be slighted and pushed aside in favor of a more average child with skill in playing marbles or spinning tops. It is not surprising, then, that the verbal

[25] For a discussion of *identification* in relation to early learning, see pages 60–63.

[26] Compare the discussion of parental concern in relation to early learning on pages 56–60.

[27] See pages 211–216. [28] See pages 382–384 and 390–392.

[29] Some striking examples of the failure of highly verbal children to win the acceptance of their peers are to be found in Hollingworth, L. S., *Children above 180 IQ*. New York: World Book Co., 1942.

child defensively renounces manipulative games and shuns his contemporaries who cry him down. Occasionally, word, thought and gesture become so highly and exclusively prized by a socially rejected individual that paradoxically he abandons their common uses in social communication entirely, and lives walled in by a private symbolic universe which he himself has built.[30] Both the consistent overestimation of symbols in our culture, and the underestimation placed upon manual skill and social interbehavior alike contribute to this distorted development and its impoverished result.

Overemphasis upon, and too rigid training in, sound ethical principles can lead to socially invalid and therefore unsound practice. The child, for example, whose overstrict and narrow moral attitudes make him conspicuously good and strangely proper, will make other children uncomfortable and resentful. They may at first content themselves with ridicule and baiting, but eventually they will ostracize him as an offender against their behavioral code. His own response to this punishment for too much goodness and correctness may direct him, in self-justification, toward an exaggeration of the skewed attitudes which initially earned him social isolation. Such an individual is likely to arrive at adolescence poorly equipped to carry on adequate social interbehavior, and with a self-evaluation that will find little to support it in the opinions of others. If he must have unreserved approval and high respect, he may be thrown back upon his own resources, and provide himself with exalted admiration and esteem through delusional self-reactions that bring him also rapid desocialization.[31]

The child who has been encouraged to indulge in excessive daydreaming, or whose human environment is so threatening, restrictive or unloving as to drive him into it, runs the danger of relying upon fantasy too heavily. If fantasy proves so attractive and secure that it is preferred to interpersonal relationships, the child may shun the company of others for the companionship of his daydreams. In the exceptional case,[32] a child becomes so overtrained in fantasy behavior that he ultimately finds difficulty in determining which for him has greater validity — the strange rituals of social interaction to which others invite him, or the more familiar fantasy to which he is himself inclined.

The offspring of anxious, insecure and socially hostile parents must also be counted among those whose socialization is unlikely to establish them firmly in their society and culture. Indeed, the distrustful child of distrustful parents carries into maturity a double burden of social inadequacy. For he is led by direct tuition to regard human companionship and reciprocal dependence,

---

[30] Compare the discussion of language and thinking in schizophrenia, on pages 506–515.

[31] For a case illustration of such a development, see pages 398–399.

[32] See, for example, Despert, J. L., "Delusional and hallucinatory experiences in children." *Amer. J. Psychiat.*, 1948, vol. 104, pp. 528–537; Kanner, L., "Problems of nosology and psycho-dynamics of early infantile autism." *Amer. J. Orthopsychiat.*, 1949, vol. 19, pp. 416–426.

outside the family circle, as more dangerous than solitude and non-coopera-tion.[33] And, because of his parents' suspicious uneasiness, he is either forbid-den to associate with neighbors, whom his parents distrust and fear, or he is moved about from place to place in a sort of migratory flight from contact with society. Thus he is denied the possibility of deep or lasting chumships and he never learns to participate as a member of a familiar social community. In consequence of such selective learning and protective denial, the child is likely to follow in his asocial parents' footsteps. When as an adolescent or adult, he is exposed to social stress from which he cannot flee, he will more readily de-socialize than his more thoroughly acculturated peers.

(b) *Adolescence and adulthood*. The period of greatest vulnerability to desocialization is unquestionably that of adolescence.[34] The social field of operations is full of ambivalence for an adolescent boy or girl. Many areas are no longer satisfactorily structured and delimited by parental behavior, and the adolescent has not yet himself acquired the behavior organization he needs for their restructuring in a self-regulatory, adult direction. Principal among these unstructured areas are those defining sex behavior, filial responsibilities and the choice of career or marital partner. Sex behavior before adolescence and after marriage is regulated by fairly simple and straightforward rules of conduct; filial relationships in childhood and emancipated adulthood are like-wise no great problem to most persons; and once the choice of career and mari-tal partner has been consummated, the lines of social role-taking are clearly drawn.

But it is during the long transition period, from childhood to biosocial adult-hood, that these dynamic structures must undergo a sweeping reorganization. The adolescent lives in a state of fluctuating uncertainty with respect to his changing social roles.[35] His contemporaries, who themselves are also flounder-ing through the adolescent bog, hold high their little banners of carefree, dauntless emancipation, but they do not share with one another their innumer-able doubts and anxieties. These doubts and anxieties, and the hunger for emancipation, intimately concern both the child-parent relationships and the parentally invoked taboos. Hence, the adolescent can rarely confide in those who wield an unwanted authority over him, and who threaten by their pro-tective kindness to deny him freedom. Under these circumstances, it is inev-itable that a great many adolescents shall undergo temporary desocialization, grow secretive and surly, confide completely in no one and trust no one, and

---

[33] For a discussion of learning by direct tuition, see pages 56–59; for a discussion of the ways in which anxiety may be learned, see pages 293–296.

[34] Adolescence is discussed in some detail on pages 141–143.

[35] Milner, E., "Effects of sex role and social status on the early adolescent personality." *Genet. Psychol. Monogr.*, 1949, vol. 40, pp. 231–325; Tryon, C., "Evaluation of adolescent personality by adolescents." *Monogr. Soc. Res. Child Develpm.*, 1939, vol. 4, pp. 1–88; Tryon, C., "The adolescent peer culture." *Yearb. Nat. Soc. Stud. Educ.*, 1944, vol. 43, pp. 217–239.

share freely neither their frustrations nor their victories. They are almost sure to find, both in their self-reactions and in the treatment they receive from others, the evidence that they are obviously like no one else and belong, therefore, to no one.

One of the most difficult tasks in adolescence and adulthood is that of achieving and maintaining a satisfactory social status.[36] Failure to accomplish this must be considered an important factor in the development of social disarticulation. Since a person's standing in the opinions of others is revealed to him only through the reactions of these others to him, the question of his social status is inevitably a source of uncertainty for him. For rarely is the social community in complete and homogeneous agreement about any one person; and even the favorable reaction of an individual today may give way tomorrow to an unfavorable one.

Moreover, one's status is seldom given explicit formulation by other individuals. It must always be inferred by indirection, so that it often seems as unstable and unsure as rumor or insinuation. Hence, as in any other ambiguous situation, a person can be expected to respond in ways that are largely determined by his particular acquired reaction-sensitivities, and therefore by his selective learning.[37] To derive one's social status realistically, from the complex interplay of one's own self-reactions and the implied attitudes of others, is in itself dependent upon a considerable degree of role-taking skill. The fortunate person learns, in his childhood and adolescent years, the technique of maintaining self-evaluative reactions that are stable enough to offset the contradictions in others' day to day evaluations, but flexible enough to accept modifications in terms of a dependable consensus.

Two other periods of vulnerability to desocialization deserve mention here — the one in middle-life, the other in old age. In middle-life, and sometimes by anticipation just before it, the realization comes with some abruptness to many persons that youth has gone forever, and with it the hopes that youth encourages.[38] One's life-span seems suddenly contracted from infinity to a finite, predictable limit. Things planned and promised to oneself and others — whether clearly formulated or not — are now clearly out of reach.

Many individuals live through middle-life as though it were fundamentally a transition period by which they reached old age. For them, senescence appears to repeat the basic problems of adolescence. Thus the insecure middle-aged person often pictures himself as passing, from a familiar well-structured

---

[36] See, for example, Centers, R., "Social class identifications of American youth." *J. Personality*, 1950, vol. 18, pp. 290–302; Gough, H., "A new dimension of status: I. Development of a personality scale." *Amer. Sociol. Rev.*, 1943, vol. 13, pp. 401–409; Gough, H., "A new dimension of status: II. Relationship of the St scale to other variables." *Amer. Sociol. Rev.*, 1948, vol. 13, pp. 534–537.

[37] For a discussion of these points, see pages 69–75 and 411–413.

[38] See, for example, Kerr, W. A., Newman, H. L., and Sadewic, A. R., "Lifetime worry patterns of American psychologists." *J. consult. Psychol.*, 1949, vol. 13, pp. 377–380.

field of social operations, into one that seems to lack both the well-defined roles and the relative freedom from anxiety that characterize earlier maturity. The waning of vigor, and in women the loss of fertility and personal attractiveness, help to reinforce this growing uncertainty and insecurity. Under these conditions, the middle-aged person — and the elderly individual also [39] — may desocialize because he feels unwanted or because he is afraid to remain in active participation and test the verity of his low self-evaluation. In some instances, as we have seen,[40] such a person desocializes by developing compensatory delusions which counteract his own self-depreciation by giving him a pseudo-community in which he takes a permanently important role.

Perpetuation of desocialization

Among those who desocialize, there are some who persist indefinitely in social detachment as a way of life, while others quickly abandon it and return to full participation in community activities.[41] Since living in social isolation always entails some personal sacrifice — in loss of close affectional relationships and even in loss of social status and of freedom — it is important to understand certain common origins of the perpetuation of desocialization. In the first place, many of the factors which we have discussed as favorable to the development of social detachment may also contribute to its continuance. This is true of the influence of the social environment; and it is true of the characteristic behavior which the individual has developed in coping with that environment, or in neutralizing its effects upon him.

Take, for example, the difficulties many persons find in deriving and accepting their social status. The adolescent or adult who remains painfully uncertain of his status, or is grossly dissatisfied with what the reactions of others to him seem to imply, may through social detachment find a personally satisfying solution that is socially disastrous. He may discover that it is possible for him to provide himself with an assured status — in his own self-reactions — which the consensus has persistently failed to provide. This accomplished, the individual is likely to resist whatever threatens to destroy his new-found sources of aggrandizement, reassurance and security. For his self-reactions give him in social isolation the comfort that society has coldly denied him. To return to full participation in the social community means to restructure the old situation with its familiar misery. To remain perpetually desocialized is

---

[39] For further discussions of isolation in old age, see pages 226–230 and 546–555.

[40] See pages 398–399.

[41] In the study of transition from Army to civilian status, described earlier, wide individual differences in efficiency of resocialization are reported. See Curle, A., "Transitional communities and social re-connection: a follow-up study of the civil resettlement of British prisoners of war. Part I." *Hum. Relation.*, 1947, vol. 1, pp. 42–68; Curle, A., and Trist, E. L., "Transitional communities and social re-connection: a follow-up study of the civil resettlement of British prisoners of war. Part II." *Hum. Relation.*, 1947, vol. 1, pp. 240–288.

to enjoy the certainty of personal significance, honor and self-respect.   And so he clings to the security of his supporting self-reactions and shuts out, as far as possible, the threat of a return to the life that originally drove him into isolation.

The most dangerous threat of all to the social isolate is that desocialization tends to perpetuate itself.   It is not only the factors initiating social detachment that favor its continuance.   The desocializing person is exposed to further hazards which may not have been present early in the process.   The diffident adolescent who has never gained the sympathetic understanding that he needs, is still less likely to be sympathized with or understood when he grows remote and disarticulated from his immediate community.   The suspicious adult who seeks to guard himself from the approach of everyone, inevitably leads others to intrude upon his highly-valued privacy by his wary, circumspect behavior.   He can retire from this threat, which his own conduct has now succeeded in augmenting, by flight and another concealment — with further social disarticulation as a consequence — or by ceasing any longer to react consistently in terms of the threatening social community, by disorganizing and living in his dreams.   One of the most complex and illuminating examples of mutual perpetuation is to be found in the dynamic interaction between desocializing and disorganizing trends, to which we now turn.

Disorganization and desocialization

Disorganization we have defined as the disruption of a unified reaction, or system of reactions, and its replacement by behavior that is fragmentary, haphazard or chaotic.   The disorganized person, we have said,[42] can no longer maintain the boundaries of his stimulating field.   His responses to simultaneous and successive stimulation are discontinuous and lack a stable background of consistent or dominant attitude.   He suffers losses in coordination, coherence and fluency of thinking, speaking and manipulation, and sometimes in stance and locomotion also.   With the disturbances in the timing of reactions, and in their functional harmony, there appear intrusive movements, words and thoughts belonging to some absent context.   Behavior is thus broken up into jumbled responses that are not interrelated and lack coherent direction.   It can thus be adequately regulated neither by the design of the environment nor by stimulation from the individual's own self-reactions.   The behavioral product of disorganization becomes therefore unpredictable and unintelligible to other persons, and often to the disorganized individual himself.

Desocialization we characterized as a reduction in the social articulation of behavior, resulting from the partial or complete detachment of the individual from participation in the activities of the full social community.   The desocialized person, either because of his segregation from the community, or

[42] For a fuller discussion of disorganization, see pages 448–469.

because he insulates himself from his human environment through his own behavior, is deprived of the sources of social validation and of opportunities to practice social role-taking. It is true that chronically ill and chronically disabled persons manage, as a rule, to maintain a reasonable degree of socialization in spite of relative isolation.[43] Like prisoners, they remain in adequate interacting relationship with whatever social field remains. Nevertheless, the exceptional invalid, like the exceptional prisoner, whose social competence has never been high, whose attitudes are unrealistic and whose main resources lie in fantasy, will stand in imminent danger of supplementing his desocialization by disorganizing trends, and thus become a schizophrenic invalid or prisoner.

The outcome of social disarticulation — whether or not it leads to and furthers disorganization — will always be greatly influenced by the social competence that an individual has earlier achieved. It will depend upon the general level of social maturity he has attained, and upon his habitual reactions to solitude or neglect. It will depend also upon the degree to which his fantasy, and particularly his symbolic self-reactions, correspond with conditions in the field of social operations. Perhaps most importantly of all, it will depend upon his past success in keeping fantasy distinct from social operations — a distinction which is essential to the preservation of behavioral organization. This means that the person who is skilled in taking social roles realistically, and in shifting perspectives easily as he shifts roles, will stand a better chance of resisting disorganization in protracted isolation or detachment than the person with unrealistic, unskilled role-taking and sharply limited perspectives.

Translated into the language of behavior disorder, this contrast finds expression in depressed and schizophrenic patients. The depressed person has usually achieved a reasonable degree of social maturity.[44] He is typically well established in his society and culture. Hence, when he falls ill, and through his illness and its consequences becomes socially detached, he is remarkably resistant to behavioral disorganization and shows a strong tendency to recover. The schizophrenic patient, on the other hand, is as a rule socially immature, unrealistic and poorly established in his society and culture, and his prognosis for recovery is poor. Indeed, the gravity of his outlook, as we shall see in now turning to a discussion of schizophrenic disorders, is directly related to this fact: that with his relative social incompetence, the schizophrenic tends to disorganize if he becomes socially detached, and to desocialize if he suffers behavioral disorganization.

[43] See pages 231–238.
[44] Compare the discussion of depressive disorders on pages 314–329.

Schizophrenic Disorders

Schizophrenic disorders are syndromes of disorganization and desocialization, in which delusion and hallucination are prominent, and in which behavior is dominated or determined by private fantasy. The signs of cerebral incompetence, the gross disorientation and the defective retentivity which help define delirious disorganization [45] are characteristically absent from schizophrenic syndromes. Indeed, one of the major unsolved problems in behavior pathology is presented by this paradox: it is a common clinical observation that schizophrenic patients, who are suffering from severe behavioral disunity and marked social disarticulation, may nevertheless exhibit no gross defects in retentivity or in orientation.[46] And this superiority over the delirious patient may be responsible in schizophrenia, as it evidently is in panic, for the striking tendencies toward self-perpetuation that the illness shows.

The normal and near-normal behavioral antecedents of schizophrenia are essentially the antecedents of disorganization and desocialization, which we have already discussed. The socially immature person who develops a schizophrenic disorder — usually an anxious and solitary person also — has entered adolescence or adulthood inadequately socialized.[47] He lacks the degree of role-taking skill necessary for ease in shifting perspectives under stress. He has learned to rely heavily on fantasy; but he has not mastered the techniques of social validation, of sharing his interpretations and conclusions, and of modifying them in accordance with the attitude of others. When, through attempted social interaction or private preoccupation, he encounters severe conflict, thwarting or delay, and develops marked anxiety, he is almost sure to show disorganization.

The crucial point here is this: that even though the same degree of frustration might arouse equal anxiety and provoke beginning disorganization in a socially mature person, he is able to fall back at once upon realistic role-taking.[48] He can gain the perspectives of others, even in his own self-reactions,

[45] For a description of delirium, see pages 469–477.

[46] This clinical observation is verified also in controlled studies of schizophrenic performance in test situations. See, for example, Rashkis, H. A., "Three types of thinking disorder: an investigation of the behavior on special tests of schizophrenics, general paretics and cerebral arterio-sclerotics." *J. nerv. ment. Dis.*, 1947, vol. 106, pp. 650–670.

[47] For studies of the early training of persons who later developed schizophrenic disorders, see Kasanin, J., Knight, E., and Sage, P., "The parent-child relationship in schizophrenia: I. Overprotection-rejection." *J. nerv. ment. Dis.*, 1934, vol. 79, pp. 249–262; Lidz, R., and Lidz, T., "The family environment of schizophrenic patients." *Amer. J. Psychiat.*, 1949, vol. 106, pp. 332–345; Tietze, T., "A study of mothers of schizophrenic patients." *Psychiatry*, 1949, vol. 12, pp. 55–65; Bonner, H., "Sociological aspects of paranoia." *Amer. J. Sociol.*, 1950, vol. 56, pp. 255–262; Fisher, S., and Fisher, R., "Value of isolation rigidity in maintaining integration in seriously disturbed personalities." *J. Personality*, 1950, vol. 19, pp. 41–47.

[48] For a discussion of *heredity* and *constitutional factors* in relation to schizophrenic disorders, see pages 28–32 and 515–517.

and he can share his interpretations and conclusions with other social persons. The socially unskilled, immature individual, on the other hand, finds himself in a personal crisis with only his private fantasy to depend upon, his individualistic interpretations and the inferior techniques of furtive watching, rumination, and validation in terms of mere plausibility. Thus, with the avenues to social help blocked by his asocial attitudes, the patient is left to face a disorganizing situation alone. He attempts to meet it by the use of further withdrawal and preoccupation — because these are his long-established techniques for dealing with frustration — and the consequence is further desocialization, and still greater disorganization. The end-result is usually a serious, and often lasting, impairment of social behavior. Indeed, it was the outcome in lasting behavioral deterioration which led nineteenth-century behavior pathologists to the conclusion that this disorganization and desocialization represented a process of dementing — comparable to pathological senility (*dementia senilis*) in course, and similar in origin.

Varieties of schizophrenic disorder

Because this supposedly dementing disorder was known to occur primarily in adolescence and adulthood, Kraepelin proposed for it the already current term *dementia praecox*, in contradistinction to *dementia senilis*. He then proceeded to differentiate four varieties — *simple, hebephrenic, catatonic* and *paranoid* [49] — and both the generic term and the division into four types were later adopted as official by American psychiatry. The types have been described as follows. (1) The *simple type* shows defective interest, gradually developing apathy, but neither delusion and hallucination, nor other strikingly peculiar behavior. (2) The *hebephrenic type* shows inappropriate smiling and laughter, silliness, bizarre thinking; the coining of words or phrases, and pleasing hallucination. (3) The *catatonic type* is characterized by peculiar conduct, negativism, phases of excitement or stupor, impulsive or stereotyped behavior, and usually hallucination. (4) The *paranoid type* is distinguished by the prominence of delusions, usually persecutory or grandiose, emotional aggressiveness, a predominantly homosexual component or fixation, and frequently hallucination.[50]

Kraepelin's *dementia praecox* has been the subject of severe criticism for half a century. Some critics objected that the behavioral deterioration in this disorder is reversible, not irreversible as in the so-called dementias. Others pointed out that the onset was frequently in the thirties, sometimes in the

[49] Kraepelin, E., *Psychiatrie: ein Lehrbuch für Studierende und Ärtze.* (4 vols.) Leipzig: Barth, 1909–1913.

[50] See American Classification of Mental Disorders, as Revised and Adopted by the Committee on Statistics and Approved by the American Psychiatric Association at its 1934 Annual Meeting. Reproduced in Strecker, E. A., Ebaugh, F. G., and Ewalt, J. R., *Practical clinical psychiatry.* Philadelphia: Blakiston (6th ed.), 1947, pp. 35–47.

forties, and occasionally in the fifties or even later. This, they said, cannot be called precocious. Bleuler recommended substitution of the now almost universally accepted term *schizophrenia*, which he defined as a disintegration "of the most varied mental functions." [51] The types have also been under fire. For not only does it prove a difficult and arbitrary task to fit a patient's behavior into a Kraepelinian type, but even when this can be achieved, the pathological behavior often shifts so that the typing is no longer appropriate. The official American classification of 1934 warns of these uncertainties, but tries to overcome them by precise definition. The United States Army medical department, during World War II, developed a revised classification, published provisionally in 1945, in which they frankly stated that schizophrenic patients need no longer be "forcibly" classified "into a Kraepelinian type." [52]

The heterogeneity we find among schizophrenic disorders, however, makes some kind of grouping necessary, if only for purposes of exposition; and the fluid state of our present-day conceptions of these syndromes favors the provisional adoption of as simple a classification as possible. In view of the fact that disturbances in the patient's relationship to the social community are fundamental characteristics of schizophrenic disorganization, we may make our grouping in accordance with this relationship. Accordingly, we shall distinguish in what follows between predominantly *aggressive, submissive* and *detached* behavior. The disorder in any of these subdivisions may be sudden or insidious in onset; its progress may be rapid or slow, episodic or uniform; and the outcome may be one of complete recovery, partial recovery or no recovery. Recurrences, even in cases with apparently complete recovery, are common in all three subdivisions.

Aggressive schizophrenic reactions. Predominantly aggressive schizophrenic patients may be hostile and vengeful toward others, believing themselves plotted against and wronged. Or, instead, their aggression may take the form of claims of omnipotence and special eminence, from which hostility and revenge are often absent. Aggressive schizophrenic patients, like depressed ones, frequently turn their enmity and vengeance against themselves, becoming actively and sometimes dangerously self-punitive, or demanding insistently of others that they be punished cruelly. We may call the first of these three *persecuted*, the second *grandiose* and the third *self-punitive*.

The aggressive *persecuted* patient builds his poorly organized pseudocommunity [53] around the threats, calumniations and frustrations that he most fears or believes he most deserves. This pseudocommunity, like any other,

[51] Bleuler, E., *Dementia praecox oder Gruppe der Schizophrenien.* Leipzig: Deuticke, 1911 (Translated as *Dementia praecox or the group of schizophrenias*, by Joseph Zinkin. New York: International Universities Press, 1950, p. 8.)

[52] United States Army Technical Bulletin no. 203. Washington, D.C.: Government Printing Office, October 19, 1945, Section 18.

[53] See pages 387–392.

will include real persons, to whom are ascribed some functions which they indeed perform, and some which they do not and often cannot. It also includes imaginary persons to whom, likewise, are ascribed functions socially valid for a social person, and functions that are unreal and for a human being frequently impossible. Against the hostile pseudocommunity thus structured, the patient may take arms, attacking, injuring and sometimes killing real persons to avenge or stave off an imagined crime. This is especially likely to follow upon a dramatic *sudden clarification*.[54] The persecuted patient may confine his attacks largely to words, using counterthreats, recriminations and demands for public vindication and redress. Or he may maintain attitudes of irreconcilable malice toward his pseudocommunity, hating and destroying in his fantasies, but giving them neither voice nor any other direct overt action.

In the following case, a person sets out in a spirit of self-vindication to achieve something for which he is unprepared, and concerning which he seems to have no socially validated plans. He gradually evolves a persecutory pseudocommunity peopled apparently by actual social individuals. To this he ascribes dangerous machinations, and then reacts against his fantastic ascriptions with aggressions in the shared field of social operations. Thus he succeeds in arousing counteraggression in the social field, and when it is found that society's weapons of confinement and shock treatment do not lead the patient to abandon his pseudocommunity, he is deprived permanently of his freedom.

> An unmarried store clerk, twenty-two years of age, was brought to the hospital in handcuffs by the police, who had been called because of the patient's sudden explosion of violence in which he swore to settle accounts with a neighbor woman. His parents dated the onset of the illness to a period, two years earlier, when their son became quite suddenly busy and seclusive. As a boy, he had always preferred his workbench in the basement, and the company of a similarly inclined chum, to competitive group play outdoors. His reading interests, which had in childhood centered about adventure and exploration stories, shifted in adolescence to biographies of great men, and to popular works on personal uplift and social reform. While still in high school, the patient repeatedly stated that he intended to devote his life to the study of people and society. When, however, he was graduated from high school at the age of nineteen, he discovered that he could not go on to college where he had expected to complete his preparation for the work of his choice. His parents could not or would not support him any longer, and his school achievement earned him neither a scholarship nor a strong recommendation that he continue with advanced studies. Accordingly, he was obliged to drop out of the running and get himself a job.
>
> The first reaction the patient gave to this disruption in his life plan was to abandon both reading and workbench in favor of convivial evenings spent with new companions. After a few months, however, he joined a church and took an active part in the young people's meetings.

[54] See pages 83–87.

At home he began talking a great deal about social betterment and the spiritual improvement of mankind. But his talk was vague and repetitious, so that his parents and his sister grew quickly bored by it, and finally told him so. To their rebuff the patient at first responded with increased talkativeness and insistent argument, against which the family defended itself by an equally insistent emphasis upon his ignorance of economic problems, of mankind's needs and of God's design. In this maneuver the family won a costly victory. For the patient finally replaced his tiresome monologues and contentious debates by a no less disconcerting angry silence and unexplained preoccupation that led up to his climactic outburst.

The patient gave up his church activities and his friends and devoted all of his spare time to solitary reading. His sister found books on architecture, city planning, social problems and psychology on the desk in his room; there was evidence that he was taking notes and drawing plans. When asked about this, he became surly and demanded that people stay out of his room. He worked fitfully at his bench in the basement, making wooden models of houses and other buildings which were not easy to identify. If anyone joined him there, he would stop work and stare at the intruder until he was left alone. When he was asked what he was trying to do, his only answer was, "You'll see." Once he said something about "changing the face of the nation."

One evening at dinner time, about six months before admission to the hospital, the patient astonished his family by pushing his plate away, and saying angrily, "I'm getting fed up with all this spying!" He then announced that his fellow-workers were all watching him and discussing him in little knots that broke up as soon as he approached. He could tell they were up to something, he said. The father discovered later that his son's fellow-workers had indeed been watching and discussing him, because he had become uncommunicative, was muttering to himself and would sometimes interrupt a controversial discussion to say that it was all being taken care of. At home, the patient kept the blinds down in his room, even in the daytime, and covered the basement window near his bench with soap. He seemed to his family more preoccupied now than angry, and he frequently stopped eating to stare into a corner or to listen.

Some three months before admission, the patient complained to his father that a certain neighbor woman was pestering him psychically, robbing him of his ideas, and interfering with his plans. He said that she had thrown a psychic spell over him which enabled her to see him in the dark, to read his mind at a distance and tune in on his thoughts. Because of the spell, he also had psychic powers. He could see this woman and several other people in his home at night and hear them talking. He thought it strange that everyone else could not see them at mealtime, even when he pointed them out; but this only confirmed his belief in his psychic powers. He later declared to his now frightened relatives that because he had thrown a stone at the neighbor's house, on his way home from work, his psychic power of seeing had been taken away from him and only that of hearing now remained.[55]

[55] For a detailed discussion of the development of such hallucinations, see pages 426–441.

The things the patient heard disturbed him greatly. At first it was mainly the one woman's voice, but after a while he could hear "her whole family and two or three boys outside." The woman talked about and to him constantly, reviling him, accusing him of filthy acts and threatening to expose him. Broadcasts on the radio, he said, referred to her and to him three or four times an evening. He became increasingly irritated that his family seemed to hear none of this; he kept insisting that they listen. In spite of his difficulties, the patient managed to keep his job until a week before admission, when his first disorganized excitement occurred. He rushed out of the basement, where he had been busily working, and tore down the street to the neighbor woman's house where he began beating on the door with a large piece of wood and shouting to her to settle the controversy once and for all. She opened the door a crack, and he shouted through it that she must stop persecuting and defaming him. Then he returned home and talked excitedly and incoherently along the same lines as before. The police arrived to investigate and the patient quieted down and promised to behave.

He seemed frightened and subdued for a few days, remaining locked in his room and refusing to come downstairs for food. He did not return to his job, but he seemed to be working steadily on his note-taking and drawing at his desk. On the afternoon of the day of his admission, he suddenly swept everything off his desk on to the floor, overturned his chair, rushed into the bathroom and jerked all the towel-racks from the walls, breaking the rods into fragments and dashing these on the floor. His mother screamed and someone called the police, who took him via the police station to the hospital.

At the hospital, the patient told the psychiatrist that the neighbor woman had it in for him because her daughter wanted to marry him, but that his mother had told him he could not go with any girl until he was financially independent. He had met the girl at a church party. Afterwards she had taken him home to meet her mother, who treated him in friendly fashion but eyed him critically and seemed to be cross-questioning him. It was after he gave up all social activities, and spent his evenings in isolation, that the woman began to work on him. "They started by apparitions — two or three, at first," he said. "Of course I didn't know what the idea was. Then they began the blackmail, calling me filthy names for six months." He sat on the porch for a few evenings and tried to make himself believe that seeing so much of him would affect their minds and stop them. But it didn't work. Then they began handling him erotically in the night. "I saw them," he said. They tortured him by threatening to abduct his parents, and to kidnap his sister, cut out her uterus and make her sterile. He could hear their threats coming from the direction of the bathroom, and he concluded that the voices were being broadcast through the towel racks. It was this conclusion that had precipitated his final outburst.

The patient was at a loss to explain the means by which his persecutors operated as they seemed to, but he had no doubt of the verity of all he reported. He said that his psychic power of hearing was on the increase, and that he wished to preserve and exercise it because it warned him of his enemies' intentions. He believed that this power was a special gift which strengthened his mental equipment. As he spoke his speech showed some fragmentation, with occasional blocking that was related to his auditory hallucination. There was otherwise nothing remarkable about his answers. He was correctly oriented for time, place and person, and he seemed reasonably conversant with current events. He was given insulin shock therapy but he made only slight and transient improvement.

When visited three years later in the hospital, the patient showed chronically disorganized behavior. His manner was exaggeratedly rigid, formal and distant. He offered little spontaneous conversation, but he listened attentively when questioned and answered readily and with clear enunciation. The structure of his talk, however, showed fragmentation, interpenetration and overinclusion [56] to a marked degree. Words and phrases belonging to his earlier vague ambitions were recognizable throughout, and so were references to the persecution that had thwarted him. He was still hearing the same voices, apparently saying the same things. He was still drawing plans, and these were stereotyped and stylistic, with notations and symbolic decorations on them. His explanations of the plans were unintelligible; but he returned the respect and forbearance of his listeners with equal courtesy and patience.

This case illustrates the development of a persecutory pseudocommunity in the behavior of an inadequately socialized young man who believed himself frustrated in achieving his life mission. There is no evidence that the patient ever formulated this mission clearly, either to other persons or to himself. His preoccupied behavior made him a focus of actual observation by fellow-workers, which he himself noticed, and this was probably the origin of his reaction-sensitivity in relation to being watched by others. In his eyes, his sexual conflict and disappointment implicated a neighbor woman — the one which his vague and socially invalidated ways of thinking permitted him to cast in the role of a kind of sorceress. The spell cast upon him by this woman performed a double function. It gave the patient something more specific to fight against than social ills, which he did not clearly understand. And it endowed him with powers that gave him a distinction which he had failed otherwise to achieve, even though in gaining this distinction he suffered behavioral disorganization.

The aggressive *grandiose* patient builds a confused pseudocommunity which casts him in the role of a distinguished or an influential person, a saint, the incarnation of some character in fiction or the reincarnation of someone famous in history, or the representative of the deity, a powerful agency or an illustrious personage. Like the persecuted patient, he mingles together real and fancied individuals with socially valid functions and socially meaningless or impossible functions. From his imaginary persons he succeeds in exacting the admiration, respect, adulation and applause he needs, but not from the actual persons. Indeed, a great deal of the aggression in grandiose schizophrenic patients arises as a response to the contradiction, resistance and ridi-

[56] For definitions of these characteristics, see pages 452–458.

cule of the social community. For the normal person can seldom recognize the potential gravity of delusions of grandeur, or understand the misery that prompts them, until they have developed into something which is completely unintelligible to him.

The aggressive *self-punitive* patient is, in effect, a persecuted individual who is his own persecutor. Indeed, it is sometimes only the prevailing disorganization — the fragmentary delusion, the interpenetration or the overinclusion — that differentiates him from the self-punitive compulsive and from a depressed person after the crucial shift.[57] He is likely also to resort to self-mutilation and self-sacrifice, such as we occasionally see in compulsive sadomasochism, and more often in depressive patients bent on expiation. In many ways, the aggressive schizophrenic patient is the greatest hazard of them all. For his behavioral disintegration — the weird and often incomprehensible character of his confused attitudes in relation to good and bad, sex and religion, cruelty, righteousness and glory — make his next step unpredictable. No one around him can share his chaotic perspectives, take his disarticulated roles, and prophesy what a person such as he will do. Some self-punitive patients, from the very start, are hopelessly unclear as to their needs, their motives and their dominant roles — a vagueness which is shared not only by many persecuted and grandiose schizophrenic persons, but by a large proportion of the submissive patients also.

Submissive schizophrenic reactions. The submissive schizophrenic patient takes the role of a passive instrument, in the hands of an obscure but powerful pseudocommunity or autistic community, which irresistibly controls him. The prevailing delusions are those of influence.[58] Many submissive patients object to and complain about what they believe is happening to them; but they do not aggressively resist, fight back or threaten reprisal. They neither actively seek help against the exploitation and control to which they feel subjected, nor do they take steps to escape it. On the contrary, they may ask to know what it is that will be done to them, or what it is that they suffer and go through, as if they were impatient for what they fear.[59]

Some submissive patients, with an air of resignation, go forth to meet the fate they anticipate. Others express an indifferent or a fatalistic attitude concerning their imagined plight and do nothing whatever about it. Some patients in the latter group puzzle relatives and clinicians by speaking about what they believe is going on around them, or inside them, with apathy or mild disdain, when what they say sounds horrible, incredible or unimaginable to the normal person.

> For example, one patient remarked casually that they were hammering nails through people's hands in the carpentry shop where he was work-

[57] See pages 320 and 358.
[58] Delusions of influence are described on pages 396–398.
[59] See pages 75–79 and 302–303.

ing, and branding them with the soldering iron. He then added that he supposed it would be his turn next. Another said that "bone pickers" had picked at her spine all the way up to her head. "They told me," she reported, "the stuff was as soft as mud." Neither patient could give an explanation for these assaults, and neither gave evidence of resenting or resisting them.

Among submissive schizophrenic patients there are also those who believe that they are expected to find out by passively observing, or by executing little ritualistic acts, the solution to some intricate puzzle of which they have some-- how become a part. Every chance event around them, even the ways in which common objects lie or are arranged, are not unfriendly challenges to their interpretation. There is often humility and a baffling willingness to learn in such patients; and occasionally one finds a patient who seems cheerful and looks upon the whole confusing business as a kind of game in which the shifting rules must be discovered by the player — like some of the games in *Alice in Wonderland.*

One patient persistently tried to interpret the meaning of everything happening about her in this way. The noon whistle must mean she is to change her position; someone drops a book as a signal for her to give something up; her nurse cups an ear to make the patient listen to an instruction although none comes; thoughts are put in her head so that she may figure them out and discern a concealed purpose; the electric floor polisher is related to something she should know but does not. "Everything in my environment is trying to tell me something and influence me," she said.

Some submissive patients obviously welcome the destiny to which their pseudocommunity or autistic community appears to dedicate them, whether this leads them to transfiguration or to martyrdom, to exaltation, debasement or oblivion. They are passive instruments in some unintelligible design to which they give tacit approval.

A young man, for example, after failing in college and making no progress in his job, came to the conclusion that he must be intended for some great hidden purpose. He started for work in his car one morning and disappeared. Two days later he turned up at a ranch house in the mountains where he was elated and confused. He said that he had a dual personality, that his mind was being read, and that messages came to him through his fingers, toes, eyes and ears. Back home he lay under his bed because signals from somewhere told him to do so. People had been signaling him from the mountains, engines were running wildly up and down the tracks flashing messages to each other, and secret service men had been stopping his car by radio. He said, "I know I'm in a trance. I'm on the edge of something big. It's something in the spiritual world — all the science and truth that has come down through the ages." He was unable to account for the situation or to give it clearer definition.

Detached schizophrenic reactions. All schizophrenic persons, of course, are to some degree socially disarticulated or detached. But our third group deserves this designation more particularly than the others because the patients in it have succeeded more nearly than the others in achieving total social isolation. Indeed, some of them retreat into the protracted social inaction we call stupor, in which they may often seem more unresponsive even than the stuporous patient suffering from cerebral incompetence.[60] There is some clinical evidence, however, to indicate that a stuporous schizophrenic person often hears and remembers for a long time things that are going on around him, especially if they fit into the fantasy activities of his autistic community. Nevertheless, stupor is the ultimate in withdrawal from social participation, although by no means necessarily either an end-stage or even a sign of grave prognosis. Patients sometimes go suddenly into schizophrenic stupor, and after a variable period — from a few minutes to a few months — come suddenly out again, and then go on to show considerable further improvement or completely to recover.

Most detached schizophrenic patients never become stuporous. They continue to react minimally to stimulation from their surroundings, so that it is possible for them with some prodding and some help to carry through the simple routines of daily living. Thus they may attend to the most essential of their body needs, eat and drink, dress and undress, get up in the morning and go to bed at night, without special assistance. Most detached patients are able to converse a little, however reluctant they may be to do it. Many of them under institutional supervision can carry through relatively simple domestic tasks — washing dishes, setting tables, cutting up food and disposing of garbage, dusting, cleaning and mending — or work as members of an outdoor gang, in such activities as shovelling, raking, carrying and stacking or road-repairing. But for all the rest — initiative and self-regulation in overt activity, participating thoroughly in shared social plan and execution, genuine communication and the interchange of information and perspective — they have no interest, and in it they play no part.

The origin of such pronounced detachment varies greatly from patient to patient. There are some patients for whom fantasied activities in an imagined context hold an irresistible fascination. Theirs is an attracted, adient attitude. Nothing in the social context is particularly frightening or revolting; but neither is there anything in it that compares with the qualities of the autistic community — however bizarre, fragmentary and chaotic its description may sound to a normal person. Many other patients, however, seem impelled primarily by overwhelming anxiety to seek refuge in the autistic community which their habitual fantasy has made easily accessible to them. Still others are driven to avoid all social interaction because it is repulsive, or because

[60] For a discussion of stupor in cerebral incompetence, see page 533.

it arouses in them an uneasy distrust or diffidence. The autistic community, which itself may not be free from threatening or disgusting aspects, at least offers the patient a sure escape from something worse. In the following case, we shall see permanent social detachment whose development illustrates these origins.

A stenographer, twenty-one years old and single, was admitted to the gynecological service of a general hospital because of pelvic complaints. When these complaints proved without foundation in organ or tissue pathology, she was transferred to psychiatry, because the nurses had observed her smiling and laughing without apparent reason, and talking softly to herself. On the psychiatric service she was uncommunicative, quiet, preoccupied and withdrawn. Her mother stated that the patient had always been reserved and unobtrusive, but extremely stubborn whenever she was thwarted. Throughout infancy and childhood she had been considered delicate and unlikely to reach adulthood because of digestive difficulties and poor sleep, both of which were aggravated by emotional disturbances of any kind.

The patient had a brother and a sister, both of whom went on to professional careers, but they were so much older than she, that they had never been her playmates. By children her own age, she was rather unnoticed than disliked. She preferred above all to stay at home and help her mother with domestic duties — "a regular little old woman," her mother used to call her. Her scholastic record was undistinguished. The patient had always been particularly shy with boys, whose company she persistently avoided. When she reached puberty, this shyness increased to such a painful degree that her avoidance changed to aversion. In consequence, she was more than ever passed over in the social activities of her peer culture. This neglect hurt her, and seems to have driven her closer than ever to her mother.

A highly important factor, both in these earlier developments and in the ultimate structure of the delusions that came later, was the fact that the patient lost her father, a physician, when she was only six years old. His death and burial made a profound impression upon her. She shared fully in her mother's grief; both mother and daughter remained in poor health for several months; and ever afterward they kept his memory green. It was agreed that she was to enter nurses' training at her father's hospital as soon as she had finished high school. But when she applied at the age of eighteen, she was denied admission on the basis of her mediocre high school record, her personal history of illness under stress, and an interview. Her initial reaction to her reverse justified at least one of these reasons, for she promptly developed digestive disturbances and abdominal pain which sent her to bed for over a week.

Her mother comforted the patient by saying that admission was entirely a matter of political influence, and that if her father had only lived, the hospital "would have considered itself lucky" to have her enroll. The patient indignantly refused to consider training in any other hospital. She insisted that she would remain at home until the school changed its mind. After she was up and about again, she was with the greatest of difficulty persuaded meanwhile to enter business college, so that she might supplement her mother's dwindling income.

The patient completed her course, qualified for civil service and obtained employment as a stenographer with a government agency. For two years she seemed to get along reasonably well, although she recounted to her mother every evening detailed criticisms of the office and its personnel. From this criticism, she always exempted the office manager whom she admired. She continued discussing her dead father with her mother. Each time something at work went particularly badly, they would comment on how different things would have been if her father had not died.

About six months before the patient came to the hospital a new office manager took charge. Following this, the office underwent a thoroughgoing reorganization, which the patient said was entirely political, and in which her job was downgraded and her work made less responsible and much less interesting. She became far more critical of the office force, especially of those who had gained by the changes, and she focussed her indignation upon the new manager as chief offender. She told her mother it was generally known that her old boss was the victim of political machinations, and that he had been "framed" in some way — she could not say exactly how.

As time went on, the patient appeared to her mother to grow more taciturn and remote. She gradually ceased speaking about the office or its personnel, and replied to her mother's inquiries curtly, by saying that things were "all right" or didn't matter. She carried through her part in domestic routines listlessly, mechanically and for the most part silently. Her evenings she devoted to the newspapers, but never seemed to finish them. She began complaining of fatigue; and she would often go off to bed right after the supper dishes were finished. She spoke vaguely two or three times of feeling sick to her stomach and of abdominal fullness. Finally, a month before her admission, she announced that she had been given a month's sick leave without pay. That was her farewell to work.

By this time the patient had become deeply preoccupied. She had to be spoken to several times before she replied, and then her answer frequently sounded irrelevant. Her mother at first gave her breakfast in bed; but the patient would then stay in bed all day, and call for food as she became hungry. The family physician could find no evidence of organ or tissue pathology. He insisted that she arise each day at a reasonable hour and go for a walk morning and afternoon. A nutritive diet was recommended and a tonic prescribed. Within three weeks, her behavior had become grossly desocialized and disorganized. She wandered about the apartment in a daze, frequently mumbling to herself, occasionally nodding or shaking her head in assent or dissent. She smiled and frowned a great deal, and sometimes coquettishly tossed her head. When asked what she was saying or doing, she would look surprised, give a snicker and reply, "Oh, nothing." Sometimes she would tell her mother rudely to "shut up." She had to be prodded constantly to get up and get dressed, to keep herself clean and tidy, to eat, and eventually even to go to the toilet.

The day before her admission to the gynecological service, the patient told the family physician in strict confidence that her father was still alive, and that she was pregnant by her former boss who, she now knew, was dead. She said that she was in communication with both of them and often could see them both. Sometimes they all three conversed together. She had found that it was unnecessary for her to speak out because they could hear her thoughts. That night she complained of recurrent severe abdominal and pelvic pains, and the next afternoon she was taken to the hospital.

After her transfer from the gynecological service to psychiatry, the patient continued to smile and laugh when she thought herself unobserved, and to talk to herself softly. To every question she was asked her reply was, "You know all about it," or "There's nothing to tell — you know it all." Otherwise she remained uncommunicative and aloof. In view of her therapeutic inaccessibility, she was transferred after two weeks to a nearby state hospital for shock treatment. Ultimately she was able to leave the hospital and return to live with her mother; she remained detached, aloof, preoccupied, and relatively uncommunicative, however, and she did not return to gainful work.

In this case we see a person, who has never become adequately socialized, reacting to neglect, disappointment and affectional need by escaping from the drab uncertainties of the social community into an autistic community of her own making. During most of her life the patient had mourned a father whom she could scarcely remember. In her adulthood, she had found a living substitute in her employer whom she could admire; but he, also, was taken from her. To this emotional stress the patient responded, as she always had, with abdominal complaints. Now, however, these acquired a new symbolism of rebirth. The man whom she alone believed dead, her former boss, now lived in her; for she was to bear him a child. And in her strangely structured autistic community her dead father was alive, while the living man who she thought had impregnated her, seemed to be dead but could still talk freely with her father and herself.

In all varieties of schizophrenic disorder, the interaction of disorganizing and desocializing trends leads to the dominance of a similar pseudocommunity or autistic community. This means, of course, that language behavior and thinking become deeply involved, since pseudocommunities and autistic communities are structured primarily in symbolic terms.[61] Indeed, one of the major foci of professional interest in schizophrenic disorder has always been the confusion and distortion of communication and socially derived thinking which disorganizing and desocializing trends produce.

Language and thinking in schizophrenia

We have said that the acquisition of a highly versatile system of interpersonal communication is essential for the effective socialization of human beings, and that it is in large part responsible for the organization and maintenance of one's socially valid thinking.[62] In the course of schizophrenic dis-

[61] See pages 387–393 and 414–426.   [62] See pages 105–113 and 478–481.

organization and desocialization, this system of interpersonal communication is utilized less and less in the service of shared participation. It becomes gradually subordinated to, and often partially replaced by, the products of private fantasy. The preoccupied patient may gesture, smile, laugh, frown, grimace and posture in accordance with what he is fantasying, and not at all with reference to what is going on in the shared field of social operations. He is likely, also, to speak to persons whom he imagines and to hallucinate their imaginary replies.

It was at one time believed and taught that the posturing, gesturing, mannerisms and facial movements which many schizophrenic patients show, were the direct product of central nervous system lesions, and presumptive evidence of heredo-degenerative disease.[63] This belief was strengthened by the fragmentary and meaningless appearance of most of these responses, to the uninitiated observer, and by the fact that sometimes they are stereotyped and repetitive, like the forced movements of irritative lesions. But in their proper context — the context of the patient's fantasied activities — the responses need be no more meaningless than those made by a preoccupied normal person who thinks he is not observed, and whose preoccupations the onlooker does not share.[64] Even the stereotyped repetitions in schizophrenia have far more often the character of compulsive ritual or hysterical autonomy than of the repetitive stereotypy in central nervous system lesions. In short, what were once considered the symptoms of brain disease are now recognized to be non-verbal fragments and remnants of previously communicative behavior.

Under ordinary conditions, language behavior continues to operate effectively as an instrument of interpersonal communication through almost constant use. Language behavior can also function in intrapersonal behavior, with socially valid results, provided this use conforms to the general structure of communication and is sufficiently tested against interpersonal usage. Similarly, thinking must be made to correspond with operations in the shared social field of interbehavior if it is to remain socially valid. For all but the exceptionally well-integrated social person, this means that one must continually engage in cooperative and competitive activities with other social persons, or at least return repeatedly to participative behavior, where conclusions privately arrived at can be publicly verified or contradicted. Otherwise, the individual runs the risk of developing language behavior and thinking which have private fantasy as their only validating context.

This is essentially the situation in the disorganization and desocialization

---

[63] For a critical discussion of this point of view, see Cameron, N., "The functional psychoses." In Hunt, J. McV. (Ed.), *Personality and the behavior disorders.* New York: Ronald, 1944, pp. 886–890.

[64] For an analysis of this point in relation to the language of preoccupied children, see Kanner, L., "Irrelevant metaphorical language in early infantile autism." *Amer. J. Psychiat.*, 1946, vol. 103, pp. 242–246.

characteristic of schizophrenic disorders. The progressive withdrawal from social participation, which we have witnessed in our cases, and the increasing preoccupation with fantasied achievement, frustration and escape, lead the patient deeper and deeper into behavior that, whatever its personal yield, has little or no social validity. Interpersonal communication, as we have seen, becomes intrapersonal communication; the patient converses less and less with other social persons, and more and more with fantasied persons in his pseudocommunity and autistic community. Not unlike a sleeping dreamer, the schizophrenic patient then finds the activities within his imagined context, to which his symbolic responses correspond, more lifelike and convincing than activities in the social context, to which these responses have little relevance.

Some of the specific effects of such absorption in intrapersonal communication are not difficult to predict. Symbolic behavior begins to lose its continuity, its conventional forms and its clarity of expression. Even the normal man, in his practical everyday life, does not render all his plans and his conclusions, his hopes, disappointments and consolations, into fully communicative social form. For his own purposes, a few disjointed exclamations suffice, a short run of fragmentary imagined acts, a line or two of socially unintelligible scribbled words and private signs. To communicate with an intimate, about material both understand, a telephone conversation can be adequate even though it is made up of ungrammatical, abbreviated jargon, loose approximation and unfinished statements. If, however, the normal man is not fully understood, or does not fully understand himself, he must be able to go on and supplement or replace his exclamations, imagined fragments, notes, signs, jargon and approximation with language and thinking that re-establish communication with others, or make his symbolic operations meaningful to himself.

The socially disarticulated schizophrenic person is one who has lost the need for retaining or for re-establishing communication with other social persons. Consequently, his symbolic behavior continues to be fragmentary, discontinuous, individualistic and approximate, even though these characteristics make his talk difficult or impossible for others to understand. The fictitious individuals who people his imagined community are far more important for the patient than any real person in the field of social operations. For them the fragmentary jargon of individualistic idiom, the shorthand and the half-formed phrase of ordinary private rumination are fully adequate. The schizophrenic patient need not even clarify his unshared thinking in terms of a consensus of his fellows. His imagined community provides its own validation in the form of his own projected and reified interpretations; and these make his conclusions seem self-evident.

Even the real persons, to whom a schizophrenic patient may assign imaginary functions in his pseudocommunity,[65] are assumed likewise to understand

[65] For a discussion of the pseudocommunity, see pages 387–393.

all that is going on in terms of an imagined context which the patient actually shares with no one. A particular delusional structure, as we have pointed out, is determined primarily by a person's reaction-sensitivities. These transform the incidental behavior of real persons — including words and gestures, of course — into imaginary signs of understanding and signals of intent. And if these signs and signals are insufficient for the patient, his immediate recourse is not as apt to be that of social testing, in which he is unskilled, as it is to be that of further hallucination, in which he is exceptionally well-practiced. The actual behavior of real persons is thus measured by its consonance with a dominant fantasy scheme, just as the imagined behavior of fictitious persons is.

As the schizophrenic patient thus gives up his previous referents in the field of social operations, his language behavior and his thinking lose their social organization. It is not simply that he now lives in a private world; he lives in a world which provides its own asocial regulation. The usefulness of language behavior is no longer determined by its success as interpersonal communication, and the validity of thinking is no longer testable in social terms. In the following example, we see language behavior that has lost much of its conventional form; it is vague and discontinuous, like dream-talk; personal idiom has developed at the expense of social intelligibility. The end-result is something that is full of unclear, ambiguous and fragmentary approximations which convey little, but seem to imply much.

> The patient, a college-trained man, is attempting to cooperate in a complicated test situation. The task confronting him is one of sorting blocks of various sizes, shapes and colors into four predetermined groups, and to formulate the principles upon which the groupings are made.[66] Here are samples of the patient's verbalization: "That's a rectangle, substantiates angle." (*What do you mean by "substantiates"?*) "'Substantiates' means to make a substantiation for a generality." (*And what does that mean to you?*) "In a word or two, to substantiate a generality, such must be written thoroughly." (*The names* [nonsense syllables] *on these two are different.*) "The names are different; one is 'CEV' and one is 'MUR'" — correct statement. (*What do you make of this difference?*) "The difference would be meaning that the words were different, and such are small for comparison of the generalities. . . . Same arrangement of letters substantiates such from the mixture. . . . Types are entirely different and that's a substantiation. A substantiation would mean to touch a flashlight; and if that was open and you come in contact with the battery, that would be a substantiation or a sensation generalization."

In this example, the patient manages to limit his comments to the shared problem. But the words he uses are privately endowed with vague and special

---

[66] For a more complete account of this procedure and an analysis of the patients' behavior, see Cameron, N., "Schizophrenic thinking in a problem-solving situation." *J. ment. Science*, 1939, vol. 85, pp. 1012–1035. The test is fully described, with plates illustrating the initial lay-out and the correct solution, in Hanfmann, E., and Kasanin, J., "Conceptual thinking in schizophrenia." *Nerv. ment. Dis. Monogr.*, 1942, no. 68.

meanings which he does not succeed in thoroughly communicating, in spite of his apparent intent to be understood. In the next examples which, for simplicity's sake, we shall take from attempted communication in the same problem-solving situation, other disorganized and desocialized characteristics appear. The patients are obviously talking about things which they assume their listener understands. Actually, however, they are unable any longer to communicate these matters intelligibly to anyone. The listener can infer the referents — and then only with considerable uncertainty — by learning about the patients' past from relatives, friends and physicians, whose communicative systems are not disorganized.

The first patient is a former school-teacher, who lost her position because of seriously decreased efficiency, and then became a practical nurse. Here she found herself the subject of neighborhood gossip, in which her name was linked with that of her unmarried male patient. In the block sorting test she is asked, "What is the difference between this group and that?" to which she replies, "Dividing by feeling your hand and calculating the rim. If I wrote on the blackboard my hand wouldn't give out anything at all, no chalk-mark. It's a certain light they leave careless with their work. It's light slatiness; and when I went out there to walk I found lots like that. Like these men working on the roof, keep slipping off. There's somebody copying that light all the time. How in God's name can a man keep spending money on a child and buy her clothes? And that's the way with Constance, and she going to school. They'll be going to fertilize her mind through our farm and get that light. My family took that up great. A woman in Missouri she worked on those children, boiled them and picked them and finished them. I like to do a work there."

The second patient is a high school graduate who worked for eight years for a wholesale grocer. The patient is described as having been studious and fond of reading the classics. He looks at the experimental board which is divided into sections. "Each man has to have his way of walking on the earth. The earth is divided up like this; and these blocks — women have to be born and carry a baby up over the stars to put them out. I live up there. (Where?) Everything's got to live over the North Sea. The moon carries the water up. That's why nobody can eat watermelons until after I've eaten. Nobody can eat a watermelon that has green hate in it. If you eat a watermelon the next comes up with your name on it. . . . I don't have any [name] through not being born yet. . . . I'm not born through food. You people have eaten food and robbed me of my birth."

In all three of these illustrations of schizophrenic talk we find obvious discontinuity and, especially in the latter two, many comments referring to matters which have nothing objectively to do with the test situation, but which the patient cannot exclude from his immediate consideration (*overinclusion*).[67]

[67] For examples of overinclusion shown by schizophrenic patients in different sorts of test situations, see Shneidman, E. S., "Schizophrenia and the MAPS test: a study of certain formal psycho-social aspects of fantasy production in schizophrenia as revealed

Discontinuity in schizophrenic patients, such as we have just observed, is a direct outgrowth of marked desocialization. Talking and thinking become divorced from the controlling influence of events in the organized social community. Hence, they may proceed almost entirely in terms of events in the fantasied context, whose temporal successions often seem haphazard and chaotic. Or there may be a failure to preserve a clear distinction between fantasy and the social context, so that events belonging to one are confused with events belonging to the other. In either case, language and thinking are characterized by an exaggerated instability of organization. Contradictory, competing and more or less irrelevant responses can no longer be excluded, and the effect of the now discontinuous and overinclusive symbolic behavior may be to confuse the patient as much as it confuses his observers.

Schizophrenic patients themselves often complain about the confusion in their talk and thinking, saying that everything seems mixed up, the words do not come as they once did, thoughts rush in and are jumbled, or seem to be blocked or suddenly to disappear. "There are a million words," one patient said. "I can't make sentences; everything is disconnected." Another patient made several attempts to speak and then gave up; the next day she complained that thoughts had been rushing through her mind so that she could say nothing.

Schizophrenic persons frequently attribute what they think, and sometimes what they say, to some irresistible power that controls them, putting thoughts into their heads and words into their mouths, or using them to speak through and to hear through. Thus a patient, usually mute, said one day, "They don't let you hear me. I used to talk to people before, but you can't hear me now. Voices out of the past talk through me." And, "You're more interested in the others, the people you're talking to through me." Then followed over fifteen minutes of inaudible lip movements.[68] (*I can't hear you.*) "It isn't passing through." Sometimes the confusion of symbolic behavior is ascribed to poison, drugs or hypnotism.

There have been innumerable attempts to reduce the compound confusion of which schizophrenic patients complain to something simpler that the normal man can understand. Thus, for example, schizophrenic talk and thinking have been characterized by Kraepelin as derailment, by Bleuler as

by performance on the make-a-picture-story (MAPS) test." *Genet. Psychol. Monogr.*, 1948, vol. 38, pp. 143–223; Zaslow, R. W., "A new approach to the problem of conceptual thinking in schizophrenia." *J. consult. Psychol.*, 1950, vol. 14, pp. 335–339; Epstein, S., "A study of overinclusion in a schizophrenic and control group." (Unpublished M.A. Thesis.) University of Wisconsin, 1951.

[68] Compare the findings of Gould on the relation between responses of the vocal musculature and auditory hallucination. Gould, L. N., "Verbal hallucinations and activity of vocal musculature: an electromyographic study." *Amer. J. Psychiat.*, 1948, vol. 105, pp. 367–372; Gould, L. N., "Auditory hallucinations and subvocal speech: objective study in a case of schizophrenia." *J. nerv. ment. Dis.*, 1949, vol. 109, pp. 418–427; Gould, L. N., "Verbal hallucinations as automatic speech. The reactivation of dormant speech habit." *Amer. J. Psychiat.*, 1950, vol. 107, pp. 110–119. These studies are summarized on pages 438–439.

reduction in associative tension, by Gruhle as loss of thought initiative, by Beringer as restriction of attention, by Stransky as intrapsychic ataxia, by Meyer as the product of habit deterioration and by Pavlov as an overdevelopment of inner inhibition.[69] The language and thought of schizophrenics has been called regressive, and likened to that of primitive man, of children and of dreaming adults. But we know nothing of primitive man — for preliterate societies are neither primitive nor characteristically schizophrenic — the logic of children does not resemble schizophrenic logic, and even seriously disorganized schizophrenic patients do not speak like normal men asleep. And, finally, a comparison of the talk of aged persons suffering from cerebral incompetence fails to support the claim that schizophrenic speech disorganization gives evidence of cerebral degeneration.[70]

During the past few decades, the principal attempts to arrive empirically at a better understanding of symbolic behavior in schizophrenia have centered about the problems of deterioration and of regression. The former has been investigated chiefly, although not exclusively, by the application of psychometric instruments developed originally for the study of normal children and adults.[71] The problem of regression has given rise to studies in verbal logic and in object sorting with the aim of determining whether or not the ability to think conceptually is lost in schizophrenic disorders. Although the original assumption, that the loss of ability to conceptualize is evidence of regression, has been seriously called into question, the results of these studies have proved valuable.

One of the early clinical observations in the schizophrenic disorders was that patients often show a remarkable tendency to interpret and use abstract, metaphorical expressions in a concrete, literal sense. Thus, for example, a patient told by another that he had better lie low refused for some time thereafter to sleep anywhere but on the floor. Another, following a nurse's comment that a letter from home should be an appetizer, began to eat the letter. The latter patient, after seeing a magazine article on holding one's tongue, went about holding her tongue with her right hand. There have been several studies designed to test this tendency toward overconcreteness by means of presenting patients with such problems as explaining proverbs and giving opposites, analogies and essential differences in relation to a standard stimulus word

[69] For a summary of these viewpoints, see Cameron, N., "The functional psychoses." In Hunt, J. McV. (Ed.), *Personality and the behavior disorders.* New York: Ronald, 1944, pp. 861–921.

[70] For a comparison of schizophrenic language with that of normal children and adults, and that of aged persons with cerebral incompetence, see Cameron, N., "A study of thinking in senile deterioration and schizophrenic disorganization." *Amer. J. Psychol.*, 1938, vol. 51, pp. 650–665.

[71] For a discussion of deterioration, see pages 518–531. Many of the psychometric studies are summarized in Hunt, J. McV., and Cofer, C. N., "Psychological deficit." In Hunt, J. McV. (Ed.), *Personality and the behavior disorders.* New York: Ronald, 1944, pp. 971–1032.

or phrase.[72] These studies all confirm the clinical observation that many, though by no means all, schizophrenic patients have greater difficulty with these tasks than do normal persons. These results are commonly interpreted as indications of an impairment in the ability to generalize.

The study of generalization in schizophrenic patients by object-sorting tests is best represented by two lines of investigation, the one carried on by Goldstein and Bolles, and the other by Hanfmann and Kasanin. Goldstein and Bolles[73] have carried over into the study of schizophrenic language and thinking, and to some extent modified, certain of the techniques which have been developed for use with cases of brain damage. These deal primarily with color-sorting, form-sorting, object-sorting, and the copying of cubes and simple geometrical figures from memory. They report results indicating an impairment of generalization or, as Goldstein expresses it, an impairment of the abstract attitude. For example, a patient in color-sorting picks out various shades of green, names each as a kind of green (e.g., emerald green, bright green, baby green) but refuses to say that they might all be called green. Goldstein emphasizes particularly the schizophrenic patient's inability to shift from one attitude to another when the second attitude is not structured for him by the experimenter. If he has sorted objects according to one principle and is told simply to sort them another way, he cannot do so.[74]

Hanfmann has carried out two investigations — one with the Healy Picture Completion Test, and one in which a single case was given a variety of tests, most of them made up of meaningful materials. From both these studies, she infers a probable impairment of conceptual thinking.[75] The work of Hanfmann and Kasanin utilized the Vigotsky sorting test. The subject faces the task of finding out empirically a predetermined solution whereby the twenty-two blocks composing the test may be sorted into four groups. It is only by combining the properties of height and plane surface that an acceptable grouping can be achieved — small-flat, small-high, large-flat and large-high. The subject's performance is scored in accordance with the time his grouping con-

[72] See, for example, Frostig, J., *Das schizophrene Denken: Phänomenologische Studien zum Problem der widersinnigen Sätze.* Leipzig: Thieme, 1929; Hadlich, H., "Schizophrene Denkstörung." *Psychol. Forsch.*, 1931, vol. 15, pp. 359–373; Wegrocki, H., "Generalizing ability in schizophrenia: an inquiry into the disorders of problem thinking in schizophrenia." *Arch. Psychol.*, N.Y., 1940, vol. 36, no. 254.

[73] Bolles, M., "The basis of pertinence." *Arch. Psychol.*, 1937, no. 212; Bolles, M., and Goldstein, K., "A study of the impairment of 'abstract behavior' in schizophrenic patients." *Psychiat. Quart.*, 1938, vol. 12, pp. 42–65.

[74] That some schizophrenic patients can, in a different type of sorting situation, learn to sort according to more than one principle, is indicated by the findings of Fey, E. T., "A study of the performance of a group of young schizophrenics and young normals on the Wisconsin Card Sorting Test." *J. consult. Psychol.*, 1951 (in press).

[75] Hanfmann, E., "Thought disturbances in schizophrenia as revealed by performance in a picture completion test." *J. abn. soc. Psychol.*, 1939, vol. 34, pp. 249–264; Hanfmann, E., "Analysis of the thinking disorder in a case of schizophrenia." *Arch. Neurol. Psychiat.*, 1939, vol. 41, pp. 568–579.

sumes, the amount of help he requires from the experimenter, and the adequacy with which he formulates his solution when he is asked to do so at the end.[76]

Hanfmann and Kasanin found it necessary to distinguish three levels of performance in relation to this sorting test. On the "primitive level" groups are made on the basis of individual block similarity; the correct solution is either not found at all or it is found accidentally and cannot be formulated. On the "intermediate level," the subject recognizes that there is some rule involved but he does not completely grasp it; he reaches the correct solution and formulates the basis for grouping correctly in terms of size, but he does not recognize that his formulation actually defines the groups. On the "conceptual level" the task is clearly understood and the subject deliberately chooses properties of the blocks as his bases, forms groups that represent classes and clearly formulates these at the end.

The schizophrenics perform on a lower level than normals of similar education; and the contrast is greatest when the comparison is restricted to college educated persons. However, there is a greater difference in level between normal college persons and normal non-college attendants than between normals as a whole and schizophrenics as a whole. One-third of the college-educated schizophrenic patients displayed superior conceptual performance as defined by Hanfmann and Kasanin. Considering the entire schizophrenic group, a reduction in the level of performance on this complex sorting test, as compared with similarly educated controls, could be demonstrated in about one-third to one-half of the cases. If such a reduction is taken as evidence of a loss in generalizing ability, then one can say that one-third to one-half of the schizophrenic patients tested show such a loss, while the others do not.

Recently Rashkis [77] has made a study of the performance of a group of schizophrenic patients in a test that calls for word-sorting and number-sorting in accordance with meaning. He reports that the performance of the schizophrenic group differs significantly from that of the arteriosclerotic and the paretic groups. He characterizes the thinking disorder in the schizophrenics as a deficit in organization but not in performance potentialities. White studied matched groups of normal and schizophrenic patients in their performance of three tasks: (a) the interpretation of indistinct, blurred words, (b) sorting clearly printed words into a group called "mine" and a group called "theirs," and (c) making up a sentence from an orally presented word. She found that schizophrenics were relatively unwilling to attempt interpreta-

---

[76] For a complete description of this test, with colored plates illustrating the materials, see Hanfmann, E., and Kasanin, J., "Conceptual thinking in schizophrenia." *Nerv. ment. Dis. Monogr.*, 1942, no. 68.

[77] Rashkis, H. A., "Three types of thinking disorder: an investigation of the behavior on special tests of schizophrenics, general paretics and cerebral arteriosclerotics." *J. nerv. ment. Dis.*, 1947, vol. 106, pp. 650–670.

tions; but when they did interpret, they showed a need to make generalizations even though the generalization "might not make sense." [78]   Moreover, the schizophrenic patients tended to group according to complex patterns, and they showed difficulty in shifting from one category to another.   White reported that they seemed to lack completeness of thought and perseverated.

From the results of empirical studies and clinical observation, we can characterize schizophrenic language and thinking as tending to become (1) *fragmentary*, (2) *approximate*, (3) *interpenetrative*, (4) *overinclusive* and (5) *literal* or *concrete*.   We must recognize, however, that these adjectives do not give us an exhaustive or even a satisfactorily definitive description of all schizophrenic symbolic behavior.   Neither do they all apply to all schizophrenic patients, by any means.   We are still far from the goal of a complete delineation of language and thought in syndromes of disorganization and desocialization.   And if, at this point, we recall Luria's important observation that language disorganization has sweeping effects upon the rest of behavior — even in normal persons [79] — we shall at once realize that a better understanding of schizophrenic language behavior and thinking may lead us toward a clearer grasp of the factors responsible for the origin and perpetuation of these important behavior disorders.

The origins of schizophrenia

To a great many persons working in this area, it is still inconceivable that schizophrenic disorders can and do arise out of behavioral disorganization and desocialization — whether the patients who succumb are socially immature or not, and regardless of their age or what their personal problems are.   For these behavior pathologists, the origin of schizophrenia must be sought in a defective germ plasm, in prenatal or early postnatal deficiencies, in a peculiarly susceptible constitution or special body type, in brain anomaly, degeneration or disease, in metabolic disturbance or in the loss of physiological homeostasis.[80]   They maintain, in effect, that the behavioral impoverishment and distortion in schizophrenia are only symptoms of an underlying disease

[78] White, M. A., "A study of schizophrenic language." *J. abn. soc. Psychol.*, 1949, vol. 44, pp. 61–74.

[79] Evidence for this has been reported in the experimental production of schizophrenic-like speech disorganization in normal adults.   See Cameron, N., and Magaret, A., "Experimental studies in thinking: I. Scattered speech in the responses of normal subjects to incomplete sentences." *J. exper. Psychol.*, 1949, vol. 39, pp. 617–627.

[80] For a discussion of heredity and constitution in relation to schizophrenia, see pages 28–32; for a review of the literature in relation to etiology, see Cameron, N., "The functional psychoses."   In Hunt, J. McV. (Ed.), *Personality and the behavior disorders.*   New York: Ronald, 1944, pp. 861–921; Bellak, L., and Willson, E., "On the etiology of dementia praecox: a partial review of the literature, 1935 to 1945, and an attempt at conceptualization." *J. nerv. ment. Dis.*, 1947, vol. 105, pp. 1–24; Bellak, L., *Dementia praecox (The past decade's work and present status: a review and evaluation).*   New York: Grune and Stratton, 1947.

process or an inborn weakness. These symptoms, however interesting as pathological products, are significant only in the sense that fever and abdominal distention are significant.[81]

The situation with regard to the origins of schizophrenic disorders is certainly no less complicated than in the rest of behavior pathology. Therefore, one can hardly afford to err in the other direction, and simply ignore the problems that structural peculiarities, physiological disturbances, degeneration and disease present. The chief difficulty often lies in the traditional formulations which are attached to these problems. For one thing, it is almost meaningless to say that only susceptible individuals develop schizophrenia, since the evidence of their susceptibility turns out to be that they are schizophrenic. The same could be said of drowning; but no useful conclusions would then follow. For another, the claim of inconceivability has nothing but prejudice to support it — whether it seems inconceivable to one behavior pathologist that so severe a disorder could result from anything but tissue pathology, or whether to another it seems inconceivable that tissue pathology is involved. Indeed, to the inexperienced layman the common symptomatology of schizophrenia, with which all behavior pathologists are familiar, seems itself utterly inconceivable.

From a biosocial point of view, it is both unnecessary and undesirable to choose between body and behavior. Anything that makes a human being less able than his fellow human beings to meet the demands of his surroundings may lead to schizophrenic disorganization and desocialization. For example, schizophrenia is found often enough in persons handicapped by developmental retardation to have earned in German a special name (*Propfschizophrenie*). Typical schizophrenia may follow cerebral intoxication, disease and degeneration.[82] It may develop during pregnancy or soon after childbirth. Acute febrile illnesses immediately precede it sometimes, and so do injuries and surgical procedures. Schizophrenia may complicate cases of pulmonary tuberculosis, diabetes mellitus, tumor, heart disease, or any other organ or tissue pathology. It may follow extreme exhaustion, starvation or prolonged exposure. Nobody working with this problem can possibly escape the potential importance of such diseases, traumas and defects.

But it is of considerable significance that the syndrome of disorganization and desocialization does develop out of such diverse backgrounds, for it argues against the specificity of any one of them. This becomes still clearer when we find that the same injury or acute illness, which immediately precedes a schizophrenic disorder in one person, may in another at least temporarily clear it up.

---

[81] An able and persuasive presentation of the case for this general point of view has been given by Hoskins, R., *The biology of schizophrenia*. New York: Norton, 1946.

[82] See, for example, Levin, M., "Transitory schizophrenias produced by bromide intoxication." *Amer. J. Psychiat.*, 1946, vol. 103, pp. 229–237.

In the end, we are driven back again to the study of our patient as a biological organism operating in a social field. And here, even though there is neither a demonstrable deficit nor evidence of intoxication, trauma, degeneration or disease, the patient may be led by his disorganization and desocialization into behavioral deterioration as devastating as any that tissue destruction can induce.

Deterioration

We have seen that in *disorganization* there is a fragmentation of previously established patterns of behavior, so that what was once a complex unified reaction is supplanted by more or less complete behavioral disunity, with perhaps a few simple stereotyped responses remaining.[1] Likewise, in *desocialization* we found that there is a replacement of behavior involving effective participation in social interaction by behavior which is not genuinely participative and fails to correspond with social fact.[2] In both disorganization and desocialization, a common result of these changes is that a person grows unable to meet many life situations at his previous level of competence. If the outcome is a distinct reduction in the general effectiveness of one's biosocial behavior, we characterize the change as deterioration.

Let us define *deterioration* as *a reduction in the general effectiveness of a person's biosocial behavior, from his usual level, to levels that are distinctly lower.*[3] It is not customary to speak of *deterioration* when a person has simply lost some previously acquired specific skill. Thus, the expert typist, who quits her job and marries, is not considered to have deteriorated just because she progressively loses her ability to type, through lack of practice and lack of interest. Neither is the skilled machine operator called deteriorated, who loses his deftness in relation to one pattern of operations, through shifting his work to a machine calling for a behavior pattern which contradicts the previously mastered one.

A further somewhat arbitrary restriction on the use of the term *deterioration* relates to the severity and the duration of change. We do not as a rule desig-

---

[1] See pages 454–456. [2] See pages 492–493.

[3] It should be noted that this definition is much broader than the definitions employed in *psychometric* studies of deterioration. For examples of psychometric approaches to deterioration, see Hunt, J. McV., and Cofer, C. N., "Psychological deficit." In Hunt, J. McV. (Ed.), *Personality and the behavior disorders*. New York: Ronald, 1944, pp. 971–1032.

nate slight or transient reductions in general biosocial effectiveness as deterioration, even though a considerable range of behavior may be involved. Thus, a man may not be as competent a salesman this year as he was last year; a woman may do a more adequate job of housekeeping one year than during a succeeding year; a child may handle his interpersonal relationships, both in school and out of it, better in one year than in the next. But unless the change in each instance represents a distinct reduction, no useful purpose is served in calling it deterioration. And of course every man, woman or child is permitted to have a day or a week of relative general incompetence without raising the suspicion that he is becoming deteriorated.

Our definition of deterioration, like our definition of fixation[4] and of regression,[5] is stated in relativistic terms. Its point of reference, however, is not that of the contemporary standards of maturity. For deterioration is gauged by the previous level of behavioral effectiveness *which a given individual has himself managed to achieve and to sustain*. Thus a ten-year-old child, whose test performance consistently earns him a mental age of seven years, cannot be called deteriorated unless it is established that this represents a distinct reduction from his previous performance. Similarly, an adult who is found incapable of remembering his own address, of dressing himself unaided, of holding a job or of maintaining adequate social relationships with others, cannot be called deteriorated unless it can be shown that at one time he was able to achieve the things which now he cannot.

It follows, from what has just been said, that a person need not have reached a high level of maturity, or of behavioral complexity, before he can deteriorate. In any phase of maturity, from childhood through adolescence and adulthood into old age, we may find — as a result of brain degeneration, regressive development or asocial withdrawal — a marked reduction in the effectiveness of an individual's biosocial reactions and relationships from his usual level. Indeed, even the behavior of an infant who has achieved little more than nursing skill, and who has acquired a meager repertory of specific reactions to environmental stimulation, may undergo so obvious a reduction in effectiveness as to deserve being called *deteriorated*.

We see deterioration also in persons who have always been *developmentally retarded*,[6] in comparison with others of the same age, sex and social status. For any one of a number of reasons — increased environmental complexity, severe restriction in living conditions, intolerable frustration, systemic illness, injury, cerebral disease or cerebral degeneration — the generally retarded person may at any age exhibit an unmistakable reduction in the level of his effec-

[4] See page 143.   [5] See pages 220–222.
[6] See Chapter 6 for a discussion of *developmental retardation*. It should be noted that, when psychometric measures of deterioration are employed, retarded individuals often *appear* to have suffered deterioration because of the earlier decline of performance in ageing retarded persons. Compare pages 157–159 and 177–178.

tiveness from what it has previously been.[7] In other words, deterioration is not a matter of absolute adequacy, but rather one of a comparison between present and previous level of effectiveness in the same person, as the following examples will illustrate.

(a) *Deterioration in chronic invalidism.*[8] The thirty-two-year-old mother of two half-grown girls complained that, following the birth of her second daughter nine years earlier, she developed a gnawing pain in her back from which she had never recovered. She was given numerous cystoscopic examinations and bladder irrigations; but the pain seemed only to increase in severity and to spread. When perineal complaints became dominant, suspension of the uterus was performed, but without benefit. A few years after this, persistent pain in the left ear was added to the complaints, and eventually there was an operation for mastoiditis, the sequel to which was chronic pain in the area. Four years before the patient was referred to the clinic, pain developed in the left leg which interfered with walking, standing and doing housework. Two years later, gastrointestinal complaints were added — indigestion, bloated feeling, belching, sour eructations, pain in the abdomen, constipation and poor appetite. Repeated thorough examinations by competent specialists failed to disclose organ or tissue pathology to account for the galaxy of complaints which now occupied a greater part of the patient's waking life.

It was not alone the multiplicity of her complaints, however, that led the patient to visit the clinic. It was also her use of them, and the reactions of her relatives toward that use. For, as her preoccupation with her symptoms increased, her concern with the affairs of other persons decreased. She gradually gave up all interest in her friends, in the movies and in community affairs. She devoted herself more and more to rest, diet and medication, to self-observation and self-care. These and her complaints became almost the sole topics of her conversation. Her care of the house, of her daughters and of her husband declined steadily, until the home lost its major functions, and the husband began threatening to break it up.

When the patient refused flatly to cooperate with the clinic in any way, to permit psychiatric or psychological examinations, or to speak of anything but her reiterated symptoms, the husband gave up the home, sent his daughters to a boarding school, and settled a monthly income on his wife. She moved first to an apartment, but she soon found that the work of keeping it up was too much for her. From there she went to a room in a boarding house where, when last heard of, she was living the life of a semirecluse. She spent her time in sparing her strength, ministering to her complaints, occasionally visit-

---

[7] For evidence concerning the effect of hospitalization upon deterioration in retarded subjects, see Cutts, R. A. and Lane, M. O'K., "The effect of hospitalization on Wechsler-Bellevue subtest scores by mental defectives." *Amer. J. ment. Def.*, 1948, vol. 61, pp. 167–182.

[8] For a discussion of *invalidism*, see pages 230–245.

ing physicians, and discussing with everyone she could the state of her health. Thus, in the course of a few years, she had reduced her general effectiveness as a human being from that of a housewife and mother, the center of her home, to that of a homeless and friendless solitary roomer, whose world was bounded by the limitations she imposed upon her own body.

(b) *Deterioration in depression.*[9] A forty-year-old woman developed a depressive illness soon after the suicide of her husband, for which she blamed herself. Previously a social leader and an excellent housekeeper who greatly enjoyed entertaining, she became increasingly withdrawn, silent, asocial, and careless of her person and her home. She was hospitalized when her relatives discovered that she was not eating, bathing, or changing her clothes. Her physicians found her tense, agitated, sleepless, self-accusatory and remote. She complained that she felt "dead inside," that everything around her seemed unreal and artificial, and that everyone hated and despised her for what she was.

For several months this patient grew steadily worse. She seldom spoke, even when addressed, and she rarely carried through the simplest routines of self-care, feeding and elimination, without constant aid. Much of the time she sat methodically pulling out her hair, or tearing her dress to pieces, thread by thread. Sometimes she urinated and defecated on her bed or in the corner, even though a bathroom opened directly off her bedroom. Because of her behavior and appearance, her relatives requested that no one but themselves be allowed to visit her. After a premature return to her home, and then a prolonged stay in another hospital, the patient improved and eventually returned to her premorbid level of social effectiveness.

(c) *Deterioration in schizophrenia.*[10] An unmarried carpenter, aged twenty-three, reacted to chronic unemployment with progressive preoccupation and loss of interest in things around him. Previously a steady worker, when work was to be had, he now adopted a vagrant way of life, drifting from town to town, and supporting himself by doing odd jobs. After a year of this, he was injured in a highway accident and sent back to his home. His mother then observed that his habitual aloofness and reserve had increased into uncommunicativeness and an insistence upon solitude. He never spoke unless spoken to, and even then only after a question had been repeated to him several times. He neither bathed nor shaved, and he let his hair grow long. He ate with good appetite, but irregularly and without regard to what it was that he was eating.

For a year he spent most of his time alone in a room upstairs. Sometimes he took long walks, from which he returned carrying bits of string, colored cloth, pieces of wire and junk, or scraps of metal. These he kept in his room. When his mother forced him to throw his collection out, he threw away with

[9] For a discussion of *depression,* see pages 314–329.
[10] Schizophrenic disorders are described on pages 494–515.

it his carpenter's tools. Occasionally he disappeared for a day or two at a time, and came back dirty, tired and unkempt. He would give no account of his actions. Finally, during three months, he lay almost continuously on his bed, apparently daydreaming. In the hospital, where he was then taken, he showed temporary improvement under insulin shock therapy; but soon afterwards his behavior again deteriorated to the point of marked social incompetence.

(d) *Deterioration in brain injury.*[11] A business executive, forty-eight years of age, received a severe head injury in an automobile collision. After prolonged hospitalization, he was discharged in good condition excepting for one major defect: he suffered from intermittent episodes of violent headache, accompanied by flashes of colored light and attacks of rage. These episodes were usually followed by a variable period of confusion, with inability to concentrate, and with marked irascibility. Medication neither prevented these episodes nor greatly diminished their severity; surgical exploration was refused.

The end-result was that the patient had first to be retired from his lucrative position, and then separated from his family. For on the job his sudden, unpredictable outbursts of temper, and the periods of confusion, made it impossible for him to continue functioning as an executive. He had no better luck at home. There he attempted to supervise the activities of the members of his family, but succeeded only in making everyone unhappy and resentful. To this he in turn reacted with more frequent attacks. A final solution was reached whereby he obtained employment in a shop where his hours were short and his duties relatively simple, and where he could get away by himself in case of an attack. He lived for the most part a restricted life alone, tending to limit his contacts to casual acquaintanceships.

(e) *Deterioration in general paresis.*[12] The patient was a thirty-eight-year-old married man with a long and satisfactory work record as a janitor. About five months before admission to the clinic, it was noticed that he began disregarding his employer's instructions, dawdling on the job and leaving tasks unfinished. As time went on, he became increasingly ineffectual and undependable, he grew angry easily and argued endlessly over trifles.

Three days before admission the patient piled all the furniture in a heap at his place of employment, and then showed himself unable to replace it when he finally agreed to do so. He was thereupon dismissed; but in a little while he returned and would not leave. When finally he went home, the patient could not be dissuaded there from taking up all the rugs, saying that he was going to paint the house. Later he disappeared, and apparently roamed about the streets for two days and a night, talking to himself, before he was picked up,

[11] For a discussion of *brain injury*, see pages 543–546.
[12] *General paresis* is discussed in greater detail on pages 541–543.

confused and disoriented, and sent to the hospital. Upon examination there, he showed the typical neurological and laboratory signs of general paresis. Under treatment he improved; but he did not recover sufficiently to leave the simplified custodial environment of a chronic hospital service.

(f) *Senile deterioration.*[13] The first change noticed in this patient, a sixty-three-year-old insurance broker, was that he was growing irritable and easily angered, whereas he had previously been always amiable and even-tempered. By the time he was sixty-five, the patient had become seriously forgetful; he misplaced things at business and at home, told the same stories over and over, and lost track repeatedly of what he was saying. He showed strikingly poor judgment in a business deal, losing a considerable sum of money as a consequence. He then complained to the state insurance commission that he was the victim of a deliberate plot to cheat him. Next he attempted unsuccessfully to bring suit against his competitors on flimsy and not altogether intelligible grounds.

At home, meanwhile, he was observed to wander about the house at night; but when questioned, he could not give an account of what he was doing or why he was up. Sometimes, especially at night and in the dark, he got lost in his own home and could not find his bedroom once he had left it. Later on, he would get lost on the way home, or on the way from his office to familiar places in the nearby downtown neighborhood. He began accusing others of stealing the things which he had himself mislaid, and once he called in the police to have an employee arrested for the theft of something that the patient had put away and then forgotten.

Eventually the patient could not even recall the names of close relatives. He frequently spoke of dead friends as if they were still living. He wandered from home unless constantly watched, grew careless of his appearance, would not bother to shave himself, and put on his clothes incorrectly or left off essential articles. Finally, he was hospitalized in a restless, confused, disoriented condition, unable to find his way about, unable to recognize day from night, or to remember whether or not he had eaten. It is worth noting that, almost to the end, this patient preserved the learned social forms of courtesy and pleasantness toward others, in spite of his gross deficits. He lived on until the age of seventy-three when an intercurrent infection resulted in his death.

Deterioration and degeneration

Our definition of deterioration, as we have formulated it, is strictly a behavioral characterization; it says nothing about the health or the integrity of tissues and organs. Indeed, as the preceding case abstracts indicate, deterioration frequently develops in persons who are not suffering from organ or tissue pathology, as well as in persons who are. It is therefore essential that

[13] Behavior in *senility* is discussed on pages 546–555.

we make and maintain a clear distinction between behavioral deterioration and biological degeneration. Accordingly, let us at this point define *degeneration* as the *occurrence of progressive ineffectiveness of organs or tissues at a physiological level of description.*

Deteriorated behavior, we have pointed out, is frequently precipitated and sustained by degenerative changes in tissues or organs. In the case of the paretic janitor cited above, for example, it was a massive invasion of the cerebral cortex by spirochaetes, and the inflammatory reaction to this invasion, that reduced the brain's competence as an organ. If the tissue degeneration which results from such an infection is allowed to progress, an obvious behavioral deterioration will sooner or later develop, and the patient will eventually be reduced to complete social incompetence. Should the progress of cortical degeneration be halted, after deterioration has become recognizable, there is usually no further behavioral deterioration and, as the cortical inflammation subsides, a certain degree of behavioral recovery may ensue.

The discovery, some four decades ago, of this comparatively simple and demonstrable relationship between cortical degeneration and behavioral deterioration has unfortunately tended to impede, rather than to hasten, progress in this field. For the behavior pathologists of that period became convinced that all deterioration would ultimately be explicable in terms of neural degeneration, if only the search were continued far enough.[14] The consequence was that, for a long time, the study of deterioration from other points of view was rejected as unscientific and visionary. During the past decade and a half, however, there has developed a growing trend away from these prejudicial attitudes.

We need not leave our example of general paresis to find reasons for the return of interest in a study of deterioration in its own right. For it is well known today that, excepting in the most advanced cases, the severity of cortical degeneration in paresis cannot be accurately inferred from the kind or degree of behavioral deterioration exhibited by the patient. One individual may show relatively good preservation of his usual level of effectiveness, while another individual, with comparable tissue destruction, cannot begin to meet adequately an environment of no greater objective complexity.

The discrepancies between tissue damage and behavior impairment become still more striking when we turn to pathological senility. Rothschild has shown that elderly persons with mild and unimportant behavioral deterioration may be found, on autopsy, to have as severe cortical degeneration as elderly persons whose deterioration was advanced.[15] Within the past two

[14] Some of these studies are reviewed in Cameron, N., "The functional psychoses." In Hunt, J. McV. (Ed.), *Personality and the behavior disorders.* New York: Ronald, 1944, pp. 863–867.

[15] An easily accessible review of this work is given in Rothschild, D., "Senile psychoses and psychoses with cerebral arteriosclerosis." In Kaplan, O. J. (Ed.), *Mental disorders in later life.* Stanford University, Calif.: Stanford University Press, 1945, pp. 233–280.

decades, increasing importance has been given to personal and environmental factors as determinants of progressive ineffectuality in the aged — the patient's premorbid personality organization, his needs and satisfactions, his freedom of action, and the preservation of a familiar but stimulating environment. The fact remains, of course, that if the brain as an organ continues to degenerate, a point will ultimately be reached at which anyone must show behavioral deterioration.

The distinction we have been making between deterioration and degeneration is most important, as well as most unmistakable, when we study behavior pathology in which deterioration is found, but not degeneration. Our first three case illustrations — of chronic invalidism, of depression, and of schizophrenia — belong in this category. The most dramatic examples occur in schizophrenic disorders, where patients often show a marked, progressive decline in effectiveness, even to the point of advanced behavioral deterioration. And yet, if death comes to such a patient through some intercurrent infection or an accident, no consistent brain changes to account for the disintegration can be demonstrated on autopsy.[16] Moreover brain biopsies, made on living schizophrenic persons, fail also to reveal any consistent disturbance in cortical structure.[17] It is clear that, even in severe behavioral deterioration, we cannot confine our search for determinants to the pathology of tissues and organs.

Deterioration and regression

A distinction between deterioration and regression is no less necessary than the distinction we have just made between deterioration and degeneration. The hypotheses of past decades, still current in the literature of behavior pathology, have linked deterioration and regression so closely together as to leave the impression that the two are identical. Schizophrenia, for example, is frequently defined as a "regression psychosis."[18] Its deterioration is then described in terms of a return to infantile fixations, a resumption of intrauterine attitudes and fetal postures, and a reversion to the ways of primitive man. Likewise, pathological senility is equated by some students with *regression*, in the sense of a return to childhood or to prehistoric adulthood; and by the same persons pathological senility is described as obvious behavioral *deterioration* in such a way as to imply that these terms are synonymous.[19]

---

[16] See, for example, Dunlap, C., "Dementia praecox: some preliminary observations on brains from carefully selected cases, and a consideration of certain sources of error." *Amer. J. Psychiat.*, 1923, vol. 80, pp. 403–421; Dunlap, C., "The pathology of the brain in schizophrenia." *Res. Publ. Assn. Res. nerv. ment. Dis.*, 1928, vol. 5, pp. 371–381.

[17] See, for example, Elvidge, H. and Reed, G., "Biopsy studies of cerebral pathologic changes in schizophrenia." *Arch. Neurol. Psychiat.*, 1938, vol. 40, pp. 227–268.

[18] For a contemporary expression of this view, see Fenichel, O., *The psychoanalytic theory of neurosis.* New York: Norton, 1945, pp. 415–424.

[19] For critical studies of this viewpoint, see Cameron, N., "A study of thinking in senile deterioration and schizophrenic disorganization." *Amer. J. Psychol.*, 1938, vol. 51, pp. 650–655; Cameron, N., "Deterioration and regression in schizophrenic thinking." *J. abn. soc. Psychol.*, 1939, vol. 34, pp. 265–270.

Thus we find a confusion in the current use of *deterioration* and *regression* that is not unlike the confusion of deterioration with degeneration, and indeed is similar in origin. For deterioration and regression designate closely related developments which often coincide or overlap. Nevertheless, a differentiation between them must be made, because — just as in the case of deterioration and degeneration — the presence or absence of one by no means necessarily implies the presence or absence of the other. This differentiation rests upon three criteria, which are themselves often interrelated: (1) *inclusiveness*, (2) *duration*, and (3) *severity*.

(1) *Inclusiveness.* We call behavior *deteriorative* when it represents a *general* reduction in a person's effectiveness, even though such a reduction does not necessarily imply relative immaturity at all. On the other hand, we call behavior *regressive* when it represents the recurrence of some more or less *specific* adaptive reaction which characterized an earlier and less mature phase in a given individual's own life history. We also call a more or less specific adaptive reaction *regressive* when it is a new occurrence in an individual's own life history, but belongs to a phase of development considered immature for persons of his age, sex and social status, in his culture.[20]

We have already seen that the case of pathological senility, cited above, underwent striking behavioral *deterioration*, and yet no important *regressive* reactions developed. By contrast, a lonely or a disappointed person may show distinct *regressive* trends without recognizably *deteriorating* from his previously effective level. Thus, a lonely child may revert to thumb-sucking when he goes to bed, a year or two after he has otherwise abandoned this source of comfort; and a disappointed adult may turn to adolescent forms of entertainment which have previously not been present in his repertory. Neither child nor adult, under these circumstances, need suffer a noticeable reduction in general effectiveness. Obviously, if a *regressive development* involves so much of a person's interbehavior that his social competence is seriously impaired, we would call this outcome *deteriorative* as well.

(2) *Duration.* We reserve the term *deteriorative* for a behavioral change downward that is enduring; *regressive* behavior may last only for a few minutes, a few hours or a few days. If, for example, a man who does not habitually engage in dependent behavior, begins to develop pronounced dependence while bedridden, we would call the change *regression.* If, however, this bedridden man should continue indefinitely to be incompetent in his interrelationships with other persons — whether his social incompetence was conspicuously immature or not — then we would call his behavior *deteriorated.* We have already pointed out that anyone is likely now and then to have a day or a week of relative social incompetence.[21] Indeed, so common are minor fluctuations in the general level of effectiveness among normal persons that,

[20] See the definition of *regression* on pages 220–222.   [21] See pages 518–520.

were we to call the somewhat less adequate performance of this or that day *deterioration*, we would reduce the whole concept of deterioration to an absurdity.

(3) *Severity*. One rarely encounters severe *regression* that is not also deteriorative — at least in the adolescent and adult years. The reverse of this, however, is not true. For deterioration may become severe without clear evidence of regressive trends that are more than incidental components of the deteriorative pattern. Our senile insurance broker illustrates this distinction clearly.

The relation between *severity* and *duration* is often simple and obvious. Thus progressive ineffectuality — with the rate of decline held constant — will go further in a longer than in a shorter time. Moreover, the further deterioration goes, as we shall see in the next section, the less become the chances that restitution will occur.

Of course, deterioration will *ultimately* lead to regressive developments if it involves behavior upon which an individual's self-reliance and initiative depend. For then the deteriorating person reaches a level of incompetence that forces him into a dependent relationship with others, just as the situation of a bedfast person compels him to be dependent.[22] This outcome is particularly common when deterioration is sudden, and when it is imposed by arbitrary environmental restriction — as in the case of the displaced aged, of prisoners, and of a considerable proportion of the patients committed to understaffed psychiatric hospitals.

The close relationship between deterioration and regression — their frequent overlapping or coincidence — is now evident. Regressive behavior is commonly a component of deterioration, just as it is also of normal activity under conditions of severe stress or unusual excitement. Moreover, what starts out as regression may proceed to deterioration because of the secondary effects of the regressive developments upon the organization of a person's behavior. For example, the bedridden man, whom we have mentioned above, undergoes deterioration because his regressive reactions are allowed to generalize to so many situations that in the end he develops severe social incompetence. Indeed, as now we turn to the conditions favoring behavioral deterioration, we must reckon the factor of regression among the most important.

Conditions favoring deterioration

(1) *Regression*. It is clear from the foregoing discussion that regressive developments frequently lead over into deterioration. From this it follows that the conditions already described as favoring regression[23] — fixation, deprivation, disorganization, frustration and dependence — may also be preludes to deterioration. In short, if regression is severe or long continued, it can

[22] See page 229.   [23] See pages 226–230.

result in the serious impoverishment or distortion of interpersonal relationships and of self-reactions. This impoverishment or distortion may in turn foster the development of behavioral deterioration, and then help to perpetuate it.

(2) *Withdrawal.*[24] Until recent years, behavior pathology has virtually ignored the important part played by social communication in preserving social competence. Indeed, the endless confusions and fruitless controversies over the relationship of deterioration to degeneration, which we have earlier discussed, are among the many unfortunate products of this neglect. Today, however, it is becoming generally accepted that continued social participation is a necessary condition for the maintenance of optimal effectiveness in the behavior of individuals.[25]

What we call human personality, it must be remembered, is not something that unfolds from within, as it matures, like a maturing plant. It is an exceedingly complex organization of kinetic behavior, the resultant of countless social interactions with other like individuals, occurring against the kaleidoscopic background of our compound culture. It is equally important to remember that human personality organization, as long as it remains effective, never becomes static. It always requires a shifting, dynamic matrix of interbehavior to support and maintain it. Hence, in a socially stagnant atmosphere, the biosocial behavior of a person tends to grow repetitive, stereotyped and automatic.

In rare instances, we have said,[26] an individual seems able to provide, in his own unshared and uncommunicated behavior, a socially valid substitute for the usually essential background of participation and interchange with other human beings. He can play the hermit and still show no loss in social effectiveness when he comes out of his retirement. But ordinarily, the social isolation resulting from withdrawal deprives a person of the stimulation and the behavioral support of others, to which he is accustomed, and upon which his personal adequacy depends. Social isolation, therefore, favors a reduction in an individual's general effectiveness and may lead to serious behavioral impoverishment and distortion.

(a) *Retirement deterioration.*[27] Some of the commonest examples of deterioration following withdrawal are to be found among those who, with or without their consent, are suddenly retired from business, profession or home-making. The critical factor in the development of *retirement deterioration* seems to be the abrupt loss of a person's sources of organized stimulation, around which his daily routines have been built. These sources include the supporting structure

---

[24] Compare the discussion of *withdrawal* on pages 230–245 and 484–491.

[25] See pages 132–134 and 480–481.

[26] For a further discussion of this topic, see pages 482–483.

[27] See Cameron, N., "Neuroses of later maturity." In Kaplan, O. J. (Ed.), *Mental disorders in later life.* Stanford University, Calif.: Stanford University Press, 1945, pp. 143–186.

of a stable work environment, and the intermittent challenges that are raised by new incidents appearing against a familiar, dependable background. They include also the predictable reactions of a person's associates to his behavior, and the patterns of organized self-stimulation which are made up of one's own habitual behavior-sequences, and one's reactions to these behavior-sequences.

In the face of such far-reaching losses, the obvious alternative to deterioration is that of reorganizing one's life so as to provide a new foundation to support new activities and untried personal interrelationships. But the difficulty is that retirement comes to most men and women relatively late in life, when they are least able to effect sweeping reorganizations in their life patterns.[28] Thus they are deprived of the conditions they need for maintaining their social competence — a familiar environmental design and the predictable interactions with other persons, which together have formed the stable framework for their own activities in the past. It is under circumstances such as these that the ageing retired man or woman loses his grip and enters upon a phase of deterioration, or shows a sudden acceleration of an already manifest reduction in general effectiveness. In neither case, do we have evidence that the change can be ascribed to a correspondingly sudden increase in cerebral degeneration.

(b) *Invalidism*. A general reduction in the effectiveness of a person's biosocial behavior and his interpersonal relationships is sometimes the outcome of withdrawal into chronic invalidism. Thus, the chronically ill or disabled patient may adopt the life of a recluse and in consequence undergo behavioral deterioration.[29] The patient, whatever his diagnosis, may devote so much time and attention to the care of his body, to its protection and treatment, that he loses contact with others, and restricts severely the scope of his own interests.[30] Under these conditions, the opportunities for engaging in participative activities with other persons diminish and may eventually disappear, while the social personality organization undergoes a corresponding impoverishment and distortion.

(c) *Isolation*. As we have elsewhere indicated,[31] if for any reason a person is cut away from adequate communication with other individuals — whether the isolation is imposed upon the person or is self-imposed — his behavioral organization is likely to deteriorate with the passage of time. In prisons, dis-

---

[28] Fried, E. G., and Stern, K., "The situation of the aged within the family." *Amer. J. Orthopsychiat.*, 1948, vol. 18, pp. 31–54.

[29] See, for example, Barker, R., Wright, B., and Gonick, M., "Adjustment to physical handicap: A survey of the social psychology of physique and disability." *Soc. Sci. Res. Council Bull. 55.* New York, 1946; Landis, C. and Bolles, M., *Personality and sexuality of the physically handicapped woman.* New York: Hoeber, 1942. Compare the discussion on pages 232–238.

[30] This is well illustrated in the case described on pages 520–521.

[31] See pages 484–491.

ciplinary barracks and concentration camps, it is frequently considered as a part of the just punishment of offenders to reduce communication to one-way commands, and to impoverish and distort the intramural patterns of social interbehavior until they bear little resemblance to normal extramural life. The behavioral deterioration induced by such enforced isolation, against the background of a grotesque caricature of a free human society, may be an important factor in subsequent failures to make a permissible social adjustment after release — and therefore a condition favoring recidivism.[32]

We have also seen that social isolation of an extreme degree may develop, not as the result of social neglect, restraint or segregation, but as the direct consequence of a person's own insulating behavior.[33] By the overuse of fantasy as compensation and a refuge, the schizophrenic person, for example, may become progressively more and more unpracticed in social interbehavior. For some time in all patients, and for an indefinite period in many, the fantasy activities can be successfully confined to periods in which social interbehavior with others is not demanded. However, the task of holding the practiced fantasy apart from the reluctantly exercised social operations proves too much for a high proportion of schizophrenic patients.

When fantasy behavior grows dominant, and it can no longer be segregated from social operations, we have one of the prime conditions favoring disorganization. And if it becomes established, behavioral disorganization, as we have seen,[34] leads inevitably to a reduction in the general level of effectiveness of the disorganized individual. Thus we see again, in the important example of schizophrenic deterioration, that progressive ineffectuality can proceed — not only without a corresponding change in the physiological competence of the organism — but also without progressive increase in the absolute complexity of the biosocial environment. The behavioral deterioration, thus begun, may go on almost indefinitely, each reduction in effectiveness leading to the development of further ineffectuality, until an end-stage is reached at which the patient can do virtually nothing for himself.

(3) *Cerebral incompetence.* We have earlier indicated, in discussing the relationship between deterioration and degeneration,[35] that one of the commonest conditions favoring behavioral ineffectiveness is that of cerebral incompetence. The biological basis of interpersonal relationships and be-

[32] Compare the difficulties reported for British prisoners of war returning to their own families. Curle, A., "Transitional communities and social reconnection: a follow-up study of the civil resettlement of British prisoners of war. Part I." *Hum. Relation.*, 1947, vol. 1, pp. 42–68; Curle, A. and Trist, E. L., "Transitional communities and social reconnection: a follow-up study of the civil resettlement of British prisoners of war. Part II." *Hum. Relation.*, 1947, vol. 1, pp. 240–288.

[33] There is some evidence, however, that insulation may be a protection against disorganization and deterioration. See pages 230 and 243–245; and Fisher, S. and Fisher, R., "Value of isolation rigidity in maintaining integration in seriously disturbed personalities." *J. Personality*, 1950, vol. 19, pp. 41–47.

[34] See pages 452–458.   [35] See pages 523–525.

havioral integration includes, as its most important single component, the activity of the brain as an organ. Anything that lowers the competence of the brain, and particularly of the cerebral cortex, places the human organism at a disadvantage in its interactions with the human environment. Of course, from what has been already said about cerebral degeneration, we should not expect the degree of behavioral deterioration to correspond always with the degree of tissue damage present.

It is well-known that individuals differ in the ease and success with which they are able to compensate for sudden or slowly progressive impairment of cerebral function. The margin within which cerebral physiology remains adequate seems to be more generous in some persons than in others. Nevertheless, it is true that no human being can count himself immune from behavioral deterioration, no matter how adaptive and resilient his physiological machinery may have been, how favorable his present environment, or how abundant his personality resources. For, if the cerebral cortex of anyone suffers enough damage, or degenerates sufficiently, then deterioration, like death, must eventually occur. It is for this reason that we have selected, as our principal illustration, the behavioral deterioration which develops in persons suffering from *cerebral incompetence.*

Syndromes of Cerebral Incompetence

The brain as an organ

Much of the behavior pathology in syndromes of cerebral incompetence cannot possibly be understood without some grasp of certain peculiarities of the brain as an organ. For us, the single most important peculiarity is that the brain is immediately and continuously dependent upon a large flow of blood, which must be well-oxygenated. This dependence has a dual source. For one thing, the level of metabolic activity in brain tissue is high, and the brain's oxygen consumption is therefore considerable.[36] And for another, brain tissue has virtually no oxygen reserve; consequently it cannot withstand severe oxygen-deprivation without quickly developing incompetence.[37]

This moment-to-moment dependence has still further consequences which help explain some of the common origins of cerebral incompetence. Because the brain is continuously dependent upon adequate oxygenation, it is highly vulnerable to any change in the oxygen-carrying capacity of the blood — a property of blood which is itself the resultant of highly complex biochemical

[36] Howell, W. H., *Textbook of physiology* (15th ed.; J. Fulton, Ed.). Philadelphia: Saunders, 1946, pp. 848–857.

[37] Nims, L. F., "Anoxia in aviation." *Annual Rev. Physiol.*, 1948, vol. 10, pp. 305–314; Russell, R. W., "The effects of mild anoxia on simple psychomotor and mental skills." *J. exp. Psychol.*, 1948, vol. 38, pp. 178–187.

mechanisms. Moreover, the maintenance of a large blood-flow through the brain makes the brain immediately responsive to innumerable physico-chemical alterations in the blood and its vessels, and therefore in the body as a whole.

Among the most important physico-chemical alterations belong the following: (*a*) changes in blood temperature; (*b*) changes in the concentration of hydrogen ions and electrolytes; (*c*) variations in systemic blood pressure, blood volume and rate of flow; (*d*) fluctuations in food supply and waste removal; (*e*) the introduction of exogenous toxins into the body;[38] and (*f*) the production of endogenous toxins within the body. If any of these alterations results in suboptimal conditions for the brain as a physiological organ, a syndrome of cerebral incompetence is likely to appear. If the changes are marked, and develop rapidly, an acute syndrome will occur. If the changes are relatively mild, and develop slowly, cerebral incompetence may not become apparent for a long time. When it does appear, its early phase may be mild and its progress insidious; or there may occur a sudden loss of compensatory adaptation to progressive change, so that there is an acute and stormy onset.

The physiological dependence of the brain, as an organ, upon its blood supply also implies a reliance upon the integrity of the intracranial blood vessels. When the blood flow in a vessel is obstructed, for example, a reduction in cerebral competence is likely to follow, the severity of which will be related to the size and location of the brain area involved, and to the suddenness and completeness of the obstruction. If a vessel is plugged by a clot formed elsewhere in the body (*embolism*), the onset is likely to be acute and abrupt, while if the clot is formed in the cerebral vessel (*thrombosis*), the onset may be gradual and slow. Similar considerations apply to inflammatory and degenerative vascular diseases such as one finds in cerebral syphilis and cerebral arteriosclerosis. Whatever impairs the physiological performance of cerebral vessels is likely to impair likewise the efficiency of the brain as an integrative organ.

A further important characteristic of the brain deserves brief mention here: the brain is a relatively soft, friable organ suspended by tough membranous structures in a rigid bony case. This situation has two consequences of immediate importance to us. The first of these is that the brain can expand very little — and then only by displacing cerebrospinal fluid and its own tissue fluid, or by interfering with its own vital blood-supply. Thus, an inflammatory process, an expanding tumor, or an accumulation of fluid within the cranial cavity, must sooner or later induce cerebral incompetence. For the effect of increasing intracranial pressure, once the narrow limits of compensatory fluid displacement have been passed, is to force cortical tissues against a bony surface — where they inevitably suffer destruction — and to obstruct the cerebral blood supply through pressure upon the vessels.

The other consequence is that, since the suspended brain is quite movable,

[38] For a partial list of common exogenous toxins, see pages 469–470.

it may suffer serious damage when the head is struck.[39] Sometimes, even in relatively slight head trauma, the brain is thrust heavily against its unyielding bony case, and sustains a crushing or a tearing injury. It may also be torn because of sudden traction along the lines of its attachment to the rigid dural membrane that serves to hold it in place. And, finally, the intracranial blood-vessels may be ruptured, for the same general reasons, so that brain tissue is bathed in blood which damages or destroys it. The comparable effects of skull fracture and of penetrating head wounds do not need special explanation. But whether brain damage comes from head injury, expanding growths, in-flammatory processes, or free blood in contact with brain tissue, the conse-quences are very apt to include at least an episode of cerebral incompetence. In many instances, as we shall see, the incompetence becomes progressive, either because of continued tissue destruction or because the initial damage leads to an irreversible degenerative process.

Acute cerebral incompetence

By *acute cerebral incompetence* we mean *a sudden episode of gross disorienta-tion, defective retentivity, and signs of central nervous system dysfunction.* We may distinguish three syndromes of acute cerebral incompetence which are, in the order of decreasing severity, *coma, stupor* and *delirium.*

Coma is a condition of *maximal* unreactivity short of death. It develops most commonly following a phase of stupor, and just preceding death; and if recovery from coma occurs, it is usually by way of stupor. Coma develops abruptly when there is a sudden head injury — what is popularly called being "knocked unconscious." It also appears abruptly when there is severe blood-loss, overwhelming intoxication — including the products of bacterial infection — cerebral hemorrhage, sudden hypoglycemia, strong electrical stimulation or surgical shock.[40]

Stupor, as a syndrome of cerebral incompetence, is a condition of *relative* unreactivity. It is customary to distinguish between stupor and coma by saying that, whereas in one the patient can be aroused through stimulation, in the other he cannot be aroused. The factors operative in producing coma will, at lower levels and when gradually applied, produce stupor. Neither coma nor stupor, in the sense used here,[41] has been the subject of organized behavioral investigation or of extended clinical study.

[39] Brock, S. (Ed.), *Injuries of the brain and spinal cord and their coverings* (3rd ed.). Balti-more: Williams and Wilkins, 1949.

[40] Hypoglycemia and electrical stimulation are used in the treatment of behavior dis-orders (see pages 591–601).

[41] The term *stupor* is also commonly used in behavior pathology to designate various degrees and kinds of unreactivity found in schizophrenic and depressive disorders, hysteri-cal attacks, mania and panic reactions. This use is often unclearly defined and some-times it is almost meaningless — as when mutism in a mobile manic patient is called *manic stupor,* and when reduced participative activity in an ambulatory schizophrenic patient is called *catatonic stupor.*

The third syndrome of cerebral incompetence, *delirium*, we have already considered in some detail as an example of behavioral disorganization.[42] Unreactivity, we have seen, is by no means characteristic of delirium. Indeed, many delirious patients are almost continuously active; and their behavior shows incoordination, fragmentation and overinclusion. By contrast, the overwhelming cerebral incompetence of coma protects the patient from disorganization, since he remains almost completely unresponsive to external stimulation. The stuporous individual shows disorganized behavior whenever he is aroused, but he quickly relapses into unreactivity as soon as he is left undisturbed, and his behavior is then the same as that of the person in coma. The delirious patient is overtly reactive to external stimulation; but his cerebral incompetence is still severe enough to prevent his maintaining complex attitudes which would support behavioral continuity.

If cerebral incompetence comes on acutely, lasts a few hours, days or even weeks, and then clears up, the development of behavioral deterioration is not a likely sequel. This is the situation that one finds in a large proportion of cases of cerebral intoxication, infection and injury. If, on the other hand, acute cerebral incompetence should result from serious and irreparable damage to the cerebral cortex, or to its projection fibers, there may develop a protracted or permanent reduction in the patient's general effectiveness. Such an outcome, of course, demands that an individual adapt himself to life at a less complex level, or that he restrict the scope of his activities, so that his reduced competence may not bring unnecessary dissatisfaction or danger to him and those around him.

It must never be forgotten that behavioral deterioration following serious, irreparable damage to the cerebral cortex is by no means always the simple direct consequence of reduced cerebral competence. There are always personal factors to be considered, and always the effects upon the patient's behavior of environmental stimulation, opportunity, challenge and restriction. For example, a person with impaired cerebral function may become secondarily anxious, discouraged, resentful or disorganized on the basis of the reactions others give to his changed behavior and to his reduced status. To these factors are almost certain to be added the person's own developing self-attitudes of inadequacy and inferiority.

Such a patient is likely to make half-hearted attempts at biosocial compensation and then give up trying to maintain or to raise his level of behavior. He may develop or reactivate relatively immature, dependent, regressive attitudes which — whether they be hostile, neutral or affectionate — only contribute to his further deterioration. In short, as the following case will illustrate, a person's cerebral incompetence may quickly become static while his behavioral deterioration continues.

[42] For a detailed discussion of *delirium*, with case illustration, see pages 469–477.

A thirty-eight-year-old successful pharmacist suffered a transient right-sided paralysis during the course of a febrile illness from which he quickly recovered. In addition to some weakness in the right hand and leg, the only important residual defect was a tendency to become confused and ineffectual in attempting to perform complex tasks. This meant, among other things, that although the patient could continue waiting on customers, making change accurately and replenishing the shelves as the stock ran low, he could no longer manage his drugstore alone or fill prescriptions.

To this reduction in status the patient reacted with understandable distress. Unfortunately, however, he could in no way be induced to accept his limitations and the losses in neighborhood prestige which they obviously entailed. Instead, he resisted all attempts at curtailing his professional activities until the situation became so grave that it was necessary to hospitalize him forcibly. This procedure the patient considered an unwarranted and a deliberately hostile act. In consequence he refused categorically to recognize or to communicate with his relatives, and to cooperate in any way with the hospital personnel. He became convinced that he was the victim of a plot to deprive him of his drugstore and his liberty. He settled down to an institutional life, reading magazines, playing cards, going to moving pictures, conversing with other patients — occasionally vilifying his relatives and the medical staff — eating and sleeping. He refused to work at anything, including occupational therapy. Fifteen years later his condition remained unchanged.

Progressive cerebral incompetence

When cerebral incompetence comes on gradually, over a long period, there is greater opportunity for compensatory adaptations to develop than there is in cases with a sudden catastrophic reduction or a rapid decline. Thus, even a moderately resourceful person may succeed in preserving behavioral adequacy for a considerable time after he has begun to show reduced retention and recall, decreased attention-span, lowered speed of reaction, and a diminishing grasp of his complex environment. The more resourceful an individual is, and the less anxious and self-demanding he happens to be, the better will be his chances of meeting the challenge of progressive cerebral incompetence, and the slower he will be in developing progressive behavioral deterioration. Nevertheless, a point must eventually be reached at which every person suffering from progressive cerebral incompetence will pass his limits of behavioral adaptability, will decompensate and deteriorate.

Let us begin with a definition. By *progressive cerebral incompetence* we mean *a syndrome of gradually decreasing retentivity, diminishing biosocial adaptiveness, and increasing central nervous system dysfunction.* As in the case of acute cerebral incompetence, we can make predictions as to the general course of the decline — that all persons undergoing progressive cerebral incompetence will ultimately develop certain typical behavioral defects, and that these defects will grow more severe and sweeping as cerebral incompetence increases. But the selectivity of one individual's behavior organization may present a strikingly different picture of deterioration from that of another individual, whose past has been different and whose repressions form a different pattern. Each person expresses his own individuality in the relative ease with which he succumbs, in the general flavor of his behavioral decline, and in the details that characterize his transient improvements and his inevitable relapses.

It is often exceedingly difficult to recognize the earliest phases of progressive cerebral incompetence. Its first signs and symptoms may seem trivial, as little worth noticing as the unimportant variations in effectiveness that everyone shows from day to day or from month to month. After the evidence has accumulated to a point where behavioral decline is obvious, however, it is usually possible to trace it back to its beginnings, months or years before. Sometimes progressive cerebral incompetence follows a sudden attack of confusion, an acute delirium or a convulsion; the subsequent course may be interrupted by further attacks which often appear to hasten the deterioration. Persons whose progressive decline has been slow and gradual may at any point develop a convulsive episode, after which the downward course is likely to show acceleration. Remissions, usually of brief duration, are not unusual in progressive cerebral incompetence; sometimes a remission persists for several weeks or months and, in the rare instance, even for a few years.

The outcome in this syndrome, unless accident, systemic disease or intercurrent infection cuts its course short, is always one of profound deterioration. Indeed, it is in progressive cerebral incompetence that we find some of the most extreme examples of behavioral deterioration. As we shall see later in this chapter, a person may have his biosocial behavior reduced through cortical degeneration almost to a vegetative level. Nevertheless, it is highly important to remember that equally devastating deterioration can also be found in persons who are not suffering from cortical degeneration at all, but from the cumulative and self-perpetuating effects of withdrawal and progressive desocialization.[43]

Defective retentivity is usually the first symptom of progressive cerebral incompetence to appear. The patient begins to complain that his memory is not what it once was. He has increasing difficulty in recalling the names of new acquaintances and of places he has recently visited. He forgets his appointments and the agreements he has entered into with other persons; he has to be reminded again and again to do the things that fall outside his well established routines. He tends to repeat statements he has just made as if he had not previously made them, and to tell stories over and over, with the same circumstantial details, to the same persons. He cannot find things which he has put away, particularly if they are new possessions or if he has put them in

[43] See pages 481–493.

a new place. If he conceals something for safekeeping he cannot recall where it is hidden, and he may even forget that he has ever handled it.

An obvious consequence of decreasing retentivity is that a person grows less and less able to take on new techniques, to make use of new information and develop new orientations. Early in his decline, he may be able to learn a novel procedure, he may welcome new information and achieve some initial reorientation in relation to an unfamiliar situation. But these gains are only temporary. The cerebrally incompetent patient's behavior soon shows little or no trace of his recent acquisitions.

One reason for the resentment which the aged so often express toward innovation is that they cannot effectively retain the changes in behavior which innovation demands. New techniques require new effort each time the elderly person tries them. New information comes and goes. Many scientists in their sixties or seventies, for example, find the time wasted that they spend reading the current technical literature; the old is already familiar, and the new cannot be retained. On a similar basis, the aged often fail to adapt effectively when they are moved away from their accustomed environment; they remain poorly oriented and gain no ease in finding their way about.

The most important consequence of impaired retentivity in progressive cerebral incompetence is that it diminishes the individual's ability to participate effectively in the social operations of his environment. It is inevitable that new elements shall repeatedly appear in the shared field of interbehavior, and that occasionally a situation will arise which is wholly novel in its design. Under such circumstances, the person whose retentivity grows progressively defective must increasingly lose interest in developments with which he cannot maintain adequate contact. In some cases, the relatively incompetent person tends to withdraw,[44] to reject the environment when he can no longer meet its demands, and thus to enter upon a process of desocialization.[45] Such withdrawal, whether or not it leads the patient to incarceration, is likely to hasten behavioral deterioration by increasing his isolation from the shared activities upon which effective personal interrelationships depend.

Most persons who suffer from progressive cerebral incompetence do not simply withdraw and give up trying to engage in participative activity. They try to compensate in one way or another for their damaged retentivity, and they protect themselves as long as possible from a recognition of the severity of their defect. One of the commonest techniques for overcoming the appearance of forgetfulness is that of *confabulation* — making up a likely story to replace what one cannot recall. In advanced cases of cerebral incompetence, where recent memory is almost completely lost, it is possible to elicit every few minutes a different account of the patient's coming to the hospital. A patient will say one moment that he walked over, another moment that his brother

[44] For a discussion of *withdrawal*, see pages 230–245.   [45] See pages 481–484.

brought him in a car, later on that he came by bus, and still later that he has been in the hospital a long time.

Another common technique is that of falling back continually upon *reminiscence*,[46] for the recall of events remote in time is as a rule not nearly as defective as that for recent happenings. This is especially characteristic of the aged who can often impress younger persons with their greater knowledge of a bygone era, and thus to some extent overcome the loss in status which defective recall entails. But, of course, reminiscence is sure to grow repetitive sooner or later, and the raconteur grows tiresome and loses more than he gains by retelling his stories. There is a common belief to the effect that as immediate recall wanes, the remembrance of early events increases in clarity and accuracy. The evidence we have at hand, however, seems to indicate that reminiscence in the cerebrally incompetent suffers from the same defects — although for a long time to a lesser degree — as those which characterize recent recall.

What a patient confabulates and what he reminisces, of course, will depend upon his own personal history. In other words, the patterns of recall, including the distortions and embroidering they exhibit, are characteristic of a given individual — of the things he has lived through and done, of his unique ways of interpreting his surroundings and himself, of his personal problems and the techniques he has evolved in dealing with them. Ultimately, the recall of both remote and recent things becomes grossly ineffectual, and confabulation is no longer well enough organized to fill in the lacunae and complete what is left unfinished in the telling. In everything but the most automatic sequences, a person's behavior grows discontinuous and fragmentary. Nearly all the old behavior patterns disappear, and no new ones can be acquired to take their place. Deterioration has reached a level at which the individual exhibits an extreme of desocialization and disorganization, in covert as well as overt behavior, in fantasy and self-reactions, as well as in shared activity and reactions to other persons.

Progressive cerebral incompetence always includes a decline in the complex functions of symbolization — of language and thinking — along with the decline in effectiveness of other complex integration. This means that communication grows more and more defective and the patient is secondarily cut off from participative behavior. His difficulties in talking oblige him to depend increasingly upon direct action, and this exposes him to frustrations not unlike those which prelanguage children face. If, as in focal injury to the brain, language functions suffer severely while the rest of behavior does not, the patient is likely to find his inability to communicate almost intolerable. Likewise, the person whose thinking is seriously impaired, but whose integra-

---

[46] It should be noted that this use of *reminiscence* in the sense of the recall of long-past events differs from the temporary increase in retention scores with time, sometimes reported in laboratory learning studies, and also termed reminiscence.

tions are otherwise relatively unaffected, is almost certain to encounter endless obstruction and interference which he can neither understand nor accept.

The emotional disturbances found in the cerebrally incompetent, as we have just indicated, are in part the consequence of inevitable frustration. The hardships which such a deteriorating person must endure can be to some extent ameliorated by the precautions that others take to remove unnecessary obstacles, shorten periods of delay, and increase their own skill in interpreting the patient's needs. But emotional problems in progressive cerebral incompetence are also a direct result of tissue degeneration. Thus, even with the greatest of consideration and skill it is impossible to eliminate, and eventually even to mitigate, the patient's emotional dysfunction.

Early in generalized cerebral degeneration, the change in emotionality is usually one of exaggeration; the emotional component of behavior is appropriate to the situation, as judged by a consensus. But tears appear where formerly there would have been only mild sympathy, and giggling or laughter comes in place of mere smiling. As a person loses his grasp of complex situations, however, he is likely to respond inappropriately by crying over harmless trivialities, and laughing over a minor incident in the presence of others' sorrow. If death does not intervene, and the patient's general behavior becomes dilapidated and disorganized, its emotional components will participate in the severe deteriorative changes. Anger, sorrow, fear and joy will replace each other easily, in relation to relatively minor incidents, and in response to fragments of environmental configurations. Eventually there may be profound apathy, punctuated by brief episodes of laughter, crying and rage.

The loss in retentivity, and the decline in the adequacy of symbolic and emotional components, are changes of the highest importance in progressive cerebral incompetence. But they are, nevertheless, only parts of the more general deteriorative picture. The person suffering from cerebral degeneration shows sooner or later a noticeable reduction in his ability to maintain the level of social organization which has previously characterized his behavior. As time passes, he loses the skills upon which competent communication depends, just as he loses also many of his mechanical skills. The business man, the factory worker and the housewife become alike inefficient, negligent and uncomprehending in relation to their accustomed work routine. They grow careless about their appearance and often uncritical of their own behavior. Many of them, because of the press of environmental stresses and the reduction in their own resourcefulness, show themselves unable any longer to cope with their personal conflicts, antisocial impulses, or asocial trends. Consequently, in a setting of cerebral inadequacy, they develop one or another of the common behavior disorders.

Behavior Disorders in Cerebral Incompetence

The development of cerebral incompetence clearly increases the likelihood of behavior disorder; but it does not in itself completely account for the occurrence of the pathological behavior. Neither does cerebral incompetence determine the precise pattern of the pathological reaction which an individual shows. It was at one time believed that for each etiological agent — toxic, infective or degenerative — there was a specific, predictable behavior disorder. Thus, a syndrome of acute cerebral incompetence which grew out of bromide poisoning was thought to have delusional and hallucinatory characteristics that distinguished it from one growing out of alcoholism; this distinction was attributed to the chemical properties of the different toxins.

A number of clinical studies indicate that this older belief is unfounded. Wolff and Curran,[47] for example, reported the presence of twenty-seven different etiological agents in 106 cases of delirium. No specific relationship could be demonstrated between the character of the behavior and the nature of the etiological agent. On the other hand, the behavior of patients who had suffered more than one delirious episode was characteristic for a given individual, even though the etiological agents in successive episodes were different. Two of their patients had previously developed behavior disorders and recovered from them; in each case there was essentially the same delusional and hallucinatory picture during the non-delirious, stress-induced episode as during the delirious one. Cameron [48] has cited two cases, one of which developed a manic attack during acute bromide intoxication and later showed the same behavior pathology under stress without intoxication. The other became manic the first time in a setting of acute economic insecurity, and many years later again became manic in an acute delirium following an operation and heavy sedation. Pfeffer,[49] in a report on withdrawal effects in morphinism, states that patients developing delusions and hallucinations in a schizophrenic-like disorganization were known to have been schizophrenic before the institution of therapy for morphinism. The great majority of patients under such treatment neither hallucinated nor developed delusions.

It is the fundamental behavior organization of the individual — the unique product of his past activities and his present situation — that determines not only what behavior disorder he will develop, but also the pathological details

[47] Wolff, H., and Curran, D., "Nature of delirium and allied states." *Arch. Neurol. Psychiat.*, 1935, vol. 33, pp. 1175–1215. See also Curran, F., "A study of fifty cases of bromide psychosis." *J. nerv. ment. Dis.*, 1938, vol. 88, pp. 163–192; Levin, M., "Transitory schizophrenias produced by bromide intoxication." *Amer. J. Psychiat.*, 1946, vol. 103, pp. 229–237; Levin, M., "Bromide psychoses, four varieties." *Amer. J. Psychiat.*, 1948, vol. 104, pp. 798–800.

[48] Cameron, N., *The psychology of behavior disorders.* Boston: Houghton Mifflin, 1947, pp. 557–559.

[49] Pfeffer, A., "Psychosis during withdrawal of morphine." *Arch. Neurol. Psychiat.*, 1947, vol. 58, pp. 221–226.

within his disorder. In acute cerebral incompetence, the disturbance in brain function must be regarded as a non-specific precipitating agent, comparable to externally applied stress.[50] In progressive cerebral incompetence the patterns of behavior disorder are similarly determined. There is a steady decrease in the efficiency of the brain as an organ until a point is reached beyond which the individual can no longer compensate for his growing deficiencies. He then reacts to his present difficulties with behavior that we call distorted, impoverished or inappropriate, just as he might have done under conditions of intolerable stress or conflict, without cerebral damage. And the specific behavior disorder that emerges in either situation is an expression primarily of the individual, not of the precipitating agent.

Thus, for example, three men in general paresis suffer comparable invasions of the cerebral cortex by spirochaetes; but one of them develops a profound depression, the second becomes seriously paranoid, and the third grows manic or severely hypochondriacal. Even the particular delusional convictions that each develops will reflect individual, personal trends; the delusions will not correspond to some special distribution of spirochaetes in the cortex. Furthermore, in the aftereffects of head injury and in senile degeneration, as we shall see, it is neither the location nor the extent of the cortical damage that determines the character or the severity of behavior disorder, if behavior disorder develops. These are determined by the individual's premorbid reactions to internal and external stress, and by the efficiency with which he has previously managed environmental pressures and private conflicts. Let us now consider three examples of cerebral damage — in general paresis, in head injury and in senile degeneration — and examine the behavioral deterioration in each.[51]

Behavior disorders in general paresis

General paresis is an encephalitis, with an accompanying meningitis, which develops as a reaction to the invasion of cortical tissue by the spirochaete of syphilis. While the invasion may be quite general throughout the cerebral cortex, the areas most seriously affected are usually the frontal and parietal regions. The tissue reaction is an inflammatory-degenerative one, the pattern of which is quite specific for paresis; the inflammatory process and the degenerative changes as they appear microscopically after death, and the presence of spirochaetes in the cortex, form an unmistakable picture. Moreover, the changes in the cerebrospinal fluid during life are highly characteristic for general paresis, so that it is difficult to make a mistaken diagnosis on the basis of tissue pathology and serology.

The neurological signs and symptoms of general paresis are less specific.

---

[50] For a discussion of this relationship in delirium, see pages 469–472.

[51] A detailed discussion of the delirium of acute cerebral incompetence will be found on pages 469–477.

All of them can be found in other forms of central nervous system disease, in varying combinations, and some of them are common in behavior disturbances that lack underlying tissue pathology completely. Among the commonest paretic signs and symptoms are pupillary changes, tremors of the fingers, eyelids, tongue and facial muscles, speech that is slow and slurred, and writing that is tremulous and often illegible, with omitted and transposed letters, muscular weakness (from which the name *paresis* comes), convulsive attacks and transitory paralyses. The course of the disease in untreated cases is one of relatively rapid decline; death occurs usually within two or three years of the onset of recognizable signs. Sometimes the progress of cerebral degeneration is interrupted by remissions, the reasons for which are unknown.

The behavioral changes in general paresis are by no means specific. In typical cases, the clinical picture is one of progressive cerebral incompetence, with an insidious onset and a gradual development, punctuated occasionally by an episode of non-specific excitement during which the patient may be highly dangerous to himself and others.[52] But the most challenging aspect of paresis for the behavior pathologist is that there is at once a high incidence and a great variety of behavior disorder in it. No other encephalitis can rival paresis in this respect.

It was at one time taught that general paresis was characterized by elated, expansive excitement, and that the clinician could recognize a paretic by his delusional grandiosity. As a matter of fact, the clinician who relied upon this behavioral criterion would miss the great majority of paretic patients and inevitably include mistakenly a large number of manic patients without cortical tissue pathology. Transient excitements, we have said, are indeed common features in this illness; but these excitements are non-specific, and they are short-lived. The elated, expansive manic picture is found in only a minority of paretics;[53] the rest, if they develop behavior disorder, suffer from depression, hypochondriacal complaints, chronic fatigue, anxiety, schizophrenic or paranoid disorder.[54]

This is only a restatement of something that we have already formulated in relation both to acute and to progressive cerebral incompetence. The cortical inflammation and destruction in general paresis create a condition favoring the development of behavior pathology; but the behavior pathology that emerges reflects the organization of the patient as a person and not the infective process. Schube enunciated this principle in a clinical paper nearly twenty years ago when he said, "The type of psychosis or psychoneurosis exhibited

[52] See the case described on pages 522–523.

[53] Strecker, E., Ebaugh, F., and Ewalt, J., *Practical clinical psychiatry* (6th ed.). Philadelphia: Blakiston, 1947, Chapter 3.

[54] Schube, P., "Emotional states of general paresis." *Amer. J. Psychiat.*, 1934, vol. 91, pp. 625–638; Cheney, C., "Clinical data on general paresis." *Psychiat. Quart.*, 1935, vol. 9, pp. 467–485

[by the paretic patient] is that which the individual would have developed at that time provided syphilis was absent and any other adequate precipitating factor was present." [55] Since that time a great deal of clinical evidence has accumulated in support of Schube's thesis, two examples of which may be cited.

Rothschild and Sharp[56] have reported manic and schizophrenic disorders which developed in a setting of cerebral incompetence, resulting from general paresis. The behavior disorders persisted for years after the complete disappearance of all clinical signs of inflammatory-degenerative cerebral disease. Postle[57] describes four cases of general paresis in patients who had been hospitalized for, and recovered from, previous behavior disorder uncomplicated by cerebral infection. One of these patients had been diagnosed in the earlier illness as schizophrenic, and the other three as manic. When later they developed paresis, each reacted with the same behavior pathology as that which had characterized his previous behavior disorder. Moreover, one suffered two additional episodes of behavior disorder, after his recovery from paresis, and these later attacks repeated the same pattern as the two he had previously had, the one without paresis and the other with paresis.[58]

Behavior disorders in head injury [59]

If, now, we examine the clinical findings in relation to head injury, we find the same general situation. Behavior disorders, when they come in the wake of head trauma, reflect the personality organization of the patient. They show a direct relationship neither to the traumatized area nor to the severity of brain damage. Indeed, as we shall see, behavior pathology which may include considerable deterioration is just as likely to develop in a person with an injured head but an undamaged brain as in one whose cerebrum has contusion or laceration. This is not to say, of course, that there may not be marked deterioration in persons with severe brain injury.[60] The important point is that behavioral deterioration is by no means confined to cases of brain damage.

It is a well-known fact that a person may suffer severe head injury without necessarily sustaining serious brain damage. The elasticity of the skull and

[55] Schube, P., "Emotional states of general paresis." *Amer. J. Psychiat.*, 1934, vol. 91, pp. 625–638.

[56] Rothschild, D., and Sharp, M. L., "Neuropathological features of general paresis in relation to mental disturbance." *Dis. nerv. Syst.*, 1942, vol. 3, pp. 310–316.

[57] Postle, B., "Pattern features and constitutional susceptibility as related to organic brain disease with special reference to general paresis." *J. nerv. ment. Dis.*, 1939, vol. 89, pp. 26–36.

[58] Compare the similar findings in acute intoxication, cited on pages 531–535.

[59] For an account of the clinical symptomatology and tissue pathology in head injury, see Brock, S. (Ed.), *Injuries of the brain and spinal cord and their coverings* (3rd ed.). Baltimore: Williams and Wilkins, 1949.

[60] See the discussion of brain damage on pages 532–533.

the movable fluid around the brain help to distribute the force of a blow. It is also a fact, however, that sometimes a relatively slight injury to the skull results in severe brain damage. The cerebral cortex may be crushed by sudden contact with the inside of the skull, which has many surface irregularities; it may be torn by the pull of its own ligamentous attachments; or a blood vessel may be ruptured, and the bleeding then damages cortical tissue.[61] If brain injury is both sudden and severe, the immediate behavioral effect is that of coma, stupor, or confusion with ataxia, dulling, and amnesia for a period that usually extends to events before and after the accident. Patients who survive serious brain injury as a rule make a rather rapid initial recovery, after which there is a protracted convalescent period before more or less complete recovery ensues.

In many cases of relatively slight brain injury — including those showing no residual impairment whatever — there is likewise an episode of confusion, ataxia, dulling and amnesia. Occasionally there is even stupor or coma ("unconsciousness"). Consequently, the immediate effects of head injury do not provide a reliable index of the severity of brain damage. The most dependable indications of brain damage are to be found in the residual neurological defects which reflect impaired functioning of the brain as an organ. Among these may be mentioned paralyses and muscular weaknesses of cortical origin, spasticity and atony, anesthesias and paresthesias, certain reflex anomalies, disturbances of speech and other coordinations, convulsive attacks and emotional storms.

The distinction between slight and severe brain injury is of considerable importance to an understanding of deterioration. For in this age, head injury is exceedingly common, and the number of persons who have undergone a reduction in the general effectiveness of their biosocial behavior, following head trauma, is very large. The problem this poses for the behavior pathologist is one of determining the degree to which posttraumatic deterioration can be attributed to brain damage, and how much of it is due to personal maladaptation. On the therapeutic side, the residuals of neurological destruction usually offer much less promise of recovery than do the products of need, conflict and anxiety. Thus, even in those cases which show definite neurological residuals, we still face the task of sorting out the signs and symptoms that reflect central nervous system damage, and promise little therapeutically, from those that reflect personal difficulties and may be decidedly worth intensive treatment. A growing interest in this task has appeared during the past few years in the clinical literature, an interest that is directing attention away from the older enumeration of "postconcussional" symptoms, and toward the study of the biosocial organization of persons who suffer head injury.

Headache was for a long time considered to be a prime symptom of brain injury, but clinical studies in recent years have not substantiated this impres-

[61] See the discussion on pages 532–533.

sion. Schaller,[62] for example, reported that this symptom occurred in only 23 per cent of his "postconcussion" cases, whereas it occurred in 97 per cent of his neurotics. Anderson,[63] in a series of chronic posttraumatic head cases, found that all the individuals who did not complain of headache showed neurological residuals of brain injury. Lewis[64] was unable to make an essential distinction between the behavior pathology in what he calls "postcontusional" cases and that of the common neuroses. Headache, according to Ruesch, Harris and Bowman,[65] is not specific for head injury. They corroborate the findings of Schaller and of Anderson that it is less often encountered in patients who show neurological residuals than in those who show none. In other words, we must look for some origin other than brain damage for the origin of this symptom.

Ruesch, Harris and Bowman have made some other interesting comparisons of the complaint picture in head injury cases. In acute head injury, the patients who gave clinical evidence of having suffered brain damage also gave a greater number of complaints than patients without such evidence. The situation is reversed, however, when persons are studied who *continue* chronically to complain. For among these persons one finds that the patients whose head injuries had originally been severe had relatively few complaints, whereas those whose head injuries had been mild had many complaints. And the longer this "postconcussional" or "postcontusional" syndrome lasted, the more numerous and the more diffuse the complaints became. The head injury had evidently furnished many individuals with a focus around which to build hypochondriacal, invalid reactions.

If brain injury is severe enough, a person's integrative behavior is bound to show adverse effects, and his social interrelationships may become relatively inadequate. This is the so-called "personality change" that often follows brain damage.[66] On the basis of their intensive study, Ruesch, Harris and Bowman came to the conclusion that in a large proportion of cases the factor of brain damage appeared to be of secondary importance, while the pretraumatic biosocial organization of the individual was the prime determinant of posttraumatic adaptation. They found that, in most of the chronic head injury patients who lacked neurological residuals, there was no evidence that

---

[62] Schaller, W., "After-effects of head injury." *J. Amer. med. Assn.*, 1939, vol. 113, pp. 1779–1784.

[63] Anderson, C., "Chronic head cases." *Lancet*, 1942, vol. 243, pp. 1–4.

[64] Lewis, A., "Discussion and differential diagnosis and treatment of postcontusional states." *Proc. roy. Soc. Med.*, 1942, vol. 35, pp. 607–614.

[65] Ruesch, J., Harris, R., and Bowman, K., "Pre- and posttraumatic personality in head injuries." In *Trauma of the Central Nervous System*. Baltimore: Williams and Wilkins, *Res. Publ. Assn. Res. Nerv. Ment. Dis.*, 1945, vol. 24, pp. 507–544; Ruesch, J., and Bowman, K., "Prolonged posttraumatic syndromes following head injury." *Amer. J. Psychiat.*, 1945, vol. 102, pp. 145–163; Ruesch, J., "Psychophysiological relations in cases with head injuries." *Psychosom. Med.*, 1945, vol. 7, pp. 158–165.

[66] See, for example, the case abstracted on page 522.

personality changes — in our sense, *deterioration* — could be attributed to the immediate consequences of the head injury itself. The majority of these persons, prior to head trauma, had shown interpersonal behavior that was definitely maladaptive.[67] Many of them seemed to have been chronically dissatisfied prior to their accident, and many were apparently able to gain sympathy, prestige or privilege which they had not previously enjoyed. Denny-Brown [68] questions the possibility of progressive deterioration as a consequence of head injury alone to a previously healthy brain.

Behavior disorders in senile cerebral degeneration [69]

The intricate interplay of biological and social factors in deterioration is nowhere better exemplified than in the cerebral degeneration of old age. We have already made the observation that, if the brain as an organ progressively degenerates, the point must eventually be reached at which behavioral deterioration will become apparent.[70] Nevertheless, excepting in the most extreme cases, one cannot reliably infer the degree of brain degeneration from senile behavior, nor estimate the level of deterioration from a study of the brain after death. The ability to compensate for progressive ineffectiveness of the brain as an organ appears to be a highly individual matter, so that individuals with comparable degeneration may operate at entirely different levels of competence. And of course the corollary of this is also true: that senile individuals, operating at comparable levels of behavioral competence, may differ greatly among themselves in the degree of brain degeneration they have suffered.

Until recent years it has been customary to ascribe all behavior pathology occurring in senile persons to the direct effect of cerebral decay. Thus, when the aged indulged in reminiscence, and depreciated the present, it was taken for granted that this was necessarily a product of diminished retentivity in relation to new happenings. When an old man or woman lost interest in personal appearance, dressed carelessly and drably, or made little effort to keep clean, it was assumed that such dilapidation must come directly from degeneration of the brain. Likewise, the impatience, tearfulness and irascibility that so often characterize the ageing person — the ill-temper, reproachfulness and emotional storms — were ascribed to changes in cerebral cortex and diencephalic nuclei. And as long as these opinions concerning senility prevailed, it

---

[67] H. Kozol comes to a similar conclusion on the basis of one of his clinical studies, "Pretraumatic personality and psychiatric sequelae of head injury." *Arch. Neurol. Psychiat.*, 1946, vol. 56, pp. 245–275.

[68] Denny-Brown, W., "Intellectual deterioration resulting from head injury." In *Trauma of the Central Nervous System.* Baltimore: Williams and Wilkins, *Res. Publ. Assn. Res. Nerv. Ment. Dis.*, 1945, vol. 24, pp. 467–472.

[69] For a detailed description of symptomatology and tissue pathology in senile and arteriosclerotic cerebral degeneration, see Rothschild, D., "Senile psychoses and psychoses with cerebral arteriosclerosis." In Kaplan, O. (Ed.), *Mental disorders in later life.* Stanford University, Calif.: Stanford University Press, 1945, pp. 233–279.

[70] See pages 524–525.

was not illogically concluded that nothing could be done about the aged but endure them and, when the limits of endurance were passed, institutionalize them.

The reason for such prejudicial attitudes toward senile behavior is that they are to some extent based upon undeniable fact. Persons with failing retentivity do resort to reminiscence; an inability to continue carrying out one's accustomed routines does characterize progressive cerebral ineffectiveness; [71] and changes in cerebral cortex and diencephalic nuclei can certainly be the origin of serious emotional disturbances. Indeed, it is an indisputable fact that a great many ageing persons show little or nothing in the way of frank behavior disorder during their progressively deteriorative course, as the following case exemplifies.

A housewife, aged seventy-three years, was brought to the hospital by relatives who found it impossible to give her the care and protection she needed. According to their account, she had been "losing her memory" during the preceding three years; for a year she had evidently shown gross disorientation, especially at night; and for six months before admission she had repeatedly wandered from the house and been unable to find her way back alone.

The day before her hospitalization, the patient had disappeared from home during the afternoon; and, in spite of their frantic search of the neighborhood, her relatives could not find her. That evening she was returned cold, dirty and dishevelled, by the police, who had observed her crossing streets against traffic, apparently oblivious to the danger she was in. She arrived home cheerful and garrulous, unable to tell where she had been, to appreciate her situation, or to understand her relatives' frightened behavior. While preparing for bed, she was only with difficulty dissuaded from climbing out of the bathroom window, which she insisted was the door. These events led to a family conference, the upshot of which was that further attempts at home care were considered to be out of the question.

Up to the age of seventy years, the patient had shown nothing unusual in her behavior. She had gone about her household duties competently, maintained her social contacts reasonably well, and kept her person well-groomed and clean. The first change that anyone noticed was a growing tendency to misplace articles at home, to leave packages in the stores, and to forget the purpose of an errand after she had started on it. The patient accepted these lapses good-humoredly as the forgetfulness that was natural to old age; and the family often joked about "grandma's absent-mindedness." After a few months, however, it became apparent that the forgetfulness was becoming a serious problem. The patient spent so much time searching for misplaced articles that she could not get her housework done, and she was unable to retrace her steps for the forgotten packages because she could not remember what they were or where she had been shopping. Eventually, about a year before admission to the hospital, she had grown incapable of

[71] Allen, E., "Changes in psychology necessitated by involution." *J. So. Med. and Surg.*, 1942, vol. 104, pp. 443–447.

making a tour of the neighborhood without getting lost, or of carrying a day's work through at home without constant prompting and help.

The family decided that the best solution for this situation was to break up the parental home and transfer the patient and her husband, a night watchman, to the home of her son and daughter-in-law and their three children. Here further difficulties arose. It soon developed that the patient could not learn the layout of her new domicile or accept her new role as a subordinate member of the household. She attempted to establish her own routines of housekeeping, ignoring or forgetting the fact that this was not her home, and that it was differently peopled from the one she had recently left. Her searching for lost articles now included not only things she had actually misplaced, but also objects which had been sold or given away when the old home was broken up. She could not remember the location of her bedroom ·or the bathroom, at first in the nighttime but finally in the daytime also. To her harassed daughter-in-law she seemed to be forever calling up or down the stairway for information as to her own whereabouts, or that of an absent article.

The daughter-in-law attempted to meet this exasperating situation by getting the patient to agree to rules which restricted the latter's movements. She was asked, for example, to confine her activities to the living room, bedroom and bathroom, and to limit the number of excursions she made up and downstairs. The maneuver failed for two reasons. The patient had always been an energetic housekeeper. Deprived of this outlet, she now became aimlessly restless. In addition, of course, she continually forgot the agreements she had made. She grew increasingly angry and indignant over the constant reminders she received of her endless transgressions, and countered with boastful accounts of her own housekeeping and disparaging statements about her present surroundings. When quiet fell upon the household, it did not always mean that the patient had fallen asleep; it frequently meant that she had left the house, and a neighborhood search would then begin.

Meanwhile, the patient gave further evidence that she was undergoing general behavioral deterioration. She required a great deal of urging before she would bathe, keep her hair combed, or change her clothing. Sometimes she put on two or more of the same articles, one over the other, and sometimes she came to breakfast with her dress on backwards. She began hoarding all kinds of things under her bed — food, newspapers, kitchenware, ornaments, clothing and toilet articles. When her daughter-in-law or her husband removed these the patient at first resisted and then wept. She became progressively confused with reference to the time of day. For example, she protested at six in the evening that it was "too early for breakfast"; soon after going to bed, she would get up and insist that it was morning; she spoke of getting ready for her husband's return from work when he had just recently left, or while he was sleeping upstairs. Not long after she had finished a meal she would ask when they were to eat, as though she had not eaten for some time.

Eventually, the patient required almost constant watching throughout the day and the night. The routines around which her adult life had been organized disappeared and the structure of her behavior grew unpredictable and unintelligible. She could no longer tell morning from evening. She spoke of its being "January or February" in July, and said she did not want to go out because of the cold. Members of the family and lifelong friends were misidentified and misnamed. She mistook her daughter-in-law once for a nurse she had known decades earlier; she could not remember from one minute to the next the names of her grandchildren; she gave her maiden name as her own and insisted that her married name belonged to her father. She repeatedly announced that she was "going home"; and then when no one was watching, she would slip out and get lost, again and again. It was this, as we have seen, that finally led to her hospitalization.

It was not only the household from which she had been removed that benefitted by the patient's hospitalization. She herself was decidedly better off in an environment where persons like herself set the pace, and she was not required to compete with the healthy, the young and the strong. Within a few weeks the patient had regained much of her former good humor which she had almost completely lost during her year of restraint and contention in her daughter-in-law's house. But the progressive cerebral incompetence from which she was suffering did not, of course, clear up. The following verbatim extracts from her formal admission examination illustrate the disorganization of thinking, the at times skillful and adroit evasion, the flight into generalities, and above all the extraordinary dilapidation which characterize profound senile deterioration. The examiner's questions are indicated, in abbreviated form, in italics.

(*Date?*) Today? I can't make it out, I can't get it. (*Year?*) 1996 or 1998. (*Month?*) Sunday. (*January?*) Yes, sir. (*October?*) Yes. (*March?*) March, April, May, June, January. (*Summer or winter?*) Summer and winter. (*Afternoon or morning?*) Morning! [actually afternoon]. (*Year?*) I can't tell you now. (*Year?*) I guess it's a new year. (*What one?*) Well, last year was a new year, wasn't it? (*Eighteen hundreds?*) No! (*Nineteen hundreds?*) No. (*What is it then?*) I don't go out much, and when I do I keep what I know to myself. I like you and I appreciate your sermons. (*Who am I?*) I don't know your name exactly. I know it's a nice name. (*What do I do?*) You attend to your business, don't you? (*What is my business?*) I'm sure I don't know. What is it? (*I'm a doctor.*) Oh, how nice. (*What am I?*) You haven't said yet, have you? ... (*Year born?*) Eighteen — I know it was eighteen something. (*Eighteen what?*) I'm trying to think. After I get home, I'll think it over and I'll just give it to you. (*When were you married?*) I was twenty-two. (*What year?*) Oh, I'd have to look at the marriage certificate. I'll ask my husband when I get home and find out for sure. ... (*Your boy born?*) Fifth of April. (*Year?*) About 1819 or 1820, or 1920. (*Old?*) He's about 25. He has three children. (*Old?*) Junior's 21, and one girl is about — the girl must be about 19 or 20 by now. ... My son is about 30 or 32, I don't know which. (*How old were you when you married?*) Thirty — ten — twenty-four. (*How many years ago was that?*) About twelve. ...

(*President?*) Roosevelt, isn't it? (*Before him?*) Bryan? (*Before him?*) Hoover. (*Before him?*) It wasn't Cleveland was it? (*Before him?*) That's too hard for me. I used to know all the presidents. . . . (*Civil War?*) It's been a good while. (*Civil War?*) Last year, wasn't it? (*Remember the first World War?*) Yes, I do. (*When was it?*) In the winter time. (*Year?*) Christmas, I think. . . . (*Capital of U.S.?*) I used to know but I can't now. (*Think it is?*) I think it's a nice state. (*What state?*) Yes, sir, the states. . . . (*What were you doing last night?*) Well, I didn't do anything much. I went down to see my father. He's been in the hospital but he's much better now. Now he's home. He makes so much of us girls that I hate to see him go out. He likes your preaching. He was there last Sunday. I fell asleep just before you came in. I like them all. That preacher's a fine man. She said to me just the other day, 'Go around and have a good time.' I said, 'Well, I love him in a way.' He's a church man, and she's a grand girl.

When behavior disorders do develop in aged and ageing persons, one finds that the behavior pathology differs little from that found in young and middle-aged adults. The differences can be accounted for on the basis of waning physiological competence — general as well as neural — of progressive changes in social status which, in our culture, are nearly always in a downward direction, and of an increasing personal realization that one's security, independence and existence can no longer be taken for granted. Individuals vary greatly in their rate of physiological waning; they vary in the real or imagined loss of status they sustain, and in their reaction to threats directed against their security, their independence and their life. Such are the origins of the wide discrepancies that have been in recent years discovered, between cerebral pathology after death and the observed ante-mortem levels of behavior.

Notwithstanding these undeniable facts, it is still true that anatomical degeneration of cortical tissue often plays a highly significant role in the production of behavior pathology during senility.[72] Indeed, under a variety of circumstances, reduced cerebral effectiveness can be in itself sufficient to precipitate a frank behavior disorder in an individual who with adequate brain function might never have developed neurosis or psychosis.

There is a great deal more to the physiological waning of senility, however, than the direct results of cerebral degeneration. One must always take into account the gradual decline in strength and endurance which comes inevitably with ageing,[73] the progressive loss of attractiveness, the diminution in the effectiveness of visceral performance and in the sensitivity of the receptors, the reduction in sexual response, and the increased lability of emotional reactions. Each of these components is capable of making a significant contribution to a person's susceptibility to behavior disorder in old age.

[72] Kahn, E., "Old age and ageing: psychiatric aspects (Discussion)." *Amer. J. Orthopsychiat.*, 1940, vol. 10, pp. 69–72.
[73] See, for example, Miles, W., "Psychological effects of ageing," in E. V. Cowdry, *Problems of ageing* (2nd ed.). Baltimore: Williams and Wilkins, 1942, pp. 756–784.

In the individual case, the relative importance of each component of physiological waning will depend in part upon the role which the corresponding function has played in a person's past life. In part it will depend upon the degree to which the function seems essential for the preservation of one's status and the support of one's personal security. Obviously, the person who has built his adult life upon a foundation of physical prowess and indefatigability will be more likely to develop behavior pathology when this foundation weakens, than will a person who has always been content with a sedentary existence and has welcomed rest. For the latter may easily accept a gradual reduction in strength and endurance since this change merely exaggerates his accustomed trends. But, for the habitually strong and tough, to reach a point beyond which effort and perseverance are no longer sufficient to keep up the usual level of activity, is to come face-to-face with a reversal in the accustomed relationships: more effort brings reduced performance, and perseverance is unavailing. The outcome then is likely to be one of sudden frustration, anxiety, self-depreciation and the expectation of losing everyone's respect and affection.

The ageing man or woman is unusual whose appearance, gait and stance improve as the years go by. To both the more energetic and the more quiescent, a loss in attractiveness to others can become the source of personal insecurity, of self-disparagement and of a withdrawal reaction.[74] This is especially apt to be the case in persons who have relied upon good looks, a pleasing build and a graceful carriage for their acceptance and their self-esteem. The inescapable shrinkage of bone and muscle, the stooped body and the uncertain gait of senility, cannot fail to impress the individual himself with his changed status among younger persons, particularly if those are related to the factors which he himself has set up as his criteria of worth.

Moreover, the emphasis a person habitually gives to any of his own characteristics will find its echo in the attitudes of others toward him. For his associates are almost certain, every once in a while, to express in public some of the disappointment over his decline that a senile person may have been trying to keep from expressing even to himself. When, however, he hears such public expressions he is unlikely to be able any longer to shield himself from a recognition of his senile status.

The senile loss in strength, endurance and attractiveness is not confined to the surface of the body and its frame, or to posture and visible movement. The internal organs, the viscera, participate also in the general decline. They tend to become noticeably less efficient as one ages, to meet increased demands poorly, to recover from stress slowly, and to require more consideration than they have earlier in life. For the individual who has never thoroughly taken his visceral performance for granted — giving his internal organs too much

[74] Atkin, S., "Old age and ageing: the psychoanalytic point of view (Discussion)." *Amer. J. Orthopsychiat.*, 1940, vol. 10, pp. 79–83.

thought, or too strongly insisting upon their robustness — a reduction in visceral competence, and the appearance of even the most unimportant signs of dysfunction, may precipitate severe overconcern, chronic watchfulness and anxiety, and perhaps lead to a withdrawal into chronic invalidism.[75]

Among the sense-organ defects that senility commonly brings, the most important clinically are those involving vision and hearing. To become half-blind or half-deaf is to lose the chief sources of pleasure in the company of other persons, to be barred from a large part of recreation and entertainment, to be deprived of the comfort of reading and the distraction provided by moving pictures and radio. It means to be restricted in the scope of one's activities and limited in one's resources, even when alone. And, perhaps most important of all, failing sight and hearing cut off the most important avenues of interpersonal communication, make participative activity more and more difficult, and isolate the aged from the interests, pleasures and hardships that they have in the past shared with others. The motives of those around the senile person become difficult to interpret, because he has lost the means for checking his inferences in terms of social interaction. Hence he may become secondarily querulous, distrustful and asocial, and in this way set the stage for paranoid or depressive developments.

Lability of emotional responsiveness and reduction in sexual competence, both of which are characteristic of old age, may open the way to behavior pathology. The joys and sorrows of everyday living may bring an exaggeratedly expressed and prolonged reaction from the senile person. His own self-reactions, as well as the reactions of those around him, are likely to impress upon him the unusual character of his behavior. He may find it difficult to acknowledge the alteration, and if he succeeds in acknowledging it, this may arouse anxiety in him because it implies a decline and suggests the approach of invalidism and death. Emotional lability, if it persists and increases, will at the very least bring home to a person that he is unable to conform to cultural expectations and perhaps lead him to regard himself as one whose behavior is no longer under his own control. This, in turn, lessens his self-esteem and lowers the opinion in which he is held by relatives, friends and business or neighborhood associates. It is the rare man or woman who does not detect such signs of his loss in emotional equilibrium and social respect; and it is only the unusually secure or unusually obtuse who can withstand the presentation of this evidence of decline with equanimity.

The reduction in sexual competence and satisfaction, like other losses in senility, will have effects upon the individual which are commensurate with his prior dependence upon his sexuality for pleasure, status and self-esteem. Likewise, the senile person who suffers the reduction is likely to meet it as he has met other disappointments — with stoicism, indifference, sullen resent-

[75] See the discussion of withdrawal into invalidism, pages 230–242.

ment, self-depreciation or overcompensation. Stoicism and genuine indiffer-ence present no problem. Resentment, in this as in other areas, may give rise to bitterness and enmity toward others which generalizes to include far more than sexual behavior; and self-depreciation on a sexual basis will tend simi-larly to spread to general self-disparagement. If refuge in autoerotism is sought by either the resentful or the self-depreciatory person, the result may be a rearousal of guilt acquired earlier in life; [76] and this in its turn may in-crease resentment and lower self-esteem.

These aspects of physiological waning and many others, favor the develop-ment of behavior disorders in senile deterioration because they reduce in one way or another the individual's ability to make, maintain and renew adequate personal interrelationships. Some reduce his vigor and injure his pride; others weaken his faith in the organs upon which he knows his life literally depends. Some damage or destroy the machinery upon which the most highly developed social interbehavior depends — the visual and auditory systems — and others bring changes that lower his standing in his own eyes, and the eyes of those around him.

The senile patient, who faces such problems, differs from the younger person who meets comparable ones, particularly in the fact that in old age there is little opportunity for adequate compensations to be developed. This is partly a consequence of the same factors which give rise to the defect or deprivation. The senile individual who declines in strength and endurance is more likely than an ailing younger person to be suffering also reductions in visual and auditory acuity. He loses his attractiveness at a time when it is harder than ever before in his life to find friends his own age, or to make friends with unlike-aged persons. He becomes emotionally unstable when he is less well tolerated by others anyway,[77] and he loses sexual competence during the same period in which he is most likely to lose the companionship and comfort of his sex partner. In our contemporary American culture, there is no other period of life that promises greater insecurity and offers as little reward. And yet senility is just the age in which it is biologically most difficult to learn new ways of living to replace the ways that are disappearing.

In stressing the biological aspects of senility, we have erected a kind of frame within which anyone must work who seeks to understand the inescapable limi-tations that old age implies, or who hopes to utilize or modify some of the mod-ern therapeutic procedures which have been developed largely in relation to adolescent and adult behavior pathology. But when one has understood the inevitability of physiological waning and the concomitant reduction in adapta-

---

[76] Hamilton, G., "Changes in personality and psychosexual phenomena with age," in E. V. Cowdry, *Problems of ageing* (2nd ed.). Baltimore: Williams and Wilkins, 1942, pp. 810–831.

[77] Henry, J., "Anthropology and psychosomatics." *Psychosom. Med.*, 1949, vol. 11, pp. 216–222.

bility, which senile persons show, he has understood only the more pessimistic half. The other half, which deals with the restrictions placed upon old people by convention,[78] the opportunities denied them by tradition, and the personal reactions to these restrictions and denials, gives us quite a different picture. For, although we must accept the fact that biological decline is inescapable, we need not, unless we wish, adopt a similar attitude toward the prohibitions and prejudices of our own society — since these are by no means irremediable.[79]

Most persons as they grow old must face the loss of their economic independence and their social status.[80] Only a small minority can look forward to retirement on more than a bare subsistence level; and that means, of course, at least partial dependence upon the charity and sufferance of others. Parents must eventually give up the freedom of their own domicile and accept housing from their grown children. Or they may be separated, and each deposited in a home for the aged, where they are placed according to sex and mobility, and not according to their previous life patterns. Under either circumstance, the ageing person is no longer able to lead his own life, to make the kind of decisions, exercise the authority or shoulder the responsibilities characteristic of the mature adult. He is reduced, in other words, to the level of a child dependent upon the good will of stronger persons who now control all his sources of gratification. A great deal of the childlike peevishness, the irascibility, querulous complaining, and the accusations of ill-treatment so often found in old age, seems to be the consequence of such enforced dependence and its attendant loss of social dignity.

The loss in social status comes not alone from economic dependence and waning authority, but also from the fact that for the great majority of old people there is no useful place. And status in our society is closely tied to usefulness. It is inevitable, of course, that older persons shall be supplanted eventually by younger ones with more vigor and resourcefulness; and to anyone who has courted dependence or idleness, this need bring little hardship. But for the factory worker, farmer or business man accustomed to earning his own way — and for the housewife who has organized a stable home around her own abilities and her person — the consequences of an imposed uselessness, with the depreciation this entails in the eyes of others, can lead to behavior pathology. The disorder thus precipitated may be exceedingly resistant to therapy, and may itself hasten senile deterioration.

[78] Lawton, G., "Psychological guidance for older persons." In E. V. Cowdry, *Problems of ageing* (2nd ed.). Baltimore: Williams and Wilkins, 1942, pp. 785–809; "Ageing mental abilities and their preservation." In G. Lawton (Ed.), *New goals for old age.* New York: Columbia University Press, 1943, pp. 11–33.

[79] Kaufman, M. R., "Old age and ageing: the psychoanalytic point of view." *Amer. J. Orthopsychiat.*, 1940, vol. 10, pp. 73–79.

[80] Piersol, G., "The problem of ageing." *Bull. N.Y. Acad. Med.*, 1940, vol. 16, pp. 555–569.

The burdens imposed by social restrictions and denials conspire with the disabling effects of biological decline to increase frustration in senility, and build up tensions of unsatisfied need and unresolved conflict. The mere fact that an old man or woman discovers that a lifelong hope is now dead, or an accustomed satisfaction now beyond attainment, does not mean that the longing disappears or the need is quenched. On the contrary, the hopelessness of the situation may make longing more insistent, and the withdrawal of satisfaction is more than likely to intensify the need. Moreover, the lack of consummation, with its tension-reduction, coming at a time when cerebral competence is decreasing, may lead to the rearousal of old needs and old conflicts — to the "return of the repressed" — which had previously been handled adequately by compensation and repression.

The chief reactions of senile individuals to increased and protracted frustration are the same as those a younger person gives: aggression and withdrawal. Sometimes, especially when cerebral competence is low or limitation of action extreme, aggression follows childish patterns which, after all, no one ever completely loses. Resistance, spite reactions, threats, sulking and temper tantrums may appear; their object, as in younger persons, may be the direct source of frustration, or it may be someone or something else to which the aggression is displaced. The aged also make use of their infirmities aggressively, both to achieve a goal otherwise unattainable and to arouse anxiety and guilt in others, and so punish them as the authors of frustration. In a similar way they may use their own inflexible routines ritualistically to cramp the freedom of younger persons, and so gain vengeance; or in a chronic depressive reaction destroy the peace of those with whom they live, by an endless reiteration of personal worthlessness and general ruin.

In the senile, as in younger persons also, withdrawal is less troublesome to others than overt aggression; but for the ageing individual, continued isolation is almost certain to have far more serious implications. As we have earlier seen, even in the absence of withdrawal the progressive cerebral incompetence of senility makes it more and more difficult for the aged to maintain their presenile levels of socialization. If, under these circumstances, a person is allowed or encouraged to develop behavioral insulation, his deteriorative trend is sure to be accelerated. Before long, the therapeutic task of replacing social incompetence with socially adequate behavior becomes extraordinarily difficult; if the process is allowed to continue, the deterioration, in the presence of a relatively incompetent cerebrum, may become irreversible.

18

Therapy in Behavior Pathology

The behavior pathologist today has at his disposal a large and growing body of clinical observation, experimental findings and empirically derived theory, which enables him to understand the development and persistence of pathological reactions. His knowledge would have little more than academic significance, however, if it did not also point the way toward effective methods of therapy. For when a patient who is anxious, confused, depressed, aggressive or desperate, comes at last to the consulting office or hospital, it is not enough for us to be able to chart the paths that have led him to his illness. We must be able also to map with him the roads leading toward biosocial health.

The therapeutic task in the field of behavior pathology is not an easy one. Pathological reactions are not readily replaced by socially appropriate behavior. Patients who have acquired behavior pathology can seldom be tutored, cajoled or persuaded into more effective ways. Nor does verbal communication alone — the formulation and discussion of reactions, in words, by patient and therapist — guarantee enduring changes in behavior. Therapy is a great deal more than this. It involves a carefully planned personal interrelationship, between a patient and a highly trained therapist, and often between patient and other patients, and other trained workers also.

It is within such an interrelationship that a patient can gain practice in the role-taking and the shift of perspective, in the formulation and the sharing of self-reactions, and in the social interchange in which he has remained ineffectual.[1] Therapy demands the active participation of a patient, not only in talk and discussion, but in emotional behavior as well. And it is successful only to the degree that the attitudes and responses, which a patient acquires in the therapeutic situation, generalize to other social situations of which he is a part, and persist as a relatively stable constituent of his behavioral repertory.

[1] See pages 114–122.

Just as there are many different routes by which patients arrive at their pathological reactions, so there are many ways which lead from pathology to socially valid behavior. No therapist can prophesy exactly what steps a given patient will take in the course of his resocialization, or even how far he will be able to progress toward normal behavior. Patients are never theoretical types or hypothetical systems. They are always human beings with their own dynamic patterns of need and frustration, of hope and anxiety, of special apathies and selective sensitivities. No one therapeutic approach is suitable for all patients. Neither, of course, is the success obtained with one approach proof that other approaches might not have been equally successful with the same patient.

Both theory and pragmatic test determine the variety of therapy employed with a given patient. At any one time, the prevailing view of the nature of behavior pathology supports certain therapeutic procedures and not others. The theory that evil spirits caused behavior pathology, for example, once justified exorcism as a therapeutic method.[2] The prevailing view today, that maladaptive social learning leads to pathology, supports therapies which involve relearning in an interpersonal situation. But there are a great many important therapeutic techniques which are used simply because they seem to work. The reasons for their effectiveness may be obscure, and the explanations advanced to justify them conflicting; but the fact remains that these techniques appear to bring desirable changes in social behavior. And for the practicing therapist, whose goal is an increase in his patient's social effectiveness, the fact that a given therapy brings improvement is far more significant than is its relationship to a particular theory.

It is for these reasons that the most conspicuous feature of contemporary therapy in behavior pathology is its diversity. Indeed, so diverse are the current views of treatment that we cannot accurately speak of contemporary therapy unless we specify in addition whether we mean office or hospital treatment, individual interview or group interaction, pharmacological assault, electrical shock or surgical interference. Even within each of these classes we can identify further varieties of therapy. Individual interviews, for example, may or may not involve free association, dream analysis, hypnosis, face-to-face discussion, or advice and direction. Therapeutic assault may range from the chemical induction of narcosis to the production of convulsions by insulin, metrazol or electroshock; or it may consist of permanent and irreversible brain damage, such as that which follows surgical lobotomy and lobectomy. Hospitalization may mean only a protective custody, which relieves the patient's friends and relatives, but favors his own progressive deterioration;[3]

---

[2] For reviews of the history of therapy in behavior disorder, see Appel, K. E., "Psychiatric therapy." In Hunt, J. McV. (Ed.), *Personality and the behavior disorders*. New York: Ronald, 1944, pp. 1107–1110; Zilboorg, G., *A history of medical psychology*. New York: Norton, 1941.

[3] Compare pages 529–531.

or it may provide an opportunity for sharing and social interaction which leads toward his recovery.

Although we cannot speak of a single variety of procedure that fairly represents contemporary therapy, we can identify certain emphases which distinguish present-day treatment from older therapies. For one thing, contemporary therapy is concerned with the individual patient as a socially effective person. Behavior pathology, as we have seen, is never restricted to one system of the body or to one area of behavior. It is always the product of broad patterns of need-satisfaction sequence, of stress and frustration, and of inappropriate adjustive techniques which flavor all aspects of the patient's social life. Consequently, treatment in behavior pathology is not restricted to one system of the body or to one organization of reactions. It encompasses the patient's total behavior, and in so doing it shifts the therapeutic emphasis away from the isolated organ and body part, which characterized earlier approaches, toward treatment of the patient as a person.

At various times in the history of behavior pathology, for example, therapy has been directed toward the patient's *symptoms*. During the eighteenth and nineteenth centuries, hysterical paralysis, seizure and amnesia were successfully relieved by hypnosis and other suggestive therapies.[4] At the same time, threats, restraint and frightening punishments were employed to quiet agitated or refractory patients.[5] Similarly, the apathy or stupor of withdrawn, desocialized patients is today sometimes interrupted by the persistent efforts of nurses in coaxing, encouraging and otherwise stimulating a patient to activity. Such procedures as these are directed toward the specific symptoms of behavior pathology. If, however, they go no further than the relief of paralysis, the reduction of excitement or the increase in general activity level, these procedures emphasize part-reactions at the expense of the total individual.

Contemporary behavior pathologists employ such symptomatic treatment chiefly when it is a necessary preliminary or adjunct to more intensive therapy. Sometimes therapy aimed at symptom-alleviation serves to interrupt a circle of self-perpetuating pathological behavior.[6] Thus a patient whose inactivation, excitement or stupor prevents him from participating fully in a therapeutic relationship may be able to begin his new social learning only after his symptoms have become less severe. Or a patient's symptoms may frighten or repel others in his social field and thus bar him from everyday social participation

---

[4] See, for example, Bernheim, H., *Suggestive therapeutics: a treatise on the nature and uses of hypnotism* (Trans. by C. A. Herter). New York: Putnam, 1900; Mesmer, F. A., *Précis historique des faits relatifs au magnetisme-animal jusqu'en en avril 1781.* London: 1781; Braid, J., *Neurypnology: (Braid on hypnotism)* (A. E. Waite, Ed.). London: George Ridway, 1899.

[5] Zilboorg, G., *A history of medical psychology.* New York: Norton, 1941, pp. 286–292.

[6] See pages 75–79.

until they lose their prominence. In such instances as these, symptomatic relief is a necessary preliminary to behavioral reorganization; but the patient as a total individual is still regarded as the focus of therapy.

Now and then in the history of behavior pathology, specific therapies have been prescribed for specific *diagnostic groups*. Neurasthenia, for example, was at one time considered the consequence of life in a highly competitive society which brought overexertion, fatigue and malnutrition.[7] Treatment of neurasthenia accordingly consisted in removing the patient from competitive situations and providing him with rest and high caloric diets. Not long ago, certain forms of behavior pathology were considered to be the simple consequence of particular toxins, and treatment was aimed at neutralizing the toxic substances involved. Thus, certain specific hallucinations were at one time attributed to specific intoxicating agents, such as alcohol and bromides.[8] As a result, treatment of the hallucinatory disorder was limited to elimination of the toxin, and little or no attention was paid to the personal factors involved.

Today the patient's official diagnosis affects the choice of therapy much less specifically than does the patient as a person, regardless of his diagnosis. There are many reasons for this change in emphasis. We have already seen that our contemporary diagnostic categories are necessarily arbitrary, and that they mask many similarities which are to be found in the reactions of patients who are grouped in widely separated classes.[9] When we come to know our patients well, we discover that their troubles stem from unsatisfied needs and persistent conflicts, and these in themselves do not differ sharply from one diagnostic group to the next. It is rather the particular patterns of reaction-sensitivity and the characteristic adjustive techniques, all of them products of social learning, which distinguish the patient in one diagnostic category from the patient in another.

Just as symptom-alleviation may be an important preliminary to intensive therapy, however, so a diagnosis may point toward therapeutic procedures which are secondary but still important. A diagnosis of depressive disorder, for example, at once alerts a competent staff to the dangers of self-injury or suicide, and demands the immediate and vigilant application of measures to protect the patient from himself. A diagnosis of manic excitement demands that similar steps be taken to protect the patient from the embarrassment, humiliation and reduction in status which may follow if he is permitted to become a public spectacle in his community. A diagnosis of paranoid disorder immediately raises the possibility that a patient may need protection from the consequences of his own unwise or unrealistic behavior. There is also an equally strong possibility that society may need protection from the retaliation

---

[7] Beard, G., *A practical treatise on nervous exhaustion (neurasthenia), its causes, symptoms, sequences and treatment.* New York: Wood, 1880; Mitchell, S. W., *Fat and blood* (8th ed.). Philadelphia: Lippincott, 1900.

[8] Compare the discussion on pages 426–433.   [9] See pages 7–9.

which a patient may attempt for real or fancied wrongs. Important as these specific therapeutic procedures may be, however, they are still preliminary to more inclusive therapy.

Varieties of Contemporary Therapy

The general principles of social learning which underlie both the development and the treatment of behavior pathology can be translated into specific therapeutic techniques in many different ways. Some therapists, for example, emphasize a close personal interrelationship between patient and therapist — an interaction which resembles in some respects the parent-child relationship within which the patient may have acquired his pathological reactions. Others specify the patient's self-inaccessible attitudes and responses as the central focus of therapy. Their procedures, consequently, aim to make accessible to the patient the reactions which he has repressed, but which are still important constituents of his distorted or impoverished behavior organization. Still other therapists stress the necessity for direct practice in sharing, role-taking and shifting perspectives in a planned group situation. Those therapists who deal primarily with persons suffering from sweeping pathology — patients who are mute, withdrawn, severely disorganized or highly excited, for example — often concentrate their efforts on chemical and electrical shock, or surgical procedures which stimulate or control the patient's responsiveness.

The varying views and procedures of contemporary therapy fall into three general groups; these are distinguished from one another by the closeness and exclusiveness of the personal interrelationships which patient and therapist develop and maintain with one another. (1) The therapeutic situation which involves *personal interaction between patient and one therapist* represents the use of a close, continuing, and exclusive relationship as a context for social learning. (2) Therapy which employs *groups of patients and therapists* emphasizes multiple personal interactions — whether it involves psychiatric ward routines, artificially structured groups, or dramatic situations in which the patient plays a prescribed role. In such therapy, there is little opportunity for the patient to form a close, lasting relationship with one person. (3) *Therapy by chemical, electrical or surgical assault* minimizes the factor of personal interaction, and emphasizes instead changes in central nervous system functioning which are presumed to be related to behavior organization. Because they are carried out in a social situation and often make possible the patient's later participation in therapeutic interaction, however, even these last procedures often bear some relation to social learning.

Personal Interaction Between Patient and Therapist

Much of contemporary therapy in behavior pathology goes on in a context of personal interaction between patient and trained therapist. In some instances, the patient comes to the therapist's office at regular intervals; between appointments he remains in his own social community, carrying on his usual work and maintaining his usual relationships with friends and family. In other instances, regular appointments with the therapist are part of the patient's life in a hospital. Between sessions the patient then remains in the therapeutic situation of the ward, where planned activities replace his usual work, and new relationships with other patients and with staff members replace his accustomed ones with family and friends. In either case, the therapist develops with his patient an interpersonal relationship which is unlike any everyday social interaction that develops outside the therapist's office. This is a unique relationship, and in its uniqueness lie its therapeutic properties.

The exact nature of this relationship, as well as exactly what is discussed and what roles are taken by the participants, has varied widely throughout the history of behavior pathology. At the turn of the present century, for example, suggestion, reasoning and persuasion were extensively employed as therapeutic tools.[10] The therapeutic interview took the form of encouraging and moralizing discussions which were designed to analyze for the patient the nature of his symptoms, and to persuade him of the possibility of cure. During the same period, some therapists employed authority and direction as their preferred techniques.[11] They advised and admonished their patients, and even organized for them routines of living planned as re-education in more desirable ways of behaving. In such relationships as these, the therapist assumed the role of leader or teacher, directly or indirectly, and the patient often learned submission and obedience to the prescriptions of his physician. The therapeutic interview consisted of highly intellectualized discussions, with a minimum of emotional participation.

Most contemporary therapists retain in their relationships with patients certain of these early therapeutic procedures.[12] They may occasionally formulate to the patient the pattern and significance of his pathology. They may give information or advice where it is needed; and they do not hesitate to

---

[10] A description of these techniques may be found in Appel, K. E., "Psychiatric therapy." In Hunt, J. McV. (Ed.), *Personality and the behavior disorders.* New York: Ronald, 1944, pp. 1111–1116. See, for example, Coué, E., *La maîtresse de soi-même par l'autosuggestion consciente.* Paris: Oliven, 1929; Dejerine, J., and Gaukler, E., *Psychoneurosis and psychotherapy.* Philadelphia: Lippincott, 1913; Dubois, P., *The psychic treatment of mental disorders.* New York: Funk and Wagnalls, 1907.

[11] See, for example, Payot, J., *The education of the will.* New York: Funk and Wagnalls, 1909.

[12] See, for example, Diethelm, O., *Treatment in psychiatry* (2nd ed.). Springfield, Ill.: C. C. Thomas, 1950; Kraines, S. H., *The therapy of the neuroses and psychoses* (3rd ed.). Philadelphia: Lea and Febiger, 1948.

support and reassure the patient when these reactions are justified. But these procedures are subordinated to a different conception of the therapeutic relationship — one which has its origins chiefly in the teachings of Freud. This relationship can best be characterized as one that is permissive, where the patient is free to talk about matters which trouble or confuse him without eliciting admonition or direction from his therapist. The patient inevitably participates emotionally, as well as verbally, in such a relationship as this; his emotional participation plays an important part in enabling him to relinquish his pathological reactions for more appropriate, mature and rewarding ones.

Although the patient-therapist relationship varies, in accordance with the patient's needs and the therapist's training, there are three general characteristics that make all such relationships valuable fields for social learning.[13]

(1) *The therapeutic relationship is one in which the therapist's reactions to the patient are accepting, or at least impartial.* The therapist is neither overprotective nor rejecting, neither punitive nor pitying toward the patient. He is able to accept with ease and impartiality the patient's fears and anxieties, his aggression or affection, his confusion or his inflexibility. In this acceptance the therapeutic relationship differs sharply from the relationships the patient has developed in his everyday life. For the people in the patient's social community are typically partisan in their attitudes toward him. They may protect, ignore, indulge, reject, punish or attack him. Indeed, it is the structure of the characteristic interactions between the patient and his social environment which has helped keep him anxious, socially unskilled or emotionally immature.

(2) *In the therapeutic relationship, a patient's anxieties are utilized to further social learning.* We have seen that severe anxieties typically underlie the inappropriate adjustive techniques and the behavioral disorganizations which characterize behavior pathology. The trained therapist is equipped to handle his patient's reactions of anxiety in such a way that they facilitate rather than retard social learning.[14]   If the anxieties become so extreme and intolerable as to place the patient in danger of developing behavior disorganization, the therapist may minimize his patient's anxiety by giving support and reassurance. In many cases, however, milder anxiety reactions are utilized, and even provoked, by the therapist as stimulants to relearning.

The impartial attitude of a trained therapist enables him to accept anxious reactions from his patient without himself becoming anxious and thereby disqualifying himself as a therapist. In these respects also, the therapeutic relationship differs importantly from the relationships which the patient has

---

[13] There is some evidence that there are few, if any, major differences among "schools" of therapists in their concept of the ideal therapeutic relationship. See Fiedler, F. E., "The concept of an ideal therapeutic relationship." *J. consult. Psychol.*, 1950, vol. 14, pp. 239–245.

[14] See pages 75–79 and 300–301.

developed in his everyday life. For in his own social community, the patient's unreduced anxiety frequently evokes from others reactions of fear, ridicule or attack; and these then serve only to increase and perpetuate his pathological behavior. The patient whose pathological reactions have been acquired and reinforced in such a context of continuing and intolerable anxiety is literally helpless to change his own behavior without the expert assistance of a therapist.

(3) *The therapeutic relationship provides a patient with the opportunity to formulate his reactions and to share them in social communication.* In a relationship with an impartial, accepting therapist, the patient may identify and verbally formulate reactions which are painful and frightening, or which have been previously inaccessible to him. Indeed, the therapist may provide training — through practice in free association, for example — which hastens the patient's formulation of his hitherto self-inaccessible behavior. Not only the formulation, but also the sharing of reactions with another person, is important in therapy. What the patient says, he hears himself say; and what he hears may surprise, frighten or repel him. When this occurs, the therapist's acceptance of the patient's words and statements, and his handling of the patient's anxieties can change an otherwise threatening situation into an opportunity for constructive learning. Nowhere is the distinction between the therapeutic relationship and the patient's everyday social community sharper than at this point. Left to himself, without opportunity to formulate and share his reactions, a patient may construct hypotheses to explain his behavior that do not correspond to a realistic interpretation of it.[15] He may develop techniques for reducing his anxiety which carry him well beyond the limits of social validity. In the therapeutic relationship, on the other hand, he has the opportunity and the technique for sharing his reactions, and consequently for controlling and altering them in socially valid directions.

These three characteristics — the therapist's accepting, impartial attitude, the therapeutic utilization of the patient's anxieties and the opportunity for formulating and sharing reactions — are to be found in all therapies which employ patient-therapist interaction. Contemporary therapists, however, differ among themselves in the particular aspects of this therapeutic situation which they choose to emphasize. These differences result in part from divergent views of the nature of behavior pathology and of its development from normal behavior. They reflect also differences among therapists as individuals, in their training, their ease in establishing particular kinds of relationships, and the sorts of patients they prefer to treat. Let us take three examples to illustrate these differences.

[15] Compare the development of pseudocommunity behavior, discussed on pages 387–392.

Non-directive therapy

Our first variety of therapeutic relationship, called *non-directive* or *client-centered*, was developed by Carl Rogers and his students.[16] This technique rests upon an assumed principle of growth, a tendency for the human organism to achieve maturity if environmental conditions are free and supporting. Pathological behavior, according to this hypothesis, is the consequence of the blocking or deviation of the normal growth process. The patient persists in his inappropriate behavior, even though he may know it is inadvisable, because it brings him present emotional satisfactions which he is powerless to relinquish. Therapy in behavior pathology is therefore directed toward present emotional reactions; it aims to remove the obstacles to development and to set the patient free to resume his normal biosocial maturation.

The non-directive therapeutic situation is a face-to-face interview, whose essential feature is the permissive and accepting attitude of the therapist toward his patient. The non-directive therapist does not advise, judge or challenge his patient; he accepts completely his patient's words and gestures, as well as the emotionalized attitudes which word and gesture seem to imply. In his own replies to his patient in the interview, however, the therapist attends less to the patient's actual words than to the emotional attitudes which seem to have prompted them. If the patient recites a list of complaints, for example, the therapist may comment that the patient feels that a great many symptoms are troubling him. If the patient asks directly for advice on a particular problem, the therapist may reply that the patient wishes that the therapist could tell him what to do. If the patient verbally attacks or resists him, the therapist neither argues nor defends himself; instead, he may say that to the patient the interview must seem unpleasant, valueless or threatening.

The following interchange between patient (P) and therapist (T) illustrates the emphasis upon emotional attitudes which distinguishes non-directive therapy. The patient is a young man who complained of recurring periods of tension and depression at a time when his imminent induction into the Army threatened his close relationship with his mother.

> P. I went home, you know. I think I have, well, a better way of getting along with Mom. I mean, take the V–12 tests, for example. She seems to understand better or something. I mean, she said I could even enlist in the Air Corps if I wanted to, and she used to just cringe when I mentioned it.
>
> T. So it seems as if you have a new understanding with her.
>
> P. Well, I think we've reached a pretty good understanding now.　　It

[16] Rogers, C. R., *Counseling and psychotherapy.* Boston: Houghton Mifflin, 1942; Rogers, C. R., "Significant aspects of client-centered therapy." *Amer. Psychol.*, 1946, vol. 1, pp. 415–422; Rogers, C. R., "Some observations on the organization of personality." *Amer. Psychol.*, 1947, vol. 2, pp. 358–368; Rogers, C. R., *Client-centered therapy: its current practice, implications, and theory.* Boston: Houghton Mifflin, 1951.

was funny . . . once around her, I got the same old feeling back I used to have when I was younger. For the past year or so, I just haven't been feeling anything, and now I got the same old feeling of love. I didn't think I could. I thought I was just cynical and hardened or something. With a different attitude you find things easier to take. (*Pause*) I don't know. (*Long pause*).

T. Feeling pretty tense about it, aren't you?

P. Yes. Is it that obvious?

T. I am aware of it, though I guess you'd rather I weren't.

P. Well . . . of course, maybe it was just because I spent such a short time at home, and Mom thought well, I was going away pretty soon, so she was more willing to hear my side. I don't know, really. I feel I am getting back to the understanding I had as a very small person.

T. Things feel more like they used to.

P. It's just a more pleasant relationship, that's all. Take an example like this. Mom used to scream if she saw me with a cigarette — tell me I couldn't smoke, and give me all sorts of reasons and everything. And this time when I was home she offered me one! I was simply bowled over. I just couldn't understand why. (*Pause*) I decided maybe she just realized I was growing up or something. Oh, she let me do little things. When I was fifteen, I worked one summer at a stock exchange. She let me do that all right, she let me go, but she didn't direct me to do it. There's never been any encouragement or guidance in getting out on my own — I just went. She let me go with a tear in her eye, you know.

T. When you wanted to do things yourself, get out on your own, there was always the tear. . . .

P. Boy, that's sure the truth! I never thought about that before, but it's sure the truth. You know, a kid doesn't realize how much effect his childhood has on him, does he? You think, well, I don't have those conflicts, I didn't have a tough adolescence, you think you're apart from all that, above it, somehow. . . . (*Pause*) So many of the other fellows act more, well, more cold toward their folks. I think I'll always need some sort of tie, somebody to come home to that I love.

Therapists who consistently employ client-centered procedures report that their patients show relatively orderly and predictable changes in behavior throughout a series of therapeutic interviews. The patient begins his therapeutic sessions with uncertainty, fear or hostility. As he comes to understand the permissive and accepting character of the situation in which he is participating, he becomes more free in expressing his ambivalent, negative or aggressive attitudes. When these attitudes have been made accessible to the patient's self-reactions, and have been formulated in words to the accepting therapist, the patient ordinarily begins to talk in more friendly, positive, mature terms. From these positive reactions, which are recognized and accepted by the therapist in the same way as are the negative ones, develops reorganization of behavior, including changes in self-attitudes. This result we call therapeutic insight.[17] And, at least in completely successful therapy, such reorganization includes the patient's formulation of possible courses of action, and his gradual and hesitant choices of more mature ways of behaving. Growth thus occurs within the therapeutic situation, and is reflected in the patient's progressively more mature reactions outside the therapist's office.

The therapists' reports have been verified to some extent by systematic analyses of electrically-recorded client-centered therapeutic sessions. In one coordinated research project based on ten completely recorded cases, for example, it was possible to rate certain dimensions of patient and therapist behavior, and to identify trends in these reactions over the entire course of therapy.[18] In this series of cases, the types of reaction most frequently employed by the therapist at all points in therapy were those restating the content of the patient's verbalization and those formulating in words the patient's emotional attitudes. The patient's statements, on the other hand, changed systematically from the early to the later therapeutic sessions. Descriptions of problems and symptoms decreased in frequency, while valid statements of the reasons for problems and their possible solutions increased. Comments indicating positive self-attitudes increased as time went on, while comments implying negative attitudes toward both self and others declined in frequency.[19]

Two separate studies in this project, employing somewhat different techniques of analysis, suggest that the patient's attitudes toward himself are closely related to his attitudes toward others,[20] and that when the patient's self-attitudes change, his attitudes toward others change in the same direction.[21] There is evidence also that as the patient's self-protective devices become self-accessible, such devices appear less and less frequently in succeeding therapeutic sessions.[22] Another study in the series analyzed those statements which describe the patient's behavior as it appears to him.[23] It is clear from this analysis that, throughout the course of therapy, patients refer to their own behavior in increasingly more mature terms. There is a consistent trend toward greater self-control and self-direction as therapy proceeds.

When therapy is successful, the systematic changes in behavior appearing

[17] Compare the discussion of insight on pages 83–87.

[18] Rogers, C. R., "A coordinated research in psychotherapy: a nonobjective introduction." *J. consult. Psychol.*, 1949, vol. 13, pp. 149–153; Raskin, N. J., "Analysis of six parallel studies of the therapeutic process." *J. consult. Psychol.*, 1949, vol. 13, pp. 206–220.

[19] Seeman, J., "The process of nondirective therapy." *J. consult. Psychol.*, 1949, vol. 13, pp. 157–168.

[20] Sheerer, E. T., "The relationship between acceptance of self and acceptance of others." *J. consult. Psychol.*, 1949, vol. 13, pp. 169–175.

[21] Stock, D., "The self concept and feelings toward others." *J. consult. Psychol.*, 1949, vol. 13, pp. 176–180.

[22] Haigh, G., "Defensive behavior in client-centered therapy." *J. consult. Psychol.*, 1949, vol. 13, pp. 181–189.

[23] Hoffman, A. E., "Reported behavior changes in counseling." *J. consult. Psychol.*, 1949, vol. 13, pp. 190–195.

in the client-centered therapeutic situation are paralleled by behavioral changes in the patient's everyday life. Research on the magnitude and nature of this generalization of reactions, from therapeutic session to life situations, however, is not yet extensive. A few studies have compared the scores made by patients on structured and projective tests, before therapy, with those achieved after therapy is over. Some of these studies show changes, from pre- to post-therapy examinations, in scores on personality inventories and on Rorschach and word association tests.[24] Other investigations, however, fail to yield significant results.[25] We need more careful analyses of the criteria of successful therapy, and more lengthy follow-up of the patients, before we can evaluate with any confidence the outcome of client-centered therapy.

It is evident, both from the therapists' descriptions and from analysis of electrically-recorded sessions, that client-centered therapy involves relationships which not every patient can establish with his therapist. Children, aged individuals, developmentally retarded persons, those suffering from severe and extensive behavior disorder, and patients who for any reason are not free to make important life decisions, are usually not suitable participants in this variety of therapeutic relationship.[26] On the other hand, persons who have developed relatively mild behavior pathology, who can learn to verbalize their difficulties, and who are capable of reorganizing their behavior in their particular social environments, often profit from participation in a client-centered relationship. For such patients, therapy seems to represent the resumption of growth toward biosocial maturity which distorted social learning and false self-reactions have interrupted.

The keynote of client-centered therapy — the patient's freedom to choose what he will discuss and what he will avoid — has been sharply criticized by many behavior pathologists.[27] It is said that a patient may refrain altogether from touching upon topics which are anxiety-provoking for him. He may accidentally overlook, or intentionally omit from his discussion, important material regarding his own life history, so that the therapist never obtains a longitudinal picture of his patient's development. Moreover, the client-centered

[24] Combs, A. W., "Follow-up of a case treated by the non-directive method." *J. clin. Psychol.*, 1945, vol. 1, pp. 148–154; Muench, G. A., "An evaluation of non-directive psychotherapy by means of the Rorschach and other indices." *Appl. Psychol. Monogr.* no. 13. Stanford University, California: Stanford University Press, 1947; Reader, N., "An investigation into some personality changes occurring in individuals undergoing client-centered therapy." (Unpublished Ph.D. thesis.) University of Chicago, 1948; Schofield, W., "Changes in responses to the Minnesota Multiphasic Inventory following certain therapies." *Psychol. Monogr.*, 1950, vol. 64, no. 5; Keet, C. D., "Two verbal techniques in a miniature counseling situation." *Psychol. Monogr.*, 1948, vol. 62, no. 7.

[25] Carr, A. C., "Evaluation of nine psychotherapy cases by the Rorschach." *J. consult. Psychol.*, 1949, vol. 13, pp. 196–205.

[26] Rogers, C. R., *Counseling and psychotherapy.* Boston: Houghton Mifflin, 1942, pp. 51–84.

[27] See, for example, Carter, J. W. (Ed.), "Symposium: critical evaluation of nondirective therapy." *J. clin. Psychol.*, 1948, vol. 4, pp. 225–263.

therapist himself, if he is consistent in his practices, is committed to just one approach for all his patients. He cannot flexibly shift his techniques to suit particular patients or particular events in the therapeutic relationship. These are serious criticisms. To what extent they are justified we cannot tell without much more controlled research on various types of therapeutic relationships than we have at present.

Psychoanalytic therapy

For comparison with non-directive therapy, let us take the variety of therapeutic relationship developed within the framework of psychoanalytic theory. For the psychoanalytic therapist, as for the client-centered one, behavior pathology is the product of the distortion, interruption or inhibition of normal growth. But the psychoanalyst conceives of the development of behavior pathology in terms much more specific than those employed by the client-centered therapist. From a psychoanalytic point of view, behavior pathology results from fixations at particular life periods, and from the inadequate resolution of those conflicts which occur inevitably in the course of normal maturation. Fixation and conflict are alike repressed or self-inaccessible, so that the patient is unable to identify them or to relinquish the inappropriate defenses he has developed against the anxieties they induce.[28]

Such a theory of the development of behavior pathology, of course, requires that certain events must occur if pathological reactions are to be altered. Repressed conflicts, including those which have developed in infancy and early childhood, must be made accessible to the patient. Inadequately solved conflicts must be resolved in more mature ways. Early fixations must be worked through and overcome. Growth occurring in the course of psychoanalytic therapy is sometimes conceived of as a recapitulation, in abbreviated and concentrated form, of the steps by which human beings proceed from infancy to mature adulthood.

Unlike the situation in non-directive therapy, there is no standard therapeutic procedure employed by all psychoanalytic therapists alike. We owe to Freud both the psychoanalytic theory of behavior pathology and the development of the first psychoanalytic therapeutic techniques. It was he, as we have seen, who early emphasized repressed conflict, frustrated need and consequent anxiety as the crucial determiners of behavior pathology. It was Freud also who turned from hypnosis as a therapeutic technique to direction and persuasion, and from these to the technique of free association which is the major tool of psychoanalysis.[29] A great many contemporary therapists follow closely the classical psychoanalytic procedures, and duplicate with their patients the

---

[28] For discussions of fixation, see pages 143–153, of conflict, pages 246–275, and of repression, pages 337–351.

[29] Freud, S., *An autobiographical study.* London: Hogarth Press, 1946.

methods Freud first used with his. A great many more contemporary psycho-analysts, however, differ from Freud both in the details of their theories of behavior pathology and in the techniques of treatment they employ. Consequently, we cannot today speak of psychoanalytic therapy and mean thereby a particular set of procedures derived from an explicit theory of behavior pathology.

Freud's interest in his earliest therapeutic tool, *hypnosis*, arose from his discussions with his colleague, Breuer. Between 1880 and 1882, Breuer was treating a young woman who suffered from hysterical inactivation.[30] In addition to her wide variety of symptoms, including paralyses of both legs and an arm, impairment of sight and hearing, and difficulties with speech, the patient occasionally seemed to be in a dreamy state, which Breuer called "absence." At these times the patient muttered to herself, as if she were busy fantasying. Breuer recorded the woman's words, and then presented them to her while she was in an hypnotic state. This procedure enabled the patient to communicate her fantasies under hypnosis, and often resulted in temporary periods of relief from her symptoms. Permanent removal of symptoms, however, occurred only when the patient recalled under hypnosis the original life situation in which the symptom developed and reacted emotionally to these recalled events. In this historically important case, the patient's troubles were found to be related to painful and frightening events which occurred during her father's long illness and eventual death. When under hypnosis the patient had reacted emotionally to these repressed reactions, she became completely well.

Freud's study of this case, in which he collaborated with Breuer, convinced him that the critical requirement for successful therapy was that the patient react emotionally to traumatic events which he had repressed. Indeed, according to Freud's view, it was the "suppressed emotion" which was responsible for the development of symptoms. Consequently, the "release" of such emotional reactions — which was called *abreaction* — seemed to be a necessary condition of the patient's recovery. And, at the beginning of his career, Freud believed that abreaction was best facilitated by hypnosis.

The therapeutic use of hypnosis was by no means original with these men, of course. A century before Freud and Breuer reported their famous case, the Austrian physician Mesmer was removing the symptoms of hundreds of patients by direct suggestion under hypnosis. Mesmer's methods were so dramatic that his cures seemed magical, and his explanations of his successes, which he made in terms of "animal magnetism," failed to meet the challenge of eighteenth-century science. For these reasons, Mesmer was dismissed as a charlatan by many of his contemporaries, and his therapeutic method fell into disrepute. Mesmer's use of hypnosis, of course, emphasized the alleviation of symptoms

---

[30] Breuer, J. and Freud, S., "Studies in hysteria." New York and Washington: Nervous and Mental Disease Publishing Co., 1936.

by direct suggestion — a technique which underlies all the *suggestive* therapies, with or without hypnosis, which we have earlier discussed.[31] In the later applications of hypnosis, culminating in the work of Breuer and Freud, there was no direct suggestion that symptoms would disappear.[32] Hypnotic techniques were used only because they made recall and emotional expression easier for the patient.

Today, therapists who employ hypnosis follow Freud in emphasizing the abreactive rather than the suggestive effects of this technique. *Hypnoanalysis*, as it is commonly called now, is often used to shorten therapy by making available to the patient material which was formerly self-inaccessible, and by facilitating his emotional reactions to it.[33] Hypnoanalysis may also be used to encourage a close, almost childlike relationship of patient to therapist. This relationship not only enables the patient to speak more freely of his own attitudes, but also provides the security he needs in order to develop more independent ways of behaving. The contemporary therapist capitalizes most fully upon these advantages of hypnoanalysis when he utilizes hypnosis in conjunction with other techniques.

Freud soon found that, in spite of the frequent and the occasionally dramatic improvements which hypnosis brought about in his patients, the technique had serious limitations. For one thing, many of his patients could not be hypnotized. For another, even intense abreaction under hypnosis did not uniformly produce permanent improvement in the patient. Often it was necessary to repeat the hypnotic procedure over and over with the same patient. These disadvantages led Freud to abandon hypnosis as his major therapeutic tool, and to substitute for it the technique of training patients to say freely whatever occurred to them. Freud found that this technique made available both to patient and therapist reactions which were otherwise inaccessible. This method of *free association* is the cornerstone of standard psychoanalytic procedure.

In utilizing free association as a therapeutic technique, the therapist first trains his patient to report in words everything that occurs to him during the therapeutic session — no matter how trivial, embarrassing, indiscreet, unpleasant or anxiety-provoking it may be. The content of the patient's free verbalizations may include events of the day, objects in the therapist's office, scraps of episodes long past, and material from fantasies and dreams. The only principle by which the patient is guided is that he must recount everything he thinks of. This is by no means an easy thing to do, for it requires the patient

[31] See page 558.

[32] Breuer, J. and Freud, S., *Studies in hysteria*. New York and Washington: Nervous and Mental Disease Publishing Co., 1936, pp. 26–27.

[33] Brenman, M. and Gill, M., *Hypnotherapy: a survey of the literature*. New York: International Universities Press, 1947; Lindner, R. M., *Rebel without a cause: the hypnoanalysis of a criminal psychopath*. New York: Grune and Stratton, 1944; Wolberg, L. R., *Hypnoanalysis*. New York: Grune and Stratton, 1945.

to inhibit his lifelong reactions of self-regulation and self-control. The therapist must give specific, repeated instructions to his patient in the methods of responding freely; often the patient lies upon a couch, where he cannot see the therapist, in order to minimize distraction and induce relaxation.

The following sample, produced by a patient already well-practiced in the technique, illustrates the fragmentary, relatively uncontrolled, dreamlike character of free verbalizations. The patient was a young man suffering from severe chronic anxieties, and from a specific phobia of high places. His fears proved to be related in intricate ways to sexual confusions, sensitivities about his own appearance and competence, and a wide discrepancy between his vocational aspirations and his achievements. His chronic anxieties were of long standing, acquired originally in a family setting of parental conflict, jealousy and depressive reactions. Even this brief excerpt from the patient's lengthy free associations includes allusions to many of his own areas of concern.

"The same thing applies to the fact that they told me some time ago about loss of sleep in the beginning of the night or the last part of the night and I insisted the first was.... I noticed for two or three nights I began waking up at 2:30 and laying awake most of the night ... or semiconscious ... two-three nights ... is that done because I'm a creature of habit on account of the suggestion of my mind ... or am I with a nervous disease. (*Pause*) Thought about nearly everything ... in general — can't recall it — nothing relating to sex ... tried to put it out of my mind and I fight to keep it out. Got the habit of thinking about things and would dream about them ... tried to keep things out of my mind ... like fighting on account of the past. My mind traced right on through these lights to the fifth floor and a blonde woman ... shows my mind runs on to sex and injury ... things like how to avoid going up in high buildings ... afraid of how high I'd go. Didn't want to tell anybody what my trouble was. Saw it was only a four or five-story building so I consented. It didn't bother me ... didn't seem a real test because it wasn't high. Still no confidence in myself ... still in the dark as to my conflicts ... two things, one 'yes' and one 'no.' Decided I'd adopt the good because the bad was lashing me...."

Occasionally, also, the therapist employs his patient's reports of his dreams as a starting-point for free association. Dreaming is an activity a good deal like fantasying or free verbalizing.[34] Consequently, the patient's dreams may include topics related to the conflicts and frustrations involved in his illness, and the free associations initiated by events or words from his reported dreams may lead the patient to painful areas he has been avoiding. The same phobic patient reported the following dream to his therapist.

"I am working in a bank. A draft is sent to me and the officers have not signed it through carelessness. I point this fact out to a high officer and tell him that under me this would not occur. The bank was in a

34 Compare the discussion on pages 420–426.

tall place, very high.   All of a sudden I become afraid I cannot get down.
There is a tall ladder and I see soft sand at the bottom.   I am in an
elevator running wild going up.   Was afraid when we reached the top
it would go down and drop.   Woke up choking.   Couldn't get my breath.
Made funny noise trying to do so.   Was scared half to death.   I leaped
out of bed when I woke up but by the time I reached the door suddenly
it cleared up and I could breathe freely."

The role of the psychoanalytic therapist whose patient has learned the technique of free association is to interpret to the patient the significance of his
reactions.   The therapist points out, at the proper times, that the patient is
attempting to avoid something, that he is employing a defense, or that he is not
reporting everything which occurs to him.   Such interpretation ordinarily
serves to show the patient his own inappropriate adjustive techniques and
eventually assists him in relinquishing or altering them.   At this point, of
course, psychoanalytic therapy differs strikingly from client-centered therapy.
The non-directive therapist verbalizes and clarifies the emotional attitudes
which seem to him to support his patients' statements in the interview.   The
psychoanalytic therapist goes beyond this and deliberately calls to his patient's attention the nature of his behavior and its probable significance to him.

In the psychoanalytic therapeutic relationship, both therapist and patient
report orderly and predictable changes in the patient's reactions.[35]   For most
persons, the initial phases of free association result in *heightened anxiety*, particularly if the patient cannot see the therapist, and cannot judge from his expression, tone or gesture the reception being given to the spoken words.   Once
an individual has acquired proficiency in the technique, however, the most
impressive features of his associations are the periods of hesitancy, blocking
and other signs of disorganization which occur.   These reactions Freud called
resistances, and from them he derived his theories of conflict and repression.[36]
Resistance, according to this theory, appears when a person's associations have
led him close to painful topics which are self-inaccessible.   Resistance may
consequently guide the therapist — and, in his turn, the patient — toward the
particular conflicts and anxieties which contribute to pathological behavior.

The interrelationship between patient and therapist in psychoanalytic
therapy also undergoes a predictable development.   Throughout the course of
treatment, the patient typically shows a variety of personal feelings for the
therapist, ranging from strong affection to equally intense antagonism.
Freud called this phenomenon *transference*, since he believed that such highly
personalized attitudes were transferred to the therapist by the patient from
relationships he had earlier developed with parents, siblings, friends or spouse.
In prolonged psychoanalytic therapy this transference may reach a point where

---

[35] See, for example, the accounts of psychologists who have undergone psychoanalysis,
published in the *Journal of Abnormal and Social Psychology*, 1940, vol. 35.
[36] See pages 249–252 and 338–340.

the patient's relationship to his therapist, and the satisfactions he obtains from him, seem to be more significant to the patient than his everyday problems and even his recovery. Such a *transference neurosis* is considered by psychoanalytic therapists to represent the patient's central conflicts; and its development and dissolution in therapy are considered essential to classical psychoanalytic treatment.

It is hardly surprising, in view of the psychoanalytic conception of behavior pathology and of its treatment, that analytic therapy is the most time-consuming of all those involving patient-therapist interaction. Under ordinary circumstances, the patient meets with his therapist for an hour each day, two to five days a week; even with such frequent sessions, psychoanalysis often extends over a period of two or three years. Of course, this is a relatively brief time for the reorganization of behavior which has itself developed over decades, and for the reworking of fixations and conflicts from infancy through adulthood. Nevertheless, classical psychoanalytic therapy is such a prolonged procedure that experimentation with briefer psychoanalytic treatments is now in progress.

Briefer psychoanalysis has been developed and most extensively used by the staff members of the Chicago Institute for Psychoanalysis, under the direction of Alexander and French.[37] This variety of treatment retains the interview procedures common to all kinds of interpersonal therapy, but it allows for much greater flexibility of approach than does the psychoanalytic technique just described. Indeed, the distinguishing mark of briefer psychoanalysis is the *principle of flexibility*. The same procedures are not employed for all patients, nor is the same approach necessarily utilized for any one patient, from the beginning straight through to the end of therapy. Alexander and French maintain that patients differ widely from one another in their need for frequent sessions, in their ability to profit from free association, and in the intensity of emotional reactions they can endure. For these reasons, the details of therapeutic procedure are altered in accordance with the patient's needs at any particular time.

In briefer psychoanalysis, the application of the principle of flexibility extends even to the crucial transference relationship. Rather than permitting a full transference neurosis to develop in all cases, Alexander and French favor restricting the transference to a few areas, or, in some cases, preventing the transference neurosis from developing at all. Flexibility also allows for the therapeutic use of events and relationships outside the therapist's office. Thus Alexander and French consider the patient's successful performance of activities outside the therapeutic relationship to be much more important than the abreaction which many other psychoanalysts single out as the most significant therapeutic factor. Consequently, in briefer psychoanalysis the patient is en-

[37] Alexander, F., and French, T. M., *Psychoanalytic therapy.* New York: Ronald, 1946.

couraged to experiment with new ways of handling his everyday relationships with his wife, his children, his friends and his competitors. Transference, according to this view, is only a training period for real-life situations; and the sooner the patient tries out his newly developing social skills in his own social community, the more promptly he may recover.

There has been much controversy over the merits and limitations of briefer psychoanalysis. Some therapists, for example, believe that the method constitutes such a simplification of the classical procedures that it should not be called psychoanalysis at all. Others believe that, because the transference neurosis is typically limited and often even omitted, the therapy cannot be more than superficial. We do not yet have the extensive and controlled follow-up observations on patients which are needed to evaluate these criticisms. Until such information is available, we can consider briefer psychoanalysis, like classical psychoanalysis and like non-directive therapy, as a procedure which, at least for some patients and some therapists, works well.

Therapy with young children

The varieties of non-directive and psychoanalytic therapy we have just discussed demand, of both patient and therapist, a high level of verbal participation in the therapeutic relationship. In non-directive interview, in free association and dream analysis, and even in hypnosis, the adult patient must be able to learn to identify, formulate and communicate his reactions to the therapist. He must also be able to comprehend and to discuss the interpretations of his behavior which his therapist may make to him. Furthermore, as we have seen, the adult patient must be capable of generalizing the reactions he acquires in his therapeutic relationship to his own life situations outside the therapist's office. The attitudes and expectations of others in his social community must permit the patient to achieve the relative independence which characterizes adult biosocial maturity.

When, however, the patient is a young child who has developed behavior pathology, such requirements as these are neither realistic nor feasible. The child lacks the language skills that are necessary for the formulation and sharing of personalized attitudes which go on in formal therapeutic interviews. He lacks the background of practice in thinking and talking about his own behavior, in specifying the motives for his acts, and in identifying and characterizing his own adjustive techniques, such as adults acquire in the course of their daily living. The lines between dreaming, fantasying, playing and thinking are much more blurred for the child than for the adult; and learning the technique of free association is for most children impossible.[38] Far from being a relatively independent individual, the child is necessarily controlled and protected by his parents; and it is to a controlling and protective family situation that the child must accommodate his behavior.

[38] See pages 106–107, 112–113, and 420–426.

It is for these reasons that therapists have developed special procedures for the treatment of children. The diversity of these methods, however, is no less when the patients are children than when they are adults. Both non-directive and psychoanalytic approaches are suitable for children, and these two broad frameworks allow for many different emphases. One therapist may stress abreaction, another the child-therapist relationship, and a third the direct interpretation of behavior to the child. One therapist may center his efforts on the child, while to another the parents may seem a more appropriate focus for treatment. What holds together these diverse approaches, and distinguishes them from the adult therapies we have just discussed, is their indirect, relatively nonverbal character. This distinctive feature appears most clearly in a procedure commonly employed by all behavior pathologists who work with young children — the therapeutic use of *play*.

For the child, as we have seen,[39] play is one of the most important paths to social maturity. In his play relationships with other children, in his use of the toys of his culture, and in the fantasies he develops with respect both to children and to toys, a growing child gains practice in role-taking, sharing and shifting perspectives; and such practice is an essential part of his biosocial maturation. As any parent knows, children often unwittingly demonstrate in their play behavior their own personal anxieties and fascinations, their half-learned roles, their groping attempts to duplicate adult activities and adult relationships. Through play also they may diminish their fears and fascinations, and transform their ill-defined roles and undeveloped social skills into a smoother behavioral organization. There are thus three components of everyday play which may be utilized in the therapeutic situation. (1) Play provides the therapist with an opportunity to observe and further understand the behavior of his young patient. (2) Play may be utilized by the child as a medium for expressing and sharing his anxieties. (3) A play situation may be a context for working out and eventually learning roles, self-reactions and adjustive techniques that are socially valid.

These three aspects of play can be translated into specific therapeutic procedures in a number of different ways. The therapist may, for example, plan and organize the play situation in advance, selecting play materials which represent particular areas of concern for his patient. If family relationships are the focus of the child's difficulties, the therapist may provide for play dolls representing the patient's parents and siblings.[40] Or he may arrange dolls and toy furniture to depict schoolroom or hospital settings if these are critical situations for the child. If the therapist believes the child needs to express hostile or aggressive reactions, which he has held under tight control, then toy weapons, amputation dolls which come apart, miniature trucks and tanks, or

[39] See pages 116–119.
[40] Compare the description of sibling rivalry on pages 287–289. Levy, D. M., "Studies in sibling rivalry." *Res. Monogr. Amer. Orthopsychiat. Assn.*, 1937, no. 2.

pounding-benches may be provided for play. Some therapists employ situations less organized than these. They may simply furnish a wide variety of dolls, pieces of furniture and other play materials, and leave the form of the play up to the child. Or they may make available only such unstructured materials as finger-paints and clay. Most therapists who work extensively with children find that the particular play objects provided are relatively unimportant. Like any person in an unfamiliar situation, the child uses what materials are available in accordance with his needs, whether the materials are fire engines, crayons, replicas of his siblings, or the dictaphone in the corner of the office.

Therapeutic play, like the interview procedure we described earlier, represents a permissive situation. The child is free to do whatever he likes with the play materials. He may use them as objects of aggression, by breaking, pounding or crushing them. He may find comfort in them when, for example, he sucks placidly on a toy nipple, or spoons up as much finger-paint as he likes for his paintings. Through timid, hesitant exploration he may learn to deprive objects of their anxiety-inducing properties, as when he undresses dolls and dares finally to talk about the perplexing matter of sex differences. Although the situation is thus a free one for the child, the therapist's role varies in accordance with his particular view of therapy. We may take, as our two examples, psychoanalytic and non-directive play therapy.

Psychoanalytic play therapy. Freud recognized the therapeutic potentialities of childhood play in the course of treating Hans, a five-year-old boy who suffered from many fears, including the specific phobia that a horse would bite him. In a paper published in 1909,[41] Freud described the boy's play behavior, both in the home situation as reported by the patient's father, and in the consulting-office where Freud once observed the boy directly. The account of the patient's behavior, and its interpretation according to psychoanalytic theories of infantile and childhood sexuality, are detailed and complex. A few play episodes stand out as dramatic illustrations of the use to which Hans was unwittingly putting his play. Thus for a few days he played he was a horse, neighing, trotting and kicking up his feet, sometimes wearing a nose bag and biting his father. During this period he seemed to confuse the "black on the horse's mouth," which particularly terrified him, with his father's black moustache; at the same time he began defying his father at home, and became less afraid of horses in the street. From this and other play incidents it appeared that Hans identified the horses he feared with his father, whom he also feared. And when, in play, he could take the role of the horse — and consequently of his father — he was somewhat less fearful of both horse and parent.

In this play episode, and in many other brief incidents in the boy's daily life,

---

[41] Freud, S., "Analysis of a phobia in a five-year-old boy" (1909). *Collected Papers,* vol. 3. London: Hogarth Press, 1946, pp. 149–289.

we can identify some of the therapeutic properties which play had for Hans. For one thing, the child's play, closely related as it was to his own fears, often constituted an abreaction. For another thing, Hans frequently seemed to try out, in his family relationships, the reactions he was learning in play; thus when he took the role of the terrifying horse, he was able to bite and defy his formerly terrifying father. Furthermore, his father, with whom Hans had a close but ambivalent relationship, promptly interpreted to him the apparent significance of each of his play and fantasy episodes. Thus abreaction, generalization to extratherapeutic situations, interpretation and personal interaction contributed to the therapeutic effect of Hans's play.

Since Freud published his early observations, other psychoanalysts have extended, refined, formalized and modified his original methods. Melanie Klein, for example, equates play therapy with adult psychoanalysis. According to her, play activity closely resembles free association, and the therapist-child relationship develops into a true transference neurosis.[42] Because of the resemblance she sees, Klein makes immediate interpretations to the child of the meaning of his own behavior. Anna Freud, on the other hand, emphasizes the adult therapist as a source of support, and as a powerful ally of the child.[43] She stresses the direct educative nature of play therapy, and discourages frequent immediate interpretation of his behavior to the child. Aichhorn, whose work has been largely with delinquent children, uses an approach similar to that represented by the principle of flexibility in briefer psychoanalysis.[44]

Perhaps the simplest of permissive play therapies, and certainly the one most heavily dependent upon abreaction, is Levy's *release therapy*.[45] In this variety of treatment, there is no attempt to create a transference neurosis; and no effort is made to interpret to the child the meaning of his play. Therapy depends entirely upon the child's expressing through his play, in the context of a permissive relationship with his therapist, the anxieties and conflicts which have led to his pathological behavior. This approach is especially suitable for children younger than ten whose difficulties stem from some relatively specific past event. Those children seem to profit especially from release therapy who are reacting in inappropriate or unrewarding ways to frightening incidents, such as the birth of a sibling, painful hospital procedures, or the death of a parent.

Non-directive play therapy. The same faith in an inherent tendency toward growth, and the same conviction that behavior pathology is the resultant of

---

[42] Klein, M., *The psychoanalysis of children.* London: Hogarth Press, 1932.
[43] Freud, A., *Introduction to the technic of child analysis.* New York and Washington: Nervous and Mental Disease Publishing Co., 1928.
[44] Aichhorn, A., *Wayward youth.* New York: Viking, 1935.
[45] Levy, D. M., "'Release therapy' in young children." *Psychiatry,* 1938, vol. 1, pp. 387–390; Levy, D. M., "Trends in therapy: III. Release therapy." *Amer. J. Orthopsychiat.,* 1939, vol. 9, pp. 913–936.

blocked growth impulses, which underlies non-directive therapy with adults, forms the basis of our second variety of play therapy. Such a growth principle enters explicitly into the play therapy outlined by Allen [46] and by Axline.[47] Allen, who has worked out his methods over a long period of time at the Philadelphia Child Guidance Clinic, emphasizes the exaggeratedly close relationship between mother and child which seems often to be the condition blocking a child's normal growth. From Allen's point of view, mother and child need to accept themselves and each other as independent individuals, rather than as together constituting an interdependent, unitary system. Consequently, the mother and the child are treated at the same time by different therapists — the mother with non-directive techniques such as were described earlier, and the child with play therapy. In the play sessions, Allen attaches greatest importance to the relationship which develops between therapist and child. Through it, the child grows to recognize himself as an individual in his own right. For this reason, Allen's method has been called *relationship therapy*. Although Allen attends primarily to the child's emotional attitudes, he still occasionally interprets a child's behavior to him.

Axline, a student of Rogers, adheres strictly in her play therapy to the principles of non-directive treatment. The therapist is permissive and accepting; he respects the child's ability to solve his own problems under proper conditions; he permits the child to lead the way. But in participating in play with his patient, the therapist consistently brings into focus the emotional attitudes which seem to support the child's specific responses. Thus if the child sucks contentedly from the toy nursing bottle, the therapist may remark that the child likes to drink from a baby's bottle. If the child in play makes one doll hit or destroy another, the therapist may say that one doll wants to hurt the other badly. It is always the attitudes which seem to support the patient's play behavior that the therapist formulates.

The same orderly process of development which characterizes non-directive adult therapy seems to occur in this type of play therapy. Negative reactions give way to positive ones; the therapist's consistent recognition of attitudes leads to behavior reorganization and often to the verbal formulation of problems. In the following illustration, for example, the basic problem of sibling rivalry is formulated finally by the child after many sessions of non-directive play therapy.

> The patient was a ten-year-old girl who refused to go to school, threatened to leave home, fought with her four older sisters and quarreled with her mother. Her five-year-old brother was clearly the favorite of the family. The girl's hostility toward her brother, her mixed reactions of acceptance and aggression toward her mother, and her confusion in

---

[46] Allen, F. H., *Psychotherapy with children.* New York: Norton, 1942.
[47] Axline, V. M., *Play therapy.* Boston: Houghton Mifflin, 1947.

her own sex role are highlighted by the therapist's recognition of her attitudes.

The therapist had been making a man's shoe out of clay. Ruth laughed about the size and asked if she was going to make a mate to it, so the therapist said she thought she would. She then made a woman's shoe, very much smaller. Ruth continued to pound her clay, remarked how sticky it was, made a rope and stretched it from ear to ear over her mouth. Then observing the progress of the woman's shoe, she laughed because it was so small. She objected that it was away out of proportion. The therapist said she would then make the man's shoe smaller. After a pause, Ruth said:

R. I think I would rather be a boy than a girl.
T. How so?
R. I don't know. Boys can play noisy things and do a lot of things a girl can't.
T. Seems like boys have more fun and girls have to act like ladies, is that it?
R. Um hm. . . . My girl friend and I would rather be boys.
T. I wonder why it seems so much nicer being a boy than a girl.
R. Oh, I don't know. . . . I think clubs should have boys in them too, instead of just girls. You know the lady next door, well she says our house looks just like a girls' dormitory. So many girls around.
T. Seems like just too many girls and not enough boys.
R. We have only one boy in our family. Sometimes people say I should have been a boy too.
T. I wonder why they say that?
R. Oh, I don't know. I guess I like to do the things boys do.

Later Ruth asks what time it is, and the following interchange takes place:

T. You have fifteen minutes more, Ruth.
R. Up at the cabin we have a sand box. You can make everything there . . . put leaves in for trees and everything.
T. And water in for lakes and rivers.
R. Yeah . . . the mother works at the Red Cross and she comes home about two o'clock every day and comes by and picks up the kids at school (*picking up the mother doll, putting her into the car, and collecting the children. Mother says:*) Sit down now. (*Boy standing on running board. The car zooms home to the garage. Mother gets out and says:*) Come into the house now.
R. She wants them to play a duet now. She's always making them do something like that.
T. While they probably don't even want to and would rather do something else.
R. Yeah, my mother makes me too. (*Boy and girl sit down at piano and after a moment boy is picked up and the girl is left sitting there.*)
R. She's going to play the piano. The girl wishes she didn't have to do things like that. . . .

T. She'd rather play the things boys do.

R. I'm a boy, you know.

T. You're a boy, Ruth? You think like a boy, you play like a boy, and you like the things boys like, and that makes you a boy? Or is it just that you wish very hard that you were a boy?

R. I *am* a boy. (*Playing with the boy doll again*) And now the mother says, "I want you children to play a duet."

T. The mother always tells them what she wants them to do, doesn't she? And like you, the children don't want to do everything she says.

R. No! (*Picks up the mother and bites her.*)

T. You're biting the mother. You want to destroy her.

R. I didn't swallow any. (*Continues to bite.*)

T. No, you didn't swallow any. But biting and eating are one way you express your feelings.

R. (*Takes mother out of her mouth and grates her teeth very hard.*) Sometimes I get mad and I feel like biting something. (*Puts the mother back in her mouth, then bites the other dolls. Mother and children are then placed in toy beds, all in the same room.*)

T. The children don't sleep in their own room, but go sleep with their mother.

R. She likes company because Daddy is away. The husband went away. They all go sleep with the mother because that's what they do on Friday night.

T. And they like to be with the mother.

R. Oh yes, they talk to all hours of the night. I sometimes sleep with her. My brother gets to sleep with her more.

T. Sometimes you wish you were that brother instead of Ruth.

R. I used to get all those things. But I'm not the littlest any more.

T. No, you're Ruth. You're not the baby. You're bigger. You can do things you couldn't do when you were smaller. And some of the things you have now you didn't have when you were little.

R. Oh, I'm bigger and I can do a lot of things my brother can't. I'm making a bird house. Should I show it to you when I come?

Systematic research on play techniques has thus far been centered more on the reactions of projection and abreaction, underlying play, than on the changes in behavior during the course of therapy. Levy's controlled studies of sibling-rivalry in a doll-play situation, which we described earlier, illustrate this variety of research.[48] Erikson reports a provocative group of studies, in which the children's play is less strictly controlled than in Levy's experiment. Erikson has been concerned with the interpretation of certain *spatial configurations* in his patients' play.[49] Thus he finds that insecure and anxious children tend to build play constructions against walls or in corners, and to show in other ways a need for support. In the same way, the height or breadth of play constructions — their open or closed-in character — may reflect the child's

---

[48] See pages 287–289.

[49] Erikson, E. H., "Configurations in play. Clinical notes." *Psychoanal. Quart.*, 1937, vol. 6, pp. 139–214.

projected sexual role. Erikson describes also the phenomenon of *play disruption*, the sudden or gradual inability to play which occurs when play no longer masks a child's anxieties.[50]

The interpretation of a given patient's play in therapy depends upon our understanding of what most normal children do when they are given an opportunity for free play. We are only beginning to collect the *normative* data which we need in order to identify certain play productions as deviant. A series of controlled experiments, conducted at the University of Iowa Child Welfare Research Station, provides an illustration of such normative studies.[51] The experimental subjects were groups of university preschool children, matched for sex, age and intelligence. The experimenters introduced into the play situations systematic variations in four dimensions: (*a*) in the extent of organization of the materials presented to the children, (*b*) in the closeness of personal interaction between adult and child, (*c*) in the degree of realism of the play materials, and (*d*) in the amount of frustration preceding and following the play sessions. Under these controlled conditions, the experimenters were able to demonstrate relationships between these experimental variables and such aspects of the children's play as its stereotypy, organization and aggressiveness.

Personal Interaction Among Groups of Patients and Therapists

A second general variety of therapy in behavior pathology involves personal interaction among *groups* of patients and therapists. This variety of therapeutic procedure is the natural consequence of our contemporary view of the development of pathological behavior. For, as we have seen throughout our whole discussion, behavior develops always in a social setting, where family constellations, the peer culture and the expectations of adult society outline the direction of social learning. And when behavioral development deviates from the group norm so severely as to become pathological, it is again the patient's social community which provides both the setting for his pathology, and the norms against which the severity of his illness is gauged. It is therefore not surprising that a great many therapists find the group situation a favorable environment for that social relearning which constitutes therapy.

The same characteristics which facilitate recovery through individual thera-

[50] Erikson, E. H., "Studies in the interpretation of play. Clinical observations of play disruption in young children." *Genet. Psychol. Monogr.*, 1940, vol. 22, pp. 557–671. Compare the description of play disruption on pages 449–450.

[51] Bach, G. R., "Young children's play fantasies." *Psychol. Monogr.*, 1945, vol. 59, no. 2; Phillips, R., "Doll play as a function of the realism of the materials and the length of the experimental session." *Child Develpm.*, 1945, vol. 16, pp. 123–143; Pintler, M. H., "Doll play as a function of experimenter-child interaction and initial organization of materials." *Child Develpm.*, 1945, vol. 16, pp. 145–166; Pintler, M. H., Phillips, R., and Sears, R. R., "Sex differences in the projective doll play of preschool children." *J. Psychol.*, 1946, vol. 21, pp. 73–80.

pist-patient interaction are to be found also in treatment involving groups of participants.[52] (1) *The therapeutic group is essentially a neutral, permissive situation.* Unlike the therapist-patient situation, the group does not provide the patient with an opportunity for a close relationship with one therapist; it does, however, supply the accepting or impartial reactions from others which favor social learning. (2) *In the therapeutic group, the patient's anxieties may be utilized to further social learning.* As we shall see, one of the functions of the hospital as a therapeutic environment is to prevent further disorganization in the patient's behavior by *reducing* his intense anxieties. In some group situations, however, as in some therapist-patient relationships, the patient's reactions of anxiety may be *employed* to provoke relearning. (3) *In the therapeutic group, the patient can formulate his own reactions and share them in social communication.* Particularly when the group includes other patients, with their own concerns and preoccupations, the patient can learn to judge the commonness of his own anxieties, and the extent of his own deviations from others. And in sharing his reactions with his peers he may be practicing the very techniques of social interaction in which he has typically remained unskilled.

There are many varieties of group interaction employed in therapy. Often several of them are used together, and combined with the patient-therapist relationship which we have earlier discussed, and with the therapies by assault which we shall describe later. Let us take three examples to illustrate the therapeutic use of groups: (1) *the psychiatric hospital setting;* (2) *artificially structured patient-groups*; and (3) *psychodrama.* These three varieties differ in their degree of organization, in the roles of the various participants, in the spans of time they cover, and in the aspects of behavior on which they focus. They all agree, however, in providing lifelike situations in which the patient can proceed with his social learning.

The therapeutic hospital

Hospitalization — or at least incarceration — is one of the oldest forms of treatment in behavior pathology.[53] As recently as 1800, patients suffering from behavior pathology were shut away from society, cast into prisons, chained in cells, or made to beg on the streets in order to survive. Toward the close of the eighteenth century and in the early years of the nineteenth, the general trend toward recognizing the dignity of the individual spread to include those who had developed pathological behavior. Hospitals were built to care exclusively for patients with behavior disorders, and the use of restraint as a means of controlling aggressive or agitated patients was gradually diminished. These changes were hastened by the efforts of such persons as Pinel,

---

[52] See pages 605–608.
[53] For a review of this form of treatment, see Henry, G. W., "Mental Hospitals." In Zilboorg, G., *A history of medical psychology.* New York: Norton, 1941, pp. 558–589.

a French physician who gained permission to unchain his patients; Tuke, a merchant who fought for decades against the restraint of patients in English hospitals; and the retired American school teacher, Dorothea Lynde Dix, whose heroic efforts to make known the low level of treatment of patients in this country and abroad led to the provision of more hospitals and better care. As a result of the work of these persons and of hundreds of others, hospitalization came to be considered more as a means of treatment and less as a mode of punishment.

It would be heartening if one could say that today hospitalized patients suffering from behavior pathology all obtain the sort of therapy that is possible in a well-organized psychiatric setting. Unfortunately this is not the case. In many hospitals and asylums in this country, patients are still restrained in cuffs or strait jackets, punished for their symptoms, or compelled to sit out their lives in dreary, unstimulating environments [54] which, as we have seen, hasten their deterioration and may render it finally irreversible. And a great many persons — often close relatives and friends of the patient — still look upon hospitalization as a welcome banishment of the patient to a place where he can no longer disturb and upset their own daily lives. These conditions are partly the result of understaffing and overwork among hospital personnel, but poorly staffed hospitals are themselves the consequence of public non-support. Indeed, the basic reason for inadequate hospital conditions today lies in the personal attitudes of fear, ridicule, distrust and repugnance which uninformed individuals still bear toward behavior pathology in others.

That hospital cannot be considered a therapeutic hospital which provides only food and shelter for its patients, and ignores the potentialities of group interaction for the treatment of its patients. Therefore, in what follows, we shall be concerned only with hospital settings which are planned in accordance with the individual needs of patients. In such hospitals the patient-group, in which an individual participates, is recognized as and used as a therapeutic agent. Likewise, the reactions of nurses and attendants to the patient, and his interactions with them, constitute as important therapeutic procedures as the relationship he makes with his therapist. In such a setting as this, restraint and punishment are regarded as grave therapeutic errors, whose occurrence indicates serious limitations in the hospital personnel. There are increasing numbers of such genuinely therapeutic hospitals in this country; and it is with their use in treatment that we are here concerned.

There are at least four functions which the well-planned therapeutic hospital can serve in the treatment of its patients.

1. *The therapeutic hospital protects the patient from the consequences of his own*

[54] See, for example, Deutsch, A., *The shame of the states.* New York: Harcourt, Brace, 1948.

behavior and from the adverse reactions of others. We have already seen the dangers of suicide, retaliation, assault, erotic advance and unwise legal transaction which threaten persons who suffer from severe behavior pathology. We have mentioned also the possibility that the disorganized or otherwise seriously disturbed patient may behave in public in ways that witnesses can never forget, so that his status in his community is irrevocably damaged. It is from such hazards as these that the therapeutic hospital protects its patients. Not only does hospitalization remove the patient from his own community and thereby interrupt the reactions of others toward him; it also provides an accepting setting within which the patient who needs to behave in threatening, agitated or excited ways, can do so without endangering his own life or the lives of others.

2. *The therapeutic hospital reduces and controls a patient's anxieties.* Often, as we have seen, if a patient remains in the environment in which his pathology has developed, he is likely to grow more and more disturbed, until his anxieties may become self-perpetuating. The same reactions of others toward him — and his reciprocal reactions toward them — which favored the acquisition of his pathological behavior, tend also to perpetuate it. Typically, neither the patient nor those close to him can comprehend or accept the extent to which the patient's customary environment may be intensifying his illness; and typically patient and family alike oppose hospitalization. For many patients, however, therapeutic hospitalization provides the neutral environment which is necessary if their anxieties are to be diminished so that they can profit from relearning. Frequently anxious patients achieve prompt and dramatic recoveries in the tension-reducing atmosphere of the therapeutic hospital.

3. *The therapeutic hospital provides routines of living which favor the reorganization of a patient's behavior.* We have met many patients whose difficulties seem to lie in the disintegration or distortion of the attitudes which support their responses. This has been particularly true of patients suffering from cerebral incompetence and of those who have developed schizophrenic disorganization.[55] The consequence of such a lack of consistent, supporting attitudes is ordinarily behavior which has suboptimal continuity or coherence. The setting of a therapeutic hospital provides a substitute behavioral background for the patient by furnishing organized daily routines which he can learn to follow. Ordered acts, such as regular rising, bathing, dressing and eating, which are simple and automatic for most persons, can often be carried through by seriously deteriorated or withdrawn patients only with the constant help and encouragement of hospital personnel. And sometimes, out of this context of artificial organization, a patient's own behavioral reorganization may develop.

4. *The therapeutic hospital provides the opportunity for social interaction*

[55] See pages 494–515 and 531–555.

among patients and staff members. In contemporary, well-planned therapeutic hospitals, patients are no longer shut away by themselves, isolated from social contacts or prevented from communicating with one another. As soon as a patient is able to move about among other people, without endangering himself or disrupting the group, he is encouraged to participate in ward activities with other patients and with staff members. Patients in modern hospitals take their meals together, assume responsibility for certain ward tasks, play group games, converse together, and attend concerts, movies and dances in the hospital. They may paint, sew, or do carpentry or metal work in informal groups; they may receive formal class training in these activities or in conventional academic subjects.

Such activities as these are neither busy work nor casual entertainment for the patient. They are selected and planned for each patient in accordance with his needs, his interests, and his social or manipulative skills. They are all carried out in a social setting. And they are all directed toward developing the competence in social interaction, in sharing and in shifting perspectives, which most patients lack. Many patients accomplish, in their groping, hesitant or aggressive approaches to trained and understanding nurses and attendants, their first steps in social relearning. Many patients also find, in the reactions of other patients with whom they share their daily activities, the acceptance, support, protection, challenge and competition which enable them to develop more valid self-reactions. Indeed, the structure of social interaction among patients in a permissive ward setting resembles closely the patterns of social interchange in any relatively stable group.[56]

By now it should be clear that a well-organized therapeutic hospital is neither a place of confinement nor a haven for rest and recreation. It is a miniature social community, planned and controlled to facilitate the social learning of its patients. It duplicates in many ways the social community from which the patient has come and to which he will one day return. The close resemblance between therapeutic hospital and an everyday social community, of course, favors the generalization of skills, which the patient acquires in the hospital setting, to situations outside the hospital environment. It is partly for this reason that a great many hospitalized patients, who are unable to develop a close relationship with one therapist, still improve and often recover completely during a period of hospitalization.

Planned therapeutic groups

In the therapeutic hospital, the relationships that a patient makes with others depend most often upon which patients happen to be residing together

---

[56] For a technique for analyzing the social interactions on the wards of therapeutic hospitals, see Hyde, R. W. and York, R. H., "A technique for investigating interpersonal relations in a mental hospital." *J. abn. soc. Psychol.*, 1948, vol. 43, pp. 287–299.

on the ward at a particular time. Few large hospitals have the facilities or the freedom necessary to distribute patients in such a way that their reciprocal reactions with other patients will be maximally therapeutic. Within a hospital, however, it may be possible to organize small groups of carefully selected patients who meet together with a therapist at regular intervals. Such planned therapeutic groups are relatively new additions to our techniques of treatment in behavior pathology. Because they make possible the simultaneous treatment of several patients, at one time and by one therapist, such planned therapeutic groups appear to be time-saving techniques, especially valuable in situations where pressure toward the prompt rehabilitation of many patients is strong. This factor was an important one in the development and wide use of therapeutic groups among psychiatric casualties in the second world war.[57]

As with all our therapeutic procedures, the varieties of planned therapeutic groups are many. At one extreme is the therapeutic group which strongly resembles a formal class situation.[58] Here the therapist serves as lecturer, and describes to a group of six to ten patients the course of maturation, the nature of conflict, frustration and adjustive techniques, and the relationship between persistent visceral activity and the development of certain symptoms. Often graphic aids add to the effectiveness of the lectures. Thus one therapist employs a series of pictures of boiling water in a tea kettle; the pictures begin with the steam leaving the kettle through the spout in the usual way, and succeeding pictures show the outcome when the spout is closed, steam accumulates, and the kettle finally "blows its top."[59] The therapist invites from his patients questions and discussion, which typically begin with factual topics, but which approach more and more closely the patients' own areas of concern as the sessions proceed. Eventually the group meetings, which have begun with theoretical lectures, evolve into opportunities for free discussion among patients of their own personal problems.

Contrasted sharply with this classroom approach is a second variety of planned therapeutic group, in which the reactions of the participating patients are made central from the beginning. The therapist is participant rather than leader, and the group's activities are guided as much as possible by the wishes of its members. In most adult patient groups of this kind, the major activity is discussion of whatever topics occur to the patients. The therapist attempts to keep the discussion going along productive lines, to see that the more withdrawn patients have an opportunity to contribute, and occasionally to reflect

[57] See, for example, Malone, T. P., "Analysis of the dynamics of group psychotherapy based on observations in a twelve-month experimental program." *J. Personality*, 1948, vol. 16, pp. 245–277; Roland, P. E., "An exploratory training technique for the re-education of catatonics." *Amer. J. Psychiat.*, 1948, vol. 105, pp. 353–356.

[58] Klapman, J. W., *Group psychotherapy: theory and practice.* New York: Grune and Stratton, 1946.

[59] Stein, M. I., "Visual aids in group psychotherapy for veterans with psychosomatic complaints." *J. clin. Psychol.*, 1948, vol. 4, pp. 206–211.

or to interpret the attitudes which seem to underlie the remarks made by the patients.

When this variety of therapeutic group method is employed with children or adolescents, on the other hand, the major activities are more likely to resemble those which recreational groups enjoy. The young patients are relatively free to select their own activities, and the choices are often those of games, parties, hikes, trips to movies and museums, or creative work with wood, paints or clay.[60] The therapist's role in such an activity group is essentially the same as his role in a company of adult patients. Usually, to be sure, he sets limits to the amount and kind of destructively aggressive behavior that is permitted. These limits are wide, however, and within them he participates as one of the group, providing opportunity for all his patients to share in the activities, and occasionally pointing up and interpreting their reactions.

Because of its free and apparently recreational nature, the technique of planned therapeutic groups is often mistakenly considered to be an easy, simple, undemanding method. There are, however, many differences between the planned therapeutic group, and the neighborhood recreational club which it superficially resembles. Indeed, the patients' need for therapy is in part the result of difficulties with interpersonal relationships; this fact alone makes it certain that a treatment group will differ from a non-treatment one. For example, seriously ill patients are always relatively ineffectual in their relationships to others. They are likely to seek more intensely for support from the authority figures in their environments, or to show unusual defiance or aloofness. They are often relatively inflexible in their attitudes, unable to share the perspectives of others, and slow to change their social reactions. Consequently, it is not surprising to find that systematic studies demonstrate that the structure of groups of patients initially shows little coherence, few lasting interpersonal relationships, and a preponderance of dependent attitudes toward the hospital or toward the therapist.[61]

The procedure of planned therapeutic groups requires as careful organizing, and as delicate handling of interpersonal relationships, as any individual or group technique in use. For one thing, the participants in a therapeutic group must be carefully selected. An outspoken or aggressive patient may be too threatening to the more withdrawn members, while a diffident, retiring patient may be submerged in a group of active, responsive ones. For another thing, the therapist's encouragement of free discussion, and his interpretation of what occurs in the group, must be done with consideration for the effect upon all the patient-participants. Some patients will be able to tolerate anxiety-provoking topics sooner than others; and some will have more ready defenses

[60] Slavson, S. R., *An introduction to group therapy.* New York: The Commonwealth Fund, 1943.

[61] Sandison, R. A. and Chance, E., "The measurement of the structure and behaviour of therapeutic groups." *J. ment. Sci.*, 1948, vol. 94, pp. 749–763.

against threat than others. Furthermore, the therapist himself may be forced into different roles by different patients. One patient may make him a target for aggression, while another may react protectively or possessively toward him. Under such circumstances, the therapist's maintenance of an impartial, accepting attitude is likely to become exceedingly difficult.

Even under these difficult conditions, however, planned therapeutic groups have been utilized with a wide variety of patients. The method has been applied, within a non-directive context, in the treatment of young children.[62] Groups of patients suffering from general developmental retardation have learned more effective social skills through participation in a therapeutic group.[63] Severely ill schizophrenic patients, who have previously been isolated because of their aggressive, destructive behavior, have come slowly and hesitatingly to participate in planned groups.[64] Some therapists now employ planned discussion groups in working with the close relatives of patients suffering from behavior pathology.[65] In such a setting, relatives have an opportunity to share their uncertainties about the patient's illness. They may also come to see the ways in which their own reactions have aggravated the patient's difficulties; and they may be able to learn more constructive and appropriate attitudes toward him and his illness.

The reasons for this extensive use of planned therapeutic groups lie to a considerable degree in the opportunity for direct social relearning which the groups provide. If the patient comes to identify with other participants, he may learn that his own reactions are neither as peculiar nor as incomprehensible as he had believed. Such "universalization" of a patient's reactions, as it has been called,[66] may in itself be tension-reducing. A patient may also find support in the reactions of other members of his group toward him, or even in the mere fact that he is accepted as one of a group of individuals. Freedom to participate with others, and acceptance by his peers — whether he is silent or talkative, retiring or forward — may provide the patient with the stable base he needs to resume his social learning.

The greatest contribution which the planned therapeutic group makes to its participants, however, is the opportunity it affords the patient to formulate and share with others his own reactions. In the group, the patient can try out his own customary ways of behaving toward others, and can see at once

[62] Axline, V. M., *Play therapy.* Boston: Houghton Mifflin, 1947.

[63] Cotzin, M., "Group psychotherapy with mentally defective problem boys." *Amer. J. ment. Def.*, 1948, vol. 53, pp. 268–283.

[64] Abrahams, J., "Preliminary report of an experience in the group psychotherapy of schizophrenics." *Amer. J. Psychiat.*, 1948, vol. 104, pp. 613–617.

[65] Ross, W. D., "Group psychotherapy with psychotic patients and their relatives." *Amer. J. Psychiat.*, 1948, vol. 105, pp. 383–386.

[66] Slavson, S. R., and Hallowitz, E., "Group psychotherapy." In Spiegel, E. A. (Ed.), *Progress in neurology and psychiatry: an annual review*, vol. 4. New York: Grune and Stratton, 1949, pp. 538–546.

the consequences which his own acts earn. He can communicate his fears and anxieties, the products of his fantasy and the fruits of his distorted thinking, and appraise them in terms of their acceptance or rejection by other persons like himself. In a sense, the reactions of participants in a planned therapeutic group constitute a consensus against which a patient can test the validity of his own reactions. The group is a lifelike social community that offers a challenge to autistic community and pseudocommunity, which these pathological developments cannot successfully meet. It provides an opportunity for socially valid thinking to prevail.

Psychodrama

More definitely structured than the hospital ward or the patient group — and organized in more minute detail than either of these — is the therapeutic technique called *psychodrama*.[67] This procedure was first employed in Vienna in 1921 by Moreno. Today the center for psychodrama is in Beacon, New York, where Moreno and his growing group of disciples utilize psychodramatic techniques in treating a variety of patients. Like all other therapeutic methods, psychodrama has its variants and subtypes, its devotees and its adversaries.

The technique of psychodrama rests upon a belief, derived in part from German personalistic psychology, that *spontaneity* is a necessary and desirable aspect of mature behavior. The individual who is socially skilled and adequate is one who is able to adapt readily to the demands of each new situation. Such ready adaptability requires, according to this theory, that the person be free and spontaneous in his reactions, rather than inflexible and stereotyped. Indeed, it is the individual lacking spontaneity who is most likely to maintain the rigid perspectives and show the inability to shift his viewpoint, which lead to pathological reactions. Consequently, therapy in behavior pathology must be directed toward the development of more spontaneous behavior; and this is what psychodrama attempts to achieve.

As it is carried out in Beacon, psychodramatic therapy takes place in a specially constructed theater, with circular stages at different levels, a balcony, and space for seating an audience. The therapist is director of the psychodramatic sessions. He publicly interviews one of the audience and outlines a dramatic scene on the basis of the interview. He then observes the action on the stage and serves as communicator between actors and spectators; or he may sit in the audience and there identify himself with the spectators as a group, or with one of them next to whom he chooses to seat himself. The action on the stage may be carried forward by one patient, a group of patients, or a company of patients and therapists together. The patient may play the role of himself, some member of his family, a close or distant acquaintance, a

67 Moreno, J. L., *Psychodrama.* New York: Beacon House, 1946.

stranger, or even the therapist. The events portrayed may be standard situations, or they may be incidents which closely resemble the patient's real-life problems, or even duplicate them. What is essential to the technique, however, is that the play-acting must always be unrehearsed.

First Moreno, and later many of his students and associates, described the successful use of psychodrama with patients. Persons who have acquired delusional and hallucinatory reactions, for example, begin their psychodramatic sessions in scenes which support their pathological behavior, and learn gradually to replace these inappropriate reactions with more valid ones. Even seriously disorganized schizophrenic patients are said to improve after practice in the spontaneity theater. Psychodrama has been employed with children and adults alike, with developmentally retarded patients, with persons legally judged delinquent, and with those who have developed mild difficulties in their interpersonal relationships. Recently Moreno has extended the technique to problems of marital maladjustment. The particular approach differs from one variety of problem to the next, but it seems clear that once the patients become engrossed in a dramatic scene, they go beyond the assigned action to situations and roles which reflect their own private conflicts.

From the descriptions of this technique, it is difficult to determine how much interpretation is made to the patient of his behavior, and how typical it is for patients to succeed in verbally formulating the needs and conflicts which have led to their pathological reactions. Nor is it easy to tell how close a relationship the patient develops with the therapist-director, how often individual interviews and planned ward activities are combined with psychodrama, or whether or not the patient is encouraged to try out his new roles off-stage. The use of stage properties, the deliberate utilization of audience-effect, and the dominant position occupied by the director further complicate the task of determining just what contributes to the reported improvement in the patient-actor's behavior.

In spite of the difficulties this method presents in relation to its evaluation, psychodrama seems definitely to provide certain of the conditions which favor social relearning. It is quite likely that spontaneous play-acting on a stage constitutes abreaction for many patients. The necessity for making appropriate responses to other characters in lifelike situations likewise affords practice in realistic interpersonal relationships. Probably more important than abreaction or personal interaction alone, however, is the direct training in role-taking which psychodrama furnishes the patient. On the psychodramatic stage the patient can develop roles which in his own life he has been able to learn inadequately or not at all. The practice in role-taking, sharing and shifting perspectives, which most persons gain in play and in fantasy, and in the contexts of parental, friendship or marital relationships, is prescribed deliberately for the patient-actor in the spontaneity theater. Psychodramatic therapy may thus be viewed as a controlled learning situation, in which the patient receives training in precisely those aspects of behavior in which he has remained immature or unskilled.

Therapy by Chemical, Electrical, or Surgical Interference

The therapeutic techniques we have been describing all require of the patient some degree of active participation. The patient must make some response to his environment. He must speak or move about; he must be able to follow ordinary routines or try out simple tasks. In order to profit from some of these therapeutic methods, he must be capable of developing a relationship with a therapist, or he must join a group without grossly disrupting the behavior of other persons. And in many of these therapies, the patient must eventually become able to speak of things which trouble him, to make self-accessible his repressed reactions, and to formulate in words his personal attitudes and responses.

There are a great many patients suffering from behavior pathology who cannot meet these requirements. There are some patients, for example, who are so negativistic, mute or stuporous that they are unresponsive to persons and objects in their environment. There are other patients who are so excited, agitated or disorganized that they cannot follow the simplest routines or join the most undemanding group. Still other patients are too preoccupied with their fantasy behavior, or too enmeshed in their own delusional thinking to develop a relationship with another person. And many patients, less seriously disturbed than these, even though they are able to participate in interviews and group activities, and to develop relationships with others, still cannot themselves make accessible and communicate the personal conflicts, anxieties and ambivalences, which form the pattern of their pathology.

Patients such as these have always been a challenge to the therapist. For if therapy is thought of as social relearning, then the patient who is to profit from therapy must be able first to make the responses upon which learning depends. The therapist who comes prepared to establish a miniature community for his patient, or to train him in free association or in group interchange, finds these approaches useless when he is faced by a withdrawn, stuporous schizophrenic patient, or stands in the presence of an excited manic patient, whose almost uninterrupted talking, singing and shouting seldom fall into the design of consecutive communication. It is to aid such patients as these that a number of auxiliary therapeutic techniques have been devised. Their aim is, or should be, to prepare the patients for the social participation, with one therapist or in a therapeutic group, which constitutes therapy. When they achieve this goal, they qualify as preliminary steps to social relearning.

Like many of our therapeutic methods, these auxiliary techniques are often the product of pragmatic test rather than the inevitable outcome of a theory of behavior pathology. They are used because they seem to work; in most of them, the question of why they work has not yet been satisfactorily answered. Sometimes these techniques used in isolation appear to be successful; the patient recovers or improves without the elaborate individual or group therapies for which the techniques may be preparatory. In such cases, the reasons for the efficacy of these auxiliary techniques are ordinarily sought in some area other than biosocial learning — for example, in physiological or anatomical changes in the central nervous system. Let us take three examples to illustrate these auxiliary chemical and surgical procedures: (1) *narcosis;* (2) *shock therapy;* (3) *cerebral damage by surgery.*

Narcosis [68]

The use of some form of sedation, producing anything from relaxation to prolonged sleep, has been an auxiliary therapy in behavior pathology for centuries. Anxious, excited, depressed or otherwise tense patients can be spared the fatigue resulting from sleeplessness and overactivity by the prescription of a mild sedative. In 1922, Klaesi suggested increasing sedation to the point where the patient remained continuously asleep for long periods of time. He reported that *continuous sleep therapy* brought improvement to excited and agitated depressed patients, and to some patients suffering from schizophrenic disorder. Klaesi explained the efficacy of continuous sleep as therapy by assuming that the patient awoke from sleep in a weakened state and consequently looked at once for help. The patient was therefore in a receptive mood for individual interview therapy. Others, however, believed that the patient's improvement was the direct result of physiological changes induced by the medication.

As therapists began following Klaesi's lead in using prolonged sleep, conflicting reports of the success of this treatment appeared. Today continuous sleep therapy is considered a symptomatic procedure only, and one which is typically unpredictable in its results. It is most successful in the treatment of severe, acute anxiety reactions of the sort which combat soldiers often develop.[69] Even in these cases, however, it is not necessarily the narcosis itself which leads to changed behavior. It may be, instead, the individual therapy, to which the patient is accessible when he awakens, that leads to his improvement.

---

[68] For reviews of this technique, see Kalinowsky, L. B., and Hoch, P. H., *Shock treatments and other somatic procedures in psychiatry.* New York: Grune and Stratton, 1946, pp. 205–206; and Sargent, W., and Slater, E., *An introduction to somatic methods of treatment in psychiatry.* Baltimore: Williams and Wilkins, 1944, pp. 100–110.

[69] For a discussion of recent applications of narcosis, see Clapp, J. S., and Loomis, E. A., "Continuous sleep treatment: observations on the use of prolonged, deep, continuous narcosis in mental disorders." *Amer. J. Psychiat.*, 1950, vol. 106, pp. 821–829.

A more common variety of narcotic treatment than continuous sleep is that which is known as *narcosynthesis*. Enough sedation is employed to make the patient relaxed and drowsy, but not enough to produce actual sleep. Occasionally the patient begins talking spontaneously at this point; more frequently the therapist must stimulate discussion by introducing topics which have some personal significance to the patient. As a rule, the patient is then able to recall past events which have remained previously inaccessible to his self-reactions. Often he recounts these events with an intensity of emotional participation that makes his recall seem like a reliving of the original episodes. During this period, the therapist provides, through his own remarks, whatever support the patient seems to need. It is while the patient is gradually awakening, however, that the therapist plays his most crucial role. He helps the patient to continue formulating and discussing the previously self-inaccessible events, but at the same time he aids the patient in seeing that these events are past, and can no longer constitute a present threat. It is this synthesis of formerly self-inaccessible reactions with the patient's current behavior organization which often leads to improvement and eventual recovery.

Like prolonged sleep, narcosynthesis has been used most extensively with military personnel suffering from severe anxiety reactions, which have been precipitated by frightening or horrifying combat incidents.[70] Whether the technique will prove equally effective in cases of civilians who develop behavior pathology remains to be seen.[71] It is clear, however, from the military applications of this method, that narcosynthesis has many of the same properties as hypnosis and free association. For these three techniques alike facilitate the formulation and sharing of behavior which is otherwise inaccessible to a patient's self-reactions. In all three, however, the continuous participation of the therapist is essential to the patient's reorganization of his behavior. Narcosynthesis, like many of the auxiliary therapies, would have little effectiveness were it not combined with a personal interrelationship between patient and therapist.

All chemical and surgical procedures have their dangers; and therapeutic narcosis is no exception to this rule. Particularly in prolonged narcosis, there is an impressive list of potential complications. Bronchopneumonia, cardiovascular collapse, toxic confusions, renal damage, urinary retention and persistent vomiting may all follow upon inadequately controlled narcotic therapy. The withdrawal of the drug after behavioral improvement is also dangerous. Most of the barbiturates employed in this variety of therapy must be cut down gradually; abrupt withdrawal produces immediate or delayed convulsions in a number of patients. Continuous vigilance on the part of medical and nursing

[70] Grinker, R. R., and Spiegel, J. P., *Men under stress*. Philadelphia: Blakiston, 1945.
[71] See, for example, Freed, H., "Narcosynthesis for the civilian neuroses." *Psychiat. Quart.*, 1946, vol. 20, pp. 39–55.

staffs is essential if the advantages of narcotic therapy are to outweigh its hazards.

Shock therapy

There are probably no contemporary therapies in behavior pathology which have been greeted with greater enthusiasm, or applied with more uncritical optimism, than chemical and electric shock. Actually shock therapies of various sorts are among the oldest treatments in behavior pathology. The purgative and blood-letting procedures which dominated ancient medical therapy were often applied indiscriminately to patients suffering from behavior pathology. Purgatives and blood-letting as therapies in behavior pathology still continued through the seventeenth and into the eighteenth century. In 1679, for example, Th. Bonet described a young woman suffering from mania who was bled until she died. To such strenuous treatments were added threats and blows, on the theory that the fearful and intimidated patient would promptly give up his wild notions and become quiet and orderly. The famous neuroanatomist Thomas Willis wrote, in the seventeenth century, ". . . maniacs often recover much sooner if they are treated with torture and torments in a hovel instead of with medicaments." [72] As late as 1812, the otherwise humane reformer Benjamin Rush advocated treating aggressive patients by pouring cold water into their armpits and down their torsos.

That such methods of treatment occasionally produced cures, no behavior pathologist can deny. Indeed, almost any experienced therapist can recall at least one of his patients who apparently recovered symptomatically after a chance shocking or frightening event which, however, was irrelevant to the main course of therapy. A patient may improve after an accidental fall down the stairs, a narrow escape from fire, an unexpected personal loss, or a fortuitous piece of good luck. It is therefore hardly surprising to find that planned and systematic applications of shock may hasten the recovery of patients today, or that these techniques are advocated by a great many contemporary therapists. Present-day shock therapies, of course, are administered without the punitive overtones which characterized their use in previous centuries, but they still depend for their effectiveness upon severe trauma to the patient's biological and social integrity.

Insulin shock treatment is the oldest of our contemporary shock therapies in this country. Around 1930, injections of insulin were employed as a means of stimulating a patient's appetite and increasing his weight. Occasionally insulin seemed also to evoke general behavioral improvement, particularly in excited patients, and in those suffering from the withdrawal symptoms of morphine addiction. During such symptomatic treatments, it was accidentally found that when large insulin dosages created an abnormal deficiency of sugar

[72] Zilboorg, G., *A history of medical psychology.* New York: Norton, 1941, pp. 261–262.

in the patient's blood (*hypoglycemia*), the patient's subsequent behavior often showed marked improvement. Consequently, therapists began to induce hypoglycemia — producing coma and sometimes convulsions in their patients — as a deliberate therapeutic measure in behavior pathology. In 1933, the Viennese psychiatrist Sakel reported the first systematic use of hypoglycemic shock therapy in patients suffering from severe behavior pathology.[73]

Since Sakel's first report, therapists have employed insulin shock widely as a method of treatment, particularly with patients suffering from schizophrenic disorders. The exact techniques vary from one hospital to another. They vary also from one patient to the next — since individuals differ greatly in their sensitivity to insulin, and in the promptness with which the normal chemical balance of their blood can be restored after hypoglycemia. In general, the procedure is to reduce the blood sugar level by means of insulin injections until the patient becomes confused, disoriented and stuporous, and finally goes into coma. The patient is kept comatose for perhaps half an hour, and the coma is then terminated by the administration of carbohydrates. Convulsions often occur early in each treatment period; somewhat less frequently there are severe seizures while the patient is comatose. Insulin treatments of this sort are sometimes given daily, with an occasional day of rest, until the patient's total behavior permits him to profit from planned or incidental forms of social relearning.

Metrazol shock therapy, which was accepted in this country somewhat later than insulin shock, stems from the belief that convulsions are themselves therapeutic in cases of behavior pathology. In 1928 Meduna[74] reported the deliberate therapeutic production of seizures in schizophrenic patients by the injection of camphor. Meduna cited the hypothesis, since called into serious question, that patients with convulsive symptoms rarely developed schizophrenic disorganization, and that schizophrenic patients who suffered also from convulsive disorders were likely to recover.[75] Because camphor is a rather unpredictable convulsant, Meduna later substituted for it *metrazol*, a preparation which produces convulsions in a prompt and predictable fashion. As in the case of insulin shock, the method, number and frequency of metrazol treatments given vary from patient to patient, and from one therapist to another. It seems clear, however, that sudden and widespread changes in the patient's total behavior sometimes follow only a few induced seizures.

Electroshock therapy is the newest and most widely employed of the contemporary shock procedures. As in metrazol therapy, it is the convulsion in

[73] Kalinowsky, L. B., and Hoch, P. H., *Shock treatments and other somatic procedures in psychiatry.* New York: Grune and Stratton, 1946, p. 4.

[74] Meduna, L. V., "Versuche über die biologische Beeinflussung des Ablaufes der Schizophrenie: Kampfer und Cardiozolkrämpfe." *Z. ges. Neurol. Psychiat.*, 1935, vol. 152, pp. 235–262.

[75] Kalinowsky, L. B., and Hoch, P. H., *Shock treatments and other somatic procedures in psychiatry.* New York: Grune and Stratton, 1946, p. 4.

electroshock treatment which is regarded by those who use it as the major
curative agent. Cerletti and Bini first proposed the use of electric current as
a convulsive stimulus at an international meeting on modern treatment in
schizophrenia, held in 1937 in Switzerland. The following year in Italy,
electroshock therapy was demonstrated for the first time. As it is used today,
the technique consists in placing electrodes bilaterally over the temporal regions
of the skull and passing an electric current, presumably through the cortex,
for a fraction of a second. The immediate effect of this electrical stimulation
is a generalized convulsion which ordinarily lasts about a minute. After the
convulsion, the patient may remain stuporous for a time, or he may awaken
at once. Most patients receive a series of electroshock treatments, two or
three times a week — sometimes more often than this — until they appear
able to profit from individual or group therapy alone.

The results of insulin, metrazol and electroshock therapy are exceedingly
difficult to appraise. Optimistic and often extravagant claims for their success
were common when these therapies were first introduced. Certainly there are
still sizeable numbers of patients who appear to recover after shock treatment.[76]
When these figures are compared with the recovery rates for patients receiving
other therapy, or for those who improve spontaneously without intensive
therapy, however, the benefits of shock therapy seem much less impressive
than the earlier claims indicated.[77] And when patients subjected to various
forms of therapy are followed up for periods as long as five years, the picture
becomes even more confusing. In some controlled follow-up studies, the advantages of shock therapy seem almost negligible; in others, the patients
treated with shock appear to maintain their recoveries longer than do patients
not so treated.[78] Patients suffering from depressive disorders seem to profit
more promptly from electroshock, and to respond little to insulin therapy.
In other disorders, however — including the schizophrenic disorganization
for which the shock therapies were originally designed — the evidence is so
conflicting that no final conclusion seems warranted.

If the statistics regarding recovery rates with shock therapy are conflicting,
the reasons advanced for those behavioral changes which do occur are even
more confusing. This is due partly to the differing procedures which are

[76] Kolb, L., and Vogel, V. H., "Use of shock therapy in 305 mental hospitals." *Amer. J.
Psychiat.*, 1942, vol. 99, pp. 90–100.
[77] See, for example, Notkin, J., Niles, C. E., DeNatale, F. J., and Wittman, G., "Comparative study of hypoglycemic shock treatment and control observation in schizophrenia."
Amer. J. Psychiat., 1939, vol. 96, pp. 681–688; "Comparative study of metrazol treatment
and control observations of schizophrenia." *Arch. Neurol. Psychiat.*, 1940, vol. 44, pp.
568–577; Craig, J. B., and Schilling, M. E., "Comparison of results of metrazol therapy with
group of matched controlled cases." *Amer. J. Psychiat.*, 1941, vol. 98, pp. 180–184; Rickles,
N. K., and Polan, C. G., "Causes of failure in treatment with electric shock; analysis of
38 cases." *Arch. Neurol. Psychiat.*, 1948, vol. 59, pp. 337–346.
[78] Finiefs, L. A., "The results of treatment of a thousand cases of schizophrenia." *J.
ment. Sci.*, 1948, vol. 94, pp. 575–580.

employed in selecting patients for shock therapy, and in the variations in details of these techniques, as they are actually applied. Furthermore, shock therapy is typically used in a hospital setting, where the patient is part of a controlled social situation, which is itself therapeutic. Shock is often combined with individual interview therapy or with planned group therapy. Under such circumstances it is impossible to assess exactly the relative contributions to the patient's recovery of shock alone, of personal interaction, and of routinized group living. This ambiguous situation invites speculation to the extent that there are at least fifty separate theories which have been advanced to account for the efficacy of shock treatment.[79]

Many of these theories hold that shock induces certain alterations in biological functioning, and that such alterations are responsible for gross behavioral changes. Among the most general are the hypotheses according to which shock stimulates the sympathetic nervous system and the cardiovascular system, thereby producing improvement in total behavior. More specific theories single out for emphasis particular changes in cellular function in the central nervous system. Thus therapists who consider that behavior pathology is the consequence of pathological cell tissue hold that shock is effective because it alters or destroys the pathological cells. Perhaps the most popular of the biological theories today is the one which ascribes the success of shock therapy to metabolic changes in brain cells, particularly to reduced oxidation in the cells of the cerebral cortex. That the various forms of shock therapy do induce sympathetic and cardiovascular changes, alter cell metabolism and result in some cell destruction seems reasonably certain. The exact relationship between these biological changes and recovery from behavior pathology — if, indeed, such a relationship exists — remains exceedingly obscure.

A great many theorists prefer to formulate their explanations of the efficacy of shock in biosocial rather than biological terms. Insulin, metrazol and electric current are said to be "shocking" to the patient in an analogous way to the shock of an icy bath, an accidental fall, or unexpected bad news. The proponents of this hypothesis claim that, for many patients, shock therapy is a terrifying treatment, representing a threat of death which must be overcome, a period of helplessness which forces the patient to seek the support of his therapist, or a deserved punishment that is itself tension-reducing.[80] Other behavior pathologists emphasize the periods of amnesia which occasionally occur in the course of, and after, shock therapy. During such periods, it is said, the patient is relieved of his conflicts and anxieties because he cannot remember them; consequently he is in a favorable position to reorganize his

[79] Gordon, H. L., "Fifty shock therapy theories." *Milit. Surg.*, 1948, vol. 103, pp. 397–401.

[80] See, for example, Alper, T. G., "An electric shock patient tells his story." *J. abn. soc. Psychol.*, 1948, vol. 43, pp. 201–210; compare also the discussion of need for punishment on pages 41–42.

behavior along new lines. Still other theorists point out that shock therapy necessarily makes the patient the center of special optimistic attention from physicians and nurses. Such special attention, particularly in large, under-staffed hospitals, may be the crucial factor which promotes recovery.

All of these theories have aroused much controversy among contemporary behavior pathologists. As yet, we lack detailed information regarding the etiology of behavior pathology, the exact effects of shock therapy, and the patients' attitudes toward shock, which we need to resolve the controversy. Shock therapy remains a therapeutic approach which is employed because, for some patients, it appears to work. The justification for this procedure is nicely put in a recent review of shock therapies: "At present we can only say that we are treating empirically disorders, whose etiology is unknown, with shock treatments whose action is also shrouded in mystery." [81]

When both the fact and the explanation of the success of therapy are in doubt, we must inquire carefully whether the advantages of the treatment outweigh its dangers. Like all chemical, electrical and surgical procedures, shock therapy has its hazards. There are complications which may follow any of the shock therapies, although they seem to be least frequent in electroshock, most frequent in metrazol therapy, and most serious in insulin shock treat-ment.[82] Pneumonia, cardiac and circulatory disturbances, and activation of tuberculosis have all been reported as sequelae of shock therapy. More com-mon than these complications are the fractures and dislocations which may occur when a patient is in a deliberately induced convulsion. Currently a great many attempts are being made to reduce these dangers.

Far more hazardous than the complications following shock therapy, how-ever, is the cerebral damage which it may induce. There is considerable evi-dence that during and immediately after shock the patient exhibits behavior characteristic of brain injury.[83] That brain injury actually may occur is indi-cated by the post-mortem studies of forty-seven metrazol and insulin deaths, which demonstrated that all these patients had suffered cerebral damage.[84] A growing number of animal investigations, in which monkeys, dogs, cats or mice are subjected to experimental shock, appear to support the belief that shock induces cerebral incompetence. Whether the damage is typically irre-versible is still unclear, although there are certainly some cases in which brain impairment appears to be permanent. This, of course, is in line with those

[81] Kalinowsky, L. B., and Hoch, P. H., *Shock treatments and other somatic procedures in psychiatry.* New York: Grune and Stratton, 1946, p. 243.

[82] Kolb, L., and Vogel, V. H., "Use of shock therapy in 305 mental hospitals." *Amer. J. Psychiat.*, 1942, vol. 99, pp. 90–100.

[83] See, for example, Watkins, C., Stainbrook, E. J., and Löwenbach, H., "Report on sub-convulsive reaction to electric shock and its sequelae in normal subjects." *Psychiat. Quart.*, 1941, vol. 15, pp. 724–729.

[84] Kinsey, J. L., "Incidence and cause of death in shock therapy." *Arch. Neurol. Psychiat.*, 1941, vol. 46, pp. 55–58.

theories of shock treatment which assign its therapeutic effect to cellular destruction in the brain.

Cerebral damage by surgery

Closely related to shock therapy, in that they deliberately produce brain damage, are certain surgical procedures for the treatment of behavior pathology. As early as 1890, a Swiss psychiatrist named Burckardt was treating his patients by means of surgical excision of parts of the cerebral cortex. This form of therapy was not generally used, however, until Moniz and Lima, in 1936, reported their observations on lobectomized monkeys, and on patients who had undergone extirpation of the frontal lobes because of the presence of brain tumor. Moniz reported that the monkeys failed to develop agitation in stressful test situations, and that the operated human patients seemed unworried and unconcerned about their personal problems. From these observations it was only a short step to the surgical damage of the frontal lobes as a mode of therapy for agitated patients.

Today there are many procedures of inducing frontal lobe impairment which are employed in an effort to change the patient's total behavior. Of these, one of the most common is the procedure developed and used extensively by Freeman and Watts [85] and called *prefrontal lobotomy*. The operation does not involve actual extirpation of brain tissue, but rather the severing of neural connections between the prefrontal area, and the thalamus and hypothalamus. It is reported that the most reliable changes in the patient's behavior follow only when there has been extensive bilateral severance of fibers, including those of the anterior thalamic radiation. Post-mortem studies of patients subjected to this surgery indicate that one effect of the procedure is that of degeneration of part of the thalamus.

Prefrontal lobotomy has now been performed on a sufficiently large number of patients to permit us to describe the typical consequences of this operation in the patient's behavior. Immediately after surgery, the patient is disoriented and either restless or apathetic. He usually shows loss of sphincter control, which is usually transient but sometimes persistent. He may develop an enormous appetite and gain markedly in weight. Not infrequently he has convulsive attacks, which may or may not recur. As these more immediate effects wane, the patient begins to reveal other characteristics which seem to be the indirect result of the surgery. He may be tactless and outspoken, careless about his personal appearance, sarcastic, vulgar and profane. He is likely to be somewhat cheerful or even euphoric, although some patients show extreme swings from depression to elation. He lacks spontaneity, rarely

[85] Freeman, W., and Watts, J. W., *Psychosurgery*. Springfield, Illinois: C. C. Thomas, 1942.

initiates activity independently, and appears inattentive and unresponsive. In extreme instances, the patient lapses into an almost vegetative existence.

This array of behavior characteristics represents a distinct change from the agitation and aggressiveness for which prefrontal lobotomy is most often recommended as therapy. Indeed, it appears as though a new set of symptoms has been substituted for the old ones. Whether such a substitution is considered desirable or not, of course, depends entirely upon the goal of therapy. If the aim is to make the patient quieter and more tractable, prefrontal lobotomy appears to be an advantageous procedure. Perhaps in some situations the apathy and inertia following induced brain damage can be regarded as preferable to the unrelieved restlessness and agitation which preceded operation.[86] If the aim of therapy is the social rehabilitation of the patient, however, the advantages of prefrontal lobotomy are questionable. Freeman and Watts emphasize the need for lengthy retraining of the patients after surgery; but even with retraining many patients show serious pathological residuals.[87]

Surgical damage as a means of therapy is still so new that extensive studies evaluating its efficacy are not yet available.[88] The extent to which patients can learn new modes of behavior after surgery is still unknown. Some studies employing psychometric tests indicate no extensive impairment of performance post-operatively; but conventional tests of this sort are not always sensitive to changes induced by brain damage. On the other hand, tasks designed to measure creativeness, reasoning and conceptualization often show lobotomized patients to be deficient in these respects.[89] Certainly prefrontal lobotomy is a radical procedure which is beset with greater dangers than either narcosis or shock. It is for this reason that its use is ordinarily restricted to chronic, severely ill patients, whose long terms of hospital residence and whose resistance to more painstaking types of therapy have led to their being designated as "incurable."

Narcosis, shock therapy and lobotomy have been defended in many different ways by different therapists. But, quite apart from the question of the validity of the rationale presented in support of one or another of these procedures, it is a fact that each is capable of producing marked changes in a patient's behavior

[86] See, for example, Jones, R. E., "Personality changes in psychotics following prefrontal lobotomy." *J. abn. soc. Psychol.*, 1949, vol. 44, pp. 315–328; Malmo, R. B., and Shagass, C., "Behavioral and physiologic changes under stress after operations on the frontal lobes." *Arch. Neurol. Psychiat.*, 1950, vol. 63, pp. 113–124.

[87] For a review of recent studies on this point, see Freeman, W., "Psychosurgery: A. Neuropsychiatric aspects." In Spiegel, E. A. (Ed.), *Progress in neurology and psychiatry: an annual review*, vol. 4. New York: Grune and Stratton, 1949, pp. 394–395.

[88] See, however, Landis, C., Zubin, J., and Mettler, F. A., "The functions of the human frontal lobe." *J. Psychol.*, 1950, vol. 30, pp. 123–138; Columbia-Greystone Associates, *Selective partial ablation of the frontal cortex.* New York: Hoeber, 1949.

[89] For a review of these studies, see Freeman, W., "Psychosurgery: A. Neuropsychiatric aspects." In Spiegel, E. A. (Ed.), *Progress in neurology and psychiatry: an annual review*, vol. 4. New York: Grune and Stratton, 1949, pp. 392–393.

— particularly in the kind and the level of his responsiveness to environmental stimulation. During narcosis, and after shock or lobotomy, patients often react differently to persons and objects around them. Consequently they may acquire attitudes and responses that differ considerably from those which have contributed to their behavior pathology. In this way, therapy by chemical, electrical or surgical interference may serve as a prelude to the social relearning which is the goal of therapy in individual and group interaction. The distinguishing mark of contemporary therapy in behavior pathology is its emphasis upon social learning. For this reason, we turn now to an explicit and detailed consideration of the learning principles involved in biosocial therapy.

19

Learning and Therapy

Throughout our study of behavior pathology, we have found a variety of conditions that initiate, intensify and perpetuate distorted and inappropriate reactions. Special reaction-sensitivities, for example, may transform neutral, uncomplicated situations into bewildering confusions and terrifying threats; the patient reorganizes an indifferent social community into a dangerous pseudocommunity.[1] Persistent stress, conflict and frustration lead to intolerable anxiety and, if unrelieved, may eventuate in widespread behavioral disorganization.[2] Some persons who succeed in minimizing their anxieties, do so by developing techniques which are themselves inappropriate, costly and in the end personally unrewarding. Others show themselves unable to identify, formulate and share their own reactions; they evidence a fascination with their own fantasy products, or reveal grave discrepancies between their self-reactions and the reactions of the consensus toward them. And in most instances of pathological behavior, we have found serious defects in role-taking skills, and an inability to shift perspectives to meet adequately the demands of the fluid, shifting field of social operations.

We have seen repeatedly that pathological reactions, such as these, emerge from normal ones through the process of social learning.[3] The patient, in his relationships with parents, siblings and peers, has acquired the special reaction-sensitivities and self-reactions, the ill-defined or meager repertory of social roles, and the ineffectual techniques of handling anxiety which have led to his illness. And, as we have also seen, it is through a similar process of social learning, in a setting of personal interrelationship, that patients acquire the more valid and appropriate behavior which leads toward recovery.[4] In the

[1] See pages 387–392.   [2] See pages 458–469.
[3] For a discussion of social learning, see pages 55–63.
[4] See pages 561–581.

course of therapy, they come to replace their pathological reactions with so-cially adaptive behavior through the same general procedures as those by which they developed their pathology — through social learning in a context of persons and cultural products. The keystone of contemporary therapy is thus *learning in social interaction.*

Behavior pathologists and learning theorists, in increasing numbers, are attempting to work out explicitly the relationships between human learning, as it is studied in the laboratory, and the changes in behavior which occur in therapy.[5] The task is by no means an easy one. For the social learning which goes on during therapy does not proceed in the orderly, step-by-step fashion which characterizes the acquisition of new behavior in the laboratory. Like the tortuous and uneven course of lifelong learning which underlies the development of pathological reactions, the acquisition of more valid behavior in therapy is complex, irregular and time-consuming. Furthermore, there are many different contemporary theories of learning, just as there are many different contemporary varieties of therapy.[6] An explanatory principle derived from one learning theory may account for the development of some single symptom, for example, and the success of one sort of therapy in alleviating that symptom; but no single present-day learning theory is complete enough to account for the efficacy of our diverse methods of therapy.

If we cannot match theory to therapy, however, we can begin with the principles of learning, which we have earlier discussed, and see how they are involved in the varieties of treatment we have already considered.[7] We shall find that certain therapies seem to be aimed only at changing the patient's level of responsiveness, while other therapies provide miniature social communities which favor relearning and generalization. Some therapeutic procedures depend upon a close personal interrelationship to produce behavioral change, while others furnish direct tuition in role-taking and shifting perspectives. Some treatment methods emphasize the formulation and sharing of self-inaccessible reactions. Other methods disregard verbal formulations almost entirely, and rely rather upon tension-reduction as a means of altering behavior. No therapy fits exactly any single theory of learning, but all thera-

---

[5] For examples of these attempts, from various viewpoints, see Dollard, J., and Miller, N. E., *Personality and psychotherapy.* New York: McGraw-Hill, 1950; Magaret, A., "Generalization in successful psychotherapy." *J. consult. Psychol.,* 1950, vol. 14, pp. 64–69; Mowrer, O. H., "Identification: A link between learning theory and psychotherapy." In Mowrer, O. H., *Learning theory and personality dynamics.* New York: Ronald, 1950, pp. 573–616; Shaffer, L. F., "The problem of psychotherapy." *Amer. Psychologist,* 1947, vol. 2, pp. 459–467; Shaw, F. J., "A stimulus-response analysis of repression and insight in psychotherapy." *Psychol. Rev.,* 1946, vol. 53, pp. 36–42; Shaw, F. J., "The role of reward in psychotherapy." *Amer. Psychologist,* 1949, vol. 4, pp. 177–179; Shoben, E. J., Jr., "Psychotherapy as a problem in learning theory." *Psychol. Bull.,* 1949, vol. 46, pp. 366–392.

[6] See pages 53–55.

[7] See Chapter 3.

pies involve one or more of the general phenomena of learning which are to be found in the development of both normal and pathological reactions.

Responsiveness and learning in therapy

Learning, we have said, can occur only when the organism makes some response to stimulation; and human organisms differ widely in the breadth and ease of their responsiveness. We have seen that individual differences in general reactivity can be demonstrated even among young infants; and that responsive children differ from relatively unresponsive ones in the reactions they elicit from others.[8] We have also seen that, early in life, different individuals acquire different reaction-sensitivities, and these prompt them to react in diverse ways in the same stimulating situations.[9] Indeed, by their own differential sensitivities to persons and objects around them, young children may acquire patterns of behavior which make them strongly susceptible, or relatively immune, to the development of behavior pathology later on.

Comparable individual differences in responsiveness characterize patients who have already acquired behavior pathology. Mute or stuporous patients, for example, are *generally unresponsive* to stimulation.[10] Excited, resistant and hyperactive patients are *generally overresponsive* to persons and objects in their environment.[11] Patients who cannot formulate and share their reactions are often *selectively unresponsive* — unable to react to stimulation which touches upon important personal topics.[12] Patients who have developed fixed viewpoints and inflexible attitudes are likewise selectively unresponsive — incapable of shifting their perspectives in the direction of social validity. It is often the case that such unresponsive or hyperactive patients can profit little, or not at all, from the stimulation to social relearning that therapy offers them.

It is for patients who are selectively unresponsive, either because of repression or because of inability to shift perspectives, that many of our most ingenious therapeutic techniques have been devised. *Free association* and the *interpretation of dreams*, often enable a patient to include reactions in his behavioral repertory which he formerly could not. *Hypnoanalysis* and *narcosynthesis* aim at extending the patient's range of responsiveness to encompass previously repressed material. *Psychodrama*, in providing training in spontaneity, encourages the patient to widen his reactivity by exchanging for his stereotyped, inflexible behavior a new facility in shifting perspectives. In less specific fashion, the *permissive attitudes* which characterize modern methods of patient-therapist interaction help to broaden the patient's area of responsiveness. A neutral environment and an impartial therapist encourage the patient

[8] See pages 22–24.   [9] See pages 69–75.
[10] Compare pages 503 and 533.
[11] See the discussion of manic disorders on pages 329–336.
[12] This point is further discussed in connection with *repression*, on pages 337–351.

to communicate reactions which he might well withhold in a more threatening situation.[13]

Any therapeutic procedure which favors optimal responsiveness in a patient may contribute to the ease of his social learning. A change in responsiveness alone, however, does not guarantee that the subsequent learning will bring a patient closer to socially valid and appropriate ways of behaving. In a sense, therefore, treatment methods which change a patient's reactivity are only prologues to the more specific and more thorough forms of learning upon which successful therapy depends. And these forms of learning involve the same six principles which we have already singled out as determinants of behavior pathology.[14] Consequently, in what follows we shall see that in therapy (1) *learning occurs in a social context;* (2) *the reactions which are acquired are patterned sequences of behavior;* (3) *learning proceeds according to the patient's needs;* (4) *learning is facilitated by tension-reduction;* (5) *excitants to learned reactions become self-accessible;* and (6) *learning often involves a sudden reorganization of ongoing behavior.*

(1) *Learning in therapy occurs in an environment of other persons and cultural products, in directions defined by the prevailing cultural pattern.* Human behavior, whether normal or pathological, is always acquired in a social context. The attitudes and self-reactions, the roles and reaction-sensitivities, which make up any person's distinctive behavior organization are always the product of social interaction. We have seen that parental emphases, sibling rivalries, and acceptance or rejection by peers may all determine the paths which an individual takes in his progress toward biosocial maturity. And we have found repeatedly, in studying the life histories of our patients, that behavioral distortion or impoverishment may result from particular kinds of interaction with parents, siblings and peers. Pathological reactions, like all other behavior, develop in a social community; it is likewise in a therapeutic social community that pathological reactions give way to more normal behavior organization.[15]

All varieties of therapy, of course, are carried out in an environment of other persons. The extent to which these persons participate in therapy, however, and the exact roles they play, differ from one sort of therapy to another. A nurse, in caring for a patient during shock treatment, or a physician, in administering an injection of insulin or metrazol, may develop no personal relationship whatever with the patient. Therapist and patient alike may view this sort of therapeutic community in such a detached fashion that its social components remain relatively unimportant. A nurse or attendant who spends months in the hospital with a patient, on the other hand, may develop with him a friendly, supportive relationship which contributes significantly to his

---

[13] *Free association* is discussed on pages 571–572, *hypnoanalysis* and *narcosynthesis* on pages 570 and 592–594, and *permissive relationships* on page 562.

[14] Compare the discussion of these principles in Chapter 3.

[15] For a detailed description of the *social community,* see pages 478–481.

social learning. In the same way, a clinician who sees the patient daily, and who carries on regular, planned therapeutic discussions with him, inevitably influences the course of his patient's learning. Other patients in the same therapeutic situation are often as important as nurses, attendants or therapists in defining the social context within which a patient reorganizes his behavior. If patients are isolated most of the time from one another, social interchange is at best meager and incidental; whereas if they participate together in organized therapeutic groups, social interaction can be extensive and planned. The social aspects of the therapeutic situation may thus be minimized or maximized, depending upon the availability and effectiveness of the reactions of other persons who share the patient's environment.

Because therapy necessarily involves other persons in addition to the patient, all varieties of therapeutic situation are to some extent social communities. These communities differ, however, in the degree to which they are structured. Some psychiatric hospital wards are tightly organized communities, molded to fit schedules of rising, eating, working and playing. By their very predictability, as we have seen, such schedules provide support and direction to the behavior of disorganized, confused, apathetic or withdrawn patients.[16] Most therapies based upon direct patient-therapist interaction, on the other hand — whether they are non-directive, psychoanalytic or eclectic, and whether they are in a hospital or out of it — employ loosely-structured situations, within which the patient is free to do and say as he likes, without fear of retaliation or punishment.

It is not sufficient, however, to characterize the therapeutic situation in terms only of the reactions of the other persons who participate in it, the extent of its organization, and its similarity to the patient's everyday existence. For by his own reactions to the persons and objects about him, by the constructions he places upon therapeutic procedures, the patient organizes the therapeutic situation in terms of his own needs.[17] An impartial therapist, for example, may be considered indifferent by one patient, amorous by another and hostile by a third. A relatively permissive play situation may spell rejection for one child, acceptance for another and neither acceptance nor rejection for a third. The same doll may be a hated sibling to one child and a devoted and sympathetic imaginary companion to another. A locked door on the hospital ward may provide comforting protection for one patient, while to another it is imprisonment. In these ways patients alter, enlarge and distort the therapeutic community, and consequently extend markedly its potentialities as a context for social learning.

As a social community, the therapeutic situation encourages, in at least three different ways, the learning of valid and appropriate behavior. (a) For

---

[16] The use of hospitalization as therapy is described on pages 582–585.
[17] Compare the discussion on pages 69–75 and 572–573.

one thing, certain therapeutic techniques require that the patient relive crucial childhood events and relationships, through which he may have acquired the beginnings of his pathological behavior. This recapitulation, it will be recalled, was the distinguishing mark of traditional psychoanalytic therapy; [18] with the help of the analyst, the adult patient identified and formulated the early conflicts and fixations which were considered to have distorted the course of his maturation. By now participating — with verbal and visceral reactions — in these recalled events, the patient resolved childhood conflicts and fixations which had persisted inappropriately into his adult years.

Some forms of play therapy emphasize the same repetition of earlier unsolved situations.[19] In release therapy, for example, and in the more conventional forms of psychoanalytic play therapy, the child repeats in play the early events and relationships which left his subsequent behavior impoverished or distorted. With both adult and child patients, however, the effective repetition of previous situations requires a close interpersonal relationship with a therapist, who can serve as supporter and interpreter, and whom the patient can cast in any part which the unfolding of events requires. In a sense, these therapies turn the clock back; they provide the patient with a second chance to follow the course of his everyday social learning and, if he can, to improve upon it.

(b) For another thing, the therapeutic social community may reconstruct the patient's present pattern of difficulties. This, of course, is one of the aims of psychodrama, of planned therapeutic groups, and of individual interview therapies which are not psychoanalytic in their orientation.[20] In psychodrama, the patient may be led directly to the focus of his troubles by the nature of the role he is assigned to play. In a planned therapeutic group, the patient often discovers, in the reactions of those who have been selected to participate with him, the outlines and consequences of his own conflicts. In a non-directive therapeutic relationship, the patient may evolve, from the therapist's consistent reactions to his emotional attitudes, the nature of his present difficulties. And in these therapeutic situations, guarded from the demands, the anxieties, the criticisms, and the responsibilities of his everyday life, the patient may be able to accomplish what he could not achieve outside therapy — the resolution of current conflicts. Like psychoanalysis, these therapies provide the patient with a new opportunity for social learning.

(c) The social aspects of the therapeutic community encourage valid learning in a third way, which is more directly related to behavioral change than are the other two. Like any social situation, the therapeutic community favors the formulation of reactions in language, and their communication to other members of the group. It is a rare patient who, for weeks at a time, remains silent before his waiting therapist, inarticulate on the psychodramatic stage, or to-

[18] See page 568.   [19] See pages 576–577.   [20] See pages 564–568 and 585–591.

tally uncommunicative in the planned therapeutic group. Most patients eventually attempt some sort of verbal interchange; and this attempt itself has therapeutic importance. For, as we have seen, patients who are silent and uncommunicative, who spend their lives in self-imposed social isolation, often undergo a reduction in their total competence which ends in behavioral deterioration.[21] Consequently, patients who participate in social interaction, whether with one therapist or with a group of patients and therapists, are to some extent defended against progressive behavioral deterioration.

The therapeutic community, of course, does much more than stimulate the patient to talk; it provides a consensus against which the patient's reactions may be validated. In our study of behavior pathology, we have seen that private fantasy and unshared rumination intensify and perpetuate many inappropriate reactions.[22] The person who does not share his attitudes with others has no check on their validity; and the person who does not validate the products of his thinking, against the reactions of others, is in danger of deviating farther and farther from the cultural norm. In the therapeutic situation, a communicative patient can test his attitudes, his fantasies and his conclusions against the reactions of other patients, of nurses, attendants and physicians. He may discover that anxieties and preoccupations he believed were unique to him are the common property of all human beings. He may find that what frightens or repels him is placidly accepted by his neighbors, and that his own unshakable convictions are not shared by the others. It is just such continuous validation that prevents the normal individual from deviating markedly from the consensus in his daily behavior. And it is thus the same continuous validation, by others in the therapeutic community, that serves often to direct the patient's learning into socially appropriate channels.

(2) *Learning in therapy involves temporal sequences of behavior.* In our earlier discussion of learning, we found that behavior organization, whether normal or pathological, could be conveniently described in terms of temporal units, such as need-satisfaction sequences, anticipant attitudes and after-reactions.[23] These temporal sequences, we said, seldom run off smoothly and automatically in everyday behavior; need-satisfaction sequences are interrupted, anticipant attitudes go unconfirmed and after-reactions change in sign. The extension of human behavior in time, however, allows for a great deal of casual, incidental learning, based upon concomitance in space and time rather than upon verbal logic. By now we have come to know a great many patients whose behavior pathology illustrates these principles. We have met patients whose unfulfilled need set the stage for pathological developments. We have met others whose ambivalent or unconfirmed anticipant attitudes brought them behavioral disorganization. And we have found patients whose specific symptoms

[21] See pages 484–492 and 529–531.
[22] See pages 387–392 and 420–426.   [23] See pages 63–69.

seem to be the product chiefly of a chance concomitance of events in space or time.

The same temporal aspects of behavior which are involved in the acquisition of pathological reactions are important in the learning that occurs during therapy. Like any person entering an unfamiliar situation, the patient goes into therapy with certain anticipant attitudes. In his own social community, he has inevitably developed relationships with other people that are characteristic for him. Perhaps he has been most comfortable when he is most domineering toward others; possibly he has made only brief, fleeting contacts which never permitted him to participate fully in interaction with other persons. But whatever their nature, his characteristic social relationships have called out reciprocal reactions from others [24] — reactions of parent-like protection, for example, of punishment, counteraggression, indifference or rejection. The reciprocal reactions which have occurred in the past between patient and the members of his social community define his social relationship. It is this preparation that determines for each patient his own anticipant attitudes as he enters a therapeutic situation.

From the very beginning, however, this novel therapeutic situation exhibits different characteristics from the one the patient expects and to which he has been accustomed. For physicians, nurses and attendants do not duplicate the behavior of a patient's friends and relatives; they maintain instead consistent attitudes of impartiality. They accept without surprise, sentimentality or challenge the patient's words, silences or gestures, his smiles, his laughter and his tears. Nor do the other patients in the situation necessarily react in predictable ways. For they are persons with their own sensitivities and preoccupations, their own sorrows and delights; and they are likely to maintain also an impersonal and detached attitude toward their fellow-patients. Consequently, in the therapeutic situation, the dependent patient's bids for support no longer gain for him protection by others. No longer do his attempts at domination bring him angry resistance or sullen submission. His shifting approaches, fleeting contacts or strange reactions no longer evoke bewilderment, fear or repulsion. The behavior of others in the therapeutic community simply does not confirm the patient's anticipant attitudes.

For most patients, the failure of the therapeutic situation to confirm their anticipant attitudes leads at first to anxiety.[25] The patient who is accustomed to the protection of others becomes helpless when his therapist fails to provide it. The patient whose life has been a series of defiant struggles with real or fantasied persons is unprepared to cope with an environment which dispassionately accepts his aggressiveness. The patient whose behavior has brought him indifference or cold rebuff is bewildered by therapists who are genuinely interested in whatever he says or does. The therapeutic community is thus in its

<hr />

[24] *Reciprocal behavior* is discussed on pages 114–116 and 134–144.   [25] See pages 289–290.

initial stages an unstructured situation for the patient; and its unstructured character may render him hesitant, uncertain, anxious and sometimes even disorganized.

The very unstructured nature of the therapeutic situation, however, favors a change in the direction of the patient's social learning. If the patient's anticipant attitudes are not confirmed — if his accustomed techniques do not work in this new social community as they did outside of it — then his former ways of behaving lose their immediate tension-reducing value. In terms of learning theory, the patient's responses are no longer confirmed or reinforced by subsequent events. Consequently the responses occur less predictably, and they may ultimately be extinguished. In terms of our earlier description of the development of behavior pathology, the circle of self-perpetuating pathological reactions is weakened and finally broken.

When the therapeutic community fails to reinforce the patient's inappropriate behavior — when the pathological reactions are no longer tension-reducing — then the patient can begin to alter his behavior. As his customary but inappropriate reactions wane in frequency and importance, the possibilities of alternative ways of behaving are enormously increased. For the patient, as for all of us, what reactions are acquired in place of the old ones depends upon space-time concomitance. Often a chance concomitance in a therapeutic situation may intensify rather than alleviate the patient's pathology. An anxious patient in an unstructured therapeutic environment, for example, may during routine procedures interpret laboratory tests as punishment or assault, and come to replace his old misinterpretations with new and more terrifying ones.[26] In a well-planned therapeutic situation, however, the factor of chance, which may have dictated the patient's incidental learning in the past, is overshadowed by an organized program designed to alter behavior in socially acceptable directions. Exactly what is learned, therefore, depends upon the particular variety of planned therapeutic situation in which the patient is participating.

If he is participating in one of the therapies which require *interaction with a single therapist*, for example, the patient is likely to learn whatever reactions this interaction calls forth. For one thing, he learns new ways of handling interpersonal relationships. And we shall see that his practice in interacting with another individual is not confined to a relationship with the therapist as a person.[27] By his own reactions to the therapist, the patient may cast him in many different roles, and thereby provide for himself practice in many different sorts of interpersonal relationship. For another thing, the patient in individual therapy may acquire different self-reactions and different perspectives in relation to his own behavior. A change in self-reactions may be facilitated, of

[26] A case illustrating the misinterpretation of examinations is given on pages 85–87.
[27] See pages 613–615.

course, when a therapist interprets the patient's behavior to him; but self-attitudes may change also in therapy where interpretation is minimized.[28] In either case, the patient comes to react to himself in terms of the public consensus rather than in terms of private rumination.

If the patient is participating in a *planned therapeutic group*, again he is likely to learn the kinds of reactions the group evokes from him. Here, however, he interacts with a variety of different individuals rather than with a single therapist who to some extent represents his own projections. Here his self-reactions are confirmed or challenged by a jury of his own peers, instead of being interpreted by a therapist. If the therapeutic method is *psychodrama*, then the patient is most likely to learn the roles he is assigned to play in the spontaneity theater, and to acquire some ease in shifting his perspectives as he shifts from one role to another. If the patient is living on a *hospital ward*, where activity is organized in terms of daily routines of eating and sleeping, he may acquire behavior in therapy which reflects in its organization the predictable events on the ward.

By now it should be clear that *learning in therapy* repeats the temporal character of all human learning in two ways. (*a*) The therapeutic situation does not confirm the patient's anticipant attitudes. Initially, therefore, a patient may be anxious or even disorganized; but anxiety and disorganization often serve to interrupt the circle of a patient's pathological behavior and free him for new learning. (*b*) What the patient now learns in therapy depends largely upon the events which take place in the therapeutic situation. Different therapeutic approaches utilize different events; but most well-planned therapeutic techniques call forth from a patient reactions which enable him to establish new relationships, develop valid self-reactions, and acquire new skill in role-taking and the shifting of perspective.

(3) *Learning in therapy proceeds according to the personal needs of the patient.* We have said that learning is always selective. Human beings typically organize situations in terms of their own needs. A person's reaction-sensitivities, which are themselves the product of learning, enable him to place his own individualized construction upon any situation of which he is a part. And if the situation is relatively unstructured to begin with, the individual can organize it almost wholly in accordance with his reaction-sensitivities. Indeed, sometimes this process is carried to the point where it is unrealistic, as measured by the actual persons and objects involved. It is this selective organization which characterizes a large share of normal and pathological behavior.[29] It underlies the differences in attitudes and skills which distinguish one normal individual from another. But it underlies also the possessive play

[28] Sheerer, E. T., "The relationship between acceptance of self and acceptance of others." *J. consult. Psychol.*, 1949, vol. 13, pp. 169–175; Stock, D., "The self concept and feelings toward others." *J. consult. Psychol.*, 1949, vol. 13, pp. 176–180.

[29] See pages 70–74 and 374–392.

of a deprived child, the progressive development of body overconcern of an anxious adult, the spread of self-punitive reactions in patients who are depressed, and the expanding autistic communities and pseudocommunities of persons suffering from schizophrenic and paranoid disorders.

In the therapeutic situation, of course, the patient shows the same selective reaction-sensitivity as he did outside of it. At least initially, he reacts in terms of his own needs to the general framework of hospital, ward, therapeutic group or interview, and to the details of therapeutic procedures. It is by no means rare, for example, to find a patient whose needs for self-protection are so intense that he is walled off from assistance as effectively as if he were sealed in a lonely cell. Such patients cannot bring themselves to participate in therapy at all, for to them participation is a public admission of illness which they dare not make. Nor is it unusual to discover patients who defend their own pathological reactions against therapeutic attack by including hospital and therapists in their pseudocommunities. All behavior pathologists are acquainted with the patient who sees hospital grounds and buildings as his own estate, who views physicians and nurses as his underlings, and who explains that he remains in the hospital not because he must, but because it is his rightful home.

In planned group therapy it is the same. The patient who faithfully plays his assigned part on the psychodramatic stage cannot help interpreting his roles in the light of his own needs and his own special sensitivities. Indeed, as we have seen, therapists who employ psychodrama report that their patients, whatever the initial character of their play-acting, seem ultimately to arrive always at their own personal preoccupations and conflicts.[30] Other planned therapeutic groups reflect similarly the behavior organizations of their participants. Initially, the patient utilizes discussion sessions or activity groups in the only way he can — by repeating, in his relationships with other patients, the reactions which have been characteristic of him in his own social community.

Even specific therapeutic procedures may be interpreted by the anxious or needful patient in accordance with his own selective reaction-sensitivities. There is always the danger, for example, that a careful chest examination will intensify one patient's conviction that he has heart disease, and another's that he has pulmonary tuberculosis or a lung tumor. A pelvic examination, similarly, may seem to one patient to indicate a suspicion of pregnancy and to another that the examiner considers her sexually atypical.[31] Therapies that are frightening or painful may confirm a depressed patient's belief in his own unworthiness, and provide him with the punishment he seeks.[32] In all such

[30] See pages 589–591.

[31] Compare the behavior of the manic patient described on pages 332–335.

[32] Compare the theory that shock therapy is effective because it may satisfy the patient's needs for punishment; see pages 597–598. See also Alper, T. G., "An electric shock patient tells his story." *J. abn. soc. Psychol.*, 1948, vol. 43, pp. 201–210.

cases, of course, the construction which the patient places upon his therapy may augment rather than diminish his behavior pathology. Consequently, it is not uncommon for experienced therapists to minimize or delay the use of examinations and of treatment which might extend or perpetuate their patients' misinterpretations.

The relationship between patient and therapist which is central to individual interview therapy also provides a comparatively unstructured field for the patient to organize in accordance with his needs. We have seen that the patient is likely to react to the neutral therapist as he has formerly reacted to his parents, siblings, spouse, friends or enemies. He attributes to the therapist the affectionate, protective or punitive attitudes which he has learned to need, or to expect, from other persons in his own social community, his pseudocommunity or his fantasy. In some varieties of therapy — particularly in the induced *transference neurosis* of psychoanalysis — such projections as these are deliberately fostered; while in other types of treatment — in briefer psychoanalysis and non-directive therapy, for example — they are minimized. They can never be completely eliminated, however, for the patient, in common with all human beings, inevitably places his own constructions upon a therapeutic relationship. In consequence, the therapist becomes many different persons, with each of whom the patient attempts to establish the kind of relationship which his needs require and his skills permit.

If, however, the therapeutic community were only a lifelike reproduction of each patient's individual behavior organization, it would have little more than diagnostic significance. Each patient would then merely duplicate, in the therapeutic situation, the pathological behavior he brought to it, and thus become more and more skilled in his inappropriate reactions. What happens in successful therapy, of course, is the opposite of this. The patient's originally distorted interpretations of the therapeutic community change in the direction of social validity. Ideally, his autistic communities and pseudocommunities give way to a valid social community anchored in real events.

Most patients, after they have spent some time in a therapeutic situation, report that their social communities now seem different to them. The same situations which formerly frightened or irritated them now seem harmless and trivial. The same persons whose reactions formerly made the patient tense, sad or hopeless, now seem indifferent or even friendly. Self-reactions undergo similar changes, so that patients often refer to their previously dominant attitudes as "nonsense" or "foolish ideas." What they are describing is actually an alteration in the pattern of their reaction-sensitivities, begun in the therapeutic community and carried over into their social community. In short, behavior that has been acquired in the patient-therapist relationship generalizes to situations outside therapy.[33]

[33] For an analysis of this point in terms of one theory of learning, see Magaret, A., "Generalization in successful psychotherapy." *J. consult. Psychol.*, 1949, vol. 14, pp. 64–69.

There are many reasons for the acquisition of new patterns of reaction-sensitivity in therapy. We have already mentioned that the therapeutic community ordinarily does not confirm the patient's anticipant attitudes.[34] We have seen also that the therapeutic community furnishes the patient with a consensus against which to test the validity of his own reactions.[35] In his own projections which occur in the therapeutic situations, the patient has actually gained practice in many of the different roles that he needs to play in his everyday life. When, therefore, he re-enters his own social community — whether this occurs between therapeutic sessions or after long hospitalization — he reacts to social persons and to social situations much as he has been reacting to them in the person of the therapist, and in the situation of the therapeutic community. His changed reaction-sensitivities enable him now to structure his social community along socially valid lines.

To these factors must be added still another. The therapist, whether he serves as daily interviewer, group discussion leader, activity director, psychodramatist or periodic visitor to the hospital ward, is selective in his reactions to the patient. His behavior toward his patient reflects the therapist's own reaction-sensitivities — a selective responsiveness which is not merely a reflection of his own needs as a person, but is in the main a product of his own professional training. And in his selective reactions to his patient, the therapist possesses a powerful instrument for changing the patient's inappropriate patterns of reaction-sensitivity.

The most important component of the skilled therapist's pattern of selective reaction-sensitivity is his consistent attitude of permissiveness and impartiality. As we have seen, the trained therapist uniformly inhibits his own reactions of condemnation, retaliation and punishment, and maintains instead a neutral attitude. For the patient who treats the therapist as if he were now a punishing parent, and perhaps later as a hated rival, and still later as an affectionate friend, this neutral attitude has one thoroughly predictable consequence. It forces the patient eventually to locate his reactions of self-punishment, hostility and affection in his own behavior, instead of attributing them to the consistently impartial therapist. It enables the patient to identify these punishing, hostile and affectionate figures as the constituents of his own pseudocommunity, the products of his own need. The therapist's impartial attitude sharpens the patient's blurred distinctions between pseudocommunity and social community, and thus encourages the development of more valid interpretations of his subsequent situations.

If simple discriminations were the only responses involved in the acquisition of reaction-sensitivity, then both the development of behavior pathology and its elimination would be mechanical, impersonal processes. Again and again in our study of patients, however, we have found that the tensions and anxieties

---

[34] See pages 608–611.   [35] See pages 607–608.

of unfulfilled personal need dictate the attitudes and responses which produce particular constellations of reaction-sensitivity. The shifts in selective responsiveness that occur in therapy are also dependent upon personal need. The patient whose hostile pseudocommunity is a projection of his own feelings of rejection, for example, cannot relinquish his fears of attack by the simple expedient of identifying his persecutors as the products of his fantasy. Unless these reactions to himself are altered from rejection to acceptance, the changes in his behavior may well remain in the realm of language only. If a permanent change in selective responsiveness is to occur, therapy must be aimed at the patient's patterns of need-satisfaction, as well as at his verbal discriminations.

To this more widespread behavior change the therapist's permissive attitude again contributes. It allows the patient to create for himself the types of situations he requires. He may fight, against the unprotesting therapist, the battles he dared not fight against his father. With his therapist, he may indulge in infantile behavior which earlier in his life his mother or his peers refused to tolerate. He can structure, from the therapist's accepting attitudes, or in the transference relationship of psychoanalysis, the affection he lacks from friend or lover. In these ways, the therapeutic community may provide, in condensed and often symbolic form, the consummation of unfulfilled need-satisfaction sequences. It is only when his needs are thus met that the patient is in a position to acquire new and more appropriate patterns of selective reaction-sensitivity.[36]

(4) *In therapy, reactions which eventuate in tension-reduction are readily acquired and tend to persist in the patient's behavioral repertory.* From infancy through maturity and old age, we have said, human learning proceeds according to the principle of tension-reduction. We have found this principle equally applicable to normal and to pathological reactions. Indeed, much of the pathological behavior we have seen in our patients has been behavior which, although it is socially inappropriate or distorted, still provides the patient with satisfaction of his need or diminution of his anxiety. Even painful or unrewarding acts often seem more tolerable to human beings than do the tensions of unconsummated behavioral sequences.

The principle of tension-reduction is employed deliberately to foster the learning involved in therapy. Its exact application, however, may vary from one sort of therapy to the next. Perhaps the simplest use of tension-reduction in therapy is to be found in hospital ward procedures.[37] Here protection of the patient from demands and responsibilities, his separation from other patients, or the provision of stable ward routines, serves to minimize the intolerable tensions and anxieties of a patient's previous everyday life. Such tension-reduc-

[36] For a more detailed discussion of the consequences of need-satisfaction, see pages 37–43.

[37] See pages 582–585.

tion through environmental simplification, as we have seen, serves rather to prepare the patient for further learning than to direct his learning into socially appropriate channels.

Tension-reduction alone seldom, if ever, changes pathological behavior into behavior which is socially more appropriate. Indeed, unless it is carefully planned to evoke valid reactions, a simplified hospital environment may actually encourage a patient to prolong and perpetuate his pathological behavior. Overcrowded, understaffed hospitals, as we have seen, are filled with patients whose social isolation, private rumination and unwarranted inferences go unchallenged and uninterrupted for weeks or months on end. Such patients find in an undemanding environment an opportunity to practice and extend their pathological tension-reducing reactions, until they are so well learned that a significant change is practically impossible. If pathology is to give way to socially valid behavior, the socially valid behavior must provide tension-reduction.

The aim of contemporary therapy, particularly that which involves patient-therapist interaction, is that of making socially appropriate behavior tension-reducing. This is usually achieved in two ways. In the first place, much of contemporary therapy initially maintains, prolongs or even provokes the unconsummated emotional reactions we have called anxiety. We have seen that the unstructured situations of interview and play therapy, as well as the free interchange of a therapeutic group, may be at first anxiety-provoking for most patients. Furthermore, most therapists — whether they are playing the role of interviewer, group participant or psychodramatist — encourage their patients to discuss unpleasant, disgusting or terrifying events and attitudes, even though this discussion may intensify the patients' anxiety reactions. Some therapists, for example, withhold altogether their own comments, or even prolong the period between contacts with their patients, in order to foster the development of optimal anxiety.[38] Such procedures, of course, demand of the therapist a nice appreciation of the limits of anxiety-tolerance for each patient. Individuals differ greatly in the degree of anxiety they can tolerate; and the therapist's task is to prevent the occurrence of disorganizing anxiety, while still allowing the development of a sufficiently high level of tension to facilitate learning.[39]

In the second place, contemporary therapists attempt to structure the therapeutic community in such a way that the reactions which terminate the patient's tension are not the earlier acquired pathological reactions which have been contributing to his behavior pathology. The therapeutic problem is thus one of obtaining closure through socially valid rather than through inappro-

---

[38] See, for example, Alexander, F., and French, T. M., *Psychoanalytic therapy.* New York: Ronald, 1946.
[39] See pages 75–79.

priate behavior. We have already seen that the therapeutic situation encourages appropriate closure in certain indirect ways. It may provide a consensus against which the patient's unwarranted conclusions stand out as invalid. It may furnish, in the reactions of other patients and therapists, a challenge to the patient's inept adjustive techniques. It may offer the patient satisfaction of his hitherto unfulfilled and frustrated needs. He may consequently come to learn that it is socially valid behavior which brings him permanent tension-reduction. And, as we have found repeatedly in our study of normal and pathological development, reactions which are permanently tension-reducing tend to persist in the individual's behavioral repertory.

There is still another way, however, in which the anxiety provoked initially in therapy may be reduced in socially valid ways. The patient who comes to communicate the frightening, repulsive or disparaging products of his own thinking may react to his attempts at communication with a sharp increase in anxiety which may initially produce mild disorganization. However, the intensity of these reactions, as we have seen, is in large part the consequence of this patient's own acquired anticipant attitudes. He has learned to anticipate punishment, rejection or attack from others on the basis of his own thoughts and attitudes. When punishment, rejection or attack is not forthcoming from his therapist, the anticipant attitudes often lose their effect. So it is that patients who are at first frightened, repelled or humiliated by their own verbalized reactions, become progressively less so, as they taste the actual consequences of their statements. It is this phenomenon which many therapists call "desensitization." From our point of view, it is an example of the general tendency of unconfirmed anticipant attitudes to wane in importance and ultimately to disappear from the patient's repertory.

(5) *In the reorganization of complex behavior in therapy, excitants to learned reactions, and the learning process itself, often become accessible to the self-reactions of the patient.* The organization of behavior always includes reactions whose excitants remain inaccessible to the self-reactions of the learner.[40] The origins of a great many important attitudes and responses are buried in the prelanguage period of development, and consequently have never been formulated in verbal symbols. Other reactions, equally important in adult behavior organization, are the resultants of space-time concomitance the significance of which has escaped the learner's notice. Still other reactions are acquired in a setting of stress or disorganization, and this setting prevents the individual from identifying the excitants at the time or recalling them later. And a sizeable proportion of any person's behavior, whether normal or pathological, becomes self-inaccessible through the selective forgetting we have called repression.

In the development and persistence of behavior pathology, it is often the

[40] See pages 79–83 and 297–298.

self-inaccessible excitants, and the self-inaccessible behavior sequences, which make the patient's reactions inexplicable to himself and unpredictable to others. The behavioral duplicity which socialization and conformity require of all growing human beings is exaggerated in the patient.[41] For him, the dichotomies between covert and overt language, and between covert and overt emotional behavior, are so wide that the overt reactions no longer specify the covert ones accurately. The patient is as little able as the prelanguage child to formulate and communicate many important aspects of his own behavioral organization.

It is not surprising, therefore, to find that much of the learning which goes on in therapy is aimed at making behavior, which has hitherto remained self-inaccessible, available to the patient's self-reactions. *Hypnoanalysis* and *narcosynthesis*, as we have seen, are attempts to aid the patient in recalling traumatic events which he has repressed. The technique of *free association* was devised originally to encourage the patient to recapture past attitudes and acts which he had forgotten or repressed; and it is still employed today as a means of circumventing the patient's critical self-attitudes. Any treatment procedure which goes on in a permissive atmosphere — whether it is individual interview, free play or group therapy — may lead the patient to specify and communicate reactions which had previously been inaccessible to him. In all these therapies, as we have seen, the therapeutic identification and interpretation of the patient's self-inaccessible reactions hasten their inclusion in his behavioral repertory.

The premature occurrence of formerly repressed reactions may intensify rather than alleviate a patient's behavior pathology. The patient whose difficulties stem from repressed attitudes of hostility toward persons he should — and overtly does — love, may develop acute anxiety and even panic if his own hostile reactions are suddenly made accessible to him. Likewise, the patient whose repressed homosexual tendencies have made him suspicious and sensitive to slights, may develop behavior disorganization or a paranoid disorder if he is abruptly confronted with the significance of his behavior. In competent therapy, the development of self-accepting attitudes to support such unwelcome responses precedes the release of repressed reactions. Otherwise, the patient has no alternative to more severe behavior pathology other than to resist and deny his own self-reactions, and thus to jeopardize his own recovery.

When reactions become self-accessible under properly controlled therapeutic conditions, relearning in socially valid directions is favored in at least four different ways. (*a*) The patient's formulation of his own behavior, and his visceral and gestural participation in this act, are in themselves tension-reducing. Freud, and most therapists after him, have remarked the relief and

[41] See pages 109–112.

relaxation which seem to follow a patient's initial formulation of previously repressed reactions. Indeed, such a formulation was originally called *catharsis*, thereby emphasizing its purgative and purifying character.[42] It is altogether understandable that the termination of repression should be tension-reducing, since, as we have seen, the maintenance of repression itself involves effort, tension and consequent fatigue.

(*b*) When the patient formulates hitherto self-inaccessible reactions in the presence of a therapist, he gains for himself the opportunity of sharing and validating these reactions. Sharing, we have said, is more easily achieved with verbal reactions than with emotional ones.[43] Even without verbal formulation, however, a patient may share his reactions with his therapist, in some respects, by acting them through in visceral and gestural language. It would be difficult to find a more lucidly communicative act, for example, than the frozen terror and mute anguish of the soldier who has just recalled in hypnoanalysis that his buddy has been mutilated in combat. Whether it goes on in language or without it, however, the sharing of reactions makes possible their validation against the consensus represented by the therapist or by a therapeutic group. And it is through such validation that reactions made self-accessible may be appraised, altered to conform with cultural expectation, or relinquished altogether.

(*c*) When self-inaccessible reactions are made self-accessible and included in his behavioral repertory, the patient is in a position to develop new social roles and to test them against the reciprocal reactions of others. It is a common observation in play therapy, for example, that when previously repressed hostility finally appears, a child is likely to become aggressive, not only toward his play materials and the therapist, but also toward his parents, his teachers, his siblings and his peers, outside the therapeutic situation. He tries out his new role recklessly with any adversary he can find, and discovers for himself the consequences of hostility in his own social community. In the same way, the unresponsive patient who identifies in therapy his own unrecognized needs to give affection may, outside the therapeutic situation, attempt to take the role of affectionate, demonstrative lover, which had previously been foreign to him. And he may find, in the reciprocal reactions of other social persons, both new gratifications of his need and new limitations to his behavior.

(*d*) When the patient has identified, in therapy, excitants and reactions which were formerly self-inaccessible, he is enabled to acquire reactions of self-control toward his own behavior.[44] We have seen that many of our patients

[42] Compare the discussion of *abreaction* on pages 569–570.

[43] See pages 125–129.

[44] The importance of verbal signs in controlling behavior, particularly in the course of therapy, has been emphasized by Dollard, J., and Miller, N. E., *Personality and psychotherapy*. New York: McGraw-Hill, 1950; Shaffer, L. F., "The problem of psychotherapy." *Amer. Psychologist*, 1947, vol. 2, pp. 459–467; Shaw, F. J., "A stimulus-response analysis of repression and insight in psychotherapy." *Psychol. Rev.*, 1946, vol. 53, pp. 36–42.

are helpless to control their own behavior because the excitants to their pathological reactions perpetually elude them. Perhaps the simplest example of this phenomenon is to be found in the behavior of patients suffering from acute anxiety attacks, who typically report that their sudden increases of anxiety seem altogether inexplicable to them. Such patients as these often discover, in therapy, that their anxiety attacks occur consistently in situations whose significance has been previously inaccessible to them — situations of rejection, hostility or affectionate approach, for example. Once the character of these precipitating situations becomes plain to the patient, he can begin to learn new ways of meeting rejection, hostility or affection, and thus of controlling the occurrence of intense anxiety. He can change from the status of helpless, dependent child to the position of mature adult, whose control of his behavior is in his own hands.

Our discussion of the self-accessibility of reactions in therapy should not lead us to overlook one final point of great importance. It is not the purpose of therapy to render available to the patient *all* of his repressed reactions. For the patient, as for all other human beings, repression has definite advantages as an adjustive technique. We have already seen[45] that repression makes for economy of behavior organization, and that it permits individuals to perform efficiently in the face of insoluble conflict or unalterable frustration. It is only when self-inaccessible reactions distort and exaggerate behavior to pathological proportions that their recognition becomes a therapeutic goal. And when such reactions are reincluded in the patient's repertory, the result may be a sudden reorganization of behavior which leads to further improvement and recovery.

(6) *Learning in therapy often involves the sudden reorganization of ongoing behavior into new patterned sequences which then persist.* By now it should be clear that if therapy is to be successful, it must induce in a patient's behavior a reorganization that will persist after he leaves the therapeutic situation for his own social community. The goal of therapy in contemporary behavior pathology is neither a superficial alteration of symptoms nor the total reconstruction of a patient's behavior. Present-day therapy aims at changes in need-satisfaction, in self-reactions, role-taking behavior and reaction-sensitivities. But the patient after therapy is not a new individual; he is the same person with somewhat increased social skills, somewhat wider perspectives and somewhat more valid self-reactions. In most therapy, as in any other form of learning, the behavioral reorganization which produces these modifications proceeds slowly and unevenly. Occasionally in therapy, however, reactions occur which produce a sudden and stable reorganization of behavior; to this phenomenon we have already given the name of *insight*.[46]

Insight, when it occurs in therapy, is not basically different from the insight we found in the problem-solving behavior of normal persons, and in the *sudden*

[45] See pages 349–350.   [46] See pages 83–87.

clarification of paranoid patients. An important distinguishing feature here is that in therapy, the abrupt reorganization of reactions must yield a pattern of behavior which has social validity. Otherwise its characteristics are the same as those which we have earlier identified. A sudden restructuring of behavior emerges in therapy from the patient's own ongoing reactions. It is ordinarily preceded by gradual shifts in attitude and by many trial formulations of his reactions by the patient. It may be precipitated by the occurrence of hitherto self-inaccessible reactions, or by a newly acquired system of accessible self-reactions. It persists in the patient's total repertory of behavior, like any other learned act, because it is tension-reducing; its persistence favors the generalization of this new pattern of reactions to situations outside the therapeutic community.

In the psychiatric literature a more restricted meaning than this is commonly given to the term *insight*. Thus, a patient is said to "have insight" if he can recognize that his own behavior is deviant, as judged by the standards of his culture. He is said to "lack insight" if to him his own pathological behavior appears quite normal. Here "insight" is defined solely in terms of the degree of agreement between the patient's verbalized self-reactions and the evaluation of his behavior by others. It is possible that the behavioral reorganization, which induces this change in self-reactions, is similar to that which defines our broader conception of insight. However, the abrupt restructuring of reactions in therapy that yields a permanently valid behavior organization — for which we reserve the term *insight* — involves a great deal more than verbal reformulation. Indeed, we have ample evidence that insight which involves only the patient's appreciation of the fact that he is, or has been ill is neither a necessary nor a sufficient condition for his recovery.[47]

Many patients, in the course of therapy, make statements in which they relate their present difficulties to some past event, or relate certain symptoms to the conditions which seem to precipitate them. Verbalizations of this sort, however, are no guarantee that a patient's subsequent behavior will change fundamentally. Indeed, they may be little more than echoes of a therapist's interpretation of the patient's behavior to him; and as such they are evidence of the patient's acceptance of and attachment to his therapist, and not genuine products of the patient's own relearning. Furthermore, the verbal formulation of these relationships often paradoxically reinforces rather than alters the patient's pathological reactions. Any experienced therapist is familiar with the sophisticated, widely-read patient who brings, to his first therapeutic session, explanations of his illness in highly technical terms which may be fairly accurate. The difficulty is that such patients may find, in their own explanations, comforting and satisfying closure which interferes with their going on from verbal statement to total behavioral change.

[47] Rennie, T., "Prognosis in manic-depressive psychoses." *Amer. J. Psychiat.*, 1942, vol. 98, pp. 801–814.

It is only when the occurrence of a system of reactions precipitates a sudden, stable restructuring of the patient's widespread behavior that we recognize the extent to which the learning in therapy involves insight. And such an extensive reorganization must include much behavior that is covert, visceral and symbolic in character, as well as that which is overt, verbal and non-symbolic. It must close, or at least narrow, the gap between overt and covert language behavior, and between overt and covert emotional reactions, which for the patient has become unbridgeable. In other words, when an abrupt reorganization of behavior occurs in therapy, the patient is enabled to confront his own behavioral duplicity,[48] and consequently to alter or even to relinquish it.

Two examples may aid in clarifying this point. Let us suppose that a patient, who is suffering from anxiety attacks, states in his first interview that his difficulties stem from lifelong hatred of his father. He makes his announcement with facility and calmness, showing in his visceral and gestural behavior no indication that his statement is anything more to him than a series of words. The words as a statement of a relationship between present symptom and prolonged conflict may be completely valid. But their vocalization nets the patient nothing in the way of widespread behavioral change, for his anxiety attacks persist and may even grow worse. Most patients themselves recognize the futility of merely stating these isolated verbal fragments of a more comprehensive conflict. They insist that they know exactly what is bothering them, but add that the knowledge alone provides them no relief. In our terms, such patients recognize only the overt symbolic aspect of a behavioral dichotomy which includes covert, symbolic and emotional reactions as well.

Let us now suppose that another patient, after a series of therapeutic interviews, or after extended participation in a therapeutic group, makes the same statement of a relationship between anxiety reactions and filial hostility. His verbal formulation is likely to be the product of gradually changing self-attitudes which now support obvious visceral and gestural responses as well as overt language. He may hesitate, block and otherwise disorganize in making his statement. He may show in flushing, tachycardia and rapid respiration the unmistakable signs that his abrupt behavioral reorganization includes emotional as well as verbal reactions. From this patient, changes in his behavior outside the therapeutic situation may be fairly expected — in his reactions toward his father, toward other adult males, and perhaps toward any person who exerts authority over him. If these changes occur, and if they persist in the patient's behavioral repertory, then we may say that learning in therapy has involved insight. For the patient, the chasm between overt and covert reactions has been narrowed to the point where both may now be included in the one new and more comprehensive pattern of behavior.

Contemporary therapy in behavior pathology favors the occurrence of in-

---

[48] For a discussion of *behavioral duplicity*, see pages 109–112.

sight by providing the conditions under which sudden behavioral reorganization is known to appear. The patient in therapy has an extended opportunity to attempt the provisional tries [49] at new self-reactions and social interactions from which insight ordinarily emerges. He is encouraged, directly or indirectly, to confront attitudes and events which have been inaccessible to him; and by formulating self-inaccessible material he sets the stage for the restructuring of his own behavior. Partly because it includes emotional reactions, and partly because it is accepted by the therapist, the new behavioral organization is ordinarily tension-reducing for the patient. Consequently, it persists in the patient's behavior, both in the therapeutic community and in the social community outside.

From this analysis it is apparent that insight in therapy is important primarily because it stimulates the generalization of reactions from the therapeutic situation to the patient's own social community. If the patient's sudden reorganization of behavior is a stable one, then he must behave in his everyday relationships in new and different ways. And if the reorganization has occurred along socially more valid lines, then these new ways of behaving will be more acceptable to other social persons than the patient's older, less adequate techniques. The reorganized patterns, in other words, are likely to prove tension-reducing to the patient, and so to persist until they become characteristic for him. When socially valid behavior organizations thus come to replace inept, inappropriate, pathological ones, both patient and therapist can justly conclude that the patient has recovered.

But whether successful therapy results from a sudden reorganization, or whether it is the outcome of a slow and gradual change, the same basic principles of learning are operative that we recognized in the everyday acquisition of new skills and new perspectives, and the same ones that we found to underlie the development of pathological symptoms. Thus, we come once more to a realization of the essential unity of the sciences of human behavior, and a clear recognition that behavior pathology is no stranger among those sciences. The behavior we individually acquire, in the field of social operations, may contribute to normal maturation and help sustain adequate socialization; it may lead to personality distortion and impoverishment; or it may constitute part of a process of recovery from behavior pathology and of the reëstablishment of effective interpersonal relationships. And the light which arises from the systematic and intelligent investigation of any one of these profoundly important areas will inevitably illuminate the others.

[49] The "provisional try" as an important aspect of learning is discussed in Hilgard, E. R., *Theories of learning.* New York: Appleton-Century-Crofts, 1948, p. 340; see also pages 83–87.

Name Index

625

$\mathcal{S}$ubject Index

Duplicity, behavioral (*see* Behavioral duplicity)

Ectomorph, 27
Effect, principle of, in learning, 76
Ego, conflict and, 249
Egocentric thinking, in developmental retardation, 164
Elimination, affectional relationships and, 139–140; body overconcern and, 149; fixation and, 149
Electroshock therapy, 595–596
Emancipation, adolescent, 142–143; conflict and, 253; in developmental retardation, 174; maturation and, 140–141; socialization and, 141–142
Embolism, 532
Emotional decompensation, in anxiety attack, 306
Emotional displacement, anxiety and, 296
Emotional excitement, learning and, 300–301; anxiety and, 279–280
Emotional reactions, 122–129; ambivalence in, 127–129; behavioral duplicity in, 127–129; cerebral incompetence and, 539; conformity and, 127–129; cumulative sequences in, 126–127; decompensation in, 126–127; definition of, 124; disorganization and, 464–466; displacement in, 125–126; hallucination and, 445–446; incommunicability of, 128–129; overinclusion and, 458; pseudocommunity and, 390–391; unshared, 128–129; visceral activity in, 122–125
Empathy, anxiety-readiness and, 295
Endocrine dysfunction, developmental retardation and, 181
Endomorph, 28
Environment, social, 478–484
Environmental change, disorganization and, 460–463
Environmental complexity, disorganization and, 468; pseudocommunity and, 390
Environmental control, infant and, 115–116
Environmental restriction, developmental retardation and, 184
Environmental stress, recurrent depressive disorders and, 326–327
Escape, impossibility of, anxiety and, 280–283
Ethics, conscience and, 285–286; feeding and, 136–137; visceral, 140; conscience and, 285–286
Excitement, manic, 330–336; normal, 329–330; as reaction to tension, 329–330
Exclusion, in behavior organization, 74–75; daydream and, 425–426; dream and, 425–426; hallucination and, 432–433; learning and, 456; repression and, 338, 341
Exhibitionism, in sex deviation, 209
Experimental method, 18–19; with infra-

human animals, 18–19; in study of conflict, 251–252
Experimental neurosis, 18–19
Expressive jargon, 91

Family similarities, adoption of prevailing pattern and, 62
Fantasy, adoption, 422; anxiety-readiness and, 294; autistic community and, 415–416; behavioral duplicity and, 416–418; compensatory, 378–379; daydream (*see* Daydream); desocialization and, 486, 488, 493, 503–504; in developmental retardation, 162; disorganization and, 463–464; dream (*see* Dream); non-verbal, 112–113; pathological lying and, 207; role-taking in, 121–122; self-reaction and, 419–420; thinking as, 112–113
Fear, anxiety and, 278; decompensation and, 126–127
Fear-reduction, experiments on, 77–78
Feeble-mindedness (*see* Developmental retardation)
Feeding, affectional relationships and, 138; disturbance of, 59–60; ethics and, 136–137; family table and, 136–137; learning and, 134–135; maturation of, 134–137; mother's techniques of, 36; tension and, 36; weaning, 135–136
Fels Institute study, 57
Field approach, 17–18
Fixation, 143–153; animal experiments and, 150–151; biosocial maturation and, 144–148; conditions favoring, 148–153; conflict and, 274–275; definition of, 143; developmental retardation and, 150; elimination and, 149; language and, 108; need-satisfaction and, 38; overprotection and, 151–152; parental attitude and, 151–153; pathological, in social deviation, 211–213; regression and, 217–222, 225; sex behavior and, 147–150; sex deviation and, 209; solitary play and, 147–148; varied pattern in, 152–153
Fixation-regression hypothesis, 217–218, 226
Flexibility, principle of, in therapy, 573
Forgery, in social deviation, case, 193–196
Foster-child delusion, 422
Fragmentation, definition of, 454
Free association, 570–571; anxiety and, 292–293; conflict and, 249; self-inaccessible excitants and, 618
Friendships, childhood, 141–142
Frustration, 47–49; in adolescence, 47; anxiety-readiness and, 294; conflict and, 49; consequences of, 51–52; definition of, 47; delay and, 47; disorganization and, 459–460; invalidism and, 233–234; pseudocommunity and, 391; regression and, 228–229; senility and, 555; stress and, 44–49;